AUTOMOTIVE ENGINEERING
Engine Performance
(Classroom Manual)

Ken Pickerill

Australia • Brazil • Japan • Korea • Mexico • Singapore • Spain • United Kingdom • United States

Automotive Engineering: Engine Performance (Classroom Manual)
Ken Pickerill

ISBN-13: 978-81-315-1296-8

Cengage Learning India Private Limited
418, F.I.E. Patparganj
New Delhi-110092

Tel: 91-11-43641111
Fax: 91-11-43641100

Cengage Learning products are represented in Canada by Nelson Education, Ltd.

For product information, visit www.cengage.co.in

Printed in India
First Indian Reprint 2010

Dedication

I want to dedicate this book to the memory of my father, Miles K. Pickerill.
Dad taught me love, honesty, and craftsmanship.

To Peggy, my wife of 32 years, and my two sons, Adam and Eric.
My family has shown nothing but support for me through the process of revising this book.

Thanks go out to:

The late John Riddle, who took me in as a young apprentice many years ago.

The management and staff of Clapp Auto Group in Clarksville, in particular Dennis Price, who always believed in my ability.

Ken Pickerill

CONTENTS

PREFACE TO THE INDIA EDITION

Unlike yesterday's mechanic, the technician of today and for the future must know the underlying theory of all automotive systems and be able to service and maintain those systems. Dividing the material into two volumes provides the reader with the information needed to begin a successful career as an automotive technician without interrupting the learning process by mixing cognitive and performance learning objectives into one volume.

Each Classroom Manual contains the principles of operation for each system and subsystem. The Classroom Manual also contains discussions on design variations of key components used by the different vehicle manufacturers. This volume is organized to build upon basic facts and theories. The primary objective of this volume is to allow the reader to gain an understanding of how each system and subsystem operates. This understanding is necessary to diagnose the complex automobiles of today and tomorrow. Although the basics contained in the Classroom Manual provide the knowledge needed for diagnostics, diagnostic procedures appear only in the Shop Manual. An understanding of the basics is also a requirement for competence in the skill areas covered in the Shop Manual.

The Shop Manual covers the "how-tos." This volume includes step-by-step instructions for diagnostic and repair procedures. Photo Sequences are used to illustrate some of the common service procedures. Other common procedures are listed and are accompanied with line drawings and photos that allow the reader to visualize and conceptualize the finest details of the procedure. This volume also contains the reasons for performing the procedures, as well as when that particular service is appropriate.

The two volumes are designed to be used together and are arranged in corresponding chapters. Not only are the chapters in the volumes linked together, but also the contents of the chapters are linked.

HIGHLIGHTS OF THIS EDITION—CLASSROOM MANUAL

The Classroom Manual reflects current changes in automotive engine performance, while retaining some of the more pertinent information on older models that are still in wide use. Engine performance technology is often seen by students as an array of complicated subjects, all of which can be difficult to understand. This is why *Automotive Engineering: Engine Performance* follows a natural progression of subjects, including basic theories, engine construction, electrical theory, and computer control, to bring all these topics together. More experienced students and working technicians can review the basic theories and then move on to more advanced areas in the latter half of the text.

This edition features expanded coverage of direct fuel injection (DFI), compression sensing ignition (CSI), and throttle actuator control (TAC), as well as updated coverage of some of the more recent developments in sensor technology and new developments to OBD II such as the thermostat and PCV monitors. The Classroom Manual also has multiple choice questions to help assess student understanding of the material. Most obvious to the casual observer will be the photos and illustrations that have been added to optimally engage students' interest in the subjects presented.

HIGHLIGHTS OF THIS EDITION—SHOP MANUAL

The *Automotive Engineering: Engine Performance (Shop Manual),* follows the same natural progression of the Classroom Manual but focuses on the skill set required to be a successful technician in today's shop. The Shop Manual starts with shop procedures and ASE certification, progresses through electrical testing, basic engine testing, and scan tool procedures, and finally through the most advanced diagnostics used today. The coverage includes new basic engine technology, such as displacement on demand, while retaining a thorough coverage of basic engine testing such as vacuum, compression, cylinder leakage, and engine balance that are the cornerstone of engine performance diagnosis. Students are then lead through electrical troubleshooting. This coverage includes basic multi-meter, test lamp, logic probe, and oscilloscope pattern reading and use. Electrical wiring and connector repair is also covered, as well as a review of battery starting and charging diagnostics. Engine performance coverage includes distributor and distributorless ignition systems, throttle body fuel injection, port-fuel and direct fuel injection. A section on computer operation and networking is included, as well as a chapter on related systems to bring the operation of the whole vehicle together for the student. This broad coverage makes this edition suitable for a wide range of student capability, from beginning technician to a more seasoned veteran.

REVIEWERS

Ron Chappell
Retired, Santa Fe Community College
Gainesville, FL

Kenneth Dytrt
Pennsylvania College of Technology
Williamsport, PA

Paul Garcia
New Mexico State University—Grants Campus
Grants, NM

Deno Garzolini
Ivy Tech Community College
Terre Haute, IN

Larry Leavitt
Pennsylvania College of Technology
Williamsport, PA

Jack D. Larmor
Baker College—Flint
Flint, Michigan

Dan Livingston
Jackson Community College
Jackson, MI

Calvin Motley
Central New Mexico Community College
Albuquerque, NM

Dan Wilson
Westwood College
Denver, CO

Christopher Woods
University of Northwestern Ohio
Lima

OVERVIEW OF ENGINE PERFORMANCE

1

Upon completion and review of this chapter, you should be able to:

- Describe the relationship of basic engine construction to engine performance.
- Describe the basic function of the cooling, fuel, and air induction systems.
- Explain similarities between distributor ignition systems and distributorless ignition systems.
- Explain the relationship of intake and exhaust systems to engine performance.
- Explain the basic function of the Exhaust Gas Recirculaton (EGR) valve.
- Explain the basic function of the Positive Crankcase Ventilation (PCV) valve.
- Describe the function of the catalytic converter.
- Describe the basic function of the evaporative emissions system.
- Examine basic differences between OBD I and OBD II.

INTRODUCTION

Congratulations! Since you are taking a course in Engine Performance, you are about to combine most of the knowledge you have gained to date and use it to start diagnosis of "drivability" problems. The Engine Performance Specialist is usually one of the most highly talented people in the shop. It takes a good foundation in electricity and electronics. It requires knowledge of the engine and how it works along with basic transmission operation. You will be surprised at how many transmission complaints are actually related to engine performance. The engine performance person also does most of the electrical diagnosis and scan tool work, so you will also need some knowledge of basic engine testing, computer operation, networking, body control modules, and so forth, which is included to help you in your career. I hope you find this text helpful in your pursuit of the most challenging and rewarding facets of automotive service.

BASIC ENGINE CONSTRUCTION

An automotive engine, whether gasoline or diesel, is classified as an **internal combustion** engine because the burning—or **combustion**—takes place inside the engine. Burning the airfuel mixture inside the engine produces large amounts of pressure which powers the engine. The engine must be strong enough to withstand the high temperatures and pressures of combustion.

The **engine block** is the largest single piece of the engine and is usually cast from iron or aluminum (Figure 1-1). The block is bored with large holes called **cylinders** which are fitted with **pistons, connecting rods**, and **crankshaft**. The crankshaft and connecting rods turn the up-and-down motion of the pistons into the rotary motion of the crankshaft (Figure 1-2). The engine block and crankshaft also contain lubrication and cooling passages.

FIGURE 1-1 *An aluminum engine block uses a steel cylinder liner for durability. (Courtesy of Chrysler Corporation)*

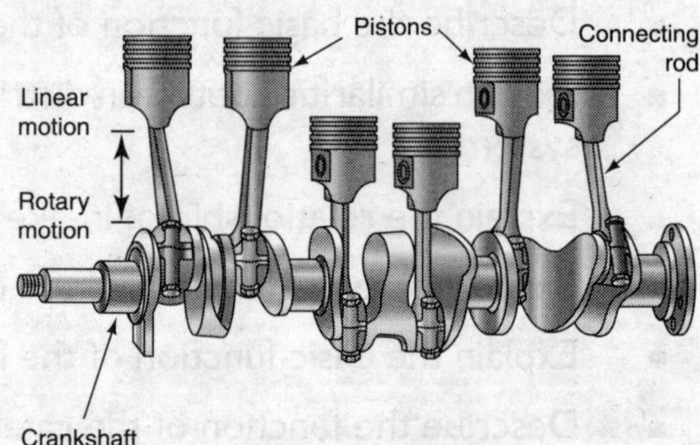

FIGURE 1-2 *The reciprocating motion of the piston is converted to rotary motion by the crankshaft.*

The **cylinder head** fits over the top of the engine block and seals the area over the piston (Figure 1-3). The cylinder head contains the valves and passages necessary to allow the air-fuel mixture into the cylinder and the exhaust out (Figure 1-4). The valves are operated by a **camshaft** that opens the **intake valves** and **exhaust valves** at the correct time during the rotation of the engine.

Four-Stroke Cycle

The four-stroke cycle is described as **intake, compression, power,** and **exhaust** (Figure 1-5). During the intake stroke, the intake valve is opened and the piston is moving down, pulling the air-fuel mix-

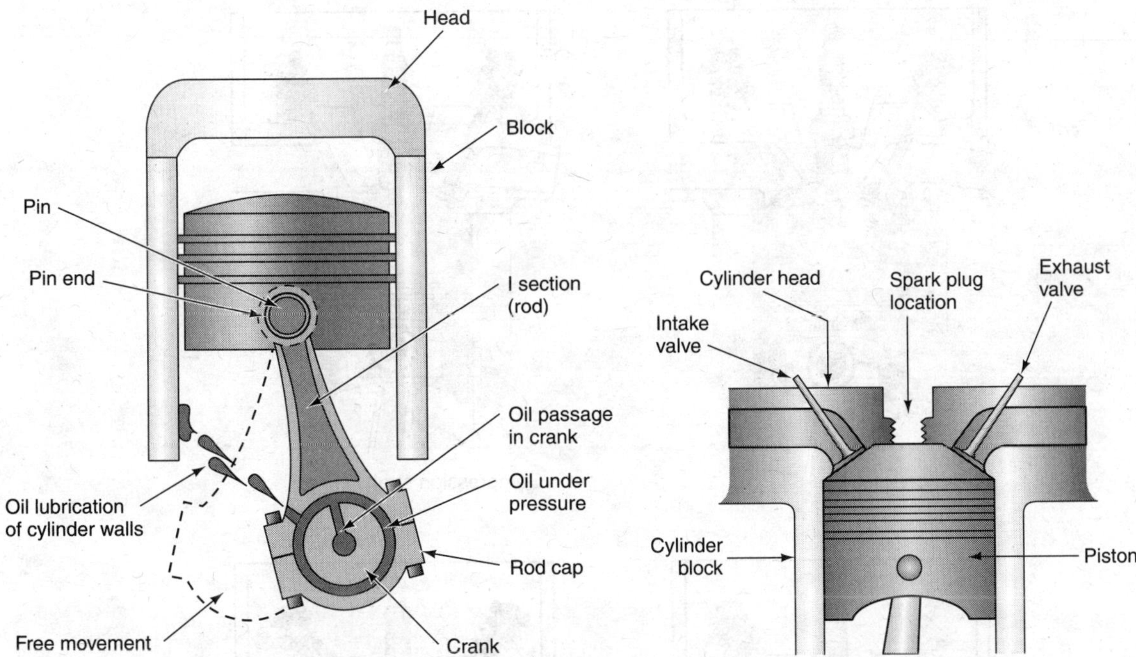

FIGURE 1-3 *Piston, connecting rod, head, and block relationships.*

FIGURE 1-4 *Placement of intake and exhaust valves.*

ture into the cylinder. The intake valve closes and the piston moves upwards compressing and heating the air-fuel mixture. The mixture is ignited by the sparkplug and the rapidly expanding gases push the piston down. The piston goes to the bottom of the cylinder, then the exhaust valve opens and the piston moves back up, ready for the process to start over with another intake stroke.

Intake and Exhaust Manifolds

The intake manifold delivers the air-fuel mixture to the cylinder head's intake passage (Figure 1-6). There are many different designs of intake manifolds depending on the injection method, but all are designed to offer the least amount of restriction to airflow. The exhaust manifold carries the exhaust and its heat away from the engine (Figure 1-7). One of the easiest ways to gain power from an engine is to make it breathe easier through less restrictive exhaust and intake manifolds.

Engine Systems

Every engine also has to include the **cooling system** (Figure 1-8). The cooling system is responsible for carrying combustion heat away from the engine and maintaining a desired operating temperature as well as providing heat for the passenger compartment. A water pump circulates the coolant through the engine and radiator. The thermostat keeps the coolant at an operating temperature that is high enough for maximum cylinder efficiency. Engines that run too cool produce excessive emissions and do not run hot enough to boil off water and residual fuel out of the oil. On the other hand, an overheating engine can cause severe engine damage in a matter of minutes.

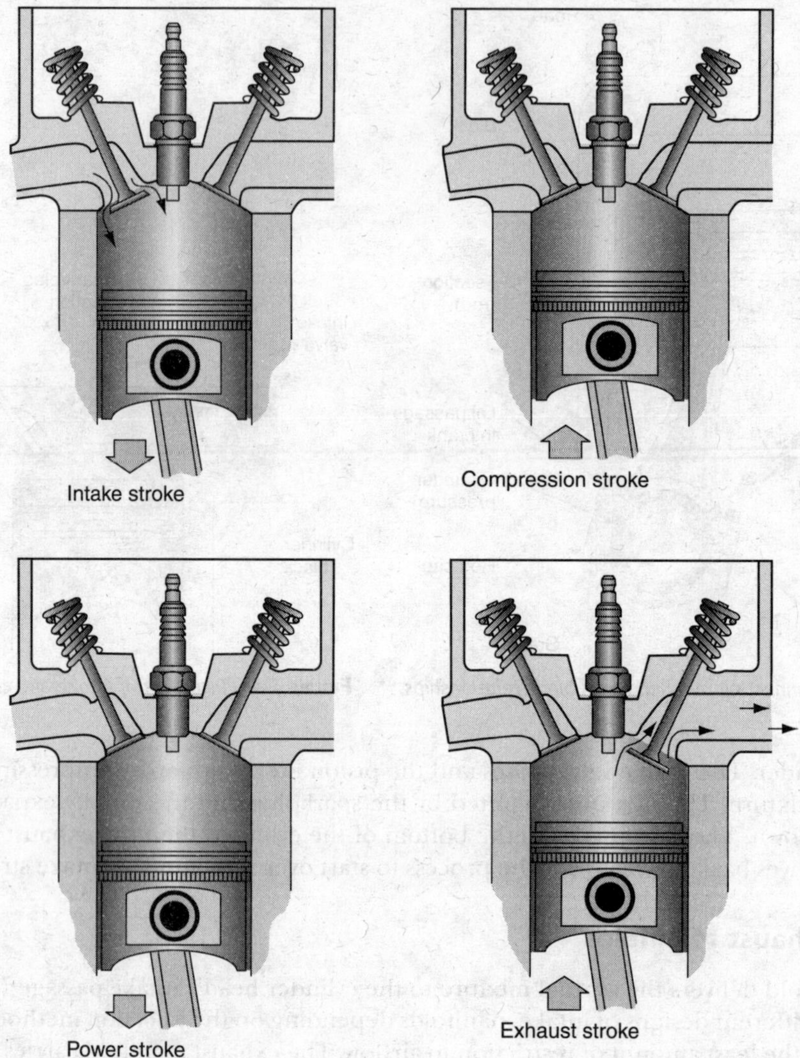

FIGURE 1-5 *The four-stroke cycle.*

Lubrication System

Another critical system is the lubrication system (Figure 1-9). The oil pump provides pressurized oil throughout the engine via drilled passages in the head, block, and crankshaft. Moving engine parts are riding on a film of oil. Obviously, if the metal parts of the engine touch, they wear rapidly and produce heavy damage to internal parts. The life of the engine depends on the operation of the cooling and lubrication systems. Make sure your customers realize the importance of maintaining these systems!

Fuel System

The **fuel system** (Figure 1-10) stores and delivers clean fuel at the proper pressure. The fuel is delivered to the fuel injector assembly. There are three principle types of fuel injection in use today; port

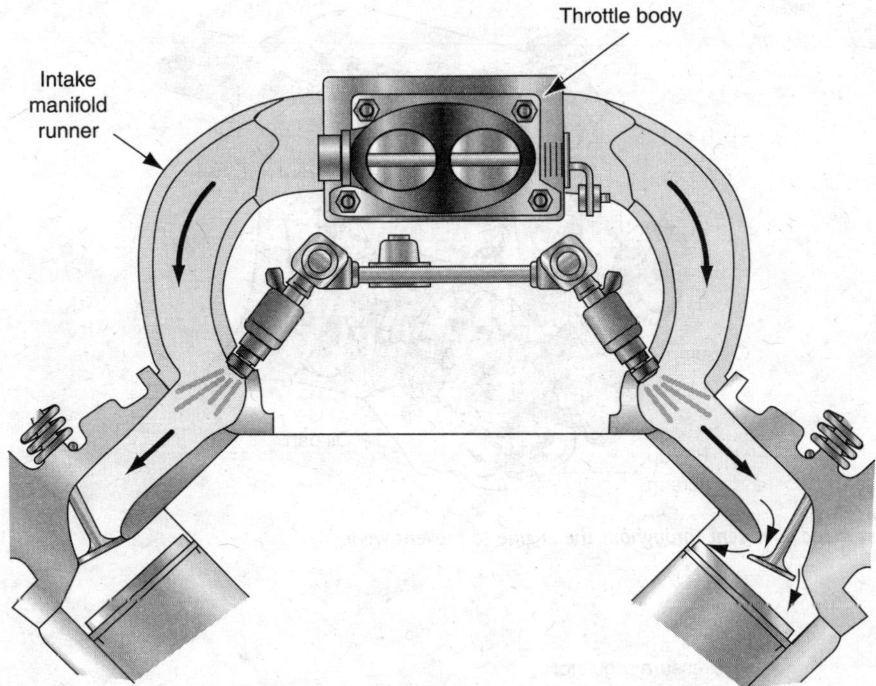

Figure 1-6 *A fuel-injected engine's intake manifold.*

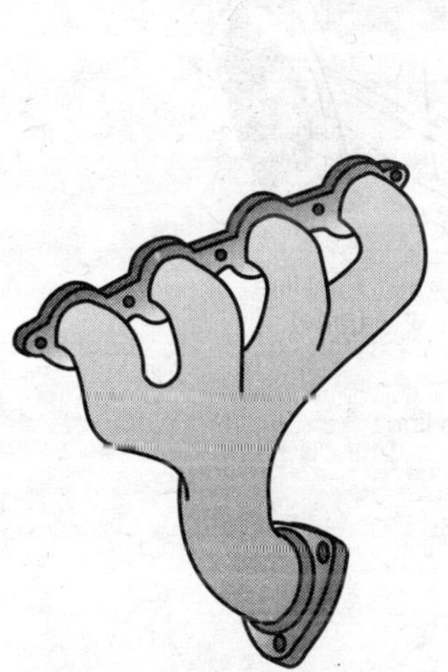

Figure 1-7 *Exhaust manifold.*

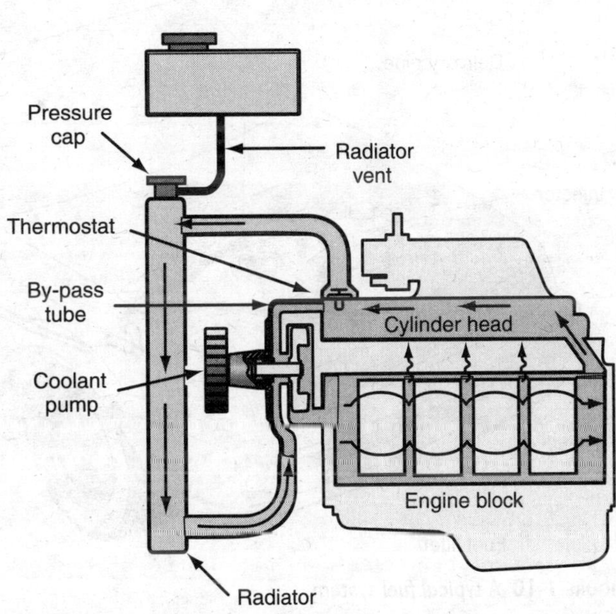

Figure 1-8 *The engine's cooling system.*

fuel injection, throttle body injection (TBI), and direct fuel injection. In port fuel injection, (Figure 1-11) each cylinder has its own injector that sprays a fine atomized mist of fuel directly behind the intake valve. Throttle body injection (Figure 1-12) utilizes one or two injectors positioned at the top of the intake manifold. Under normal operating conditions, the computer tries to produce a

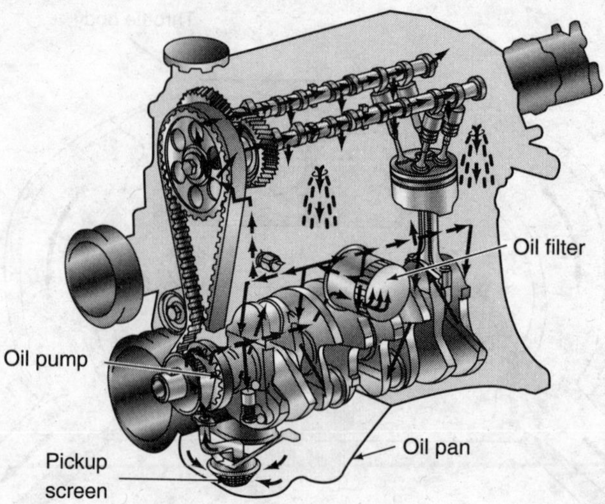

FIGURE 1-9 *Pressurized oil is sent throughout the engine to prevent wear.*

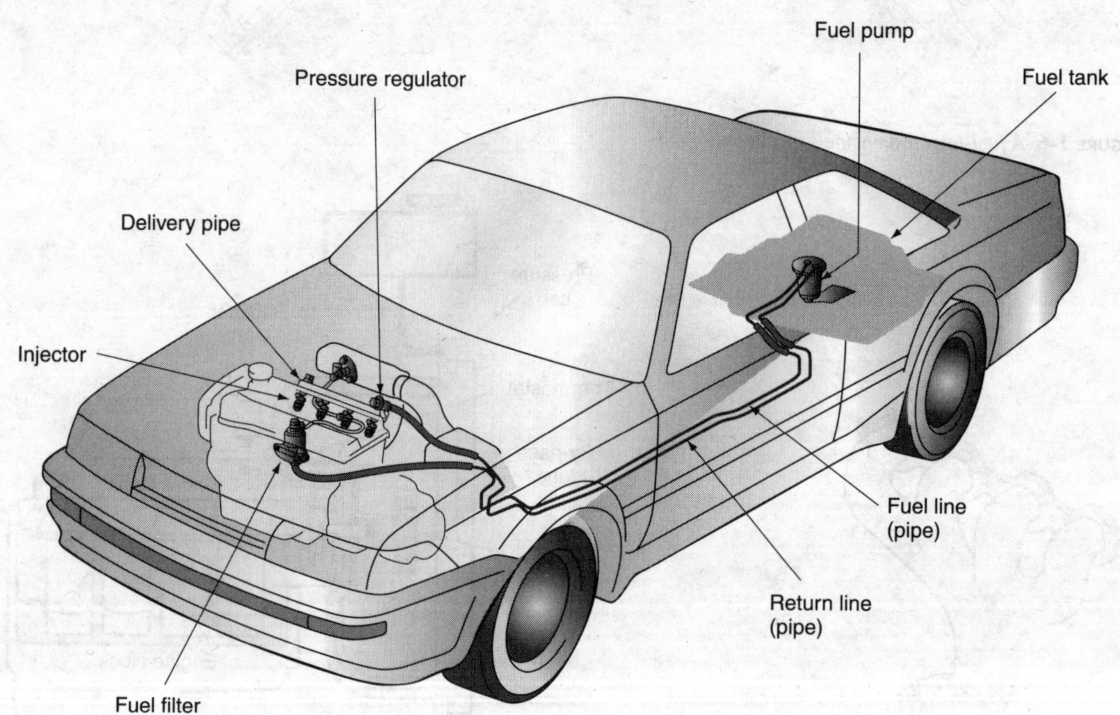

FIGURE 1-10 *A typical fuel system.*

mixture which is 14.7 parts air to one part fuel, but under some conditions such as a cold engine or acceleration, the mixture must be much richer. The fuel and air mixture are changed by the amount of time the fuel injectors are left on. The injectors are left on longer when conditions require more fuel. The computer can control fuel delivery based on engine sensors such as coolant, intake air, manifold pressure, mass air flow, and throttle position sensors. Direct fuel injection has some major

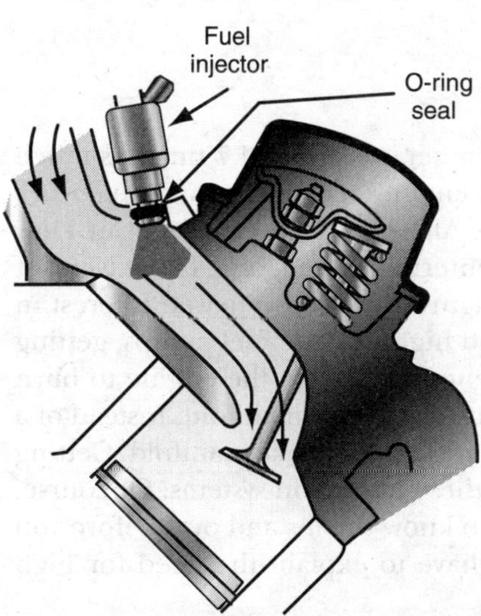

FIGURE 1-11 *A port fuel injection system.*

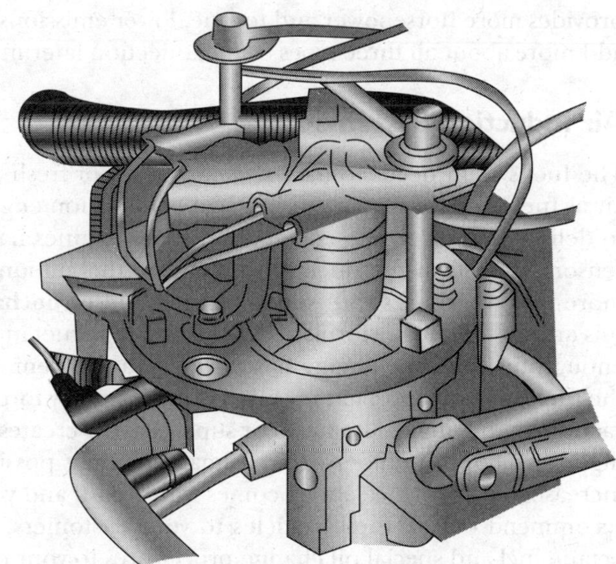

FIGURE 1-12 *A throttle body injection system.*

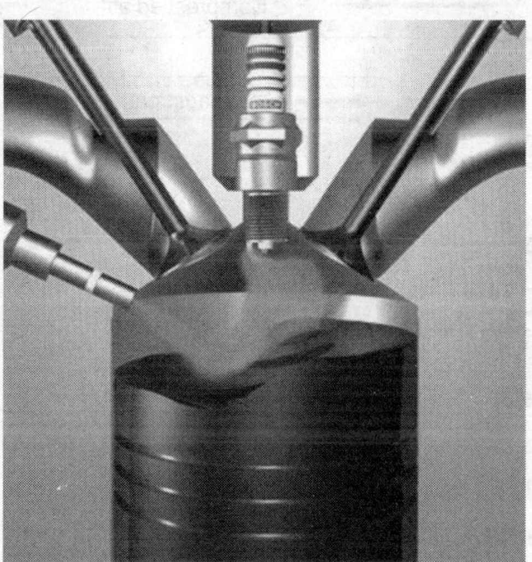

FIGURE 1-13 *Direct fuel injection.*

differences from Throttle Body Injection (TBI) and port fuel injection (PFI). The fuel is injected directly into the cylinder instead of behind the intake valve (Figure 1-13). The advantage of injecting fuel directly into the cylinder is the ability to deliver fuel without restriction from the intake valve and the ability to inject the fuel at any time during the intake cycle, nearly to top dead center (TDC). The fuel is injected at a much, much higher pressure than port fuel or TBI (over 2,000 psi). Most of the direct injection engines also have a special piston that keeps the direct injected fuel near the sparkplug so a very small amount of fuel (corresponding to a very lean mixture) can be ignited. The engines that use direct injection also have much higher compression than other fuel injection types. The added fuel pressure provides more atomization, which helps cool the combustion chamber and allows for higher compression ratios without contributing to spark knock. Direct fuel injection provides more horsepower and torque, lower emissions, and better fuel economy. Of course, we will add more about all three types of fuel injection later in the text.

Air Induction Systems

The fuel system needs to have a clean supply of fresh air. Remember, we need 14.7 times as much air as fuel in order to run our internal combustion engine. Most engines have a system of ductwork to deliver cool air to the engine, and some engines have a Mass Air Flow (MAF) or Vane Air Flow sensor installed in the ducting to measure the amount of air entering the engine. The advent of more factory vehicles with **supercharging** and **turbocharging** (Figure 1-14) has renewed interest in this area of engine performance. By using large fuel injectors and highpressure fuel pumps, getting enough fuel into the engine has not been a problem. Getting enough air into the engine to burn the fuel *is* a problem. That problem is overcome by forcing air into the intake manifold. Instead of a vacuum in the intake, the turbo or supercharger creates pressure inside the intake manifold. Getting high horsepower numbers from a small engine is possible with these induction systems. Of course, increased performance always comes with a cost, and you need to know the ins and outs before you recommend one of these vehicles to your customers. You will have to explain the need for high octane fuel and special oil change procedures to your customers.

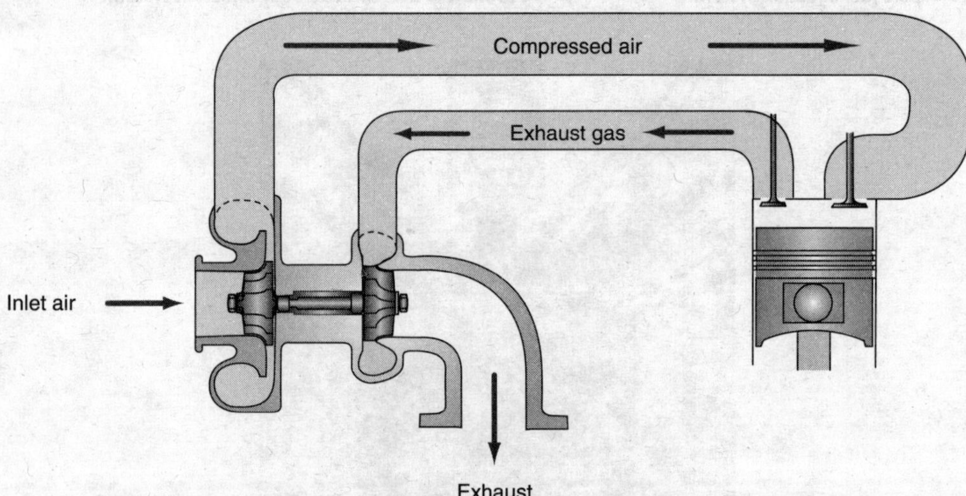

FIGURE 1-14 *Turbocharging forces air into the combustion chamber.*

EMISSION CONTROL SYSTEM

There are principally three emissions that have to be controlled on the automobile: **hydrocarbons** (HC), **carbon monoxide** (CO), and **oxides of nitrogen** (NO_x). The Environmental Protection Agency (EPA) has established guidelines for the emission of these gases. Great strides have been made since the 1960s in controlling these pollutants, but because more miles are being driven by more vehicles each year, there are still problems with these pollutants. HC is unburned fuel, CO is partially burned fuel, and NO_x is nitrogen that has been burned in the engine. Nitrogen is difficult to burn, and this usually forms due to high combustion temperatures. We will give you a quick overview of some of the most important systems that are used to control emissions (Figure 1-15).

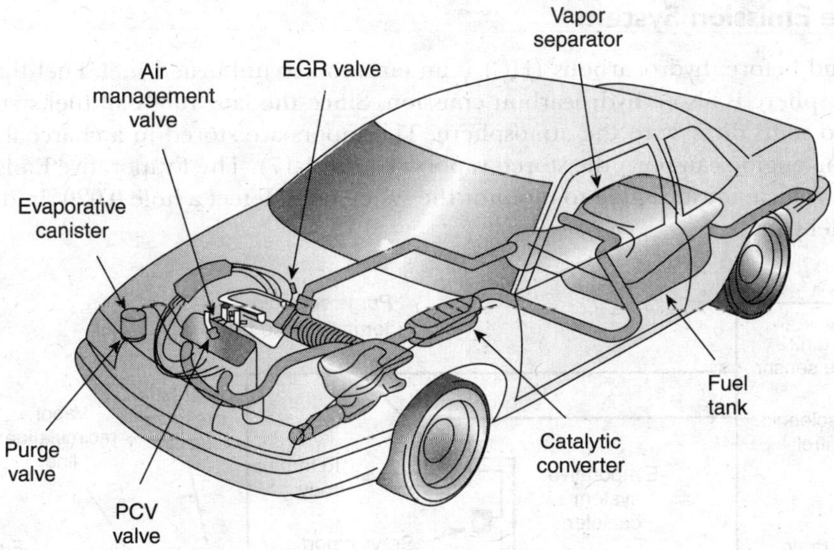

FIGURE 1-15 *Overview of basic emission systems.*

Positive Crankcase Ventilation

The **positive crankcase ventilation** (PCV) system controls "blow-by." Blow-by is the combustion gas that finds its way past the piston rings and into the crankcase. This would cause the crankcase to become pressurized, causing leaks and hydrocarbon (HC) emissions. Additionally, the combustion gases contain unburned fuel and water that would eventually contaminate the oil. The PCV system removes the crankcase pressure and burned blow-by gases (Figure 1-16). The PCV is among the earliest emission control system.

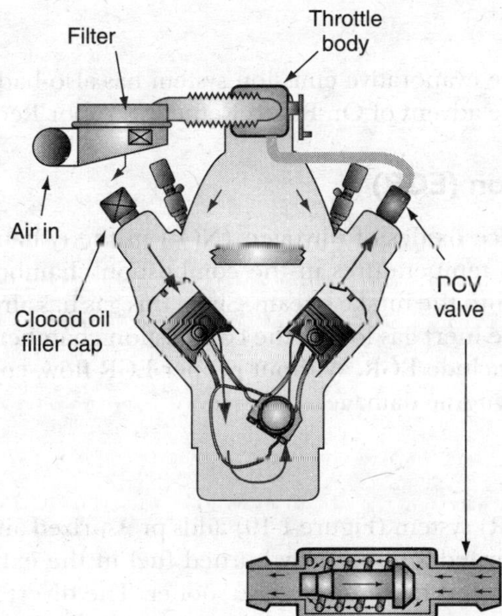

FIGURE 1-16 *The PCV system helps eliminate crankcase pressure, along with water and unburned fuel.*

Evaporative Emission System

As we have said before, hydrocarbons (HC) is an emission of unburned fuel. Fuel that evaporates into the atmosphere is also a hydrocarbon emission. Since the late 1960s all fuel systems must be sealed with no vents directly to the atmosphere. The vapors are stored in a charcoal canister and stored until the engine can burn the stored vapors (Figure 1-17). The Evaporative Emissions System on an OBD II vehicle must be able to monitor the system and detect a hole 0.020″ in diameter as of the 2002 model year.

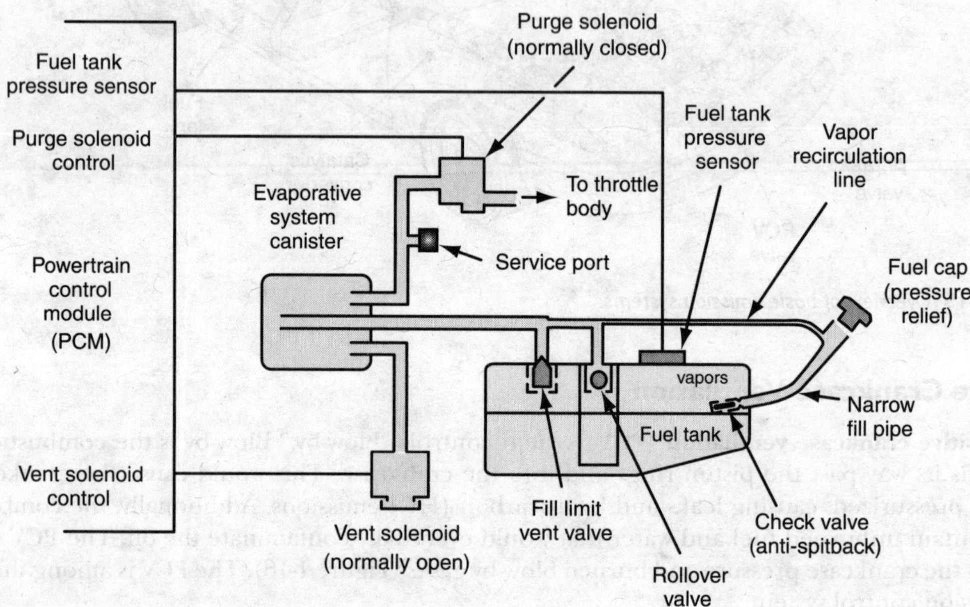

FIGURE 1-17 *Enhanced evaporative emission controls.*

Additionally, since 1998 the evaporative emission system has also had to store all the vapors produced while refueling with the advent of On-Board Refueling Vapor Recovery, or ORVR.

Exhaust Gas Recirculation (EGR)

The EGR valve helps to reduce oxides of nitrogen (NO_x) in the exhaust (Figure 1-18). Oxides of nitrogen are formed by high temperatures in the combustion chamber. The EGR valve meters a small amount of exhaust gas into the intake stream. Since this gas has already been burned, it is basically inert. The addition of the inert gas lowers the combustion chamber temperature. Fuel delivery is calculated by the PCM to include EGR. Without proper EGR flow, combustion temperatures are too high and can even cause engine damage.

Air Injection System

The **air injection reaction** (AIR) system (Figure 1-19) adds pressurized air into the exhaust manifold. This burns some of the unburned and partially burned fuel in the exhaust manifold which helps to heat the catalytic converter and make it effective sooner. The diverter valve diverts air from the pump into the exhaust stream under some conditions (such as deceleration) to prevent backfire.

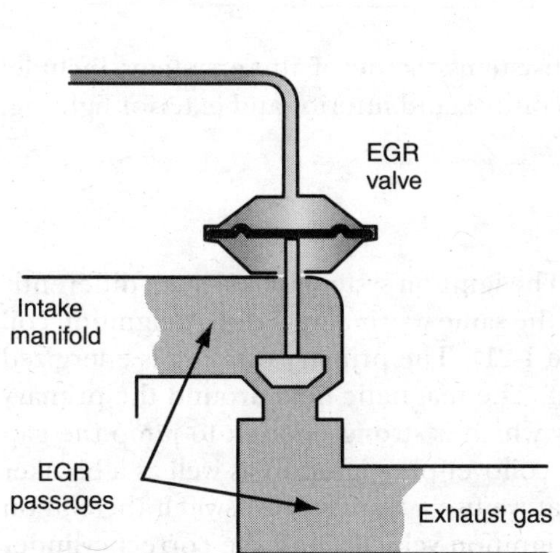

FIGURE 1-18 *EGR cools down combustion temperatures by introducing some exhaust gas into the intake manifold.*

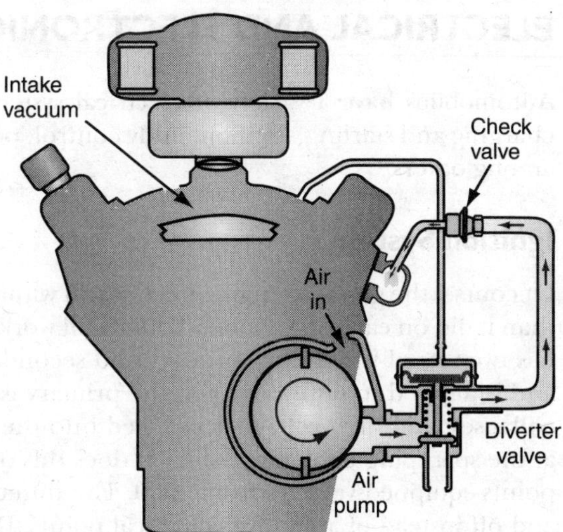

FIGURE 1-19 *The air injection reaction (AIR) system injects air directly into the exhaust manifold.*

The check valves prevent exhaust from backing up into the rubber hoses of the AIR system. Older systems also directed air into the catalytic converter after the engine was warm.

Catalytic Converter

The catalytic converter is designed to clean up vehicle exhaust by the oxidation and reduction of exhaust gases (Figure 1-20). A catalyst is anything that promotes a reaction with its presence but is not changed by the reaction. Problem exhaust gases are carbon monoxide, hydrocarbons, and oxides of nitrogen. Carbon monoxide and hydrocarbons are **oxidized** (burned) in the converter. Oxides of nitrogen are **reduced**, which means the nitrogen and oxygen are split apart.

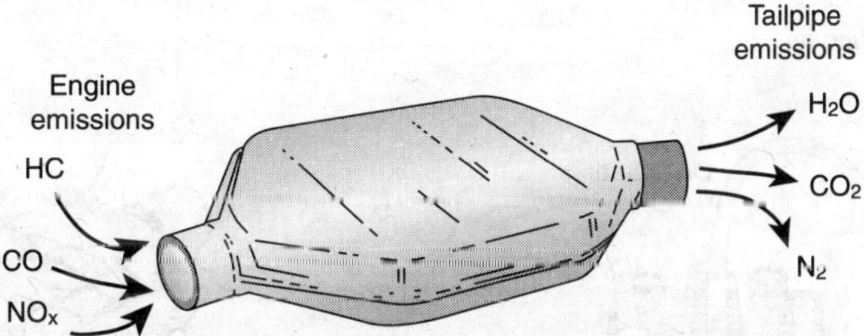

FIGURE 1-20 *The catalytic converter oxidizes HC and CO and reduces NO_x.*

Exhaust System

The exhaust system carries the toxic exhaust fumes away from the vehicle and makes the engine quiet. The catalytic converter is also part of the exhaust system. The exhaust system requires pipes, heat shields, mufflers, resonators, and hangers.

ELECTRICAL AND ELECTRONIC SYSTEMS

Automobiles have a variety of electrical systems and subsystems. Some of these systems include: charging and starting, ignition, body control, powertrain control, and interior and exterior lighting, among others.

Ignition System

Of course, the gasoline engine cannot run without spark. The ignition system looks much differently than it did on early automobiles, but it still works basically the same way it always did. An ignition coil has two sets of windings: a primary and secondary (Figure 1-21). The primary winding is energized and is allowed to saturate. Then the primary is turned off. The magnetic field around the primary collapses, and high voltage is induced into the secondary which is strong enough to jump the gap at the sparkplug on compression. It does this on modern coilover-plug ignition as well as a breaker points-equipped vehicles from 1960. The difference is that we use a transistor to switch the coil on and off instead of a set of mechanical points. Distributor ignition vehicles find the correct cylinder to fire because it is indexed mechanically when the rotor button points to the correct cylinder in the distributor (Figure 1-22). Coil-overplug and distributorless ignition systems (Figure 1-23) find

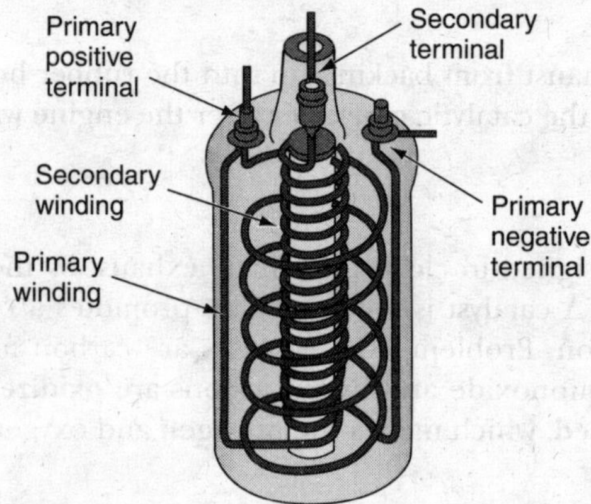

FIGURE 1-21 *Typical ignition oil.*

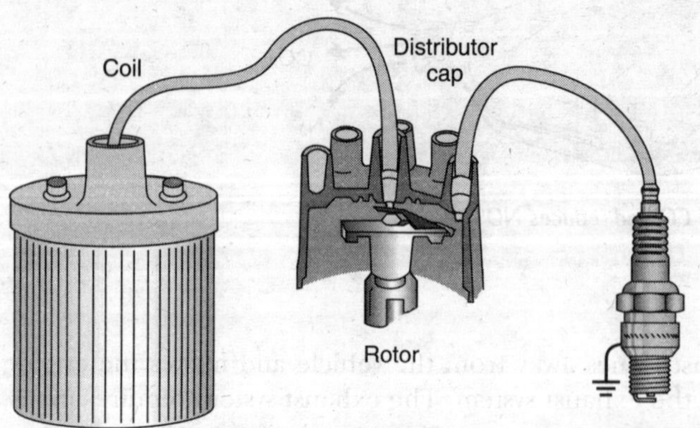

FIGURE 1-22 *Typical distributor ignition.*

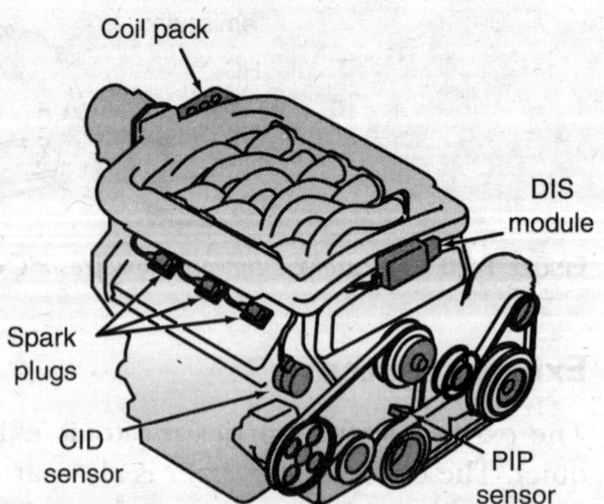

FIGURE 1-23 *Ford's distributorless ignition components.*

which cylinder needs to fire by using sensors and a computer. The computer's sensors allow very precise control of timing, resulting in increased fuel mileage and power. The computer knows or calculates the amount of air entering the engine, the gear the transmission is in, the engine load, the engine temperature, the temperature of the air entering the intake, whether or not the engine is spark-knocking.... You should start to get an idea of how the manufacturers managed to meet fuel economy standards and still have cars that are fun to drive.

Starting System

The starting system is of course to start the vehicle. A small current from the ignition switch is used to close the contacts on the starter solenoid or relay which sends full battery current to the starter motor (Figure 1-24). The starter motor turns the crankshaft, the ignition fires the plugs at the right time, and if successful in starting, the engine takes over on its own and the key is allowed to return to the run position. The starter has to be able to turn the engine at a high enough speed to allow compression temperature to rise to a suitable level or starting may not take place.

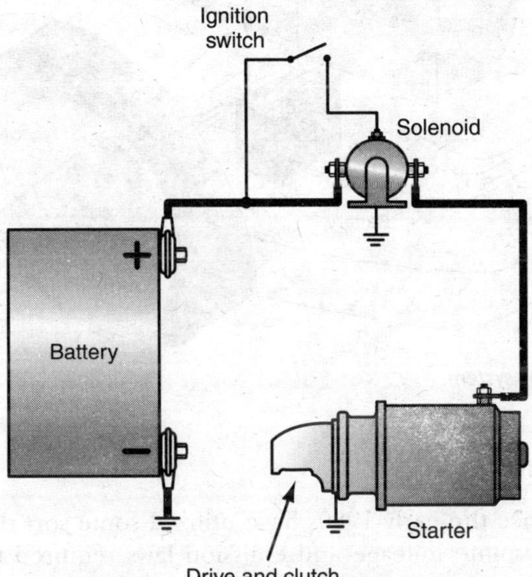

FIGURE 1-24 *Small current from the ignition switch activates a solenoid which connects battery power to the starter motor.*

Charging Systems

The charging system (Figure 1-25) exists to recharge the battery. Engine starting drains much of the battery power, and the charging system replenishes the battery for the next start. The charging system also powers accessories when the engine is running. The load on the electrical system is sensed by the voltage regulator, and the alternator responds with an appropriate charge. The battery is there to help fill any temporary gaps the charging system may have, such as sitting still at a stop light, air conditioning or cooling fan turned on, etc. If the alternator is charging the battery, it is said to be charging. If more current is flowing from the battery than the alternator, it is said to be discharging.

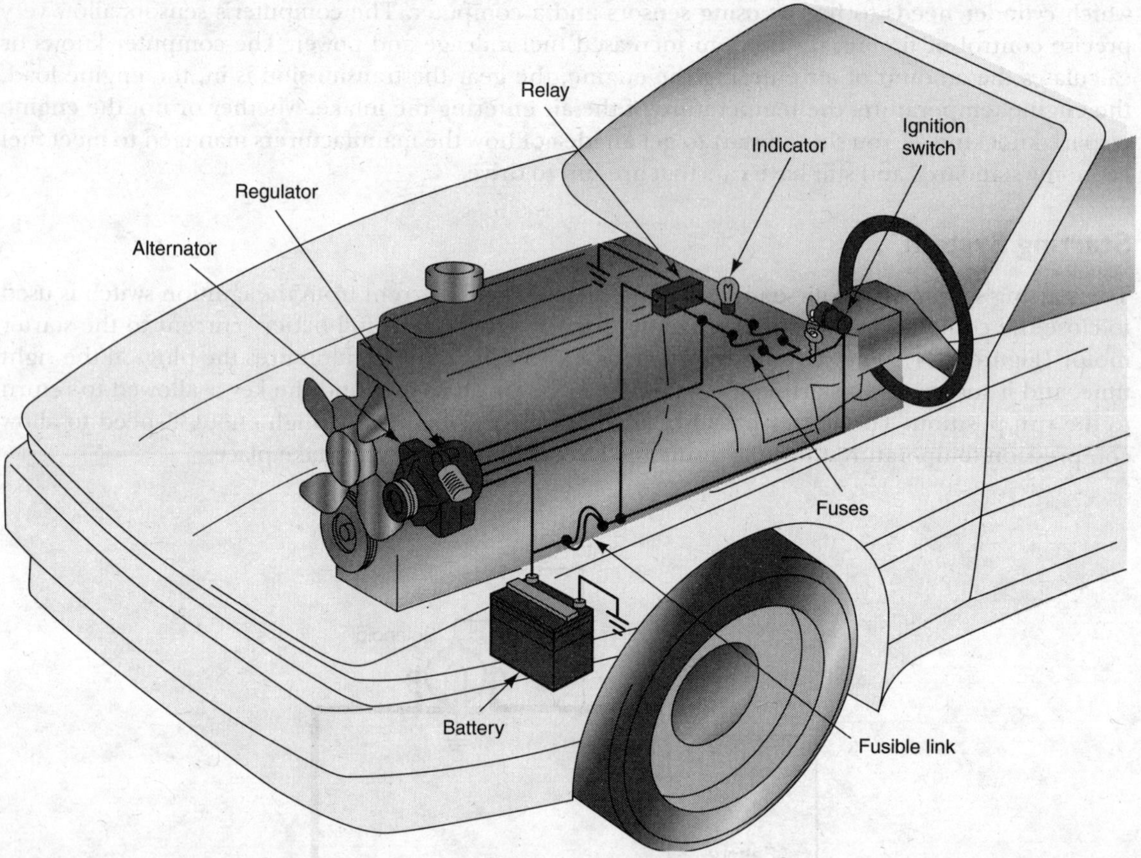

FIGURE 1-25 *Parts of the charging system.*

Electronic Engine Controls

Most vehicles produced since the early 1980s have utilized some sort of electronic control system (Figure 1-26). Stringent gasoline mileage and emission laws required the accuracy of computers using a variety of sensors that have brought us to where we are today: good fuel economy and low emissions with good performance. Electronic systems have fewer moving parts to wear out or lose calibration than their electronic counterparts. Fewer repairs are needed, and maintenance is reduced.

The first computer-controlled emission system has been termed **OBD** (On Board Diagnostics), or **OBD I**. These systems were made from the late 1970s until the implementation of **OBD II** in 1996. The OBD I systems were meant to be serviced using tools that every shop owned at the time. For example, on a General Motors (GM) vehicle, a dwell meter on the sixcylinder scale was used to read the commands the computer was sending for the air-fuel mixture. These systems had **flash codes** that anyone could access, such as Chrysler's method of turning the key on and off three times in rapid succession to start the "Check Engine" lamp flashing engine codes. OBD I was designed to catch faults in sensor circuits and output devices.

OBD II vehicles are designed to not only catch faults in sensor circuits and output devices, but to be able to test components for proper operation while driving. Flash codes are not generally available for OBD II vehicles, so a scan tool will be necessary to access codes. However, OBD II computers are much faster and more capable than those of the OBD I vehicles. More codes and information is

Inputs from sensors	Computer processing	Outputs using actuators
Mass airflow (amount of air entering the engine) Crank sensor (engine speed) Cam sensor (camshaft position) Throttle position sensor Coolant temperature sensor Intake air temperature Oxygen sensor/air-fuel ratio Knock (spark knock) sensor	Computer takes inputs and processes them according to its programming and then determines the appropriate outputs. The computer also compensates fuel delivery for such conditions as a cold engine, wide open throttle, or idle.	Fuel injectors Timing control Exhaust gas recirculation (EGR) Idle control

FIGURE 1-26 *Computer controlled systems receive inputs from sensors and perform outputs based on their programming.*

available than ever before, and these continue to grow every year. The technician who embraces and understands this technology can use this wealth of information to make his or her job easier.

Electronic control systems have three main components: input sensors to determine operating conditions, a computer programmed to interpret these results, and output devices designed to carry out the commands of the computer. Electronic control systems can also be reprogrammed as necessary to correct many problems that may arise after the vehicle has been produced. In the past, calibration changes meant changing or modifying parts.

REVIEW QUESTIONS

Short Answer Essays

1. Explain why the engine performance technician is probably one of the most skilled technicians in the shop.
2. Explain why diesel and gasoline engines are termed internal combustion engines.
3. Explain the purpose of the cylinder head.
4. Explain the four-stroke cycle.
5. Explain how a turbo or supercharger raises engine power.
6. Explain why a PCV valve is needed.
7. Explain how the EGR valve lowers combustion temperatures.
8. Explain the basic operation of the catalytic converter.
9. Explain what type of emission is controlled by the evaporative emissions and how it is accomplished.
10. Explain how the lubrication system prevents wear.

Fill-in-the-Blanks

1. The evaporation of fuel is a _______________ emission.
2. We need _______________ times as much air as fuel in order to run our internal combustion engine.
3. An ignition coil has two sets of windings: a _______________ and _______________.
4. One of the easiest ways to gain power from an engine is to make it _______________ easier through less restrictive exhaust and intake manifolds.
5. A _______________ _______________ circulates coolant through the engine and radiator.
6. Moving engine parts are riding on a _______________ of _______________.
7. There are two principle types of fuel injection in use today: _______________, and _______________ _______________.
8. The fuel-air mixture is changed by the _______________ of _______________ the fuel injectors are on.
9. The oldest emission control is the _______________ valve.
10. The _______________ valve meters a small amount of exhaust gas into the intake stream.

Multiple Choice

1. The EGR valve is designed to reduce:
   A. Oxides of oxygen
   B. Carbon Monoxide
   C. Carbon dioxide
   D. Oxides of nitrogen
2. Technician A says that the catalytic converter oxidizes hydrocarbons (HC). Technician B says that the catalytic converter oxidizes CO (carbon monoxide). Who's right?
   A. Technician A
   B. Technician B
   C. Both Technicians
   D. Neither Technician
3. Technician A says that the evaporative emissions system (EVAP) on a 2003 vehicle must detect a leak from a hole 0.020" in diameter. Technician B says that the ORVR portion of the evaporative emissions system is designed to capture fuel vapors produced during refueling. Who is correct?
   A. Technician A
   B. Technician B
   C. Both Technicians
   D. Neither Technician
4. The alternator does all of the following ***except:***
   A. Recharges the battery after starting the engine.
   B. Senses electrical load with the diodes
   C. Responds with more current when additional electrical loads are added.
   D. Powers accessories when the engine is running

5. Technician A says that overheating can damage an engine in a matter of minutes. Technician B says that overcooling an engine by removing the thermostat prolongs engine life.
   A. Technician A
   B. Technician B
   C. Both Technicians
   D. Neither Technician
6. All of the following are types of fuel injection ***except***:
   A. Port-fuel Injection
   B. Intermittent Injection
   C. Throttle body injection
   D. Direct fuel injection
7. The proper sequence for the four-cycle engine is:
   A. intake-exhaust-power-compression
   B. compression-power-intake-exhaust
   C. power-intake-compression-exhaust
   D. intake-compression-power-exhaust
8. Technician A says that the PCV system was introduced in 1998. Technician B says the PCV system helps eliminate blow-by and oil contamination by unburned fuel. Who is correct?
   A. Technician A
   B. Technician B
   C. Both Technicians
   D. Neither Technician
9. In Figure 1-27, Technician A says the solenoid is used so a small amount of current through the ignition switch can be used to control the much larger starter current. Technician B says current to start the vehicle travels directly through the ignition switch and them to the starter. Who is correct?
   A. Technician A
   B. Technician B
   C. Both Technicians
   D. Neither Technician

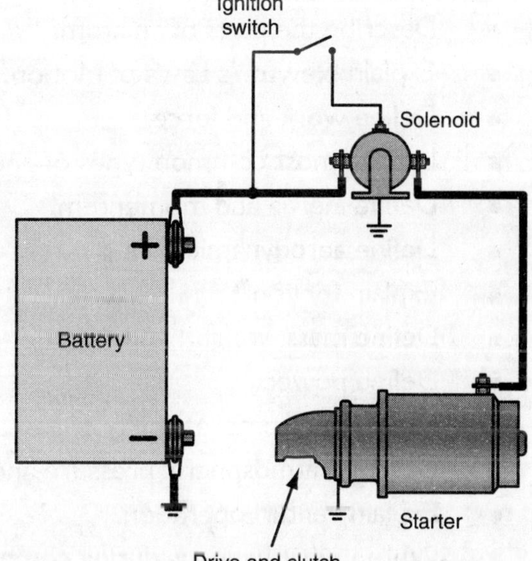

FIGURE 1-27 *Starter Circuit*

10. Technician A says that direct injection is an earlier version of port fuel injection. Technician B says that direct injection systems inject fuel directly into the intake manifold. Who is correct?
    A. Technician A
    B. Technician B
    C. Both Technicians
    D. Neither Technician

BASIC THEORIES 2

Upon completion and review of this chapter, you should be able to:

- Define atoms and elements.
- Define compounds and molecules.
- Describe the parts of an atom.
- Explain Newton's Laws of Motion.
- Define work and force.
- List the most common types of energy and energy conversions.
- Define inertia and momentum.
- Define aerodynamics.
- Explain friction.
- Define mass, weight, and volume.
- Define power.
- Explain the compressibility of gases and the noncompressibility of liquids.
- Describe atmospheric pressure and vacuum.
- Explain venturi operation.
- Explain what happens during combustion.
- Describe acids and bases.
- Explain basic gear theory.

INTRODUCTION

An understanding of the basics is absolutely essential before a study of complex systems and components is attempted. Basic engine theories such as force, work, torque, and power must be understood prior to a study of engine components, systems, and diagnosis in this book. To truly understand how an engine works, you must have a basic understanding of these principles of chemistry and physics. Other important concepts that you must understand are those related to electricity and electronics. These topics are covered in much detail in the next chapter of this book. If you have previously studied engine theory and physics, the information in this chapter may be used as a review. A thorough study of this chapter will provide all the necessary background information before you study the information in this book.

THE BASICS

Atoms and Elements

An **atom** may be defined as the smallest particle of an element in which all the chemical characteristics of the element are present. An **element** is defined as a liquid, solid, or gas that contains only one type of atom. For example, copper contains only copper atoms.

Compounds and Molecules

A **compound** is a liquid, solid, or gas that contains two or more types of atoms. Water is a compound that contains hydrogen and oxygen. A **molecule** is the smallest particle of a compound in which all the chemical characteristics of the compound are present.

Electrons, Protons, and Neutrons

A **proton** is a small, positively charged particle located at the center, or nucleus, of each atom.

An **electron** is a small, very light particle with a negative electrical charge. Electrons move in orbits around the nucleus of an atom.

A **neutron** does not have an electrical charge. These particles add weight to an atom. Neutrons are positioned in the nucleus of an atom.

Acids and Bases

An **acid** is a compound that breaks into hydrogen ions (+H) and another compound in a water solution. An ion is an atom or group of atoms with a positive or negative charge. Ions determine whether a compound is an acid or base. For example, H_2SO_4 is sulfuric acid, and in water would break into +H and $-SO_4$ ions. Acids have a sour taste. For example, a lemon contains citric acid. Acids attack some metals and produce hydrogen gas. Acids turn litmus paper from blue to red. Acids also react with alkalis (bases) to form salts. For example, NaOH (or sodium hydroxide, a powerful base) could combine with HCl (or hydrochloric acid) to form table salt and water. A **base** (alkali) is a compound that produces hydroxide (–OH) and another compound in water. Bases feel slippery to the touch and turn litmus paper from red to blue. Soaps are usually weak bases.

Electron Movement

The outer ring on an atom is called a **valence ring**. The number of electrons on the valence ring determines the electrical characteristics of the element.

NEWTON'S LAWS OF MOTION

First Law

A body in motion remains in motion, and a body at rest remains at rest unless some outside force acts on it. When a car is parked on a level street, it remains stationary unless it is driven or pushed. If the gas pedal is depressed with the engine running and the transmission in drive, the engine delivers power to the drive wheels, and this force moves the car.

Second Law

A body's acceleration is directly proportional to the force applied to it, and the body moves in a straight line away from the force. For example, if the engine power supplied to the drive wheels increases, the vehicle accelerates faster.

Third Law

For every action there is an equal and opposite reaction. A practical application of this law occurs when the wheel on a vehicle strikes a bump in the road surface. This action drives the wheel and suspension upward with a certain force, and a specific amount of energy is stored in the spring. After this action occurs, the spring forces the wheel and suspension downward with a force equal to the initial upward force.

WORK AND FORCE

When a force moves a certain mass a specific distance, **work** is produced. When work is accomplished, the mass may be lifted or slid on a surface (Figure 2-1). Since force is measured in pounds and distance is measured in feet, the measurement for work is foot-pounds (ft.-lb). In the metric system, work is measured in Newton meters (N·m). If a force moves a 3,000-pound vehicle for 50 feet, 150,000 foot-pounds of work are produced. Mechanical force acts on an object to start, stop, or change the direction of the object. It is possible to apply force to an object and not move the object. Under this condition, no work is done. Work is only accomplished when an object is moved.

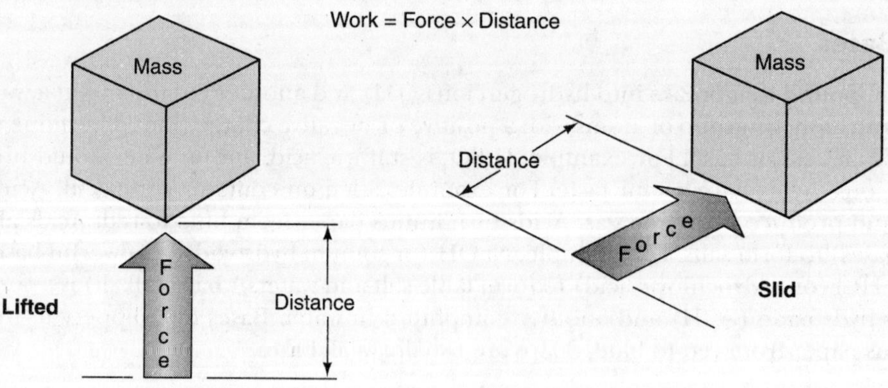

FIGURE 2-1 *Work is accomplished when a mass is lifted or slid on a surface.*

ENERGY

When **energy** is released to do work, it is called kinetic energy. This type of energy may also be referred to as energy in motion. Stored energy may be called potential energy. Energy is available in one of these seven forms:

1. Chemical energy is contained in the molecules of atoms. In the automobile, chemical energy is contained in the molecules of gasoline, and also in the molecules of electrolyte in a battery.
2. Electrical energy is required to move electrons through an electric circuit. In the automobile, the battery is capable of producing electrical energy to start the vehicle, and the alternator produces electrical energy to power the electrical accessories and recharge the battery.
3. Mechanical energy is defined as the ability to move objects. In the automobile, the battery supplies electrical energy to the starting motor, and this motor converts the electrical energy to mechanical energy to crank the engine.
4. Thermal energy may be defined as energy produced by heat. When gasoline burns, thermal energy is released.
5. Radiant energy is defined as light energy. In the automobile, radiant energy is produced by the lights.
6. Nuclear energy is defined as the energy within atoms when they are split apart or combined. Nuclear power plants generate electricity with this principle. This type of energy is not used in the automobile.
7. Solar energy is defined as a light-source energy that can be converted to heat or electricity. The photovoltaic effect is applied to convert light energy directly into electrical energy. Solar cells, consisting largely of semi-conductor materials, are the basic elements used for conversion.

ENERGY CONVERSION

Energy cannot really be destroyed or eliminated. It can only be changed or converted from one state, or form, to another. Energy conversion occurs when one form of energy is changed to another form. Since energy is not always in the desired form, it must be converted to a form we can use. Some of the most common automotive energy conversions are these:

Chemical to Thermal Energy Conversion

Chemical energy in gasoline or diesel fuel is converted to thermal energy when the fuel burns in the engine cylinders.

Thermal to Mechanical Energy Conversion

Mechanical energy is required to rotate the drive wheels and move the vehicle. The piston and crankshaft in the engine and the drive train are designed to convert the thermal energy produced by the burning fuel into mechanical energy (Figure 2-2).

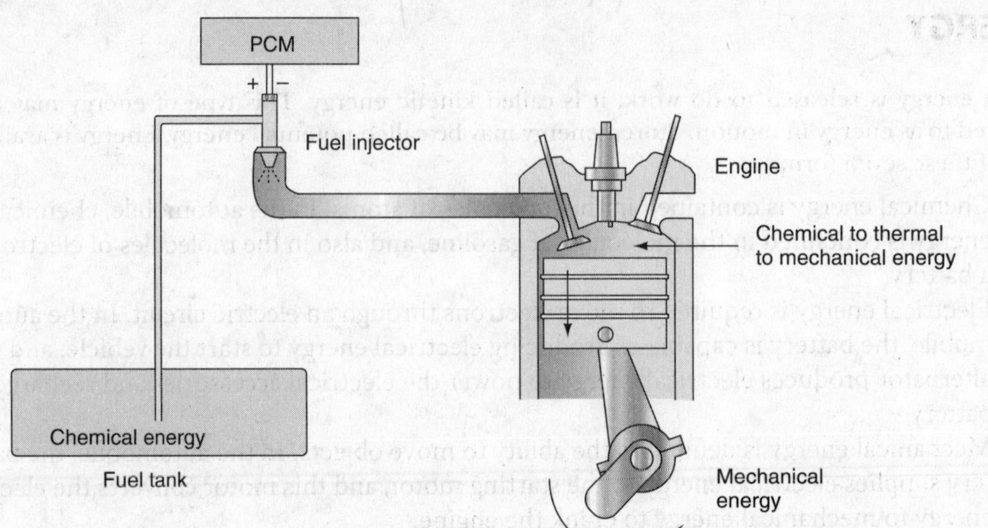

FIGURE 2-2 *Thermal energy in the fuel is converted to mechanical energy in the engine cylinders. The piston, crankshaft, and drivetrain deliver this mechanical energy to the drive wheels.*

Electrical to Mechanical Energy Conversion

The windshield wiper motor converts electrical energy from the battery or alternator to mechanical energy to drive the windshield wipers.

Mechanical to Electrical Energy Conversion

The alternator is driven by mechanical energy from the engine. The alternator converts this energy to electrical energy, which powers the electrical accessories on the vehicle.

Mechanical to Thermal Energy Conversion

The brakes of a vehicle change the mechanical energy of the moving vehicle to heat energy, in the form of **friction**, created by the action of the brake linings rubbing against the rotating brake drums or rotors.

Solar to Electrical Energy Conversion

Solar energy can be converted to electrical energy using special semi-conductors. One type of solar cell is a photoelectric cell or sensor. This converts the light signal into a voltage signal. It can be found on vehicles that have automatic headlamps that turn on when the sensor detects a specified amount of ambient light. When the voltage level reaches a specified point proportionate to the ambient light level, the headlamps will go on.

INERTIA

The **inertia** of an object at rest is called static inertia, whereas dynamic inertia refers to the inertia of an object in motion. Inertia exists in liquids, solids, and gases. When you push and move a parked vehicle, you overcome the static inertia of the vehicle. If you catch a ball in motion, you overcome the dynamic inertia of the ball.

MOMENTUM

Momentum is the product of an object's weight times its speed. Momentum is a type of mechanical energy. An object loses momentum if another force overcomes the dynamic inertia of the moving object.

FRICTION

Friction may occur in solids, liquids, and gases. When a car is driven down the road, friction occurs between the air and the car's surface. This friction opposes the momentum, or mechanical energy, of the moving vehicle. Since friction creates heat, some of the mechanical energy from the vehicle's momentum is changed to heat energy in the air and body components. The mechanical energy from the engine must overcome the vehicle inertia and the friction of the air striking the vehicle. Body design has a very dramatic effect on the amount of friction developed by the air striking the vehicle. The total resistance to motion caused by friction between a moving vehicle and the air is referred to as **coefficient of drag (Cd)**.

The study of Cd is very complicated and also very important. At 45 miles per hour (mph), or 72 kilometers per hour (kph), half of the engine's mechanical energy is used to overcome air friction, or resistance. Therefore, reducing a vehicle's Cd can be a very effective method of improving fuel economy.

AERODYNAMICS

Engineers are always looking for ways to make the automobile more efficient. Aerodynamics is the study of how objects like automobiles move through the air (Figure 2-3). Fuel mileage as well as handling is adversely affected by boxy shapes and flat surfaces facing forward. Ideally, air will follow the contours of the vehicle as it moves down the road. Early in the design of a new vehicle, a model is tested in a wind tunnel to assess the way it is going to slice through the air. Even the bottom of the vehicle must be taken into account because if the air gets an opportunity to lift up under the vehicle, it can make handling difficult and dangerous, as well as increasing drag. Air dams and spoilers are used to redirect air around the vehicle instead of beneath.

MASS, WEIGHT, AND VOLUME

A lawn mower is much easier to push than a 2,500-pound vehicle because the lawn mower has very little inertia compared to the vehicle. A spaceship might weigh 100 tons here on earth where it is affected by the earth's gravitational pull, but the mass remains the same. In outer space beyond the earth's gravity and atmosphere, the spaceship is almost weightless. Here on earth, **mass** and **weight** are measured in pounds and ounces in the English system. In the metric system, mass and weight are measured in grams and/or kilograms.

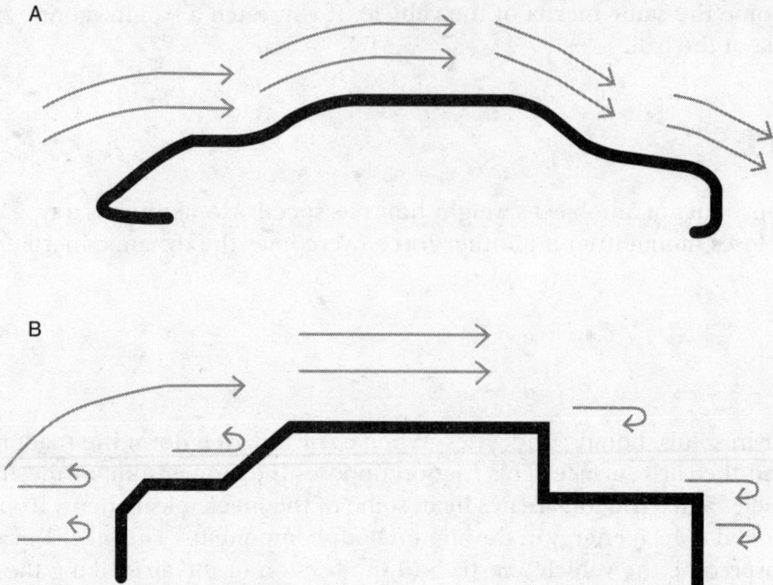

FIGURE 2-3 *(A) Vehicle with low aerodynamic drag. (B) Vehicle with high aerodynamic drag.*

Volume is a measurement of size, and it is related to mass and weight. For example, a pound of gold and a pound of feathers both have the same weight, but the pound of feathers occupies a much larger volume. In the English system, volume is measured in cubic inches, cubic feet, cubic yards, or gallons. The measurement for volume in the metric system is cubic centimeters or liters.

TORQUE

When you pull a wrench to tighten a bolt, you supply **torque** to the bolt. This torque, or twisting force, is calculated by multiplying the force and the radius. For example, if you supply 10 pounds of force on the end of a 2-foot wrench to tighten a bolt, the torque is 10 times 2 = 20 foot-pounds (ft.-lb.) (Figure 2-4). If the bolt turns during torque application, work is done. When a bolt does not rotate during torque application, no work is accomplished.

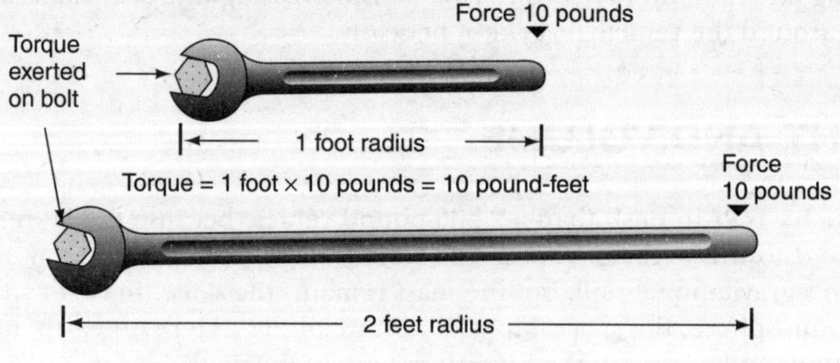

FIGURE 2-4 *Force applied to a wrench produces torque. If the bolt turns, work is accomplished.*

GEAR THEORY

Referring to Figure 2-5, you can see that the driving gear is turning the driven gear. The radius of the driving gear is 1 foot and is turned with a force of 25 pounds. This means that the driving gear has a torque of 25 foot-pounds. If this torque is applied to a gear with a radius of 2 feet, the final output of the driven gear is 50 foot-pounds. This means that the torque at the driven gear has been doubled. Since the driven gear is twice as large as the driving gear, the ratio between the two gears would be referred to as 2:1. This relationship is also called a **gear reduction** since the speed of the driven gear will be less than that of the driving gear.

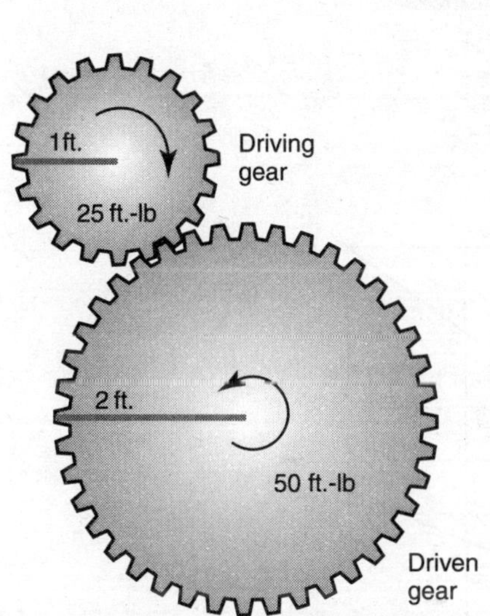

FIGURE 2-5 *The driven gear will turn at half the speed but twice the torque because it is two times larger than the driving gear.*

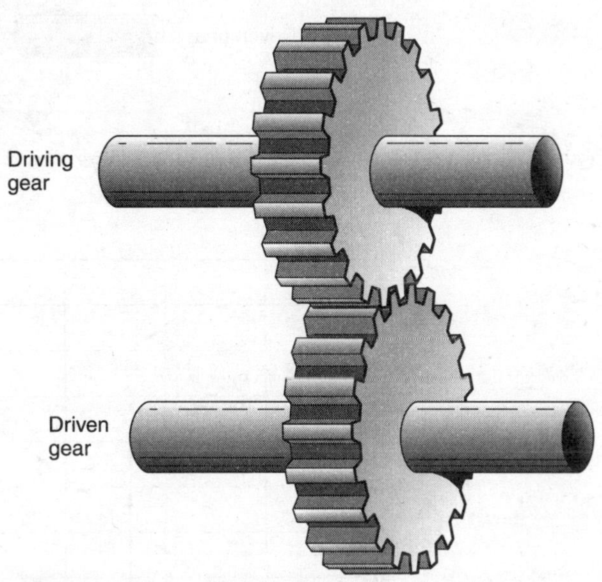

FIGURE 2-6 *If both gears are the same size, the gear ratio is expressed as 1:1.*

If the two gears were the same size (Figure 2-6), there would be no torque or speed change. This would be a 1:1 ratio, or sometimes called **direct drive**.

Finally, if the driving gear were larger than the driven gear, there would be a speed increase and a torque decrease (Figure 2-7). This ratio is expressed as a ratio of less than 1:1, such as a typical automotive **overdrive** ratio of around 0.8:1. Overdrive has little torque, so a vehicle in an overdrive gear range is likely to downshift quickly when climbing a hill or accelerating. Of course, the power through the transmission is still sent through a final drive or differential which is generally a gear reduction of about 3:1. This means that there is not a true overdrive at the wheels, but the broader range of modern transmissions gives designers the opportunity to use a large gear reduction for good acceleration from a stop when more torqued is needed and still able to produce speed and good fuel mileage for the highway when large amounts of torque are not necessary. Figure 2-8 shows the relationship of gear selection torque and speed.

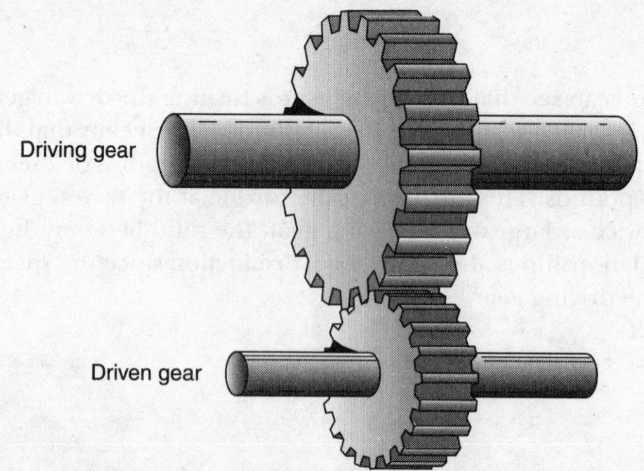

FIGURE 2-7 *In an overdrive ratio, the driving gear is larger than the driven gear.*

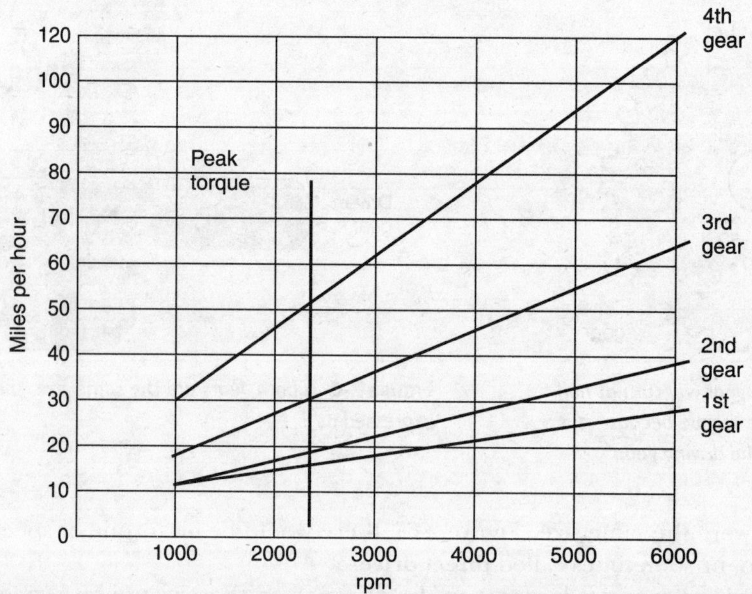

FIGURE 2-8 *Peak torque of the engine is at 2200 rpm. Using gears, the vehicle speed at peak torque can be charged to increase speed.*

POWER

James Watt, a Scotsman, is credited with being the first person to calculate **power**. He measured the amount of work that a horse could do in a specific amount of time. Watt calculated that a horse could move 330 pounds for 100 feet in 1 minute. If you multiply 330 pounds by 100 feet, the answer is 33,000 foot-pounds of work. Watt determined that one horse could do 33,000 footpounds of work in 1 minute. Thus, one horsepower is equal to 33,000 foot-pounds per minute, or 550 foot-pounds per second (Figure 2-9). Two horsepower could do this same amount of work in one-half minute, or four horsepower would be capable of completing this work in one-quarter minute. If you push a

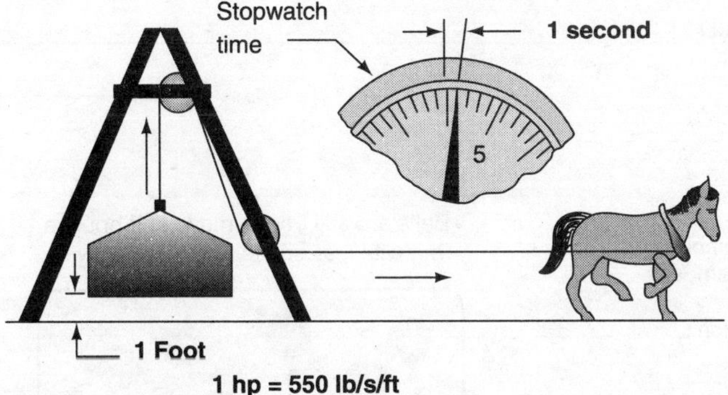

FIGURE 2-9 *One horsepower is produced when 550 pounds are moved 1 foot in 1 second.*

3,000 pound, 1,360 kilograms (kg), car for 11 feet (3.3 meters) in onequarter minute, you produce four horsepower. From this brief discussion about horsepower, we can understand that as power increases, speed also increases, or the time to do work decreases.

PRINCIPLES INVOLVING LIQUIDS AND GASES

Molecular Energy

Remember that kinetic energy refers to energy in motion. Since electrons are constantly in motion around the nucleus in atoms or molecules, kinetic energy is present in all matter. Kinetic energy in atoms and molecules increases as the temperature increases. A decrease in temperature reduces this kinetic energy. Molecules in solids move slowly compared to those in liquids or gases. Gas molecules move quickly compared to liquid molecules. Since gas molecules are in constant motion, they spread out to fill all the space available. At higher temperatures, gas molecules spread out more, whereas lower temperatures cause gas molecules to move closer together.

Temperature

Temperature affects all liquids, solids, and gases. The volume of any matter increases as the temperature increases. Conversely, the volume decreases in relation to a reduction in temperature. When the gases in an engine cylinder are burned, the sudden temperature increase causes rapid gas expansion, which pushes the piston downward and causes engine rotation (Figure 2-10).

Pressure and Compressibility

Since liquids and gases are both substances that flow, they may be classified as fluids. If a nail punctures an automotive tire, the air escapes until the pressure in the tire is equal to atmospheric pressure outside the tire. When the tire is repaired and inflated, air pressure is forced into the tire. If the tire is inflated to 32 pounds per square inch (psi), or 220 kilopascals (kPa), this pressure is applied to every square inch on the inner tire surface. **Pressure** is always supplied equally to the entire surface of a container. Since air is a gas, the molecules have plenty of space between them. When the tire is inflated, the pressure in the tire increases, and the air molecules are squeezed closer together, or compressed. Under this condition, the air molecules cannot move as freely, but extra molecules of air can still be forced into the tire. Therefore, gases such as air are said to be **compressible**.

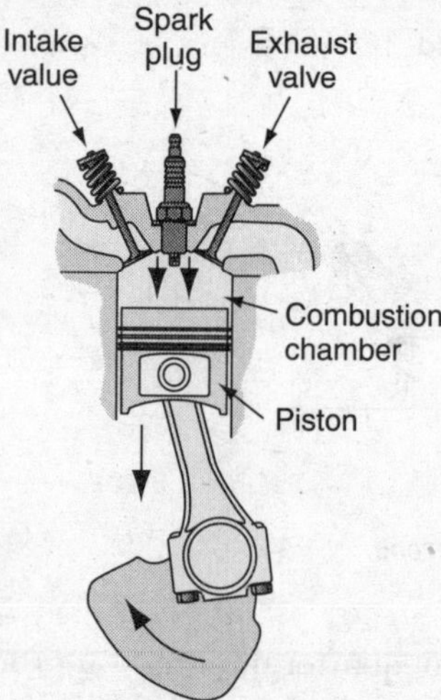

FIGURE 2-10 *Hot expanding gases push the piston downward and rotate the crankshaft.*

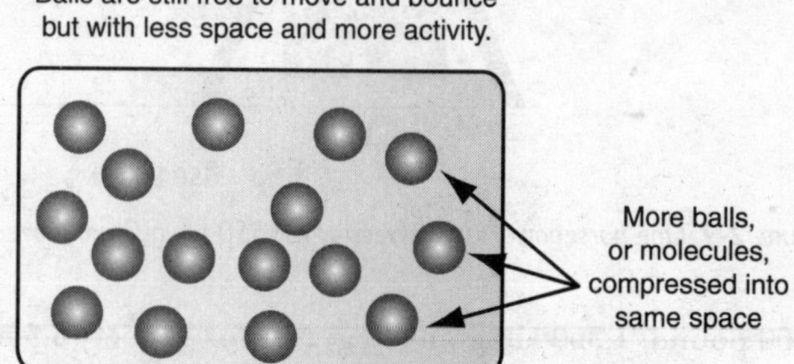

FIGURE 2-11 *Gases can be compressed because there is empty space between the molecules.*

The air in the tire may be compared to a few balls on a billiard table without pockets. If a few more balls are placed on the table, the balls are closer together, but they can still move freely (Figure 2-11).

If the vehicle is driven at high speed, friction between the road surface and the tires heats the tires and the air in the tires. When air temperature increases, the pressure in the tire also increases. Conversely, a temperature decrease reduces pressure.

If 100 cubic feet (2.8 cubic meters) of air is forced into a large truck tire and the same amount of air is forced into a much smaller car tire, the pressure in the car tire is much greater.

Molecules in a liquid may be compared to a billiard table without pockets that is completely filled with balls. These balls can roll around, but no additional balls can be placed on the table because the balls cannot be compressed. Similarly, liquid molecules cannot be compressed (Figure 2-12).

FIGURE 2-12 *Liquids are non-compressible because there is no empty space between molecules.*

Liquid Flow

If a tube is filled with billiard balls and the outlet is open, more balls may be added to the inlet. When each ball is moved into the inlet, a ball is forced from the outlet. If the outlet is closed, no more balls can be forced into the inlet (Figure 2-13).

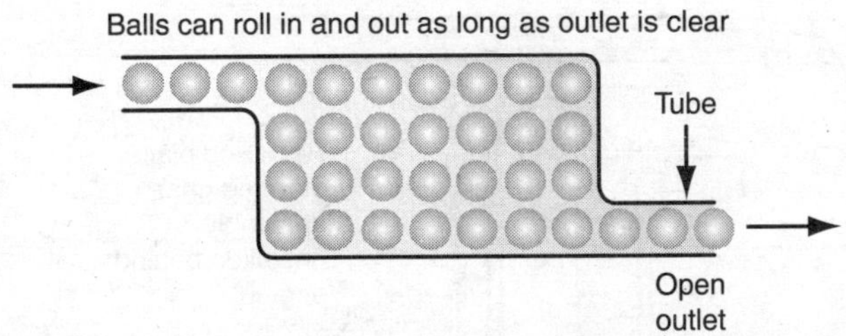

FIGURE 2-13 *Billiard ball movement in a tube filled with balls compared to liquid flow.*

The billiard balls in the tube may be compared to molecules of power steering fluid in the line between the power steering pump and steering gear. Since **noncompressible** fluid fills the line and gear chamber, the force developed by the pump pressure is transferred through the line to the gear chamber (Figure 2-14).

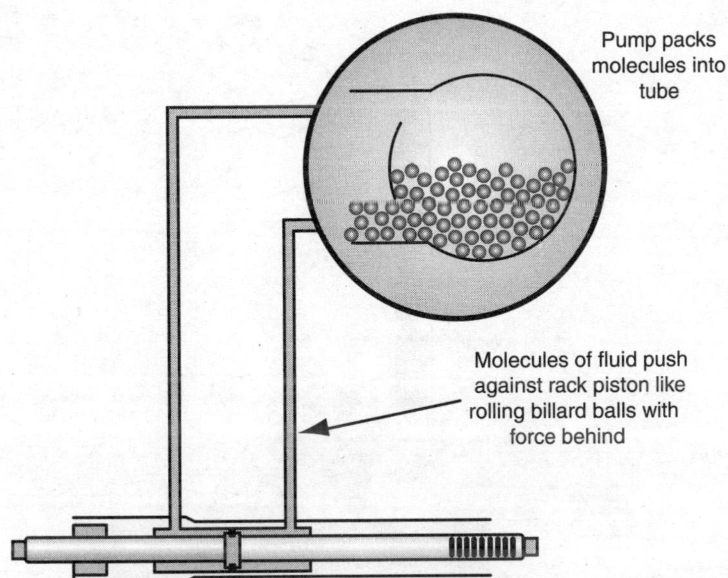

FIGURE 2-14 *Power steering pump pressure supplied to the steering gear chamber.*

This pressure is applied equally to every square inch in the gear chamber. This pressure applied to the rack piston in the gear chamber helps to move the rack piston. Since the rack is connected through steering linkages and arms to the front wheels, the force on the rack piston helps the driver to move the front wheels to the left or right during a turn (Figure 2-15).

ATMOSPHERIC PRESSURE

Since air is gaseous matter with mass and weight, it exerts pressure on the earth's surface. A onesquare-inch column of air extending from the earth's surface to the outer edge of the atmosphere weighs 14.7 pounds at sea level. Therefore, **atmospheric pressure** is 14.7 psi at sea level (Figure 2-16). The atmospheric pressure at sea level is 29.92 inches Hg (inches of mercury). Atmospheric pressure

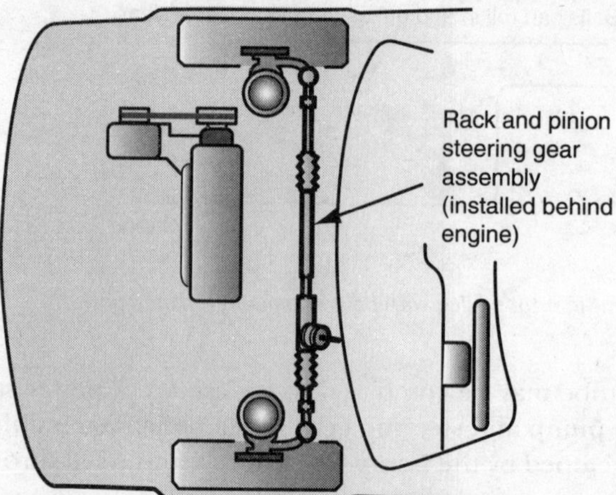

FIGURE 2-15 *Steering gear, linkages, and arms connected to the front wheels.*

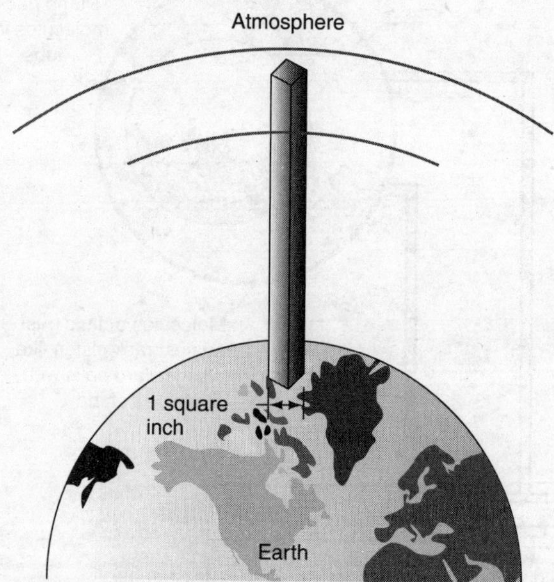

FIGURE 2-16 *A column of air one-inch square extending from the earth's surface at sea level to the outer edge of the atmosphere weighs 14.7 pounds.*

measured in the metric system at sea level is 100 kPa. You might also see a measurement called "bar." A bar is one atmosphere of pressure and equals 100 kPa or 14.7 psi. Bar can also be used in terms of pressure measurements for oil and fuel. The relationship of the change of pressure and altitude is inversely proportionate. The lapse rate is 1 inch Hg per 1,000 feet increase in altitude. Water vapor is $^5/_8$ of the density of air; therefore, air that is saturated with moisture has seemingly less oxygen compared to the same volume of air with less moisture. Hot, dry air is less dense than cooler air and therefore has more space between the molecules. Cooler air is denser, with less space between the oxygen molecules.

Atmospheric Pressure and Temperature

When air becomes hotter, it expands. This hotter air is lighter than an equal volume of cooler air. This hotter, lighter, air exerts less pressure on the earth's surface compared to cooler air. If the temperature decreases, air contracts and becomes heavier. Therefore, an equal volume of cooler air exerts more pressure on the earth's surface compared to hotter air. Cool air is said to be denser than warm air.

Atmospheric Pressure and Altitude

As you climb above sea level, atmospheric pressure decreases. At 5,000 feet (1,524 meters) above sea level, a one-square-inch column of air from the earth's surface to the outer edge of the atmosphere is 5,000 feet (1,524 meters) less than the same column of air at sea level. Therefore, the weight of this column of air is less at an elevation of 5,000 feet (1,524 meters) than at sea level. As altitude continues to increase, atmospheric pressure continues to decrease. At an altitude of several hundred miles above sea level, the earth's atmosphere ends. There is zero atmospheric pressure at that point. In addition to lower atmospheric pressure, the higher the altitude the less oxygen there is proportionately in the air. Less density due to lower pressure means less oxygen per unit of measurement. The altitude also has an effect on the boiling point of liquids. As the altitude increases, the boiling point decreases.

VACUUM

When air has a pressure higher than atmospheric pressure, a **positive pressure** exists. When air has a lower pressure than atmospheric, it has a **negative pressure**. **Vacuum** is the term commonly used to describe negative pressures. Vacuum is best described as any pressure less than atmospheric. A total or complete vacuum is the total or complete absence of air pressure.

The understanding of pressure and vacuum is one of the keys to understanding how an engine works. It also explains how things work and why things may not work the way they are supposed to. The reaction of a high pressure to a lower pressure defines the action of many engine components. Whenever there is a high (positive) pressure and a lower (less positive) pressure, the higher pressure will move toward the lower in an attempt to equalize the pressures.

We all are quite familiar with this. A balloon expands as we blow in more air, simply because we are increasing the pressure inside the balloon. The high pressure inside is pushing out against the lower pressure outside the balloon.

Vacuum could be measured in pounds per square inch (psi), but inches of mercury (in. Hg) are most commonly used for this measurement. Let us assume that a plastic "U" tube is partially filled with mercury, and atmospheric pressure is allowed to enter one end of the tube. If a vacuum is supplied to the other end of the "U" tube, the mercury is forced downward by the atmospheric pressure. When this movement occurs, the mercury also moves upward on the side where the vacuum is supplied. If the mercury moves downward 10 inches, or 25.4 centimeters (cm), where the atmospheric pressure is supplied, and upward 10 inches (25.4 cm) where the vacuum is supplied, 20 in. Hg is supplied to the "U" tube. The highest possible, or perfect, vacuum is 29.9 in. Hg (Figure 2-17), which is 0 psi of pressure.

Vacuum and atmospheric pressure are used in several automotive systems. For example, atmospheric pressure is available outside the engine air intake. When a piston moves downward with an intake valve open, a vacuum is created in the cylinder above the piston. The air moves rapidly from the high pressure outside the air intake to the lower pressure in the cylinder (Figure 2-18).

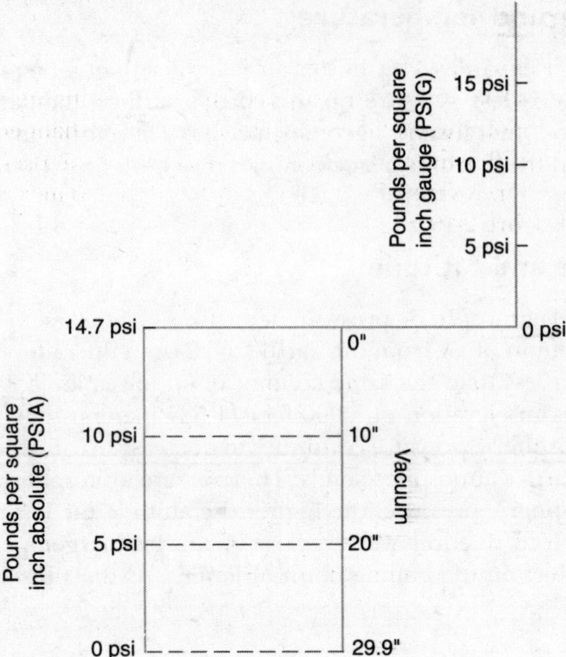

FIGURE 2-17 *A comparison of pressure and vacuum readings.*

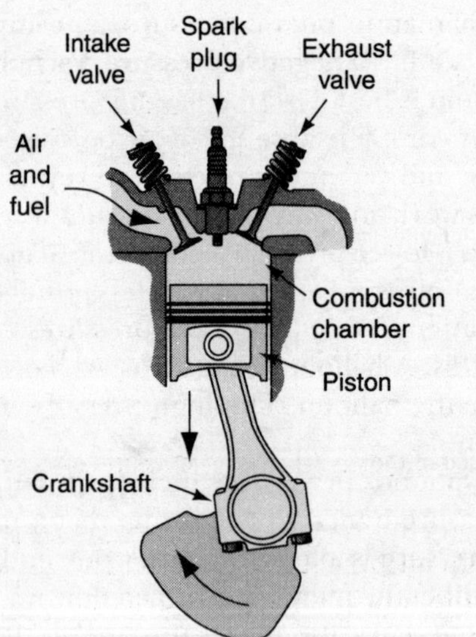

FIGURE 2-18 *Air moves from the outside atmosphere, which is a high pressure, to the lower pressure in the cylinder during the engine's intake stroke.*

Pumps use high and low pressure to move liquids or gases. For example, as a water pump rotates, it creates a high pressure at the pump outlet and a low pressure at the inlet. This pressure difference causes coolant to flow through the cooling system.

VENTURI PRINCIPLE

Pressures of a liquid or gas can be increased or decreased by applying more pressure onto it or by relieving some of the pressure on the liquid or gas. Pressure is also changed by putting a restriction in whatever the liquid or gas is flowing through. At the restriction, the pressure increases. After the restriction, the pressure is lower. A **venturi** is a restriction designed to increase the speed of the flow and decrease its pressure (Figure 2-19).

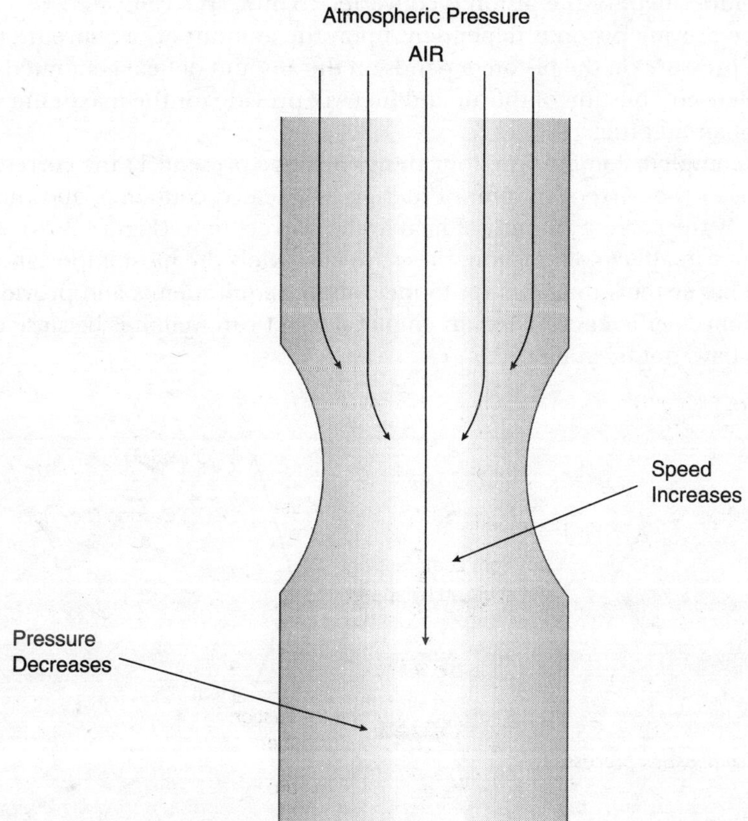

FIGURE 2-19 *A venturi increases the speed of the incoming air and creates a vacuum below the venturi.*

Let's assume we have a tube with air flowing through it. The air is moving from the high pressure side to the low pressure side. In the tube we have a restriction or venturi. As the moving air enters the venturi, the center column of air has no direct contact with the restriction. The air surrounding the center column is directed, by the venturi, toward the center column. This pushes the column through the venturi faster than it would on its own.

On the other side of the restriction, the size of the tube returns to normal. Although the speed of the air increased through the venturi, the volume of air entering into this larger area is less than the amount of air on the other side of the venturi. As a result, a lower pressure or vacuum is present at the outlet of the venturi.

COMBUSTION

An engine converts the energy found in fuel into heat energy, which is changed to mechanical energy that can be used to move a vehicle. The conversion of energy results from the mechanical design of the engine and through combustion. Combustion is a burning process. During this burning process, a chemical reaction takes place between the air and the fuel that entered the engine's cylinders. During this chemical reaction, heat energy is released. With the release of the heat, the pressure of the air in the cylinders increases. This high pressure pushes on the engine's piston causing it to move. The movement of the piston is converted to move the vehicle.

The energy of the moving piston is dependent upon the amount of pressure there is on the piston. The amount of pressure on the piston depends on the amount of heat generated by the combustion process. Complete combustion of the air and fuel will provide for the maximum amount of heat from that amount of air and fuel.

In order to have complete combustion, four things must be present: 1) the correct amount of air must be mixed with; 2) the correct amount of fuel in; 3) a sealed container, and this mixture must be; and 4) shocked by the correct amount of heat at the correct time (Figure 2-20). Although there are other factors that can affect combustion, these are absolutely the most important factors. As you will see, the engine has systems that attempt to meet these requirements and provide for complete combustion or maximum efficiency. When an engine doesn't run well, it is because one or more of these requirements have not been met.

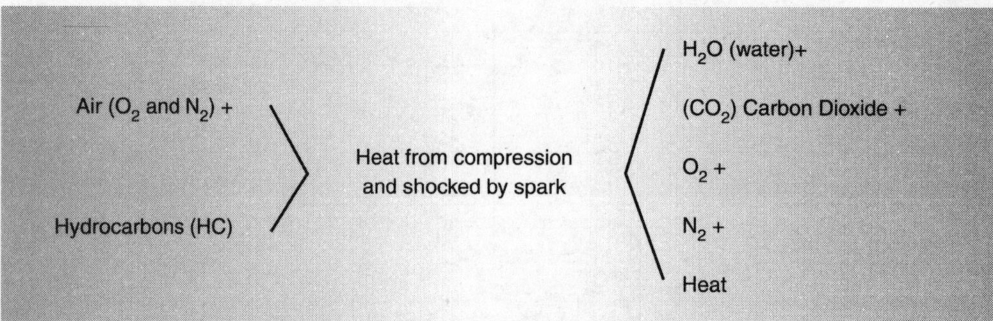

FIGURE 2-20 *The ideal combustion process.*

All components of the engine are designed in an attempt to achieve total combustion. Although no engine can achieve complete combustion during all operating conditions, total combustion is the goal. Incomplete or inefficient combustion results from neither having a sealed cylinder nor the right amounts of air, fuel, and/or heat in the cylinder. The more incorrect any of these requirements are, the less complete the combustion will be.

The result of total combustion is the generation of great heat and the conversion of all of the cylinder's air and fuel into water and carbon dioxide. When total combustion does not take place, full conversion of the fuel and air also does not take place. This results in the release of pollutants from the engine.

REVIEW QUESTIONS

Short Answer Essays

1. Define an element and a compound.
2. Name the four factors that are necessary for complete combustion.
3. Define a molecule.
4. Describe three particles found in an atom, including the electrical charge and location of each particle.
5. Explain why a venturi decreases pressure.
6. What is atmospheric pressure?
7. What happens to air pressure as the temperature of the air changes?
8. Describe Newton's three laws of motion.
9. Describe six different forms of energy.
10. Describe four different types of energy conversion.

Fill-in-the-Blanks

1. At sea level, atmospheric pressure is ______________ psi.
2. In nature, a ______________ pressure always moves toward a ______________ pressure.
3. The nucleus of an atom is comprised of a(n) ______________ and a(n) ______________.
4. Work is calculated by multiplying ______________ times ______________.
5. Energy may be defined as the ability to do ______________.
6. When one object is moved over another object, the resistance to motion is called ______________.
7. Weight is the measurement of the earth's ______________ ______________ on an object.
8. Torque is a force that does work with a ______________ action.
9. Power is a measurement for the rate at which ______________ is done.
10. Negative pressure may be called ______________.

Multiple Choice

1. Technician A says that the valence ring of an atom is the innermost ring of electrons. Technician B says that the valence ring is the second ring of electrons. Who is correct?
   A. Technician A
   B. Technician B
   C. Both technicians
   D. Neither technician
2. In order to have complete combustion, we must have all of the following *except*:
   A. correct amount of air
   B. correct amount of fuel

C. unsealed container

D. shocked by the correct amount of heat at the right time

3. One horsepower, as calculated by Watt, is equivalent to:

A. moving 550 pounds 100 feet in 1 minute

B. doing 33,000 foot-pounds of work in 1 hour

C. doing 550 foot-pounds of work in 1 second

D. both A and B

4. Technician A states that the inertia of a vehicle at rest is called static inertia. Technician B says that the inertia of a vehicle in motion is called dynamic inertia. Who is correct?

A. Technician A

B. Technician B

C. Both technicians

D. Neither technician

5. Technician A says that torque is measured in the metric system as gram-centimeters. Technician B says torque is measured in the metric system as Newton-meters. Who is correct?

A. Technician A

B. Technician B

C. Both technicians

D. Neither technician

6. Technician A says that weight is the measurement of the Earth's gravitational pull on an object. Technician B says that Mass is the measurement of an object's inertia. Who is correct?

A. Technician A

B. Technician B

C. Both technicians

D. Neither technician

7. A perfect vacuum is said to have been reached at:

A. 18.8 in. Hg

B. 17.3 in. Hg

C. 29.9 in. Hg

D. 35.9 in. Hg

8. Technician A says that energy released to do work it is called kinetic energy. Technician B says that energy that is stored is called theoretical energy. Who is correct?

A. Technician A

B. Technician B

C. Both technicians

D. Neither technician

9. While discussing gases, Technician A says that when pressure increases so does temperature. Technician B says that when temperature increases so does pressure. Who is correct?

A. Technician A

B. Technician B

C. Both technicians
D. Neither technician

10. All of the following are measurements of atmospheric pressure ***except***:
    A. bar
    B. psi.
    C. kPa
    D. kg-cm

ENGINE DESIGN AND OPERATION

3

Upon completion and review of this chapter, you should be able to:

- Define the methods used for engine classification.
- Describe the four strokes in the four-stroke cycle.
- Explain compression ratio.
- Explain the purpose of the camshaft, pushrods, and rocker arms.
- Explain volumetric efficiency.
- Describe the difference between an overhead cam engine and an overhead valve engine.
- Describe four different types of engine block design.
- Briefly describe the different engine systems.
- Define cylinder bore and stroke.
- Explain how to calculate engine displacement.
- Describe three different methods of measuring engine efficiency.
- Name and describe the components of a typical lubricating system.
- Describe the purpose of a crankcase ventilation system.
- Explain oil service and viscosity ratings.

- List and describe the major components of the cooling system.
- Describe the operation of the cooling system.
- Describe the function of the water pump, radiator, radiator cap, and thermostat in the cooling system.

INTRODUCTION

Modern engines are highly engineered power plants. These engines are designed to meet the performance and fuel efficiency demands of the public. The days of the heavy, cast-iron V8 engine with its poor gas mileage are quickly drawing to a close. Today, these engines have been replaced by compact, lightweight, and fuel efficient engines. Modern engines are made of lightweight engine castings and stampings, non-iron materials (for example, aluminum, magnesium, fiber-reinforced plastics), and fewer and smaller fasteners to hold things together. These fasteners are made possible through computerized joint designs that optimize loading patterns. Each of these newer engine designs has its own distinct personality, based on construction materials, casting configurations, and design.

These modern engine building techniques have changed how technicians make their money. Before these changes can be explained, it is important to explain the "basics" of engine design and operation.

ENGINE CLASSIFICATIONS

Today's automotive engines can be classified in several ways, depending on the following design features:

- *Operational cycles.* Most technicians will generally come in contact with only four-stroke cycle engines. However, a few older cars have used—and some cars in the future may use—a two-stroke engine.
- *Number of cylinders.* Current engine designs include 3-, 4-, 5-, 6-, 8-, 10-, and 12-cylinder engines.
- *Cylinder arrangement.* An engine can be flat (opposed), in-line, or V-type. Other more complicated designs have also been used.
- *Displacement.* The volume of the engine's cylinders added together.
- *Valve train type.* Engine valve trains can be either the **overhead camshaft (OHC)** type or the camshaft in-block **overhead valve (OHV)** type. Some engines separate camshafts for the intake and exhaust valves. These are based on the OHC design and are called **dual overhead camshaft (DOHC)** engines. V-type DOHC engines have four camshafts—two on each side.
- *Ignition type.* There are two types of ignition systems: spark and compression. Gasoline engines use a spark ignition system. In a spark ignition system, the air-fuel mixture is ignited by an electrical spark. Diesel engines, or compression ignition engines, have no spark plugs. An automotive diesel engine relies on the heat generated as air is compressed to ignite the air-fuel mixture for the power stroke.
- *Cooling systems.* There are both air-cooled and liquid-cooled engines in use. Nearly all of today's engines have liquid-cooling systems.
- *Fuel type*. Several types of fuel are currently used in automobile engines including gasoline, natural gas, diesel, and propane. The most commonly used is gasoline. Recently, electric vehicles have been introduced for sale to the public. These vehicles do not rely on a fuel for power.

ENGINE LOCATION

The engine is typically placed in one of three locations. In the vast majority of vehicles, it is located at the front of the vehicle, forward of the passenger compartment. Front-mounted engines can be positioned either longitudinally or transversely with respect to the vehicle.

The second engine location is a mid-mount position between the passenger compartment and rear suspension. Mid-mount engines are normally transversely mounted. The third, and least common, engine location is in the rear of the vehicle. The engines are typically opposed type engines. Each of these engine locations offers advantages and disadvantages.

CHARACTERISTICS OF FOUR-STROKE ENGINE DESIGN

Depending on the vehicle, either an in-line, V-type, slant, or opposed cylinder design can be used. The most popular designs are in-line and V-type engines.

In-Line Engines

In the in-line engine design (Figure 3-1), the cylinders are all placed in a single row. There is one crankshaft and one cylinder head for all of the cylinders. The block is cast so that all cylinders are located in an upright position.

In-line engine designs have certain advantages and disadvantages. They are easy to manufacture and service. However, because the cylinders are positioned vertically, the front of the vehicle must be higher. This affects the aerodynamic design of the car. Aerodynamic design refers to the ease with which the car can move through the air. When equipped with an in-line engine, the front of a vehicle cannot be made as low as it can with other engine designs.

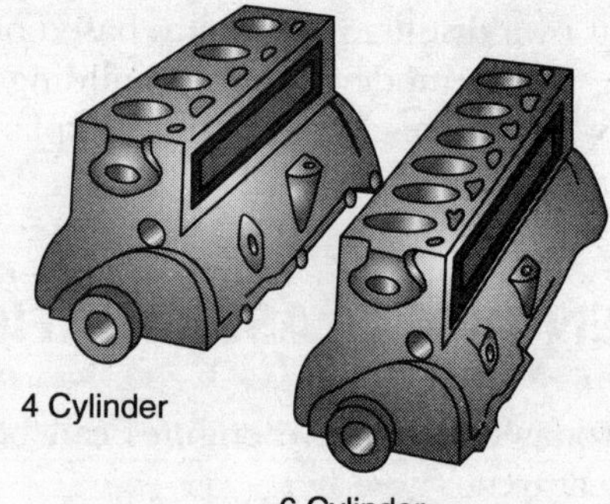

FIGURE 3-1 *In-line engine designs.*

V-Type Engines

The V-type engine design has two rows of cylinders (Figure 3-2) located 60 to 90 degrees away from each other. A V-type engine uses one crankshaft that is connected to the pistons on both sides of the V. This type of engine has two cylinder heads, one over each row of cylinders.

One advantage of using a V configuration is that the engine is not as high or long as an in-line configuration. The front of a vehicle can now be made lower. This design improves the outside aerodynamics of the vehicle. If eight cylinders are needed for power, a V configuration makes the engine much shorter, lighter, and more compact. Many years ago, some vehicles had an in-line eight-cylinder engine. The engine was very long and its long crankshaft also caused increased torsional vibrations in the engine.

Slant Cylinder Engines

Another way of arranging the cylinders is in a slant configuration (Figure 3-3A). This is much like an in-line engine except that the entire block has been placed at a slant. The slant engine was designed to reduce the distance from the top to the bottom of the engine. Vehicles using the slant engine can be designed more aerodynamically.

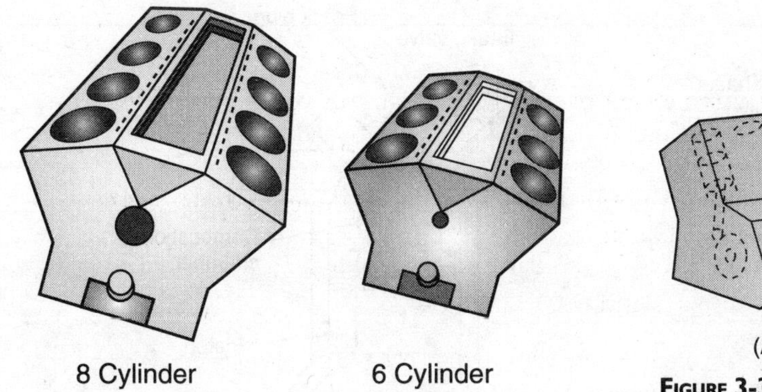

Figure 3-2 *V-type engine designs.*

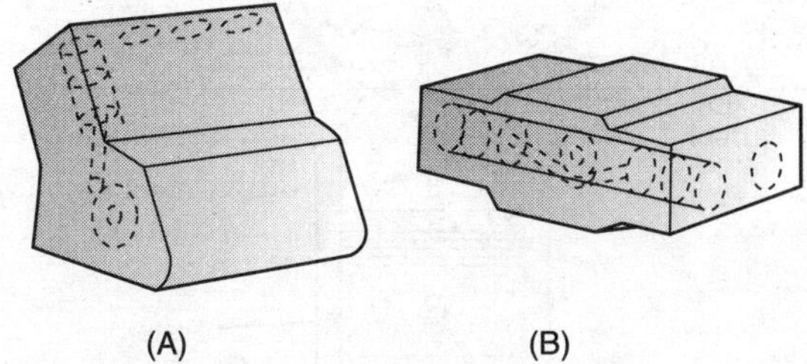

Figure 3-3 *(A) Slant engine and (B) opposed cylinder engine designs.*

Opposed Cylinder Engines

In this design, two rows of cylinders are located opposite the crankshaft (Figure 3-3B). Opposed cylinder engines are used in applications where there is very little vertical room for the engine. For this reason, opposed cylinder designs are commonly used on vehicles that have the engine in the rear. The angle between the two cylinder heads is typically 180 degrees. One crankshaft is used with two cylinder heads.

FOUR-STROKE GASOLINE ENGINES

In a passenger car or truck, the engine provides the rotating power to drive the wheels through the transmission and driving axles. All automobile engines, both gasoline and diesel, are classified as internal combustion because the combustion or burning takes place inside the engine. These systems require an air-fuel mixture that arrives in the combustion chamber at the correct time and an engine constructed to withstand the temperatures and pressures created by the burning of thousands of fuel droplets (atomized fuel).

The combustion process is the result of several engine systems working independently *and* in concert to bring together the precise amount of air, fuel, heat, pressure, and spark at precisely the right time to create power. The internal combustion engine can be compared to an air pump. The engine operates, in part, on the principles of thermodynamics. It is responsible for compressing the incoming air-fuel charge to raise its pressure and, in turn, raise its temperature close to the self-ignition temperature. The ignition system is responsible for supplying the required amount of spark to adequately ignite the air-fuel mixture under various pressures. The air intake and fuel systems are designed to deliver varying ratios of mixture to meet varying operating requirements. Of course, each cylinder should receive the same amounts of mixture, pressure, and spark if the engine is to run smoothly and efficiently. The construction of the engine and its different parts is engineered and manufactured to withstand a harsh operating environment, both internal and external to the **combustion chamber**.

Most vehicles today use a four stroke, reciprocating gasoline engine. As the name implies, four strokes of the piston are required to complete one engine cycle (Figure 3-4). A stroke is the full up or down travel of the piston in the cylinder bore. The piston is connected to the crankshaft by a connecting rod and moves up and down within the cylinder (reciprocating motion). The reciprocating motion of the piston is converted to a rotary motion via the crankshaft (Figure 3-5).

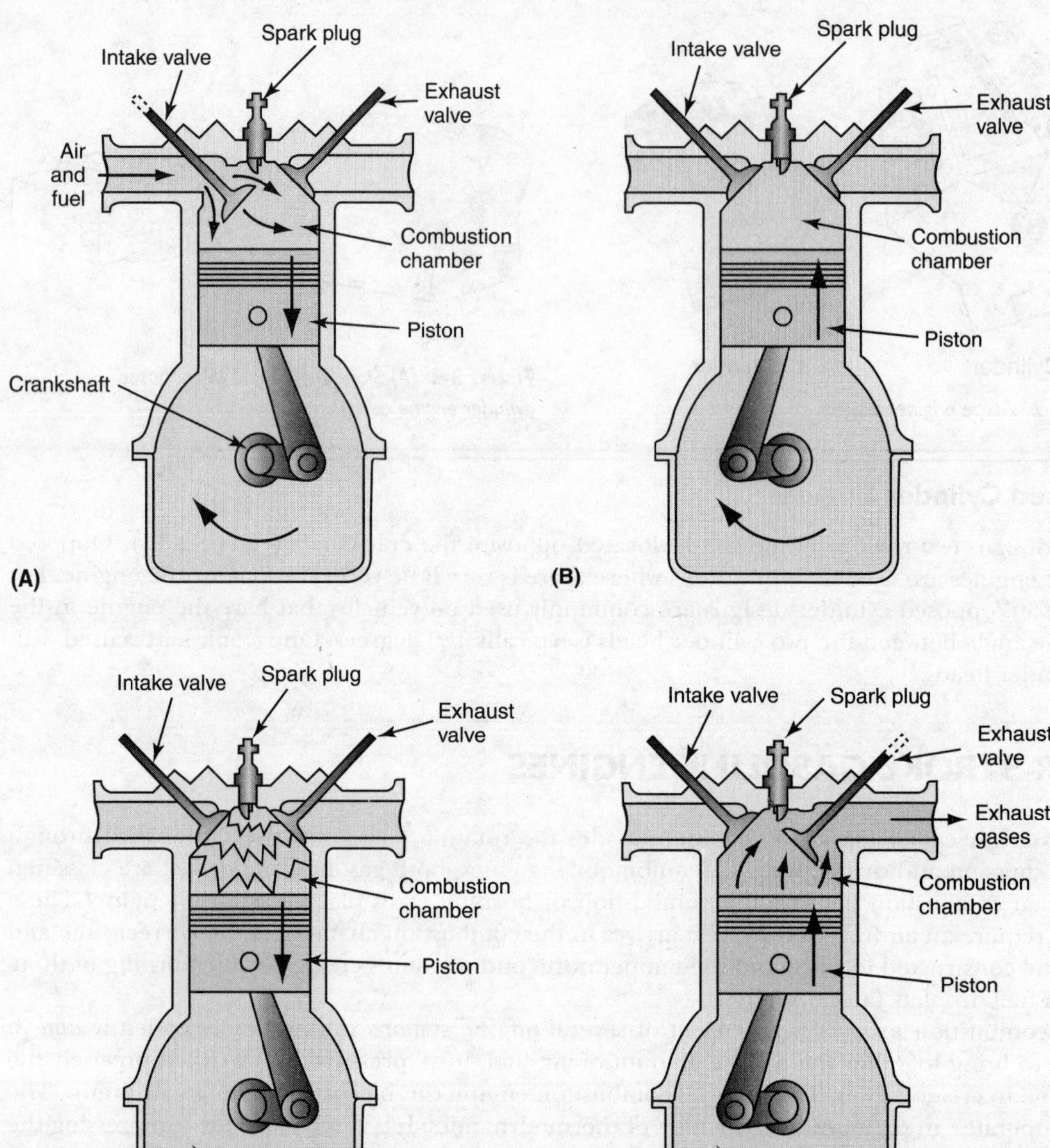

FIGURE 3-4 *(A) Intake stroke, (B) compression stroke, (C) power stroke, and (D) exhaust stroke.*

At the point of ignition, the air-fuel mixture burns rapidly, beginning the power stroke. The virtual immediate expansion of gases as heat energy is released from the gasoline due to ignition creates a sudden rise in temperature and pressure, forcing the piston downward and rotating the crankshaft. The next cylinder in the firing order immediately repeats this process, and so on for each cylinder. It takes two complete crankshaft revolutions, or 720 degrees, and one revolution of the camshaft to complete one engine cycle, firing all cylinders once. For example, a four-cylinder engine will fire a cylinder every 180 degrees of crankshaft rotation. Figure 3-6 maps the crankshaft

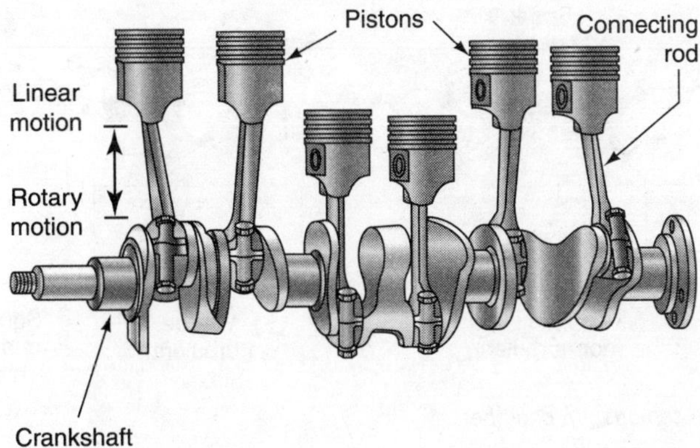

FIGURE 3-5 *The reciprocating motion of the pistons is converted to rotary motion by the crankshaft.*

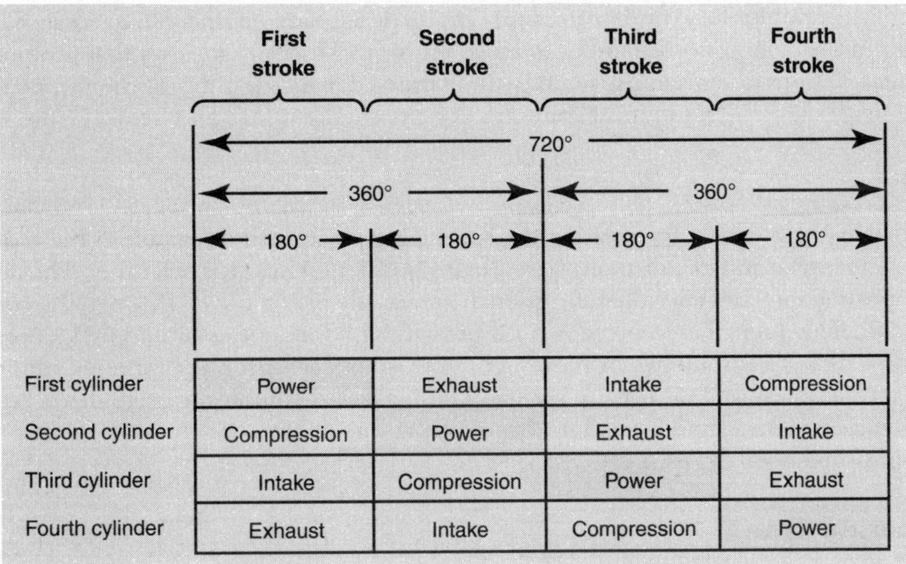

	First stroke	Second stroke	Third stroke	Fourth stroke
First cylinder	Power	Exhaust	Intake	Compression
Second cylinder	Compression	Power	Exhaust	Intake
Third cylinder	Intake	Compression	Power	Exhaust
Fourth cylinder	Exhaust	Intake	Compression	Power

FIGURE 3-6 *A four-cylinder engine has one cylinder on a power stroke every 180 degrees of crankshaft rotation.*

position, measured in degrees, and the cylinder event for one complete engine cycle in a four-stroke, four-cylinder engine.

A flywheel (manual transmission) or flexplate-torque converter (automatic transmission) is connected to the end of the crankshaft. The flywheel is a heavy mass that stores some of the engine's energy (inertia) to even out the power pulses as each cylinder fires. It does this by helping to keep the crankshaft moving beyond bottom dead center (BDC) after the power stroke occurs for each cylinder, in addition to maintaining momentum to assist the piston on the compression stroke. In addition, the flywheel couples the transmission to the engine for the transfer of power created by the engine to be delivered to the drive wheels.

The combustion chamber is the space in which the air-fuel mixture is compressed and ignited to create a controlled explosion. It is not really an explosion by definition, but rather a rapid, calculated, and controlled burn. The term helps to describe the sudden violent release of heat energy from a precise fuel mixture. Made up of the area between the valve surface side of the cylinder head and

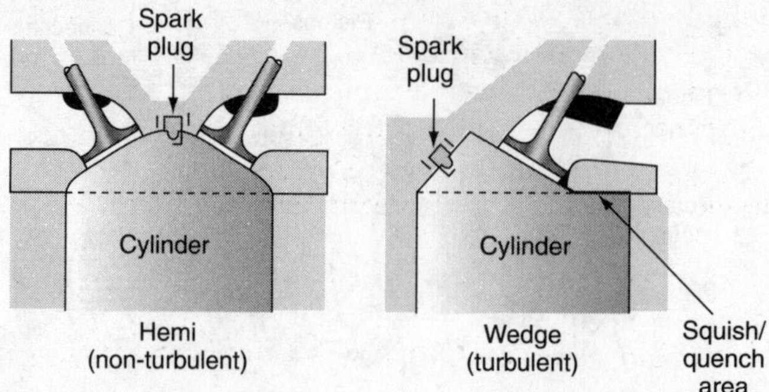

FIGURE 3-7 *Hemi and wedge combustion chambers.*

the top of the piston as it approaches top dead center (TDC), the combustion chamber is where the actual production of power begins. The design of the combustion chamber is determined by the size and shape of the cylinder head and piston top. Certain designs are engineered to create a type of turbulence within the combustion chamber to move the air-fuel mixture in a way that promotes a more efficient burn. Various designs in use today include the wedge, hemispherical (hemi), pent-roof, "D" shape, and heart shape. The two most common designs are the wedge and hemi (Figure 3-7).

Wedge Type

The wedge-type combustion chamber has the spark plug positioned off-center in the widest part of the wedge. The intake and exhaust valves are usually positioned next to each other. The air-fuel mixture is compressed into an area called the quench area as the piston travels through the compression stroke to TDC. The quench area promotes a thorough blending of the air and fuel before combustion. This also causes a turbulence or movement of the mixture within the cylinder, causing a more complete burn at lower and mid-cruise speeds. The high-swirl combustion chambers are the result of raised surfaces on the cylinder head surface of the wedge design that creates a specific amount of combustion turbulence.

Hemispherical Type

The main characteristic of the hemispherical combustion chamber is that it is rounded. When the piston is at TDC, the combustion chamber resembles a half-ball, hence the name. This design allows the intake and exhaust valves, typically located across from each other with the spark plug placed between them, to be angled in the cylinder head. This crossflow arrangement of the valves helps create a less restricted airflow entering and exiting the cylinder. The central location of the spark helps ignite and maintain a centralized burn of the flame front. This type of combustion chamber is also referred to as a non-turbulent design. A variation of this style uses a domed piston that creates a tighter quench area that also creates some turbulence.

Other Types

A design that is popular with the four-valve-per-cylinder engines is the "V" shaped, pent-roof combustion chamber. This and other newer types are designed to improve combustion efficiency and emissions.

The concept of these types of combustion chambers is to enhance the air-fuel mixture movement during the combustion process. The turbulence causes the burning air-fuel molecules to blend with and help quickly ignite the unburned molecules, resulting in a more complete combustion.

Although the combustion must occur in a sealed cylinder, the cylinder must also have some means of allowing heat, fuel, and air into it. There must also be a means to allow the burnt air-fuel mixture out so that a fresh mixture can enter and the engine continue to run. To accommodate these requirements, engines are fitted with valves (Figure 3-8).

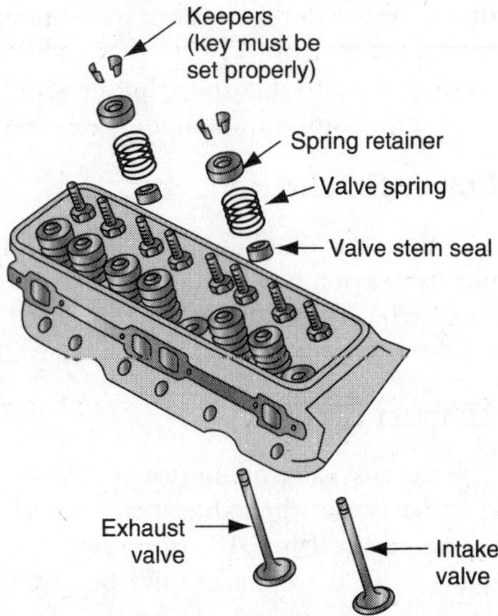

FIGURE 3-8 *Parts of a cylinder head.*

There are at least two valves at the top of each cylinder. The air-fuel mixture enters the combustion chamber through an intake valve and leaves (after having been burned) through an exhaust valve. The valves are accurately machined plugs that fit into machined openings. A valve is said to be seated or closed when it rests in its opening thus creating a "seal." When the valve is pushed off its seat, it opens.

A rotating camshaft, driven by the crankshaft, opens and closes the intake and exhaust valves. **Cams** are raised sections of a shaft that have high spots called **lobes**. As the camshaft rotates, the lobes rotate and push the valve open by pushing it away from its seat. Once the cam lobe rotates out of the way, the valve, forced by a spring, closes. The camshaft can be located either in the cylinder block or in the cylinder head.

When the action of the valves and the spark plug is properly timed to the movement of the piston, the combustion cycle takes place in four strokes of the piston: the intake stroke, the compression stroke, the power stroke, and the exhaust stroke.

The up-and-down movement of the piston on all four strokes is converted to a rotary motion by the crankshaft. It takes two full revolutions of the crankshaft and one revolution of the camshaft to complete the four-stroke cycle.

Intake Stroke

The first stroke of the cycle is the intake stroke. As the piston moves away from TDC, the intake valve opens. The downward movement of the piston increases the volume of the cylinder above it. This reduces the pressure in the cylinder. This reduced pressure, commonly referred to as engine vacuum, causes the atmospheric pressure to push a mixture of air and fuel through the open intake valve. (Some engines are equipped with a super- or turbocharger that pushes more air past the valve.) As the piston reaches the bottom of its stroke, the reduction in pressure stops. This causes the intake of air-fuel mixture to slow down. It does not stop because of the weight and movement of the air-fuel mixture. It continues to enter the cylinder until the intake valve closes. The intake valve closes after the piston has reached BDC. This delayed closing of the valve increases the volumetric efficiency of the cylinder by packing as much air and fuel into it as possible.

Compression Stroke

The compression stroke begins as the piston starts to move from BDC. The intake valve closes, trapping the air-fuel mixture in the cylinder. At TDC, the piston and cylinder walls form a combustion chamber in which the fuel will be burned. The upward movement of the piston compresses the air-fuel mixture to one-eighth of its volume (in an 8:1 compression ratio engine), raising its pressure to over 100 pounds per square inch (psi). The sudden rise in pressure and temperature increases fuel volatility, thereby bringing the air-fuel mixture almost to the point of self-ignition. The displacement of the piston is the amount of cylinder volume change that takes place within the cylinder as the piston travels from TDC to BDC. The volume at TDC is the clearance volume of the cylinder. If the volume measured in the cylinder with the piston at BDC is eight times the clearance volume, it is an 8:1 compression-ratio engine.

Power Stroke

The power stroke begins as the compressed fuel mixture is ignited. An electrical spark across the electrodes of a spark plug ignites the air-fuel mixture. The burning fuel rapidly expands, creating a very high pressure against the top of the piston. This drives the piston down toward BDC. The downward movement of the piston is transmitted through the connecting rod to the crankshaft.

Exhaust Stroke

The exhaust valve opens just before the piston reaches BDC on the power stroke. Pressure within the cylinder causes the exhaust gas to rush past the open valve and into the exhaust system. Movement of the piston from BDC pushes most of the remaining exhaust gas from the cylinder. As the piston nears TDC, the exhaust valve begins to close as the intake valve starts to open. The exhaust stroke completes the four-stroke cycle. The opening of the intake valve begins the cycle again. This cycle occurs in each cylinder and is repeated over and over, as long as the engine is running.

VALVE AND CAMSHAFT PLACEMENT CONFIGURATIONS

Two basic valve and camshaft placement configurations of the four-stroke gasoline engines are used in automobiles (Figure 3-9).

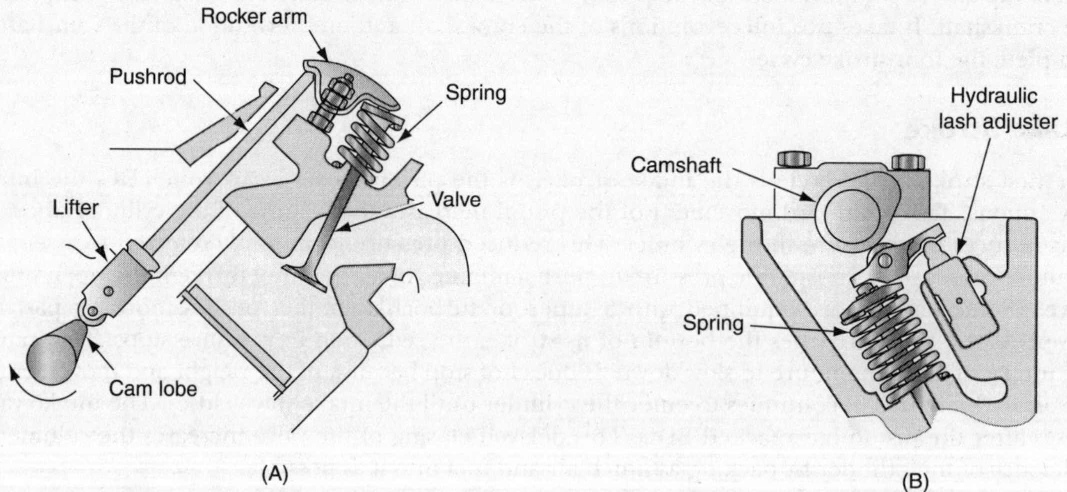

FIGURE 3-9 *Basic valve and camshaft placement in an (A) overhead valve and (B) overhead camshaft engine.*

Overhead Valve (OHV)

As the name implies, the intake and exhaust valves in an overhead valve engine are mounted in the cylinder head and are operated by a camshaft located in the cylinder block. This arrangement requires the use of valve lifters, pushrods, and rocker arms to transfer camshaft rotation to valve movement. The intake and exhaust manifolds are attached to the cylinder head.

Overhead Cam (OHC)

An overhead cam engine also has the intake and exhaust valves located in the cylinder head. But, as the name implies, the cam is located in the cylinder head. In an overhead cam engine, the valves are operated directly by the camshaft or through cam followers or tappets, typically eliminating the pushrods and rocker arms.

VALVE AND CAMSHAFT OPERATION

In OHV engines with the camshaft in the block (Figure 3-10), the valves are operated by valve lifters and pushrods that are actuated by the camshaft. In OHC engines, the cam lobes operate the valves directly, and there is no need for pushrods nor lifters.

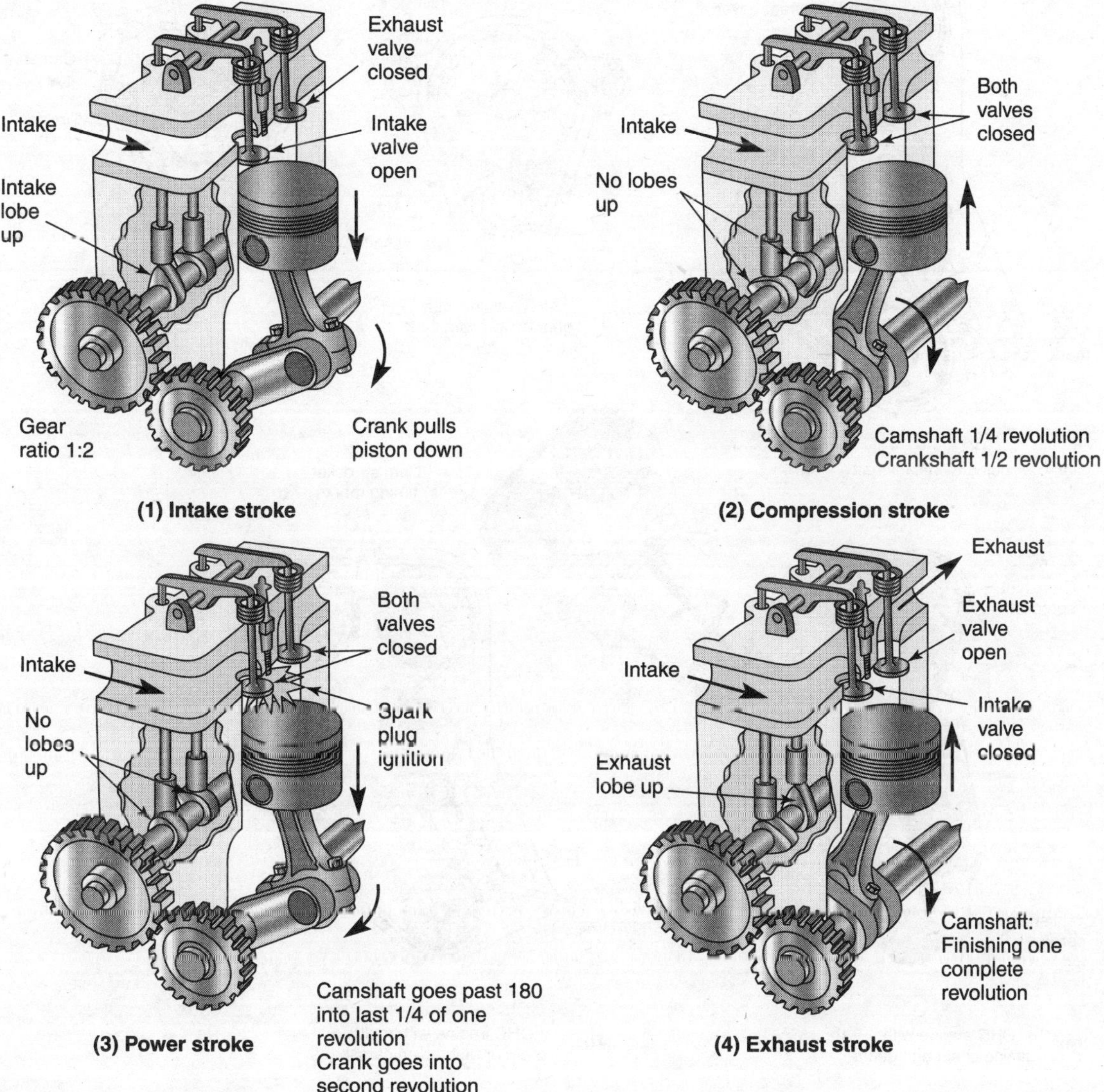

FIGURE 3-10 *Valve operation in an OHV engine.*

Cam lobes are oval shaped. The placement of the lobe on the shaft determines when the valve will open. Design of the lobe determines how far the valve will open and how long it will remain open in relation to piston movement.

Timing Gears, Belts, and Chains

The camshaft is driven by the crankshaft by way of gears, a timing chain, or a timing belt (Figure 3-11).

Routine maintenance is essential to prevent valvetrain problems, especially with regard to timing belts. Certain engines have a recommended mileage interval in which the belt should be replaced.

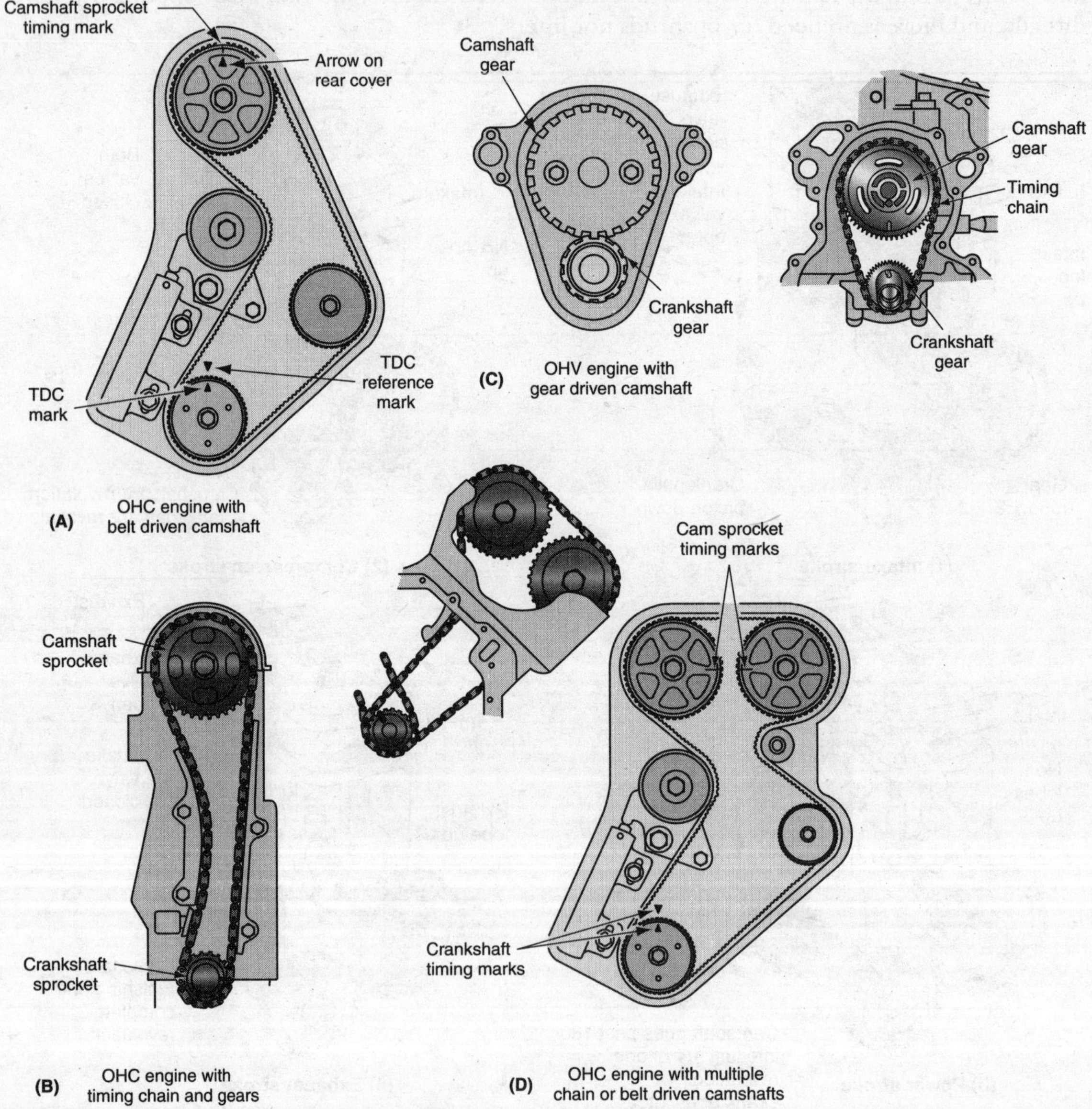

FIGURE 3-11 *The different timing drive mechanisms used today.*

Some timing chains—and all timing belts—use a tensioner to push against the chain or belt to keep it tight, compensating for stretch and normal wear. Maintaining proper tension helps to ensure the belt or chain will stay tight against the gears or sprockets to prevent slipping and maintain precise valve timing. Some tensioners are adjustable, while others are self-adjusting. If a timing belt or chain becomes excessively worn, it is possible that a change in valve timing accuracy will result. In addition, if the timing belt becomes damaged and breaks while the engine is running, the camshaft will stop suddenly while the crankshaft continues for a brief moment before the engine quits. Depending on engine design, damage may result to the valves, cylinder head, and pistons due to the valves coming in sudden contact with the tops of the pistons. Some engines have a small but adequate clearance between the open valve and the piston at TDC. Should a timing belt failure occur, this will likely prevent damage if the crankshaft and camshaft happen to come to rest in that particular position. If the timing chain or belt jumps from its correct position on the timing gear or if the tension is not correct, drive-ability problems or engine damage may occur. This is because the valves open and close at the wrong time relative to crank and piston position, resulting in incorrect airflow into and out of the cylinder. While timing gears seemingly require no maintenance, they can wear or break just like any other part. Today's advanced electronic engine management systems can actually mask some driveability symptoms caused by these or other mechanical problems in an effort to maintain emission control.

Valve Timing and Overlap

Volumetric efficiency is a measure of how much of the cylinder volume is filled during various operating conditions. The timed flow rate of a given volume is the basis for understanding this concept. For example, if a given volume of air at a given pressure flows through a fixed opening, it is a time-related event. If that same volume were under pressure, more air would flow through the fixed opening in the same period of time. This is true up to the point where additional pressure no longer yields an increased amount of flow. This is because the area through which the air is flowing stays the same. Therefore, it is the size of the fixed opening that limits the flow. This explains why valve-train-related problems such as a worn cam lobe, carbon-restricted intake valve, lifter adjustment, or faulty lifters can reduce compression in the cylinder. Due to such restrictions, the time the valve is open is reduced, thereby creating less time for the air-fuel charge to flow into the chamber and resulting in less volume in the cylinder. To summarize, it can be simply stated that the ratio of ambient air density to that in the cylinder when filled is that particular engine's volumetric efficiency at a given rpm.

For the intake and exhaust valves to open and close properly, they must be timed precisely to the crankshaft position. Refer to Figure 3-12 to aid in illustrating the relationship of the valves to the four strokes of the piston. As the piston approaches the intake stroke, the intake valve begins to open at about 20 degrees before the piston reaches TDC. The piston moves past TDC, enters the downstroke, and passes BDC at about 50 degrees when the intake valve closes. The movement of the incoming air continues although the piston has begun its upward travel. The compression stroke begins while the intake valve is closing, at about 50 degrees after BDC. The compression stroke continues toward TDC. Ignition occurs just before the piston reaches TDC to ensure that peak combustion pressure occurs when the piston is about 15 degrees after TDC. This maximizes the power from ignition because the combustion pressure is effective for approximately 90 degrees of the total crankshaft rotation. That translates to about 15 percent of the crankshaft movement that is used to create power. The combustion continues to push the crankshaft to about 60 degrees before BDC, when the exhaust valve opens. The exhaust stroke continues to occur as the crankshaft rotates to about 20 degrees after TDC. Depending on the engine design, for about 30 or more degrees both the intake and exhaust valves are open. This period of time when both valves are open is called valve overlap. Overlap helps control the volume of the fresh air-fuel charge being drawn into the cylinder.

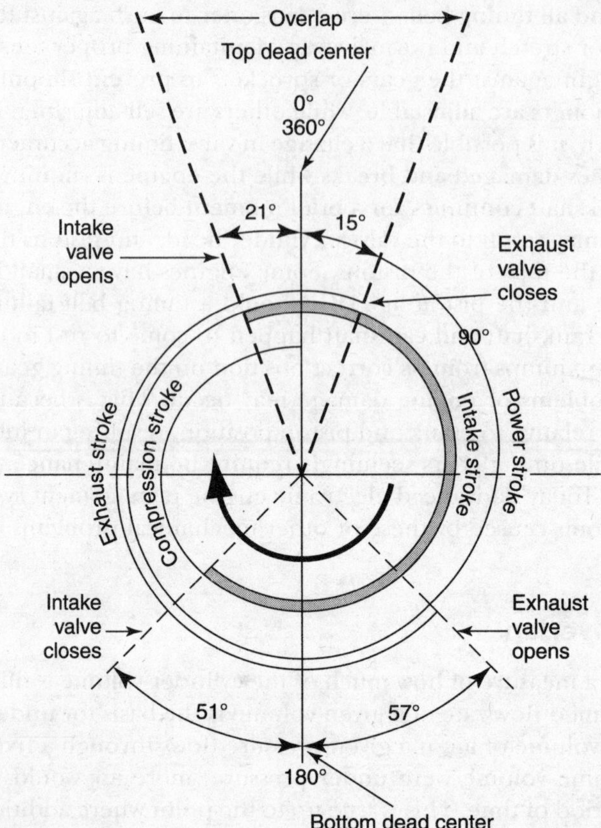

FIGURE 3-12 *Typical valve timing diagram.*

The movement of the outgoing exhaust gases creates a lower pressure in the cylinder that acts on the intake charge. This action is called scavenging. This scavenging effect allows the fresh mixture to begin to flow into the cylinder even before the piston begins the intake stroke. If anything affects the valve timing or the valve opening, the flow will be reduced or interfered with, reducing mixture intake, airflow, volumetric efficiency, and compression.

Multivalve Engines

Volumetric efficiency relates to the concept of more air input equals more power output. Multivalve engines allow more volume to enter the cylinder in a specific period of time. The velocity of the intake air is actually higher with smaller multiple valve ports as compared to a single larger passage. Multivalve engines today come in a variety of arrangements and number of valves. A dual-valve engine is a bit of a misnomer in that there are actually four valves per cylinder—two, or dual, intake valves and two exhaust valves. Other combinations use three or five valves per cylinder. With the three-valve system, there are two intake valves and one exhaust, while the five-valve arrangement uses three for the intake and two for exhaust. In many of the multivalve applications, two camshafts are used and are referred to as dual overhead camshafts (DOHC). Any multivalve engine will require a more complex camshaft operation, which requires more components that add cost to the engine.

Variable Cam Timing

As with any camshaft design, a good compromise is engineered into the valve timing to optimize high-end performance while maintaining good, low speed and idle quality. High-performance camshafts have a high duration (the amount of time the valves stay open) to enhance high rpm performance. However, the idle quality is erratic at best. To achieve the best of the entire performance spectrum, some engines use variable camshaft timing. By controlling camshaft and valve operation for best idle quality, low speed performance, and higher horsepower output at high speeds, the incoming air-fuel charge can be adjusted specifically and precisely for the varying conditions and demands. Engine speed and load determine when the valves will open and for how long. Several types of variable cam timing designs are in use today. On some, camshaft rotational timing is controlled hydraulically through commands from the powertrain control module (PCM). Others use computer-controlled solenoids to control rocker arms to vary the intake and exhaust valve timing by alternating between separate cam lobes featuring two different lift and duration profiles.

Variable Displacement Engines

At light loads, such as during steady cruising, only a small percentage of available power is needed. Also, at these light engine loads, the throttle is almost completely closed, which limits the engine's ability to breathe; and in turn the cylinders do not get enough air for an efficient combustion. With some of the cylinders deactivated, the throttle is opened further, which contributes to cylinder fill. In a way, four cylinders are better than eight under a light load. Engineers have developed ways to shut down some of the cylinders in an engine but still have them available for action quickly when needed. So far, V-8 and V-6 engines have been fitted with the technology. Every other cylinder in the firing order is shut down when cylinder deactivation is available (Figure 3-13). Special engine mounts, computer programming, variable valve timing technology, and a partial cylinder fill keep the engine from running rough as you might suspect. The cylinders are generally deactivated by closing the exhaust valve on the exhaust stroke. This keeps the exhaust charge in the cylinder. This charge provides some cushion for the piston on the way up. Also, if there is no charge at all in the cylinder, oil would be pulled up through the piston ring gaps when the piston was on the way down the cylinder due to the vacuum created. The fuel injectors are also turned off, but the spark at the plug is still fired. The reasoning for this is the fact that the plug could cool down and foul out during periods of inactivity. Generally, there are two ways used to shut down cylinders: lifter deactivation and rocker arm deactivation. General Motors' Active Fuel Management and Chrysler's Multiple Displacement System MDS uses a special lifter (Figure 3-14) that collapses when oil pressure sent from a PCM-activated solenoid acts on a pin in the lifter. The lifter collapses, so the pushrod is no longer lifted and the valve stays closed. A spring located on the lifter takes up the lash created and prevents the valve train from being noisy. Honda uses a version called variable cylinder management (VCM). This system utilizes the rocker arms and cam followers that are locked together by a **synchro** pin. When the cylinders are deactivated the pin is pulled out and the valves are no longer opened by the rocker

FIGURE 3-13 *This V-8 engine is running on 4 cylinders under certain conditions to greatly improve fuel economy.*

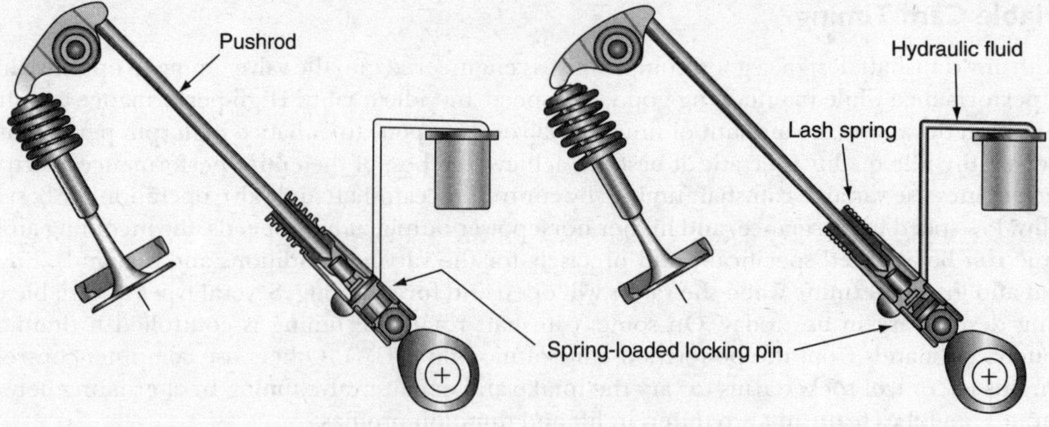

FIGURE 3-14 *Special valve lifters used in variable displacement engines from GM and Chrysler.*

arms. When all cylinders are needed, the pins are reinserted and the cam follower and rocker arms are reconnected.

GASOLINE ENGINE SYSTEMS

The operation of an engine relies on several other systems. The efficiency of these systems affects the overall operation of the engine.

Air-Fuel System

This system makes sure the engine receives the right amount of both air and fuel needed for efficient operation. For many years, air and fuel were mixed in a carburetor, which supplied the resulting mixture to the cylinder. Today, most late-model automobiles have a fuel injection system that replaces the carburetor but performs the same basic function.

Ignition System

This system delivers a spark to ignite the compressed air-fuel mixture in the cylinder at the end of the compression stroke. The **firing order** of the cylinders is determined by the engine's manufacturer and can be found in the vehicle's service manual. Typical firing orders are illustrated in Figure 3-15.

Lubrication System

This system supplies oil to the various moving parts in the engine. The oil lubricates all parts that slide in or on other parts, such as the piston, bearings, crankshaft, and valve stems. The oil enables the parts to move easily so that little power is lost and wear is kept to a minimum. The lubrication system also helps transfer heat from one part to another for cooling.

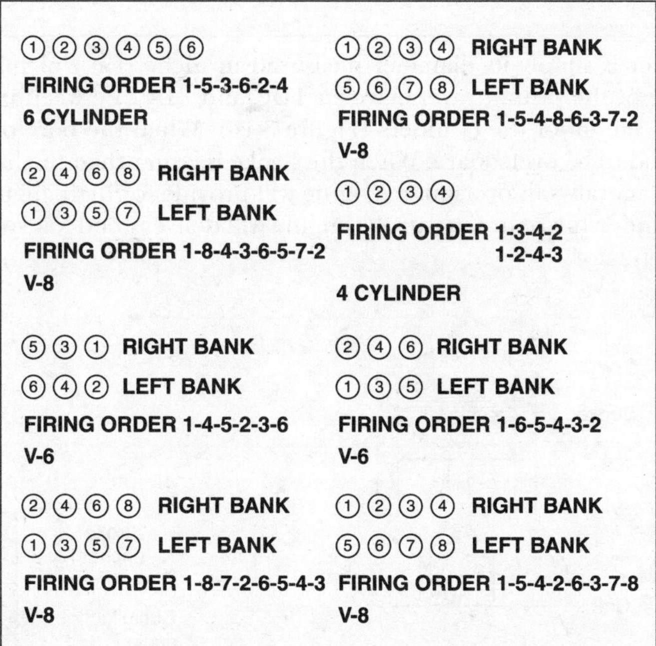

FIGURE 3-15 *Common firing orders.*

Cooling System

This system is also extremely important. Coolant circulates in jackets around the cylinder and in the cylinder head. This removes part of the heat produced by combustion and prevents the engine from being damaged by overheating.

Exhaust System

This system removes the burned gases from the combustion chamber and limits the noise produced by the engine.

Emission Control System

Several control devices, which are designed to reduce the amount of pollutants released by the engine, have been added to the engine. Engine design changes, such as reshaped combustion chambers and altered valve timing, have also been part of the manufacturers' attempt to reduce emission levels.

ENGINE MEASUREMENT AND PERFORMANCE

Some of the engine measurements and performance characteristics that a technician should be familiar with follow.

Bore and Stroke

The **bore** of a cylinder is simply its diameter measured in inches (in.) or millimeters (mm). The **stroke** is the distance of the piston travel between TDC and BDC. Between them, bore and stroke determine the displacement of the cylinders (Figure 3-16). When the bore of the engine is larger than its stroke, it is said to be oversquare. When the stroke is larger than the bore, the engine is said to be undersquare. Generally, an oversquare engine will provide for high engine speeds, such as for automobile use. An undersquare or long-stroke engine will deliver good low speed power, such as an engine for a truck or tractor.

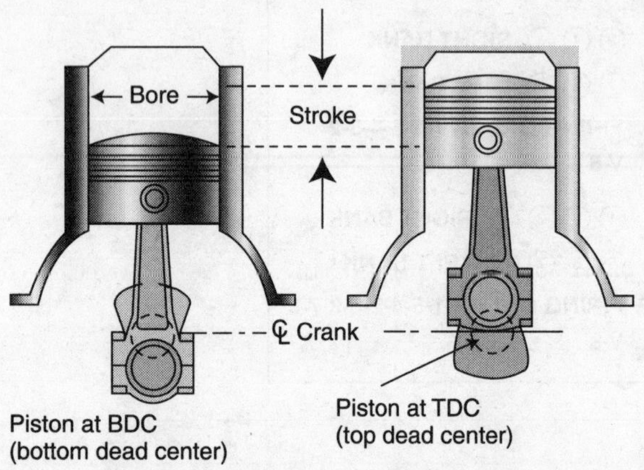

FIGURE 3-16 *The bore and stroke of an engine.*

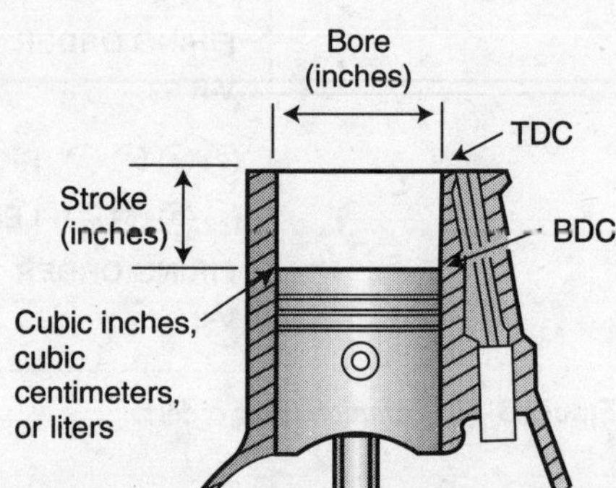

FIGURE 3-17 *Displacement is the volume of a cylinder between TDC and BDC.*

Displacement

Displacement is the volume of a cylinder between the TDC and BDC positions of the piston. It is usually measured in cubic inches, cubic centimeters, or liters (Figure 3-17). The total displacement of an engine (including all cylinders) is a rough indicator of its power output. Displacement can be increased by opening the bore to a larger diameter or by increasing the length of the stroke. Total displacement is the sum of displacements for all cylinders in an engine. Cubic inch displacement (CID) may be calculated as follows.

$$\text{CID} = \text{pi} \times R^2 \times L \times N$$

where pi = 3.1416

$$R = \text{bore radius or } \frac{\text{bore diameter}}{2}$$

L = length of stroke

N = number of cylinders

Example: Calculate the cubic inch displacement (CID) of a six-cylinder engine with a 3.7-in. bore and 3.4-in. stroke.

$$\text{CID} = 3.1416 \times 1.85^2 \times 3.4 \times 6$$
$$\text{CID} = 219.66$$

Most of today's engines are described by their metric displacement. Cubic centimeters and liters are determined by using metric measurements in the displacement formula.

Example: Calculate the metric displacement of a four-cylinder engine with a 78.9-mm stroke and a 100-mm bore.

$$\text{Displacement} = 3.1416 \times \left(\frac{100}{2}\right)^2 \times 78.9 \times 4$$

$$\text{Displacement} = 2479 \text{ cubic centimeters (cc)} = 2.5 \text{ liters (L)}$$

Larger, heavier vehicles are provided with large displacement engines. Large displacement engines produce more torque than smaller displacement engines. They also consume more fuel. Smaller, lighter vehicles can be adequately powered by lower displacement engines that use less fuel.

Compression Ratio

The **compression ratio** of an engine expresses how much the air and fuel mixture will be compressed during the compression stroke. The compression ratio is defined as the ratio of the volume in the cylinder above the piston when the piston is at BDC to the volume in the cylinder above the piston when the piston is at TDC (Figure 3-18). The formula for calculating the compression ratio is as follows.

$$\frac{\text{volume above the piston at BDC}}{\text{volume above the piston at TDC}}$$

or

$$\frac{\text{total cylinder volume}}{\text{total combustion chamber volume}}$$

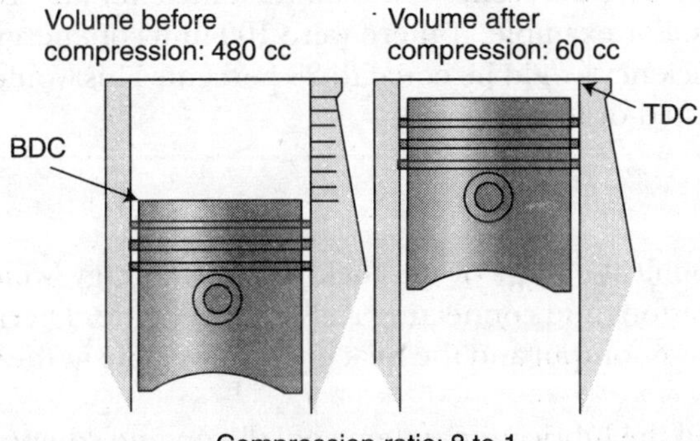

FIGURE 3-18 *Compression ratio measures the amount the air and fuel mixture will be compressed.*

In many engines, the top of the piston is even or level with the top of the cylinder block at TDC. The combustion chamber is in the cavity in the cylinder head and cylinder bore above the piston. This is modified slightly by the shape of the top of the piston. The volume of the combustion chamber must be added to each volume in the formula in order to achieve an accurate calculation of compression ratio.

Example: Calculate the compression ratio if the total piston displacement is 45 cubic inches and the combustion chamber volume is 5.5 cubic inches.

$$\frac{45 + 5.5}{5.5} = \text{compression ratio}$$

$$9.1 \text{ to } 1 = \text{compression ratio}$$

(Be sure to add the combustion chamber volume to the piston displacement to achieve the total cylinder volume.)

The higher the compression ratio, the more power an engine theoretically can produce. Also, as the compression ratio increases, the heat produced by the compression stroke also increases. Gasoline with a low octane rating burns fast and may explode rather than burn when introduced to a high-compression ratio. This can cause detonation. The higher a gasoline's octane rating, the less likely it is to explode.

As the compression ratio increases, the octane rating of the gasoline also should be increased to prevent abnormal combustion.

ENGINE EFFICIENCY

Engine **efficiency** is a measure of the relationship between the amount of energy put into the engine and the amount of available energy from the engine. Engine efficiency is expressed in a percentage. The formula for determining efficiency is:

$$\text{efficiency} = \frac{\text{output energy}}{\text{input energy}} \times 100$$

There are other aspects of the engine that are expressed in efficiencies. These include mechanical efficiency, volumetric efficiency, and thermal efficiency. They are expressed as a ratio of input (actual) to output (maximum or theoretical). Efficiencies are expressed as percentages. They are always less than 100 percent. The difference between the efficiency and 100 percent is the percentage lost during the process. For example, if there were 100 units of energy put into the engine and 28 units came back, the efficiency would be equal to 28 percent. This would mean that 72 percent of the energy received was wasted or lost.

Thermal Efficiency

An engine converts the chemical energy of the fuel into heat energy, which is then converted into mechanical energy by the pistons and connecting rods of the engine. Thermal energy is the relationship between the engine power output and the heat energy available in the fuel. A percentage is used to express this relationship.

As the cooling system and the lubrication system cool the engine components, these systems carry away much of the heat energy in the fuel. However, this cooling action is necessary to prevent the destruction of engine parts. Part of the heat energy in the fuel is dissipated through the exhaust system. Some of the heat energy in the fuel is consumed to overcome the internal friction in the engine and powertrain. From the total energy in the fuel, these average losses may occur:

- 35 percent loss to the cooling and lubrication system
- 35 percent loss to the exhaust gas
- 5 percent loss to engine friction
- 10 percent loss to powertrain friction

After these losses, only 15 percent of the thermal energy in the fuel is left to drive the vehicle. In recent years, engine components have been designed to reduce engine friction, and improved lubricants reduce engine and powertrain friction. However, the average engine thermal efficiency still remains below 30 percent. Some engine manufacturers are designing ceramic engine components that are capable of operating at higher temperatures than metal and aluminum components. The use of ceramic engine components increases engine thermal efficiency.

Mechanical Efficiency

Mechanical efficiency is the relationship between the engine power delivered and the power that would be delivered if the engine operated without any power loss. The mechanical efficiency of an engine is expressed as a percentage.

Volumetric Efficiency

As discussed earlier, volumetric efficiency is the relationship between the amount and density of air actually taken into the cylinder on the intake stroke compared to the amount of air required to fill the cylinder at atmospheric pressure. Volumetric pressure is also expressed as a percentage. The volumetric efficiency of an engine is affected by intake manifold design, valve timing, and exhaust system design.

TORQUE AND HORSEPOWER

Torque is a turning or twisting force. The engine's crankshaft rotates with a torque that is transmitted through the drivetrain to turn the drive wheels of the vehicle. **Horsepower** (HP) is the rate at which torque is produced.

Engines produce power by turning a crankshaft in a circular motion. To convert terms of force applied in a straight line to a force applied in a circular motion, the formula is:

$$\text{torque} = \text{force} \times \text{radius}$$

Example: A 10-pound force applied to a wrench 1 foot long will produce 10 pound-feet (lb.-ft) of torque. Imagine that the 1-foot-long wrench is connected to a shaft. If 1 pound of force is applied to the end of the wrench, 1 pound-foot of torque is produced. Ten pounds of force applied to a wrench 2 feet long will produce 20 pound-feet of torque (Figure 3-19).

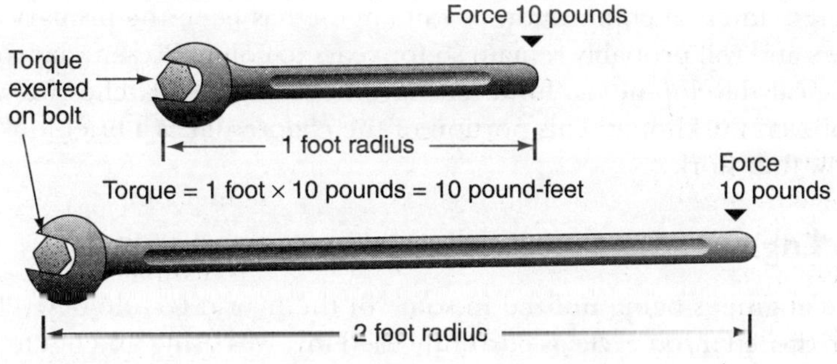

FIGURE 3-19 *Force applied to a wrench produces torque.*

The technically correct torque measurement is stated in pound-feet (lb.-ft). However, it is rather common to state torque in terms of foot-pounds (ft.-lb). In the metric or SI system, torque is stated in Newton-meters (Nm) or kilogram-meters (kg-m).

If the torque output of an engine at a given speed (rpm) is known, horsepower (HP) can be calculated by the following formula.

$$\text{HP} = (\text{torque} \times \text{rpm}) \div 5{,}252$$

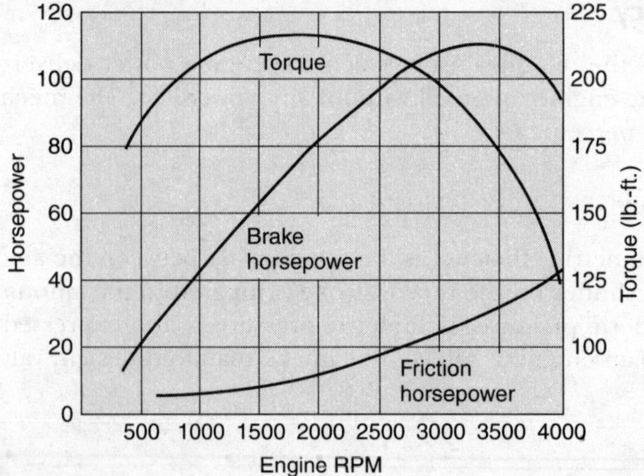

FIGURE 3-20 *The relationship between horsepower and torque.*

An engine produces different amounts of torque based on the rotational speed of the crankshaft and other factors. A mathematical representation, or graph, of the relationship between the horsepower and torque of one engine is shown in Figure 3-20.

This graph shows that torque begins to decrease when the engine's speed reaches about 1,700 rpm. Brake horsepower increases steadily until about 3,500 rpm. Then it drops. The third line on the graph indicates the horsepower needed to overcome the friction or resistance created by the internal parts of the engine rubbing against each other.

OTHER ENGINE DESIGNS

The gasoline-powered, internal combustion piston engine has been the primary automotive power plant for many years and will probably remain so for years to come. Present-day social requirements and new technological developments, however, have necessitated searches for ways to modify or replace this time-proven workhorse. This portion of the chapter takes a brief look at the most likely contenders and how they work.

Atkinson Cycle Engine

The Atkinson cycle engine is being utilized in some of the hybrid technology vehicles on the market today. Basically, the Atkinson cycle as currently used involves using an engine with a long stroke and a unique arrangement on the intake valve. It is a four-stroke engine with the normal intake-compression-power-exhaust strokes. The Atkinson cycle involves leaving the intake valve open on the intake stroke past BDC. This way, the start of the compression stroke is delayed until the intake valve is closed. This affects the compression ratio of the engine. The variable valve timing of the engine allows it to respond to conditions as needed. The advantage of the Atkinson cycle is the long power stroke which squeezes every bit of energy out of the fuel burned during the short compression stroke. A conventional four-stroke engine has a power and compression stroke that last for the same amount of time. With the long stroke of the Atkinson cycle, this would result in an engine that had a compression ratio too high to pump gasoline. The engine is not known for high power unless supercharged, which is known as a Miller cycle engine.

Two-Stroke Gasoline Engines

In the past, several imported vehicles have used two-stroke engines. As the name implies, this engine requires only two strokes of the piston to complete all four operations: intake, compression, power, and exhaust. As shown in Figure 3-21, this is accomplished as follows.

1. Movement of the piston from BDC to TDC completes both intake and compression.
2. When the piston nears TDC, the compressed air-fuel mixture is ignited, causing an expansion of the gases. Note that the reed valve is closed and the piston is blocking the intake port.
3. Expanding gases in the cylinder force the piston down, rotating the crankshaft.
4. With the piston at BDC, the intake and exhaust ports are both open, allowing exhaust gases to leave the cylinder and air-fuel mixture to enter.

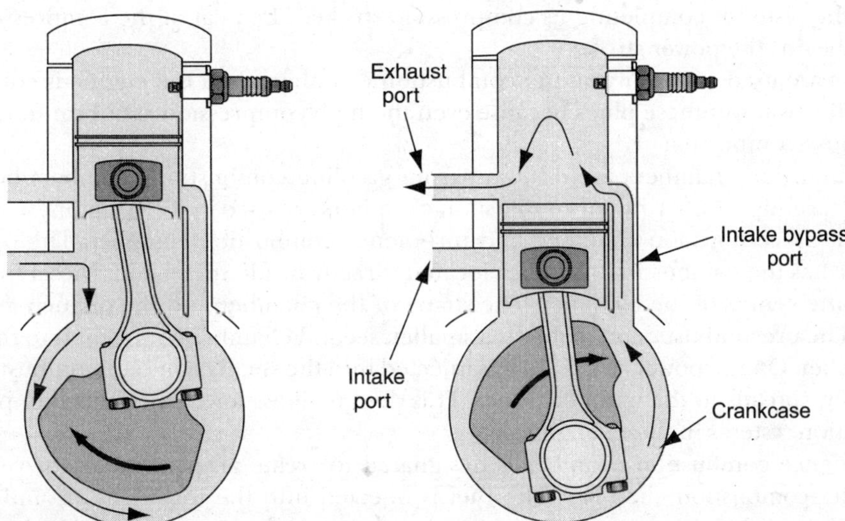

FIGURE 3-21 *The two-stroke engine.*

Although the two-stroke-cycle engine is simple in design and lightweight because it lacks a valve train, it has not been widely used in automobiles. They tend to be less fuel efficient and have dirtier exhaust than four-stroke engines. Oil is often in the exhaust stream because these engines require constant oil delivery to the cylinders to keep the piston lubricated. Some of these engines require that a certain amount of oil be mixed with the fuel.

In recent years, however, thanks to a revolutionary pneumatic fuel injection system, there has been increased interest in the two-stroke engine. The injection system, which works something like a spray paint gun, uses compressed air to flow highly atomized fuel directly into the top of the combustion chamber. The system becomes the long sought-after answer to the fuel economy and emissions problems of the conventional two-stroke engine. This fuel injection system is the basis for orbital two-stroke direct injection piston engine, which may be used in cars in the future.

Diesel Engines

Diesel engines represent tested, proven technology with a long history of success. Invented by Dr. Rudolph Diesel, a German engineer, and first marketed in 1897, the diesel engine is now the dominant power plant in heavy-duty trucks, construction equipment, farm equipment, buses, and marine applications.

During the late 1970s and early 1980s, many predicted small diesel engines would replace gasoline engines in passenger vehicles. However, stabilized gas prices and other factors dampened the enthusiasm for diesels in these markets. The use of diesel engines in cars and light trucks is now limited to a few manufacturers.

Diesel engines and gasoline-powered engines share several similarities. They have a number of components in common, such as the crankshaft, pistons, valves, camshaft, and water and oil pumps. They are both available in four-stroke combustion cycle models. However, the diesel engine and four-stroke compression-ignition engine are easily recognized by the absence of an ignition system. Instead of relying on a spark for ignition, a diesel engine uses the heat produced by compressing air in the combustion chamber to ignite the fuel. The systems used in diesel-powered vehicles are essentially the same as those used in gasoline vehicles.

Fuel injection is used in all diesel engines. Injectors spray pressurized fuel directly into the cylinders, just as the piston is completing its compression stroke. The heat of the compressed air ignites the fuel and begins the power stroke.

Glow plugs are used only to warm the combustion chamber when the engine is cold. Cold starting is impossible without these plugs because even the high-compression ratios cannot heat cold air enough to cause combustion.

Diesel combustion chambers are different from gasoline combustion chambers because diesel fuel burns differently. Three types of combustion chambers are used in diesel engines: open combustion chamber, precombustion chamber, and turbulence combustion chamber. The open combustion chamber has the combustion chamber located directly inside the piston. Diesel fuel is injected directly into the center of the chamber. The shape of the chamber and the quench area produces turbulence. The precombustion chamber is a smaller, second chamber connection to the main combustion chamber. On the power stroke, fuel is injected into the small chamber. Combustion is started there and then spreads to the main chamber. This design allows lower fuel injection pressures and simpler injection systems in diesel engines.

The turbulence combustion chamber is designated to create an increase in air velocity or turbulence in the combustion chamber. The fuel is injected into the turbulent air and burns more completely. The prechambers in a diesel engine head must be properly indexed with the head and correctly installed. They must be perfectly flush (not above or below) with the cylinder head. Failure to follow this will cause the head gasket to fail.

Rotary Engine

The **rotary** engine, or **Wankel engine**, is somewhat similar to the standard piston engine in that it is a two-cycle, spark ignition, internal combustion engine. Its mechanical design, however, is quite different. For one thing, the rotary engine uses a rotating motion rather than a reciprocating motion. In addition, it uses ports rather than valves for controlling the intake of the air-fuel mixture and the exhaust of the combusted charge.

The heart of a rotary engine is a roughly triangular rotor that "walks" around a smaller, rigidly mounted gear. The rotor is connected to the crankshaft through additional gears in such a manner that for every rotation of the rotor the crankshaft revolves three times. The tips of the triangular rotor move within the housing and are in constant contact with the housing walls. As the rotor moves, the volume between each side of the rotor and the housing walls continually changes.

Referring to Figure 3-22, when the rotor is in position A, the intake port is uncovered and the air-fuel mixture is entering the upper chamber. As the rotor moves to position B, the intake port closes and the upper chamber reaches its maximum volume. When full compression has reached position C, the two spark plugs fire, one after the other, to start the power stroke. At position D, rotor side A uncovers the exhaust port and exhaust begins. This cycle continues until position A is reached where the chamber volume is at minimum and the intake cycle starts once again.

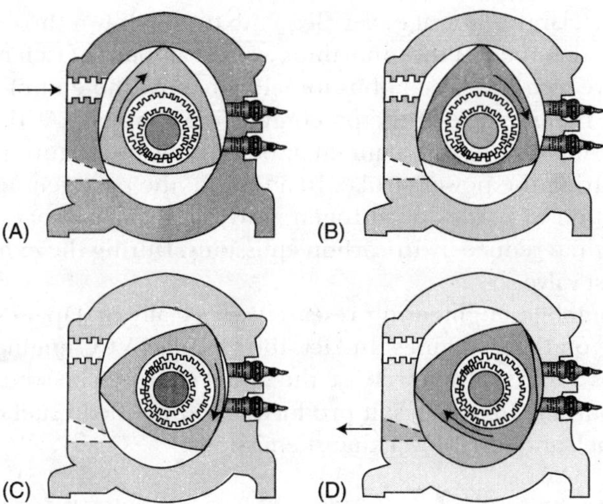

FIGURE 3-22 *Rotary operational cycles.*

The fact that the rotating combustion chamber engine is small and light for the amount of power it produces makes it attractive for use in automobiles. Using this small, lightweight engine can provide the same performance as a larger engine. But the rotary engine, at present, cannot compete with the piston gasoline on durability, exhaust emission control, and economy.

Stratified Charge Engine

The stratified charge engine (Figure 3-23) combines the features of both the gasoline and diesel engines. It differs from the conventional gasoline engine in that the air-fuel mixture is deliberately stratified to produce a small rich mixture at the spark plug while providing a leaner, more efficient and cleaner burning main mixture. In addition, the air-fuel mixture is swirled for more complete combustion.

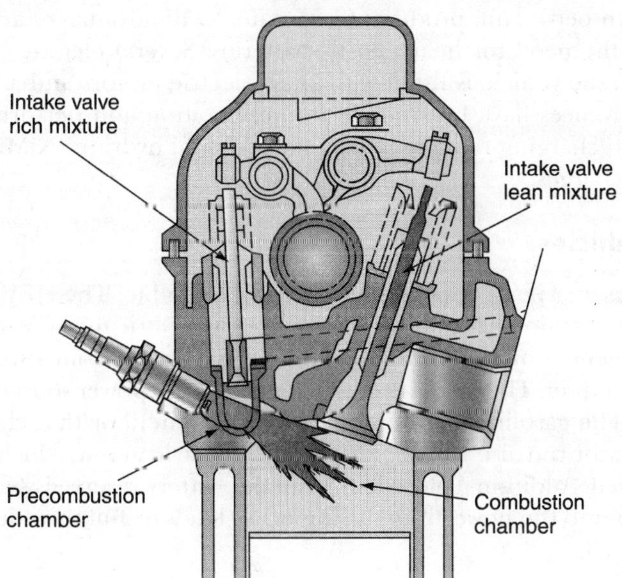

FIGURE 3-23 *Typical stratified charge engine.*

On the intake stroke, a large amount of very lean mixture is drawn through the main intake valve to the main combustion chamber. At the same time, a small amount of rich mixture is drawn through the auxiliary intake valve into the precombustion chamber. At the end of the compression stroke, the spark plug fires the rich mixture in the precombustion chamber. As the rich mixture ignites, it in turn ignites the lean mixture in the main chamber. The lean mixture minimizes the formation of carbon monoxide during the power stroke. In addition, the peak temperature stays low enough to minimize the formation of oxides of nitrogen, and the mean temperature is maintained high enough and long enough to reduce hydrocarbon emissions. During the exhaust stroke the hot gases exit through the exhaust valve.

A great deal of automobile engineering research, especially by Japanese and European manufacturers, is being done on these engines. In fact, the Honda CVCC engine uses a stratified charge design. This engine uses a third valve to release the initial charge. The stratified charge combustion chamber has three important advantages: it produces good part-load fuel economy, it can run efficiently on low-octane fuel, and it has low exhaust emissions.

Miller-Cycle Engines

This engine design is a modification of the four-stroke-cycle engine. During the intake stroke, a supercharger feeds highly compressed air to an intercooler. This cooled, but compressed, air is fed to the cylinders. During the compression stroke, the intake valve remains open for longer than normal. This prevents compression from occurring until the piston has moved one-fifth of its upward travel. Then the valve closes and compression occurs. The shortened compression stroke keeps the compression ratios and cylinder temperatures low. The power stroke begins as soon as the piston is ready to move down its bore and continues until it reaches BDC. This longer power stroke provides more torque and increased efficiency. The exhaust stroke is much the same as that in a four-stroke-cycle engine.

Electric Motors

In the early days of the automobile, electric cars outnumbered gasoline cars. An electric motor is quiet, has little or no emissions, and has few moving parts. It starts well in the cold, is simple to maintain, and does not burn petroleum products to operate. Its disadvantages are limited speed, power, and range, as well as the need for heavy, costly batteries. Several electric cars have recently been introduced. Generally, the vehicle is fitted with large electric motors and a large bank of lead-acid batteries. Although advances have been made for acceleration and performance, the issue of distance traveled before recharging remains. Using nickel metal hydride (NiMH) batteries will extend the intervals between charges.

Hybrid Electric Vehicles

Hybrid electric vehicles, or HEVs, have recently become available. The HEV uses both a small gasoline engine and an electric motor for power. Power for the electric motor is stored in a battery pack, which is charged by a generator. When the vehicle begins to move from a stop, the electric motor is the primary source for power. The gasoline engine becomes the power source during normal driving and load conditions. The gasoline engine also drives the generator that charges the battery pack. In addition, the generator can also supply power to the electric motor, which is run to add power to the powertrain if needed. Additional electricity from the battery reserve is sent to the electric motor, increasing power output to the powertrain during heavy loads or full throttle.

Hybrid Types

Hybrid vehicles are classified as either **mild, parallel,** or **series**. In a mild hybrid, which is also known as a CAS for Combined Alternator Starter type, a gas or diesel engine runs to charge the batteries for the electric motor. The electric motor only runs when the small internal combustion motor needs assistance during acceleration or hill pulling.

The series hybrid uses a small internal combustion engine to charge the batteries when they become discharged. The electric motor provides power to the drive wheels. The series hybrid uses a complex controller to provide seamless acceleration from the electric motor.

The parallel hybrid uses both the electric motor and the internal combustion engine to power the drive wheels. The electric motor in the parallel system is small and uses principally the internal combustion engine except during times of low load, such as in town driving or freeway cruising.

Fuel Cells

Although commonly used in spacecraft and submarines, emerging technological advances are making the fuel cell a contender for automotive use. In the simplest terms, the fuel cell is a component that converts hydrogen to electricity. The electricity that is converted from hydrogen (derived from methanol or gasoline) will be used to power an electric motor that powers the car. The fuel cell is perhaps the answer to the problems associated with a conventional electric vehicle. The advantage of the fuel cell vehicle is that the batteries are lighter and are charged by the fuel cell, as compared to other electric vehicles, which have to be plugged in. The fuel cells do not store electricity, but rather convert it to be used as required to drive the electric motors. When power requirements exceed the fuel cell's capacity, power is provided by storage batteries. The hydrogen will likely come from methanol. Methanol can be handled and stored much the same way gasoline is. Currently under development for automotive application, fuel cell technology as an alternative to gasoline-powered engines will be the focal point throughout this decade.

ENGINE LUBRICATION

An engine's lubricating system performs several important tasks. It holds an adequate supply of oil to cool, clean, lubricate, and seal the engine. It also removes contaminants from the oil and delivers oil to all necessary areas of the engine.

Engine Oil

Engine oil is a clean or refined form of **crude oil**. Crude oil, when taken out of the ground, is dirty and does not work well as a lubricant for engines. Crude oil must be refined to meet industry standards. Engine oil is just one of the many products that come from crude oil. Engine oil is specially formulated so that it has the following properties.

- Prompt circulation through the engine's lubrication system
- The ability to lubricate without foaming
- The ability to reduce friction and wear
- The ability to prevent the formation of rust and corrosion
- The ability to cool the engine parts it flows on
- The ability to keep internal engine parts clean
- The ability to suspend and carry small particles to the oil filter

To provide these properties, engine oil contains many additives. Because of these additives, choosing the correct oil for each engine application can be a difficult task. However, the **American Petroleum Institute** (**API**) has developed service ratings for motor oil that greatly simplify oil selection.

Performance requirements, test methods, and limits for motor oil are cooperatively established by vehicle and/or engine manufacturers and technical societies such as the American Society for Testing and Materials (ASTM) and the **Society of Automotive Engineers (SAE)**.

The API uses two types of marks: the API Service Symbol and the API Certification Mark (Figure 3-24). The API Service Symbol indicates the performance level and grade of the oil. The API Certification Mark, introduced in 1993, helps consumers identify engine oil that is suitable for use in gasoline engines. Motor oils licensed to use the API Certification Mark meet the latest standards of the International Lubricant Standardization and Approval Committee (ILSAC), which is comprised of US and Japanese automobile manufacturers.

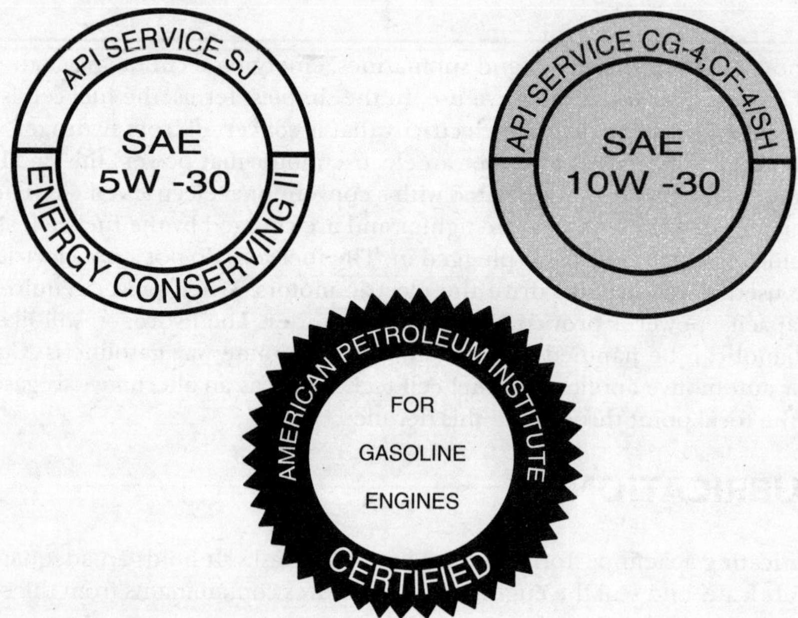

FIGURE 3-24 *Identification label on oil containers.*

The API Service Symbol has been around for many years and is well recognized. It is divided into three parts:

The top portion describes the performance level of the oil.
The center section displays the SAE viscosity grade of the oil.
The lower section indicates whether the oil has energy-conserving properties.

The top portion of the API Service Symbol indicates the oil's performance for gasoline or diesel engines. The API classifies engine oil as an S (Service) class for passenger cars and light- and medium-duty trucks with gasoline engines and as a C (Commercial) class for heavy-duty diesel applications. As a coincidence (not a true definition), think of the S-class oils for a spark-ignited engine and the C-class oils for compression-ignited engines. The second letter following both the S and C categories is generally assigned alphabetically in order of development.

The following service rating examples for gasoline engines are:

SG—Obsolete (was introduced in 1993)
SH—Obsolete (was introduced in 1996)
SJ—Obsolete (was introduced in 1997)
SL—Obsolete (was introduced in 2001)
SM—Introduced in 2004 for current and older engines

It is important to note that each gasoline engine category above exceeds the performance properties of all the previous categories and can be used in place of the lower one(s). SM rated oil, for example, can be used for any previous category. It is expected that the next API change will move the S rating one step higher. The tests that the oil must pass will be more stringent, so the letter rating will go up to reflect that new standard.

The following are the service ratings for diesel engines:

CE—Obsolete—Introduced in 1987 for high-speed, four-stroke, naturally aspirated, and turbocharged engines

CF—Current—Introduced in 1994. The CF-rated oil can be used in place of CD-rated oils

CF-4—Current—Introduced in 1990 for high-speed, four-stroke, naturally aspirated, and turbocharged engines.

CG-4—Current—Introduced in 1995 for severe-duty, high-speed, four-stroke engines using fuel with less than 0.5 percent weight sulfur. The CG-4 rated oil can be used in place of CD, CE, and CF-4 oils.

CH-4—Current—Introduced in 1999 for high-speed, four-stroke engines designed to meet 1998 emission standards using fuel with up to 0.5 percent weight sulfur. The CH-4 rated oil can be used in place of CD, CE, CF-4, and CG-4 oils.

CI-4—Current—Introduced in 2002 for four-stroke engines meeting 2004 emission standards. Can be used in place of CD, CE, CF-4, and CH-4 oils.

CJ-4—Introduced for 2007 and later diesels to be compatible with the diesel particulate filter installed on these engines to limit particulate emissions. This oil has limited amounts of sulfates and phosphorus because they are incompatible with the particulate filter.

The center section of the API Service Symbol indicates the SAE viscosity grade of the oil. The SAE classifications are the internationally accepted standard for defining viscosity. However, this standard provides no information specific to the quality of the oil. Although single-grade oils are still used in certain applications, the multi-grade oils are most widely used in today's automotive applications.

Friction Modifiers

Oil refiners add a number of different additives to their oil that improve oil performance in the engine. Friction modifiers in the engine oil reduce friction between moving parts that contact each other. The oil film between two moving surfaces is actually sheared by the moving components. During this oil-shearing process, there is a certain amount of friction in the oil. This friction within the oil is referred to as viscous friction, and this type of friction is reduced by friction modifiers in the oil.

Antifoaming Agents

Oil foaming may be caused by the rotating action of the crankshaft and connecting rods. Since oil foam contains oil and air, excessive oil foaming causes air in the lubrication system, which partially destroys the oil film on moving components in contact with each other. This action allows these moving components to contact each other, causing excessive friction and wear. Antifoaming agents added to the engine oil reduce oil foaming in the engine. Oil foaming may be caused by overfilling the crankcase; therefore, it is important to maintain the oil at the proper level on the dipstick.

Corrosion and Rust Inhibitors

Since the engine experiences severe temperature changes, condensation may form water in the engine. Condensation on engine components may cause rust. When rust inhibitors are added to the oil, they help to disperse moisture from the metal surfaces. Certain acids may be formed in small quantities during the combustion process, and these acids get past the rings into the engine oil. Acids cause corrosion on engine components as they circulate through the lubrication system with the oil. Acids in the oil are neutralized by corrosion inhibitors added to the oil.

Extreme Pressure Resistance

When an engine is operating under heavy load, the pistons and connecting rods produce an extremely high downward force on the crankshaft journals. Under this condition, the film of oil in the connecting rod and main bearings may be subjected to pressures up to 1,000 psi (6,900 kPa). This high pressure tends to squeeze the oil out of the crankshaft bearings. If the oil is squeezed out of the bearings and the bearing insert contacts the crankshaft, bearing damage results. Extreme pressure resistance additives help to prevent the oil from being squeezed out of the bearings.

Detergents and Dispersants

Carbon is a normal by-product of the combustion process. This carbon collects on the combustion chamber surfaces. However, some of this carbon collects on the top ring lands and compression rings. Detergents added to the oil help to clean these carbon deposits from the piston and rings, and this action keeps the rings working freely in the ring grooves.

A dispersant added to the engine oil helps to prevent carbon particles from sticking together to form larger particles. Oil passages may be plugged by large carbon particles. The smaller carbon particles are removed by the oil filter, while some larger particles may remain in the oil pan. These carbon particles in the oil pan are removed when the oil is changed.

Oxidation Inhibitors

The rotation of the crankshaft causes oil agitation in the crankcase. Air combines with high-temperature oil when the oil is agitated. During this combination of air and high-temperature oil, the oxygen in the air combines with the oil and forms a sticky substance that is similar to tar and contains corrosive compounds. This tar-like material may plug oil passages or destroy the oil film on some of the engine components. The corrosive compounds may attack and erode bearing materials. Oxidation of engine oil is reduced by oxidation inhibitors added to the oil.

Viscosity

In addition to the additives and performance rating of the motor oil, viscosity is another important aspect of oil selection. Viscosity is merely the resistance of the oil to flow. Thin oil flows freely and is less resistant to flow, whereas thick oil has a higher resistance to flow and flows more slowly. Testing standards are established to measure the specific amount of oil that flows in a given period at specific testing temperatures, both hot and cold. The multi-grade oils have additives called viscosity index improvers that allow the oil to flow as evenly when cold as when hot. In other words, with a multi-grade oil there is a less noticeable difference in oil flow characteristics between temperature extremes. Engines operate in a wide range of temperatures and conditions: climate, stop-and-go city driving, prolonged highway speeds, pulling loads, and so on. Engines must function reliably in the harshest of operating environments. Consider today's engine designs, some of which have complex valvetrains, block and piston arrangements, tight clearances, and engines that run hotter in a smaller engine compartment. Generally, the largest percentage of critical engine wear occurs within the first 15 seconds of starting a cold engine. The properties of the oil must allow it to flow properly to provide lubrication and not break down, regardless of the conditions.

The SAE has established a classification system that standardizes oil viscosity ratings. This system is a numeric rating in which the higher viscosities, or thicker oils, receive the higher numbers (Figure 3-25).

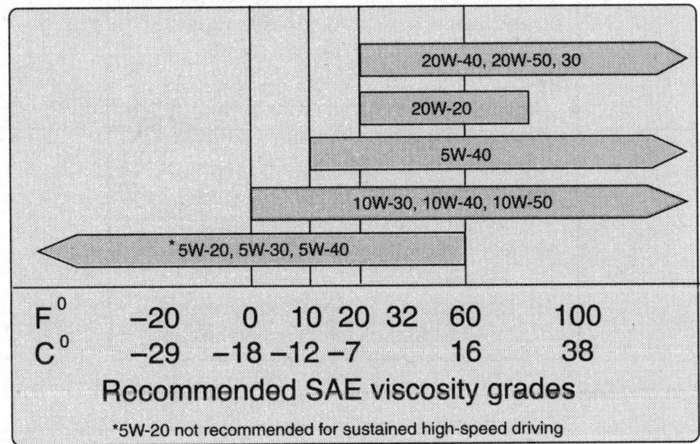

FIGURE 3-25 *SAE oil viscosity ratings in relationship to ambient temperatures.*

For example, an SAE 40 oil is thicker and flows slower than an SAE 5 oil. Obviously, a cold engine needs to have the oil flow quickly and freely. Because heat can cause the oil to flow easier, thicker oil is needed for high temperatures. Straight-viscosity oils will have a single number or rating, such as SAE 40. There are no viscosity index improvers added to extend the flow properties. The multi-grade has two numbers, indicating a cold flow rate and a hot flow rate. The numbers are assigned as a result of the oil's performance during the cold- and hot-flow rate tests performed. For example, SAE 5W-30 has the flow characteristics of a 5 "weight" oil when cold and the hot flow rate of a 30 "weight." The number before the "W" indicates the cold rating. The "W" actually stands for "winter," not "weight" as some may assume. The oil testing standards are being made more stringent, and the motor oils are constantly evolving with new compounds and additives to keep pace with engineering advances. Oil change intervals have been extended due to these improvements. A longer interval between oil changes not only saves money for the consumer, but also makes sense environmentally. Engine life will be prolonged by using the proper rated oil recommended specifically by the manufacturer in addition to changing the oil and oil filter at the recommended intervals.

The SAE classification and the API rating are usually indicated on the oil container (Figure 3-26). Selecting oils that specifically meet or exceed the manufacturer's recommendations and changing the oil on a regular basis will allow the owner to achieve the maximum service life from an engine.

Engine oils can be classified as **energy-conserving** (fuel-saving) **oils**. These are designed to reduce friction, which in turn reduces fuel consumption. Friction modifiers and other additives are used to achieve this. Energy-conserving oil is identified as such on the top of the oil can. Some oils are specially formulated for turbocharged engines. This oil is identified on the container with a marking such as "Turbo Formula."

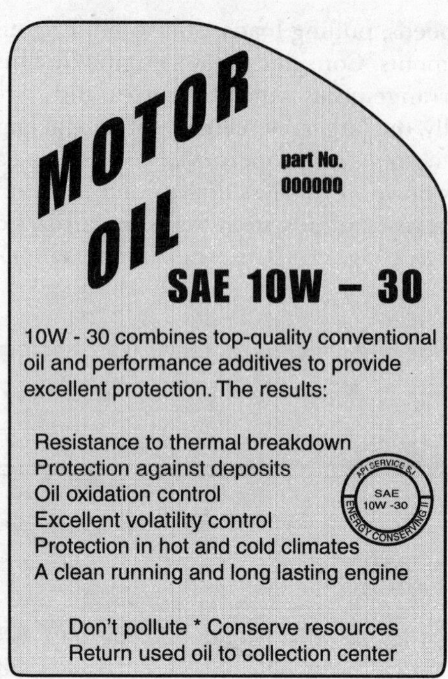

Figure 3-26 *API designation and SAE rating.*

Synthetic and Recycled Oils

Synthetic oils are recommended by a few engine manufacturers. These oils are manufactured in a laboratory rather than being refined. Synthetic oils have improved stability over a wide temperature range, and they have improved viscous friction qualities. When synthetic oil is used in an engine, there may be a slight improvement in fuel economy and cold weather cranking speed.

The introduction of synthetic motor oils dates back to World War II. It is often described as the oil of the future. Synthetic oils are manufactured in a laboratory rather than pumped out of the ground. They offer a variety of advantages over natural oils including better fuel economy, stability over a wide range of temperatures and operating conditions, and longevity. They are more costly than natural oil.

Engine oil that is based on petroleum and synthetic products is available. These oils combine some of the better attributes of synthetics with the lower-cost petroleum-based oils. Typically, these oils are 80 percent petroleum and 20 percent synthetic.

Used oil that has been processed to remove impurities and restored to original standards is called recycled oil. Many oil recycling plants have been built in North America, and the recycled oil from these plants should be equivalent to new refined oil. Most states have strict laws regarding the dumping of used oil.

LUBRICATING SYSTEMS

The main components of a typical lubricating system are described here.

Oil Pump

The oil pump is the heart of the lubricating system. Just as the heart in a human body circulates blood through veins, an engine's oil pump circulates oil through passages in the engine.

The oil pump is usually located in the oil pan. Its purpose is to supply oil to the various moving parts in the engine. To make sure the parts are lubricated, an adequate amount of oil must be delivered to the parts. To get the oil to move through the engine and into the various parts, the oil must be pressurized. Oil pumps are designed to move a certain volume of oil and pressurize it to a certain amount. The amount of oil flow through the engine depends on the volume of oil available, the pressure of the oil, and the clearance (or space) the oil must flow through (Figure 3-27).

Oil Pump Pickup

The **oil pump pickup** is a line from the oil pump to the oil stored in the oil pan (Figure 3-28). It usually contains a filter screen, which is submerged in the oil at all times. The screen serves to keep large particles from reaching the oil pump.

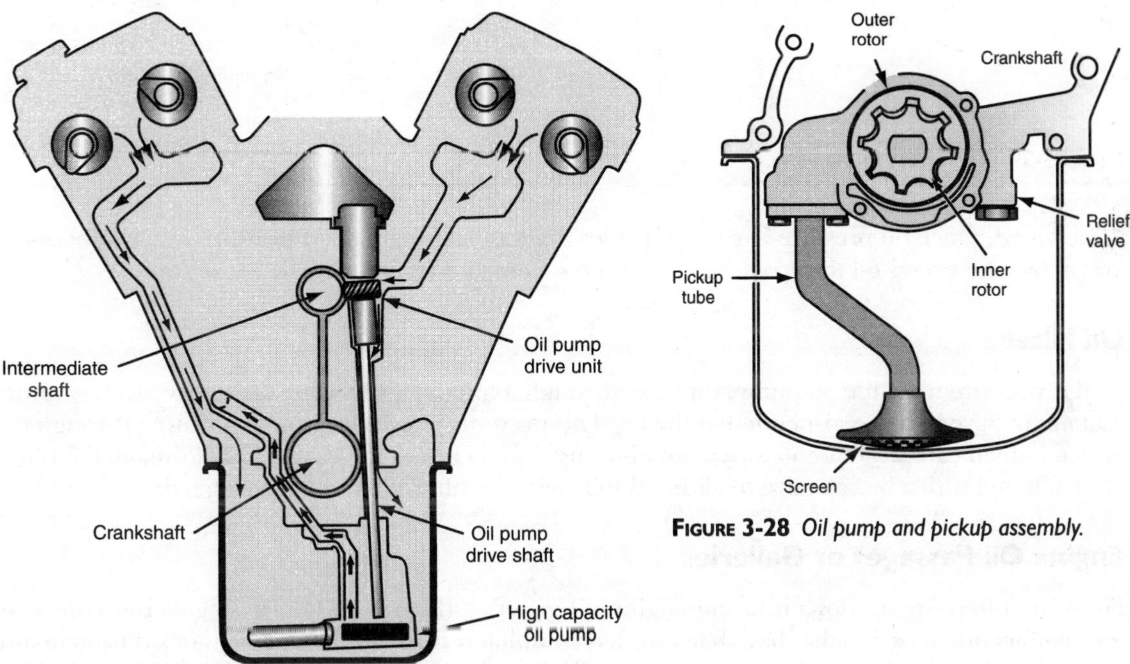

FIGURE 3-27 *Oil pump and drive assembly.*

FIGURE 3-28 *Oil pump and pickup assembly.*

Oil Pan or Sump

The oil pan attaches to the crankcase or block. It serves as the reservoir for the engine's oil. It is designed to hold the amount of oil that is needed to lubricate the engine when it is running, plus a reserve. The oil pan helps to cool the oil through its contact with the outside air.

Pressure Relief Valve

Since the oil pump is a positive displacement pump, an oil pressure relief valve (Figure 3-29) is included in the system to prevent excessively high system pressures from occurring as engine speed

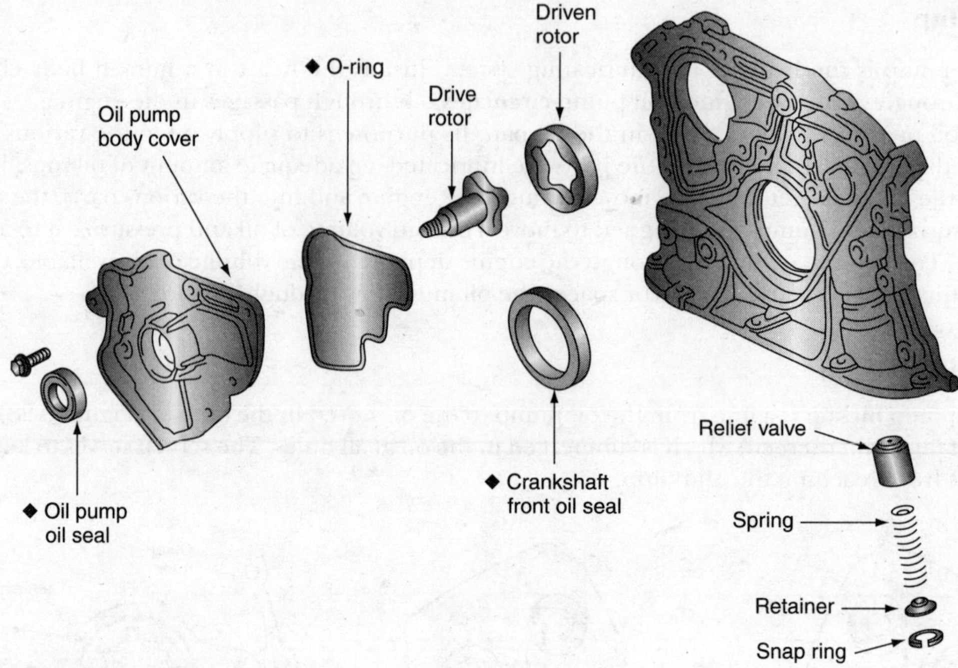

FIGURE 3-29 *Oil pressure relieve valve.*

is increased. Once oil pressure exceeds a preset limit, the spring-loaded pressure relief valve opens and allows the excess oil to bypass the rest of the system and return directly to the sump.

Oil Filter

Under pressure from the oil pump, oil flows through a filter (Figure 3-30) to remove any impurities that might have become suspended in the oil. This prevents impurities from circulating through the engine, which can cause premature wear. Filtering also increases the usable life of the oil. Oil filters are equipped with a bypass valve to allow oil to bypass the filter if the filter is clogged.

Engine Oil Passages or Galleries

From the filter, the oil flows into the engine oil galleries (Figure 3-31). These galleries consist of interconnecting passages that have been drilled completely through the engine block during manufacturing. The outside ends of the passages are blocked off so the oil can be routed through these galleries to various parts of the engine. The crankshaft also contains oil passages (oilways) to route the oil from the main bearings to the connecting rod bearing surfaces.

Engine Bearings

Since oil is delivered to the engine bearings by an oil gallery, an oil hole is machined in the bearing for alignment with the oil gallery in the engine block. Many engine bearings are manufactured with an oil groove to help distribute the oil over the surface of the bearing. Once the oil has been used by the bearing, it flows out of the oil clearance space and is replenished with a fresh supply of oil under pressure from the oil pump.

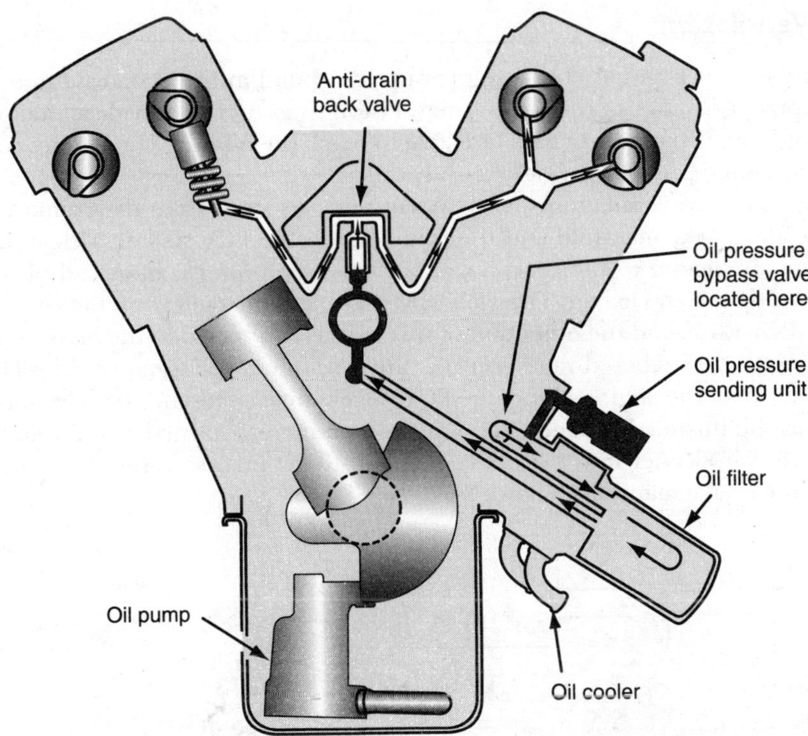

FIGURE 3-30 *Oil passes from the filler through the anti-drain back valve to the lifters and the camshaft journals.*

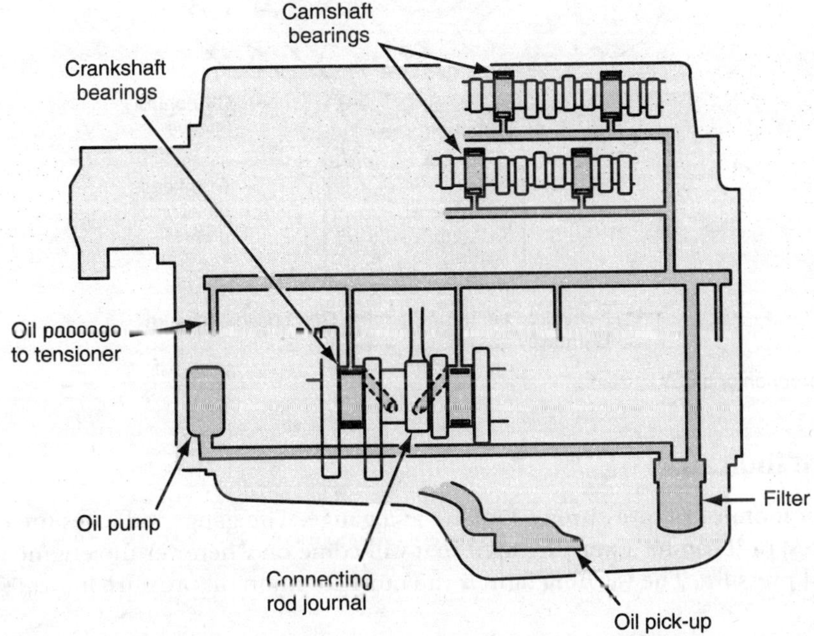

FIGURE 3-31 *Oil passes from the main oil galley to the main bearings and connecting rod journals.*

Crankcase Ventilation

Crankcase ventilation is necessary because pressure can build in the crankcase due to combustion pressure. This pressure passes by the piston rings. Piston rings do not provide a total seal of the combustion area, and some combustion gases are able to reach the oil pan. These gases contaminate the oil and apply unwanted pressure on gaskets and seals.

The positive crankcase ventilation (PCV) system removes gases from the crankcase and delivers them back into the intake manifold and the cylinders. In the PCV system, a clean air hose is connected from the air cleaner to the rocker arm cover. A small filter is mounted on the end of this clean air hose inside the air cleaner. The PCV valve hose is connected from the rocker arm cover to one end of the PCV valve, and the other end of this valve is connected to the intake manifold. Inside the PCV, a spring-loaded, tapered valve controls the flow of crankcase vapors in relation to engine vacuum and load. With the engine idling, the PCV valve is nearly closed. The valve moves toward the open position as the throttle is opened and engine load increases. Intake manifold vacuum moves clean air from the air cleaner into the crankcase, and the crankcase gases are moved through the PCV valve into the intake manifold (Figure 3-32).

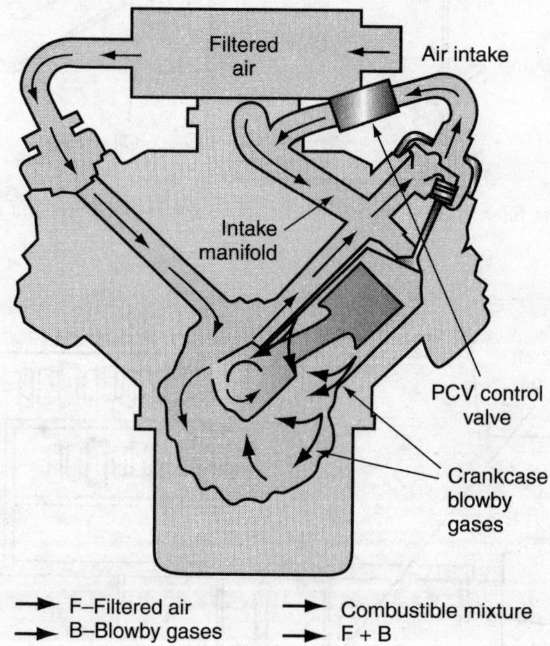

FIGURE 3-32 *Operation of a PCV system.*

Oil Pressure Indicator

The driver can monitor oil pressure by looking at a gauge. The gauge indicates the engine oil pressure at all times, or it can be a warning light that will come on whenever the engine is running with insufficient oil pressure. The warning light is the most common oil pressure indicator.

Oil Seals and Gaskets

Oil seals and gaskets are used throughout the engine to prevent both external and internal oil leaks. The most common materials used for sealing are synthetic rubber, soft plastics, fiber, and cork. In critical areas, these materials might be bonded to a metal. It is important to note that because of today's engines with computer-controlled management systems, a seemingly innocent gasket or seal leak can actually affect driveability. A damaged or leaking seal or gasket can allow extra air to be drawn into the crankcase through the PCV system. This results in unmetered air entering the intake manifold. Although minor, depending on the type of system the computer uses to read air intake, the engine can idle rough, idle high, or have other symptoms.

Dipstick

The dipstick is used to measure the level of oil in the oil pan. The end of the stick is marked to indicate when the engine oil level is correct. It also has a mark to indicate the need to add oil to the system (Figure 3-33).

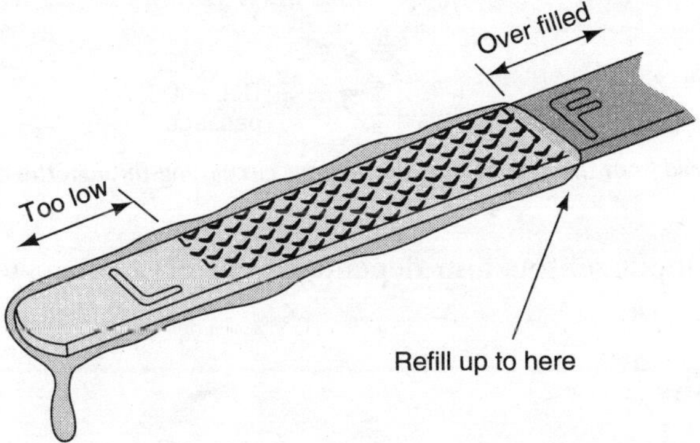

FIGURE 3-33 *The dipstick indicates the oil level in the crankcase.*

Oil Coolers

Some engines, such as diesel engines or turbocharged engines, use an external oil cooler. These typically look like a small radiator mounted near the front of the engine. Heat is removed from the oil as air flows through the cooler. Normal maximum engine oil temperature is considered to be 250°F. Hot oil mixed with oxygen breaks down (oxidizes) and forms carbon and varnish. The higher the temperature, the faster these deposits build. An oil cooler helps keep the oil at its normal operating temperature.

COOLING SYSTEMS

During the combustion process, temperatures can reach 4,500°F (2,468°C). While the engine is idling or operating at moderate speeds, the average combustion chamber temperature is 2,000°F (1,080°C). These temperatures in the cylinder are high enough to melt aluminum pistons, distort the cylinder walls, warp the cylinder head, and destroy the lubricating oil. Coolant circulation through the jackets in the cylinder head and block must absorb heat and lower component temperatures to a safe operating level (Figure 3-34).

Heat may be transferred by conduction, convection, or radiation in an engine cooling system. However, most of the heat is transferred by conduction from the hot engine components to the lower-temperature coolant. Coolant temperature also affects combustion and engine efficiency.

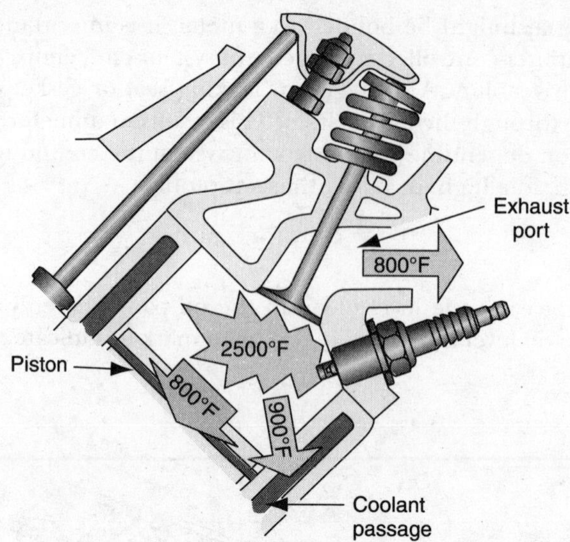

FIGURE 3-34 *Heat is transferred from the cylinders to the coolant circulating through the coolant jackets.*

Some computer system input sensors also depend on correct coolant temperature to produce a normal signal.

Liquid-Cooled System

By far, the most popular and efficient method of engine cooling is the liquid-cooled system (Figure 3-35). In this system, heat is removed from around the combustion chambers by a heat-absorbing liquid (coolant) circulating inside the engine. This liquid is pumped through the engine and, after absorbing the heat of combustion, flows into the radiator where the heat is transferred to the atmosphere. The cooled liquid is then returned to the engine to repeat the cycle. These systems are designed to keep engine temperatures within a range where they provide peak performance.

The engine's thermostat controls the temperature and amount of coolant entering the radiator. While the engine is cold, the thermostat remains closed, allowing coolant to circulate only inside the engine. This allows the engine to warm up uniformly and eliminates hot spots. When the coolant reaches the opening temperature of the thermostat, the thermostat begins to open and allows the flow of coolant to the radiator. The hotter the coolant becomes, the more the thermostat opens, allowing more coolant to flow through the radiator. Once the coolant has passed through the radiator and has given up its heat, it reenters the water pump. Here it is again pushed through the passages surrounding the combustion chambers to pick up heat and start the cycle once again.

The thermostat also maintains proper coolant temperatures to keep the emission control systems working properly. Many vehicles fail the emissions test because they are operating at a temperature that is too low.

Coolant

Coolant is a mixture of antifreeze and water. The antifreeze contains ethylene glycol and anti-corrosion chemicals. If water is used alone in a cooling system, the water promotes rust, corrosion, and electrolysis. The water in the cooling system may become slightly acidic because of minerals and metals in the cooling system. Metals such as brass, copper, aluminum, and cast iron alloy are contained in the cooling system. A small amount of electric current may flow from one of these metals to the

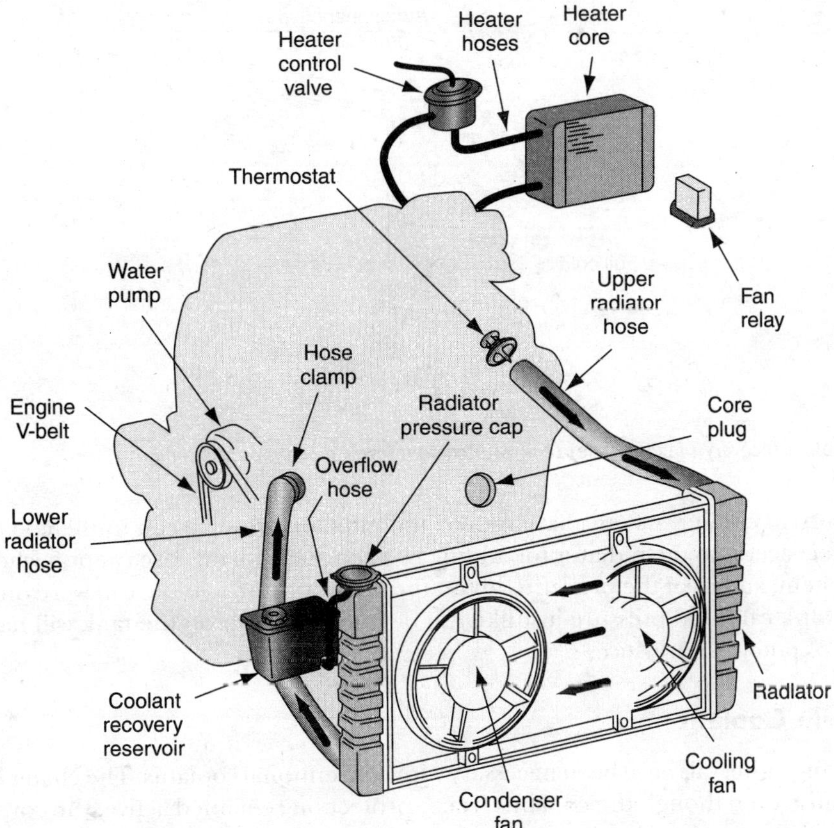

FIGURE 3-35 *Major components of a typical liquid-cooled engine. Arrows show coolant flow.*

other through the acid formed in the water. This electric current has a corrosive effect on cooling system metal components.

The antifreeze protects the coolant from freezing. Since water expands when it is frozen, the coolant jackets in the block and head may be cracked by frozen coolant. The radiator and heater core are also damaged by frozen coolant.

If the coolant boils, the liquid is no longer in contact with the cylinder walls and combustion chamber surfaces in the head. Under this condition, the heat is no longer transferred from these surfaces to the coolant, and the cylinder walls and combustion chamber surfaces become overheated. This action may score or collapse pistons and crack or warp cylinder heads.

A mixture of 50 percent antifreeze and water has a boiling point of approximately 230°F (103°C) at atmospheric pressure compared to water, which has a boiling point of 212°F (100°C) at sea level. This mixture of antifreeze and water provides extra protection from boiling. The same mixture of 50 percent antifreeze and water provides freezing protection to approximately –40°F (–35.5°C).

Most cooling systems today use an **expansion** or **recovery tank** (Figure 3-36). Cooling systems with expansion tanks are called closed-cooling systems. They are designed to catch and hold any coolant that passes through the pressure cap when the engine is hot. As the engine warms up, the coolant expands. This eventually causes the pressure cap to release. The coolant passes to an expansion tank. When the engine is shut down, the coolant begins to shrink. Eventually, the vacuum spring inside the pressure cap opens and the coolant in the expansion tank is drawn back into the cooling system.

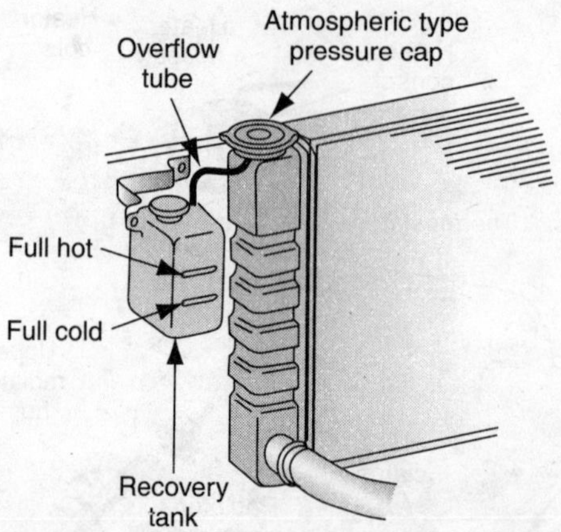

FIGURE 3-36 *Coolant recovery (degas bottle) tank with coolant levels marked on the tank.*

Recently, certain cooling systems have moved the radiator pressure cap to the coolant reservoir, leaving no direct access to the radiator for adding or checking coolant. Use caution when servicing a hot cooling system, and treat the pressure cap on the recovery tank as if the cap were on the radiator. The recovery tank can hold pressure just like the radiator. The cap on the tank will have a warning on it advising of potential pressure.

Extended Life Coolant

Anti-freeze change intervals have been necessary with conventional coolants. The change intervals are necessary because even though the coolants freeze protection remained active, the corrosion inhibitors would diminish over time, leaving engine components vulnerable to corrosion. Automakers and anti-freeze manufacturers have developed newer formulations such as DEX-COOL®.

These anti-freeze formulations are based on Ethylene Glycol, the main ingredient in conventional anti-freeze, but the corrosion protection is different, being based on carboxylates instead of silicates, phosphates, borates, nitrites, nitrates, and amine additives to eliminate corrosion. In addition to the fact that the carboxylates' corrosion protection does not tend to diminish over time, they are not as abrasive to water pump seals.

Water Pump

The heart of the cooling system is the water pump. Its job is to move the coolant through the cooling system. Typically, the water pump is driven by the crankshaft through pulleys and a drive V-belt or ribbed V-belt. The pumps are centrifugal-type pumps (Figure 3-37), with a rotating paddle wheel type impeller to move the coolant. The shaft is mounted in the water pump housing and rotates on bearings. The pump contains a seal to keep the coolant from passing through it. At the drive end (the exposed end), a pulley is mounted to accept the belt. The pulley is driven by the crankshaft. The pump housing usually includes the mounting point for the lower radiator hose.

When the engine is started, the pump impeller pushes the water from its pumping cavity into the engine block. When the engine is cold, the thermostat is closed. This stops the coolant from reaching the top of the radiator. In order for the water pump to circulate the coolant through the engine during warmup, a bypass passage is added below the thermostat, which leads back to the water pump. This passage must be kept free to eliminate hot spots in the engine during warmup. It also allows hot coolant to pass through the valve, which will open the thermostat when it reaches the proper temperature.

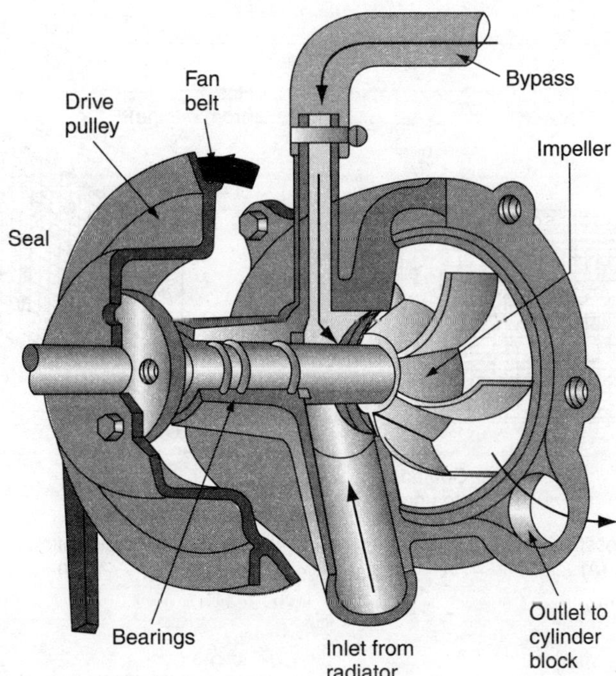

FIGURE 3-37 *Impeller-type water pump.*

Radiator

The radiator is basically a heat exchanger, transferring heat from the engine to the air passing through it. The radiator itself is a series of tubes and fins that expose the heat from the coolant to as much surface area as possible. This maximizes the potential of heat being transferred to the passing air. The inlet tank in the radiator contains a baffle to distribute and de-aerate the coolant.

Factors influencing the efficiency of the radiator are the basic design of the radiator, the area and thickness of the radiator core, the amount of coolant going through the radiator, and the temperature of the cooling air.

A radiator's efficiency can be greatly increased by increasing the difference between the temperature of the coolant and the outside air flowing through it. This can be done by only raising the temperature of the coolant. Doing this permits the use of a smaller radiator or the use of the same size radiator to cool a larger engine. This is the primary reason manufacturers have been specifying higher start-to-open temperatures for thermostats and higher pressure ratings for radiator pressure caps.

The radiator is usually based on one of these two designs: crossflow or downflow. In a crossflow radiator (Figure 3-38A), coolant enters on one side, travels through tubes, and collects on the opposite side. In a downflow radiator (Figure 3-38B), coolant enters the top of the radiator and is drawn downward by gravity. Crossflow radiators are seen most often in large-engine or late-model cars because all the coolant flows through the fan air stream, which provides maximum cooling.

There are two types of radiator core construction: honeycomb or cellular type and tube and fin. There are also two radiator core construction materials used—the copper/brass, soft solder coolers and the vacuum-brazed, aluminum cores cinched to nylon tanks.

The aluminum type is thin, lightweight, and less costly. (The initial price of aluminum is less than copper.) For these reasons, aluminum core radiators are being used more and more in newer model vehicles.

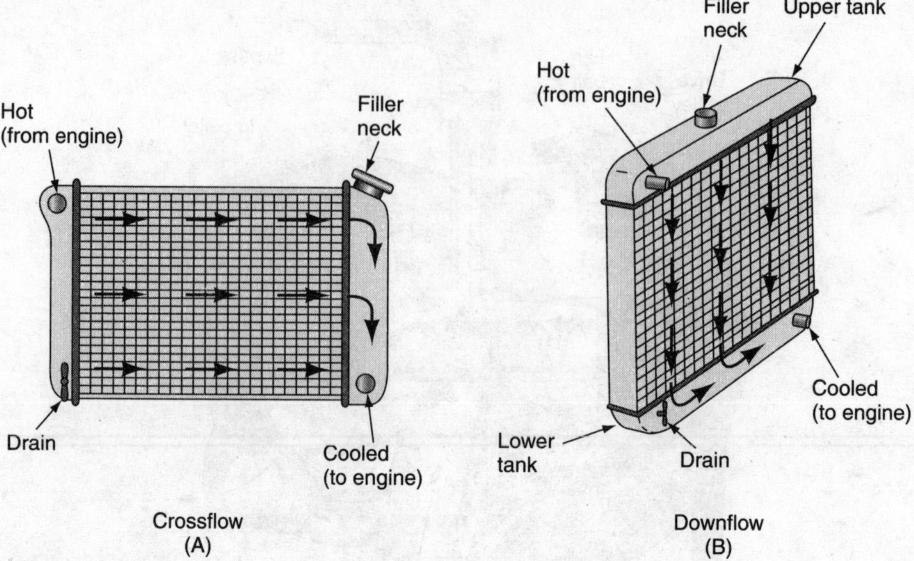

FIGURE 3-38 *Radiator coolant flow.*

Most radiators feature petcocks or plugs that allow a technician to drain coolant from the system. Coolant is added to the system at the radiator cap or the recovery tank depending on the type of system being used.

Radiator Pressure Caps

Atmospheric pressure is 14.7 psi at sea level, and this pressure decreases as elevation increases above sea level. At elevations below sea level, atmospheric pressure increases. Water boils at 212°F (100°C) at sea level, and this boiling point decreases at higher elevations with reduced atmospheric pressure. The radiator cap contains a spring-loaded lower sealing gasket that contacts the lower sealing surface in the radiator filler neck (Figure 3-39).

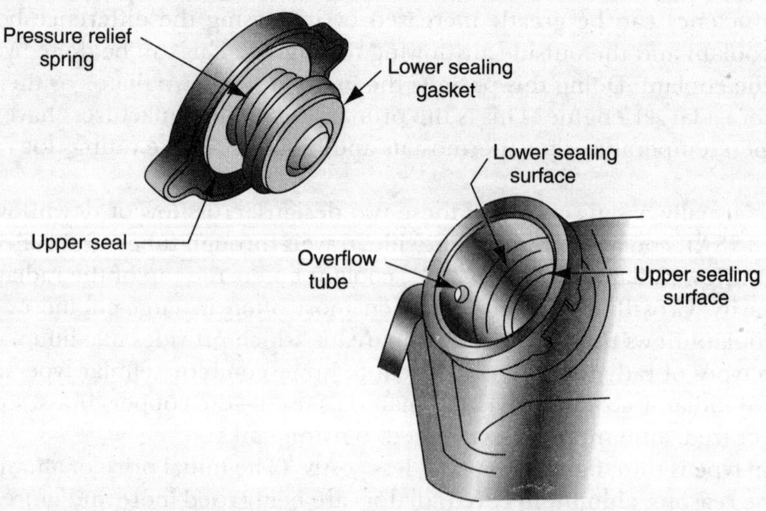

FIGURE 3-39 *Radiator pressure cap assembly.*

On many radiator caps, the spring and sealing gasket are designed to maintain 15 psi (103 kPa) in the cooling system. While the cooling system pressure remains below 15 psi (103 kPa), the spring keeps the sealing gasket closed. For each 1 psi (6.8 kPa) of pressure increase, the boiling point of the water increases approximately 3°F (1.6°C). Therefore, the boiling point of water at 15 psi (103 kPa) is about 257°F (125°C). The 50 percent antifreeze and water solution increases the coolant boiling point to approximately 266°F (134°C). A pressurized cooling system provides additional protection against coolant boiling.

If the coolant overheats and the cooling system pressure exceeds 15 psi (103 kPa), this pressure forces the sealing gasket open against the spring tension. This action allows coolant to escape from the filler neck through the overflow tube into the coolant recovery system.

Water Outlet

The water outlet is the connection between the engine and the upper radiator hose through which hot coolant from the engine is pumped back into the radiator. The water outlet has been called a gooseneck, elbow, inlet, outlet, or thermostat housing. Generally, it covers and seals the thermostat and, in some cases, includes the thermostat bypass.

Hoses

As already mentioned, the primary function of a cooling system hose is to carry the coolant between different elements of the system. Nearly all automobiles have an upper and lower radiator hose and two heater hoses. Some may also have a bypass hose. The majority of cooling system hoses are made of butyl or neoprene rubber. Many hoses are wire reinforced, and some are used to connect metal tubing between the engine and the radiator. Normally, radiator hoses are designed with expansion bends to protect radiator connections from excessive engine motion and vibration.

The upper radiator hose is subjected to the roughest service life of any hose in the cooling system. It must absorb more engine motion than any of the other hoses. It is exposed to the coolant at its hottest stage, and it is insulated by the hood during hot soak periods. These conditions make the upper hose the most likely to fail.

Nearly all original equipment radiator hose is of the molded, curved design. Aftermarket products may be of this type or of a wire inserted flex type. This flex-type hose allows greater vehicle coverage per part number, but may not be designed for some cars that require radical bends and shapes. Lower radiator hoses are normally wire reinforced to prevent collapse due to the suction of the water pump. Hose clamps are used to secure the hoses to the inlets and outlets of the cooling system.

Thermostat

An automotive thermostat works somewhat like a typical home thermostat. It attempts to control the engine's operating temperature by routing the coolant either to the radiator or through the bypass or sometimes by a combination of both.

Today's thermostat is composed of a specially formulated wax and powdered metal pellet, which is tightly contained in a heat-conducting copper cup equipped with a piston inside a rubber boot. Heat causes the wax pellet to expand, forcing the piston outward, which opens the valve of the thermostat. The pellet senses temperature changes and opens and closes the valve to control coolant temperature and flow. Today's thermostats are also designed to slow down coolant flow when they are open. This helps to prevent overheating, which can result from the coolant moving too quickly through the engine to absorb enough heat.

While the thermostat might be situated in several locations, the most common spot is at the front of the engine on top of the engine block (Figure 3-40). The heat element fits into a recess in the

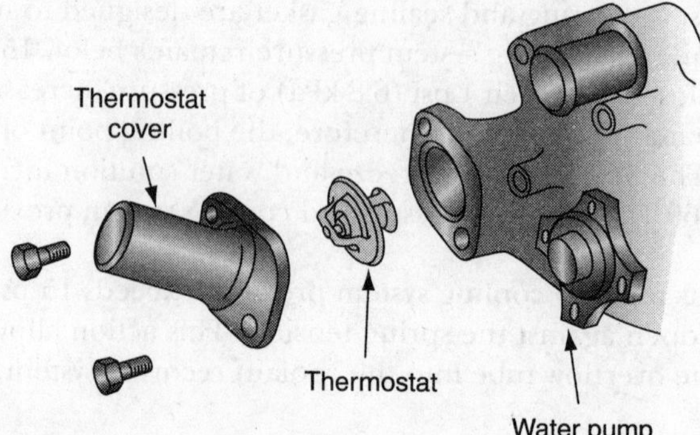

FIGURE 3-40 *Typical thermostat location.*

block where it will be exposed to hot coolant. The top of the thermostat is then covered by the water outlet housing, which holds it in place and provides a connection to the upper radiator hose.

There are two basic types of thermostats on the market today. Both function in the same manner, but each has distinct differences.

The reverse poppet thermostat (Figure 3-41A) opens against the flow of the coolant from the water pump. The coolant, under water pump pressure, is used to help the reverse poppet thermostat stay closed when it is cool. The valve is self-aligning and also self-cleaning.

The balanced sleeve thermostat (Figure 3-41B) eliminates pressure shocks by allowing pressurized coolant to circulate around all of its working parts. By reducing pressure shocks, it provides coolant temperature stability during the most difficult operating conditions.

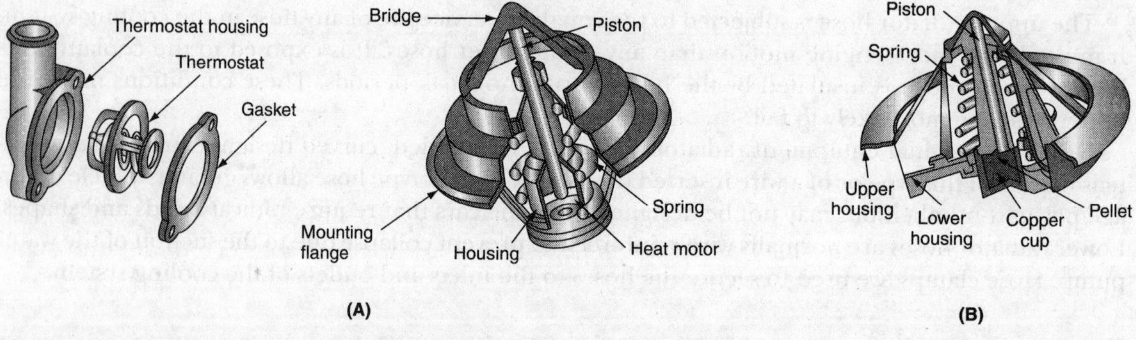

FIGURE 3-41 *Types of thermostats: (A) reverse poppet; (B) balanced sleeve.*

The thermostat permits fast warmup of the engine after it has been started. Slow warmup causes moisture condensation in the combustion chambers, which finds its way into the crankcase and causes sludge formation. The thermostat keeps the coolant above a designated minimum temperature required for efficient engine performance. Most engines are equipped with a coolant bypass, either outside the engine block or built into the casting. Some thermostat models are equipped with a bypass valve that shuts off the engine bypass after warmup, forcing all coolant to flow to the radiator.

Thermostats must start to open at a specified temperature, normally 3°F above or below its temperature rating. It must be fully opened at about 20°F above the "start to open" temperature. It must also permit the passage of a specified amount of coolant when fully open and leak no more than a specified amount when fully closed.

Belt Drives

Belt drives (Figure 3-42) have been used for many years. V-belts and serpentine belts are used to drive water pumps, power steering pumps, air-conditioning compressors, alternators, and emission control pumps (Figure 3-43). The flexibility of belt drives has allowed many inexpensive improvements in the modern automobile.

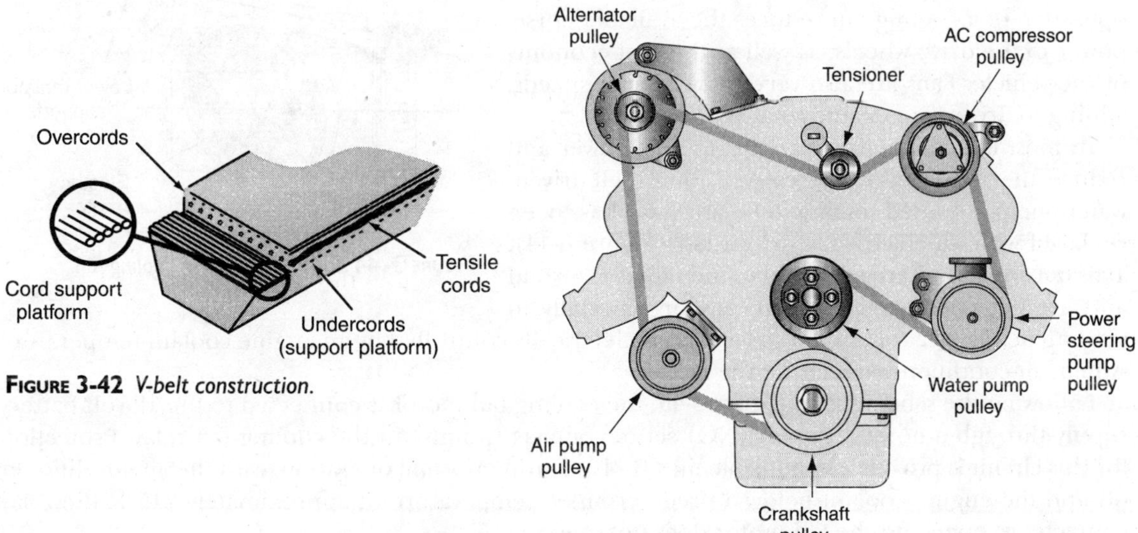

FIGURE 3-42 *V-belt construction.*

FIGURE 3-43 *A single belt may drive many components.*

The belt system is popular for a number of reasons. It is very inexpensive and quiet when compared to chains and gears. It is also very easy to repair. Because the belts are flexible, they will absorb some shock loads and cushion shaft bearings from excessive loads.

Serpentine belts are kept under constant tension by an idler pulley or tensioner. This pulley is designed to compensate for belt stretch and to keep a proper amount of tension on the belt.

Many drive units consist of two matched belts that run over parallel pulleys. If one pulley or belt should wear excessively, the belts will run at slightly different speeds, thus one will be constantly slipping. Matched belts should always be replaced in pairs so they wear together, thus maintaining the same length to prevent slippage and problems.

Fans and Fan Clutches

The efficiency of the cooling system is based on the amount of heat that can be removed from the system and transferred to the air. The system needs air. At highway speeds, the ram air through the radiator should be sufficient to maintain proper cooling. At low speeds and idle, the system needs additional air. This air is delivered by a fan.

The design of fans varies with the air requirements of the engine's cooling system. Diameter, pitch, and the number of blades can be varied to attain the needed flow. Fans are usually shrouded to maintain efficiency by causing all of the flow to pass through the radiator. This shrouding also allows the fan to be placed relatively far from the radiator, thus allowing the engine to be set back in the car while the radiator is left near the front of the vehicle.

Five- or six-blade fans are found on some cars. Fans may be made of steel, nylon, or fiberglass, and are precisely balanced to prevent water pump bearing and seal damage. Since fan air is usually only necessary at idle and low speed operation, various design concepts are used to limit the fan's operation at higher speeds. Horsepower is required to turn the fan. Therefore, the operation of a cooling fan reduces the available horsepower to the drive wheels, as well as the fuel economy of the vehicle. Fans are also very noisy at high speeds, adding to driver fatigue and total vehicle noise.

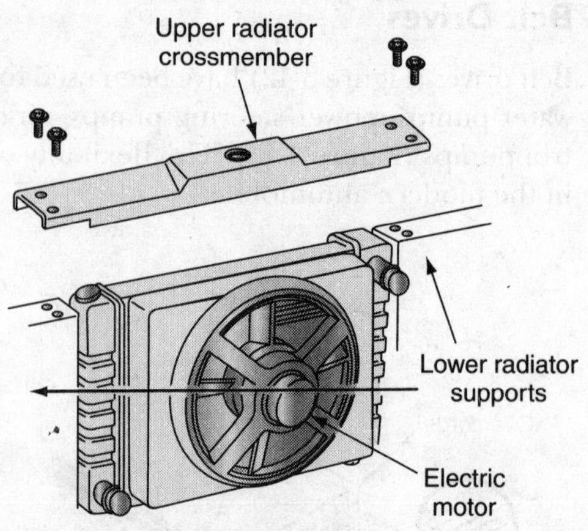

FIGURE 3-44 *Electrically driven cooling fan.*

In most late-model applications, to save power and reduce the noise level, the conventional belt-driven, water-pump-mounted engine coolant fan has been replaced with an electrically driven fan (Figure 3-44). This fan and motor are mounted to the radiator shroud and are not connected mechanically or physically to the engine. The 12-volt, motor-driven fan is electrically controlled by an engine coolant temperature switch, air-conditioner switch, or the PCM.

Following the schematic in Figure 3-45, the cooling fan motor is connected to the 12-volt battery supply through a normally open (NO) set of contacts (points) in the cooling fan relay. Protection for this circuit is provided by a fusible link (F/L). During normal operation, with the air conditioner off and the engine coolant below a predetermined temperature of approximately 215°F, the relay contacts are open and the fan motor does not operate.

Should the engine coolant temperature exceed approximately 230°F, the engine coolant temperature switch closes. This energizes the fan relay coil, which in turn closes the relay contacts. The contacts provide 12 volts to the fan motor if the ignition switch is in the on position. The 12-volt supply for the relay coil circuit is independent of the 12-volt supply for the fan motor circuit. The coil circuit is from the on terminal of the ignition switch, through a fuse in the fuse panel, and to ground through the relay coil and temperature sensor.

There are many variations of electric cooling fan operation. Some provide a cooldown period whereby the fan continues to operate after the engine has been stopped and the ignition switch is turned off. The fan stops only when the engine coolant falls to a predetermined safe temperature, usually about 210°F. In some systems, the fan does not start when the airconditioner select switch is turned on unless the high side of the air-conditioning (A/C) system is above a predetermined safe temperature.

Most late-model cars control the cooling fan by completing the ground through the engine control computer. Check the service manual to see how an electric cooling fan is controlled before working with it.

Another way of controlling fan noise and horsepower loss is by using a fan clutch (Figure 3-46). This unit connects the fan to the drive pulley (usually on the water pump shaft). The clutch slips at high speeds, therefore it is not turning at full engine speed.

Cooling fan clutches may be speed controlled or temperature controlled. The obvious advantage of the temperature-controlled unit is that it knows when air is needed to cool the system. A silicone fluid couples the fan blade drive plate to a driven disc via a series of annular grooves in the two pieces. The fluid fills these grooves and drives the fan until the differential torque between the fan and the drive disc causes the fluid to shear or slip. The unit has a bimetallic element that senses the air temperature behind the radiator (Figure 3-47). This bimetal is calibrated to open and close a valve in the clutch that dispenses the silicone at particular temperatures. When the fluid is returned

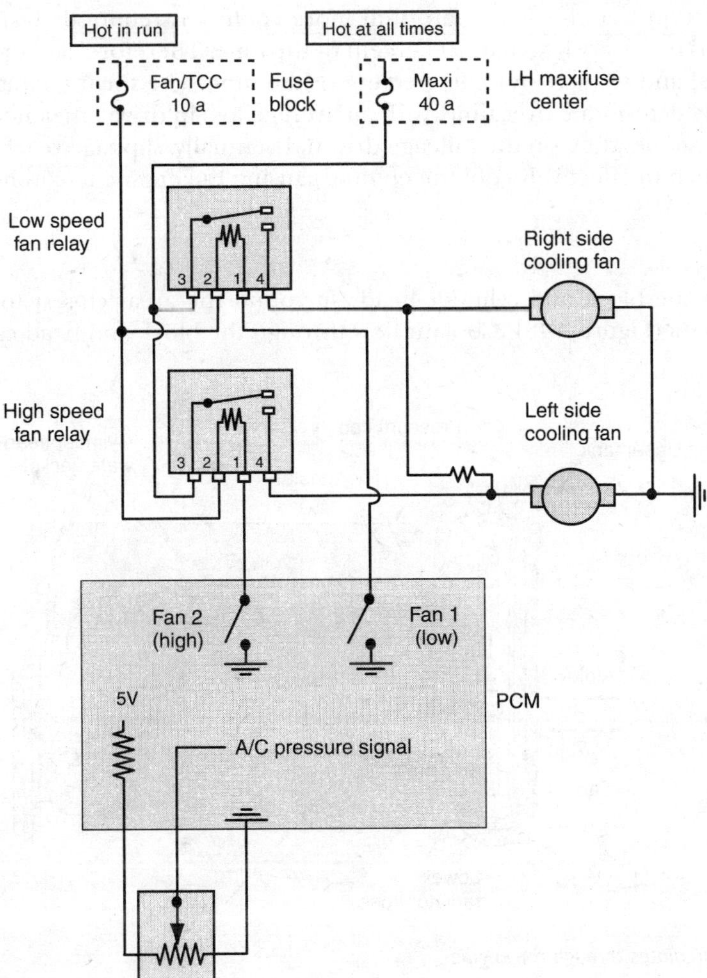

FIGURE 3-45 *Electric cooling fan circuit with two cooling fans.*

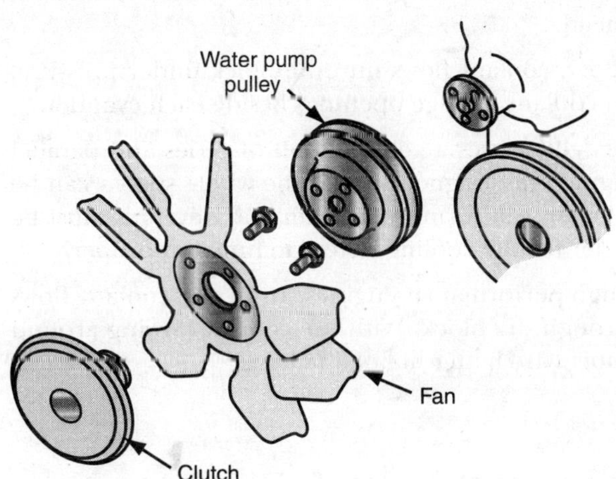

FIGURE 3-46 *Viscous-drive fan clutch mounting.*

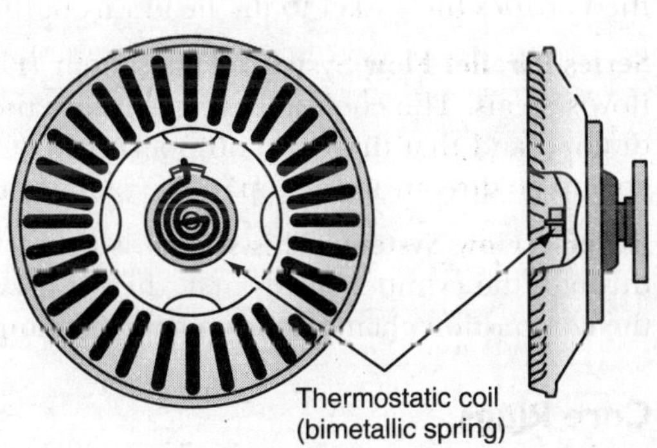

FIGURE 3-47 *Thermostatic coil on a viscous-drive fan clutch.*

to its reservoir, the unit freewheels the fan until more cooling is required. Tests have proven that maximum cooling is necessary less than 10 percent of the time. Therefore, a temperature-controlled fan clutch saves fuel and reduces noise 90 percent of the time. The shear characteristics of the silicone fluid gradually deteriorate over time, with an average loss in drive efficiency of about 100 rpm to 200 rpm per year depending on the mileage driven. Eventually, slippage reaches the point where the fan slips too much to effectively cool the engine, causing the engine to run hot.

Water Jackets

Hollow passages in the block and cylinder heads surround the areas closest to the cylinders and combustion chambers (Figure 3-48). Coolant flow through the block and head can be in one of the following ways.

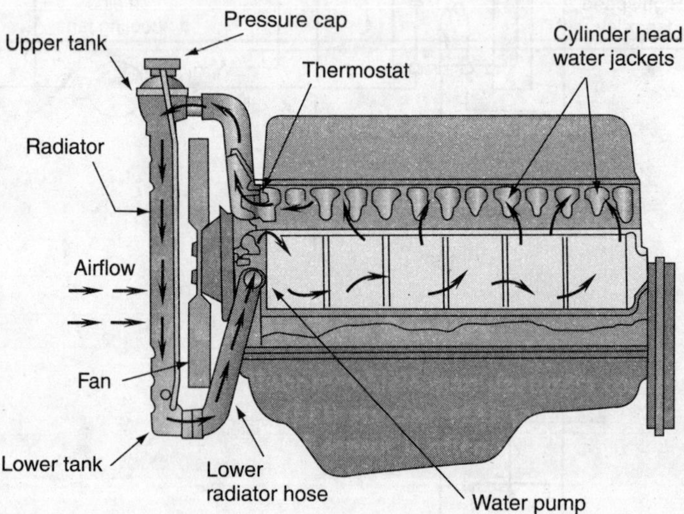

FIGURE 3-48 *Coolant circulates through the engine.*

Series Flow System. In this system (Figure 3-49A), the coolant flows around all the cylinders on each bank as it flows to the rear of the block. Large main coolant passages at the rear of the block direct the coolant through the head gasket and to the head.

Parallel Flow System. In this system (Figure 3-49B), coolant flows into the block under pressure, then crosses the gasket to the head through main coolant passage openings beside each cylinder.

Series-Parallel Flow System. This system (Figure 3-49C) uses a combination of series and parallel flow systems. The cooling passages inside the engine are designed so that the whole system can be drained and that there are no pockets in which steam can form. Any steam that develops must be able to go directly to the top of the radiator in order for the cooling system to function properly.

Reverse Flow System. This system is on a few high-performance engines. In it, the coolant flows through the cylinder heads first, then it flows through the block. With the coolant flowing around the combustion chamber first, chamber temperatures are better maintained.

Core Plugs

Included in the water jackets are soft (core) plugs and a block drain plug. The soft plugs and drain are usually removed during engine teardown. New ones are installed during reassembly. Core plugs

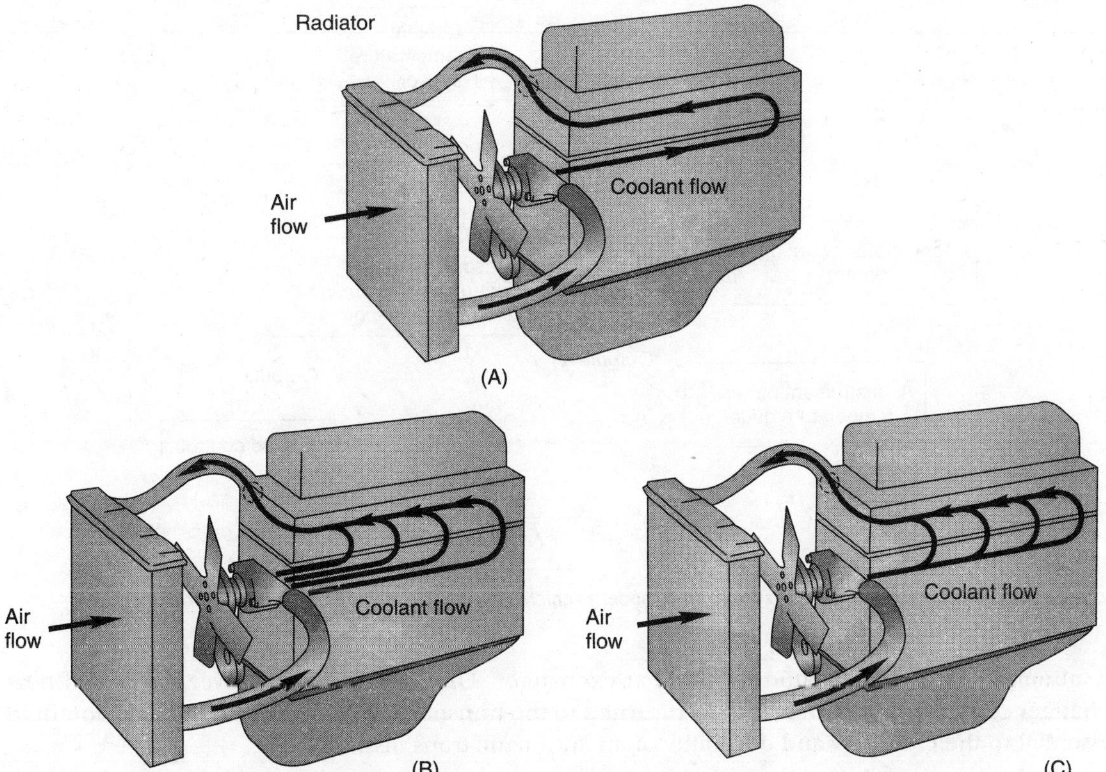

FIGURE 3-49 *Different coolant flow designs. (A) series flow; (B) parallel flow; and (C) series-parallel flow.*

are prone to rust and corrosion, and therefore will weep coolant or rust through completely. When this happens, the core plugs should be replaced.

Temperature Indicator

The coolant temperature sensor (CTS) is screwed into the water jacket and sends a voltage signal to the PCM. Older vehicles used several CTSs. Many times there would be a separate sensor for the cooling fan, hot lamp, gauge, and the computer's engine controls. Modern vehicles use the engine CTS signal processed by the PCM to control all of these functions (Figure 3-50).

Heater System

A hot liquid passenger compartment heater is part of the engine's cooling system. Heated coolant flows from the engine through heater hoses and a heater control valve to a smaller heater core, or radiator, located in a hollow container on either side of the fire wall. Air is directed or blown over the hot heater core, and the heated air flows into the passenger compartment. Movable doors can be controlled to blend cool air with heated air for more or less heat.

Oil Cooler

Radiators used in vehicles with automatic transmissions have a sealed heat exchanger, or form of radiator, located in the coolant outlet tank of the regular radiator. Metal or rubber hoses carry

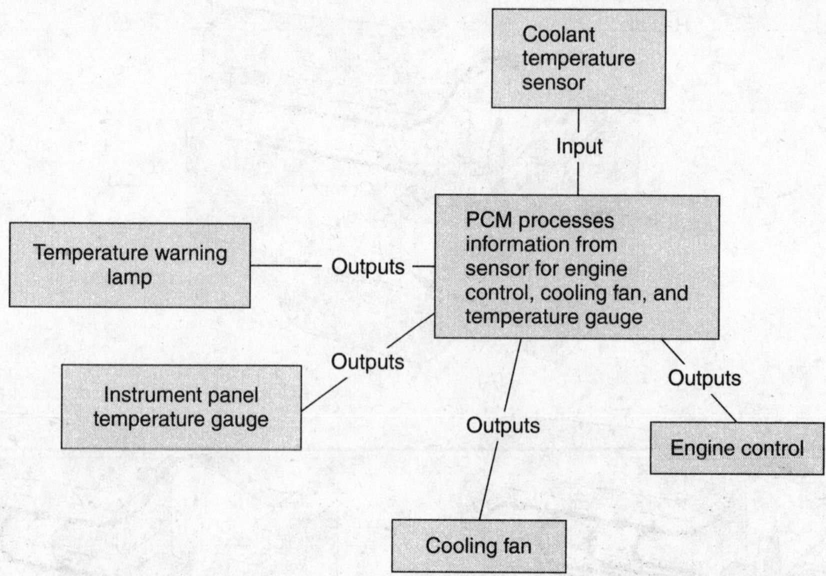

FIGURE 3-50 *The coolant temperature sender on a modern vehicle is used by the PCM to control several functions.*

hot automatic transmission fluid to the heat exchanger. The coolant passing over the sealed heat exchanger cools the fluid, which is then returned to the transmission. Cooling the transmission fluid is essential to the efficiency and durability of an automatic transmission.

Air-Cooled System

As mentioned at the beginning of this chapter, a few engines (such as the Porsche 911 and 930 models) use a cooling system that relies on air rather than a liquid to transfer heat from the engine to the atmosphere. Cylinders and heads have fins that are enclosed in a shroud to control airflow. The fins expose more of the surface area to airflow for better heat dissipation. Ducts and shrouds direct the airflow over the engine components, especially over the hotter cylinder head area. A belt-driven or electric blower provides for airflow. Fresh air is taken in and heated air expelled into the atmosphere. A thermostat connected to a control valve or door regulates airflow to control engine temperature.

REVIEW QUESTIONS

Short Answer Essays

1. Explain how compression ratio is calculated.
2. Describe two different methods of camshaft drive in an overhead camshaft (OHC) engine.
3. Explain the advantage of a pressurized cooling system.
4. Describe thermostat purpose and operation.
5. Explain the reason for adding friction modifiers to engine oil.
6. Describe the difference between a 5W-40 oil and a 10W-30 oil.

7. How is the oil pump driven?
8. What is the name of the component in the lubrication system that prevents excessively high system pressures from occurring as engine speed increases?
9. Name the four strokes of a four-stroke cycle engine.
10. Explain what volumetric efficiency is and what can affect it.

Fill-in-the-Blanks

1. In most automotive applications, the water pump is driven by the ______________ .
2. The stroke of an engine is ______________ the crank throw.
3. In a four-stroke engine, the exhaust valve opens ______________ ______________ bottom dead center (BDC) on the power stroke.
4. In a four-stroke engine, the camshaft is rotating a ______________ the crankshaft speed.
5. Lubricating oil cleans, cools, lubricates, and ______________ engine components.
6. Engine displacement may be increased by increasing the bore diameter or the ______________.
7. In a four stroke engine, the point at which both the intake and exhaust valves are open is called ______________ ______________.
8. For every pound per square inch (psi) of cooling system pressure, the boiling point of the coolant is increased about ______________ degrees.
9. In a reverse flow cooling system, immediately after the coolant leaves the water pump, it flows through the ______________ ______________.
10. An automatic transmission cooler is usually mounted in the ______________ ______________.

Multiple Choice

1. All of the following are examples of engine designs ***except***:

   A. horizontally opposed
   B. inclined cylinder
   C. slant engine
   D. inline

2. *Technician A* says that a hemispherical combustion chamber is nonturbulent.
   Technician B says that a wedge combustion chamber is also nonturbulent.
   Who is correct?

   A. Technician A   C. Both technicians
   B. Technician B   D. Neither technician

3. Two technicians are discussing the intake stroke;
   Technician A says that the intake valve is open during the intake stroke.
   Technician B says that the piston is moving from top dead center to bottom dead center.
   Who is correct?

   A. Technician A   C. Both technicians
   B. Technician B   D. Neither technician

4. *Technician A* says that the time that both valves are open is called overlap.
   Technician B says that valve overlap creates a scavenging effect.
   Who is correct?
   A. Technician A   C. Both technicians
   B. Technician B   D. Neither technician

5. *Technician A* says that the Atkinson cycle engine is a two-stroke engine.
   Technician B says that the Atkinson cycle engine delays the compression stroke by varying the time the exhaust valve is closed.
   Who is correct?
   A. Technician A   C. Both technicians
   B. Technician B   D. Neither technician

6. Two technicians are discussing 10W-30 motor oil.
   Technician A says that the "W" stands for "winter."
   Technician B says that the oil will have the viscosity of a 30 "weight" oil when warm.
   Who is correct?
   A. Technician A   C. Both technicians
   B. Technician B   D. Neither technician

7. *Technician A* says that the pressure regulator valve limits oil pressure to a preset value.
   Technician B says oil filters have a bypass valve that allows oil to bypass the oil filter in case it becomes clogged.
   Who is correct?
   A. Technician A   C. Both technicians
   B. Technician B   D. Neither technician

8. All of the following are true of modern radiators ***except***:
   A. Radiators are pressurized to 15–18 psi
   B. Most radiators are diagonal flow
   C. Radiators can be made of plastic and aluminum
   D. A 50/50 mix of antifreeze and water is best

9. *Technician A* says that the thermostat should be fully open about 10°F above the rating of the thermostat.
   Technician B says that radiators are pressurized to help raise the boiling point of the coolant.
   Who is correct?
   A. Technician A   C. Both technicians
   B. Technician B   D. Neither technician

10. The three measures of engine efficiency are:
    A. mechanical, volumetric, isometric
    B. mechanical, theoretical, thermal
    C. exocentric, theoretical, volumetric
    D. mechanical, volumetric, thermal

Electricity and Electronics

4

Upon completion and review of this chapter, you should be able to:

- Explain the basic principles of electricity.
- Define the terms voltage, current, and resistance.
- Name the various electrical components and their uses in electrical circuits.
- Use the Ohm's Law formula to calculate volts, amperes, or ohms in a circuit.
- Explain the differences between series, parallel, and series-parallel circuits.
- Define an electromagnet.
- Explain electromagnetic induction.
- Describe the operation of a diode in forward and reverse bias.
- Explain the operation of a transistor.
- Describe briefly how an integrated chip is manufactured.
- Explain the purposes of the battery in the vehicle electrical system.
- Describe the design of a cell group in an automotive battery.
- Describe the chemical changes that occur while the battery is charging and discharging.
- Explain four different battery ratings.

- Describe the operation of the neutral safety switch, starter relay, and theft deterrent computer.
- Explain the current flow through the solenoid windings and starting motor while the starter is engaging.
- Describe the current flow through the solenoid windings and starting motor while the engine is cranking.
- Explain the starter drive operation when the engine is cranking and while the starting motor is disengaging.
- Explain how a voltage regulator limits the AC generator voltage.
- Describe how the voltage is induced in the AC generator stator windings and explain the current flow from the stator windings through the charging circuit when the engine is running.

INTRODUCTION

Many complicated electronic systems such as electronic fuel injection and distributorless ignition systems are described in this text. A study of electric and electronic fundamentals is necessary before you begin to learn about these systems. If you have studied the fundamentals of electricity before, the information in this chapter may be used as a review. To understand the operation of many of the components that affect engine performance, you must have a good understanding of electricity and electronics.

There is often confusion concerning the terms electrical and electronic. In this book, electricity and electrical systems will refer to wiring and electrical parts. Electronics will mean computers and modules used to control engine and vehicle systems.

A basic understanding of electrical principles is important to proper diagnosis of any system that is monitored, controlled, or operated by electricity. Although the subject is normally covered in a separate course, a quick overview of electricity and its principles is presented here. This chapter also covers the battery, starting motor, and AC generator, which are very important components of an automobile. The battery supplies the voltage and current to operate the starting motor to crank the engine. If the electrical accessories are turned on when the engine is not running, the battery supplies the power to operate these accessories. When the engine is running and the charging system cannot meet the power requirements of the electrical system, some power is supplied by the battery.

BASIC ELECTRICITY

All things are made up of atoms. An atom is the smallest particle of something. Atoms are very small and cannot be seen with your eye. This may be the reason many technicians struggle to understand electricity. The basics of electricity focus on atoms. Understanding the structure of the atom is the first step in understanding how electricity works. The following principles describe atoms, which are the building blocks of all materials.

- In the center of every atom is a nucleus.
- The nucleus contains positively charged particles called protons and particles called neutrons that have no charge.
- Negatively charged particles called electrons orbit around every nucleus.
- Every type of atom has a different number of protons and electrons, but each atom has an equal number of protons and electrons. Therefore, the total electrical charge of an atom is zero, or neutral.

In all atoms, the electrons are arranged in different orbits called shells. Each shell contains a specific number of electrons. The outer shell of electrons is called a valence ring. The number of electrons on the valence ring determines the electrical characteristics of the element. For example, a copper atom, which is a good conductor of electricity, has 29 electrons and 29 protons (Figure 4-1). The 29 electrons are arranged in shells. The outer shell has only 1 electron. This outer shell needs 32 electrons to be completely full. This means that the 1 electron in the outer shell is loosely tied to the atom and can be easily removed.

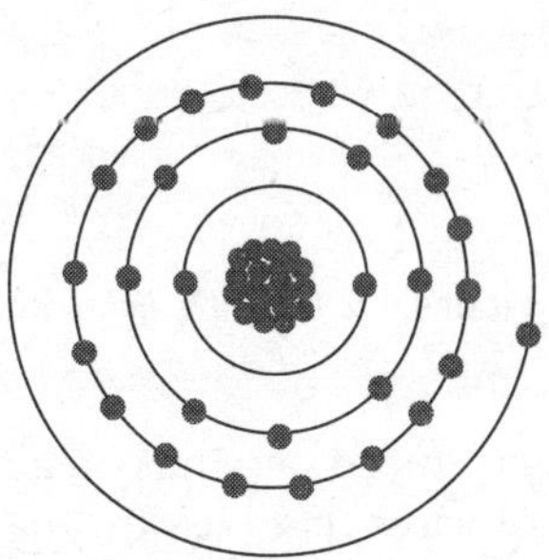

FIGURE 4-1 *Basic structure of a copper atom.*

The looseness or tightness of the electrons in orbit around the neutron of an atom explains the behavior of electricity. Electricity is caused by the flow of electrons from one atom to another. The release of energy as one electron leaves the orbit of one atom and jumps into the orbit of another is **electricity**. The key behind creating electricity is to give a reason for the electrons to move.

There is a natural attraction of electrons to protons. Electrons have a negative charge and are attracted to something with a positive charge. When an electron leaves the orbit of an atom, the atom then has a positive charge. An electron moves from one atom to another because the atom next to it appears to be more positive than the one it is orbiting around. An electrical power source provides for a more positive charge and, in order to allow for a continuous flow of electricity, it supplies free electrons. In order to have a continuous flow of electricity, three things must be present: an excess of electrons in one place, a lack of electrons in another place, and a path between the two places.

An AC generator and battery are used in an automobile's electrical system; these are based on a chemical reaction and on magnetism. A car's battery is a source of chemical energy. A chemical reaction in the battery provides for an excess of electrons and a lack of electrons in another place. Batteries have two terminals—a positive and a negative. Basically, the negative terminal is the outlet for the electrons and the positive terminal is the inlet for the electrons to get to the protons. The chemical reaction in a battery causes a lack of electrons at the positive (+) terminal and an excess at the negative (−) terminal. This creates an electrical imbalance causing the electrons to flow through the path provided by a wire. A simple example of this process is shown in the battery and light arrangement in Figure 4-2.

The chemical process in the battery continues to provide electrons (power) until the chemicals become weak. At that time, either the battery has run out of electrons or all of the protons are matched with an electron. When this happens, there is no longer a reason for the electrons to want to move to the positive side of the battery. It no longer looks more positive. Fortunately, the vehicle's charging system restores the battery's supply of electrons. This allows the chemical reaction in the battery to continue indefinitely.

Electricity and magnetism are interrelated. One can be used to produce the other. Moving a wire (a conductor) through an already existing magnetic field (such as a permanent magnet) can produce electricity. This process of producing electricity through magnetism is called induction. In a generator, a coil of wire is moved through a magnetic field. In an AC generator, a magnetic field is moved through a coil of wire. In both cases, electricity is produced. The amount of electricity that is

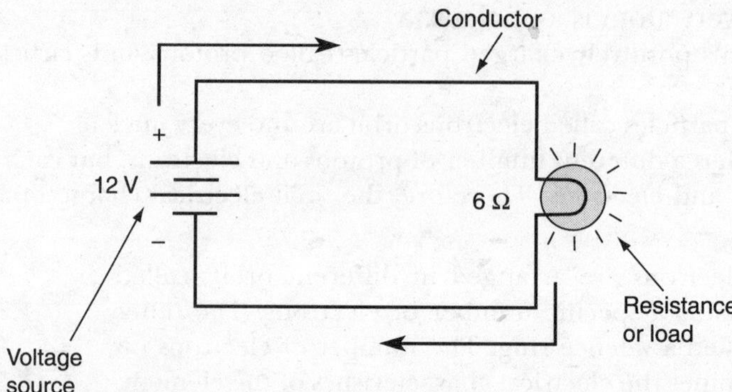

FIGURE 4-2 *A simple light circuit consists of a voltage source, conductors, and a resistance or load.*

produced depends on a number of factors, including the strength of the magnetic field, the number of wires that pass through the field, and the speed at which the wire moves through the magnetic field.

Measuring Electricity

Electrical **current** is a term used to describe the movement or flow of electricity. The greater the number of electrons flowing past a given point in a given amount of time, the more current the circuit has. This current, like the flow of water or any other substance, can be measured. **Voltage** is electrical pressure. Voltage is the force developed by the attraction of the electrons to the protons. The more positive one side of the circuit is, the more voltage is present in the circuit. Voltage does not flow, rather it is the pressure that causes current flow. When any substance flows, it meets resistance. The resistance to electrical flow can be measured.

Electrical Flow (Current)

The unit for measuring electrical current is the **ampere**, usually called an amp. The instrument used to measure electrical current flow in a circuit is called an **ammeter**.

In the flow of electricity, millions of electrons are moving past any given point at the speed of light. The electrical charge of any one electron is extremely small. It takes millions of electrons to make a charge that can be measured.

There are two types of electrical flow or current: **direct current (DC)** and **alternating current (AC)**. In direct current, the electrons flow in one direction only. The example of the battery and light shown earlier is based upon direct current. In alternating current, the electrons change direction at a fixed rate. Most automobile circuits operate on DC current, while the current in homes and buildings is AC.

Resistance

In every atom, the electrons resist being moved out of their shell. The amount of resistance depends on the type of atom. As explained earlier, in some atoms (such as those in copper) there is very little resistance to electron flow because the outer electron is loosely held. In other substances, there is more resistance to flow because the outer electrons are tightly held.

The resistance to current flow produces heat. This heat can be measured to determine the amount of resistance. A unit of measured resistance is called an **ohm**. Resistance can be measured by an instrument called an **ohmmeter**.

Pressure

In electrical flow, some force is needed to move the electrons between atoms. This force is the pressure that exists between a positive and negative point within an electrical circuit. This force, also called electromotive force (EMF), is measured in units called **volts**. One volt is the amount of pressure (force) required to move 1 ampere of current through a resistance of 1 ohm. Voltage is measured by an instrument called a **voltmeter**.

Voltage Drop

As current passes through a resistance, heat is generated. With this generation of heat comes a loss in voltage. The voltage that is converted to heat by a resistance is called the voltage drop. In all circuits, all of the voltage provided by the source of power is dropped across the circuit. When a circuit has only one resistance, source voltage is dropped across that resistance. If a circuit has more than one resistance, the voltage drop across each resistance depends upon the resistance value of each resistor.

For example, if a 12-volt circuit has two 3-ohm resistors, each resistor will drop 6 volts. If we add a 6-ohm resistor to the circuit, each 3-ohm resistor will drop 3 volts and the 6-ohm resistor will drop 6 volts.

Ohm's Law

To understand the relationship between current, voltage, and resistance in a circuit you need to know the basic law of electricity, **Ohm's Law**. This law states that it takes 1 volt of electrical pressure to push 1 ampere of electrical current through 1 ohm of resistance. As such, the law provides a mathematical formula for determining the amount of current, voltage, or resistance in a circuit when two of these are known. The basic formula is: Voltage = Current multiplied by Resistance.

Although the basic premise of this formula is calculating unknown values in an electrical circuit (Figure 4-3), it also helps to define the behaviors of electrical circuits. A knowledge of these behaviors is important to an automotive technician.

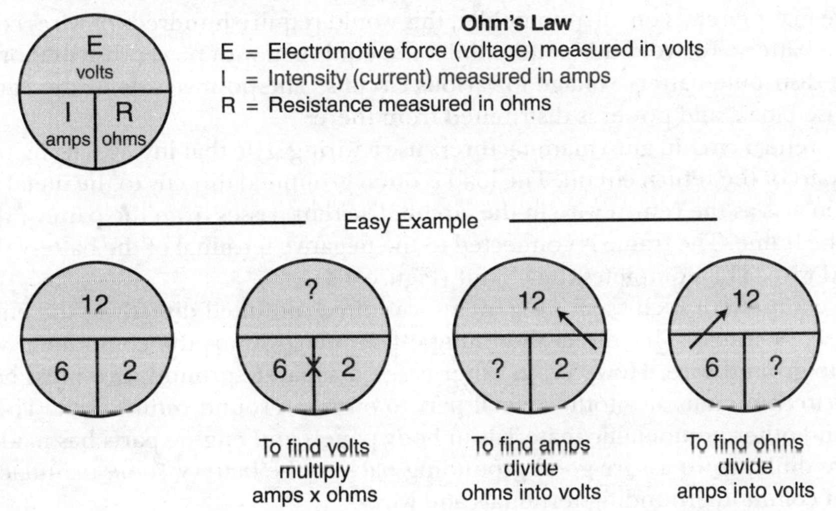

FIGURE 4-3 *Ohm's Law.*

If voltage does not change but there is a change in the resistance of the circuit, the current will change. If resistance increases, current decreases. If resistance decreases, current will increase. If voltage changes, so must the current or resistance. If the resistance stays the same and current decreases, so will voltage. Likewise, if current increases, so will the voltage.

Circuits

When electrons are able to flow along a path (wire) between two points, an electrical circuit is formed. An electrical circuit is considered complete when there is a path that connects the positive and negative terminals of the electrical power source. Somewhere in the circuit there must be a load or resistance to control the amount of current in the circuit. Most automotive electrical circuits use the chassis as the path to the negative side of the battery. Electrical components have a lead that connects them to the chassis. These are called the chassis ground connections. In a complete circuit, the flow of electricity can be controlled and applied to do useful work, such as light a headlamp or turn over a starter motor. Components that use electrical power put a load on the circuit and consume electrical energy.

The amount of current that flows in a circuit is determined by the resistance in that circuit. As resistance goes up, the current goes down. The energy used by a load is measured in volts. Amperage stays constant in a circuit, but the voltage is dropped as it powers a load. Measuring voltage drop determines the amount of energy consumed by the load.

A complete electrical circuit exists when electrons flow along a path between two points. In a complete circuit, resistance must be low enough to allow the available voltage to push electrons between the two points. Most automotive circuits contain four basic parts.

1. **Power sources** such as a battery or AC generator that provide the energy needed to create electron flow.
2. **Conductors** such as copper wires and the vehicle's frame that provide a path for current flow.
3. **Loads** which are devices such as light bulbs, electric motors, or resistors that use electricity to perform work.
4. **Controllers** such as switches or relays that direct the flow of electrons.

A complete circuit must have a complete path from the power source to the load and back to the source. With the many circuits on an automobile, this would require hundreds of wires connected to both sides of the battery. To avoid this, automobiles are equipped with power distribution centers or fuse blocks that distribute battery voltage to various circuits. The positive side of the battery is connected to the fuse block, and power is distributed from there.

As a common return circuit, auto manufacturers use a wiring style that involves using the vehicle's metal frame as part of the return circuit. The load is often grounded directly to the metal frame. The metal frame then acts as the return wire in the circuit. Current passes from the battery, through the load, and into the frame. The frame is connected to the negative terminal of the battery through the battery's ground wire. This completes the circuit (Figure 4-4).

An electrical component such as an AC generator is often mounted directly to the engine block, transmission case, or frame. This direct mounting effectively grounds the component without the use of a separate ground wire. However, in other cases, a separate ground wire must be run from the component to the frame or another metal part to ensure a sound return path. The increased use of plastics and other nonmetallic materials in body panels and engine parts has made electrical grounding more difficult. To assure good grounding back to the battery, some manufacturers now use a network of common grounding terminals and wires.

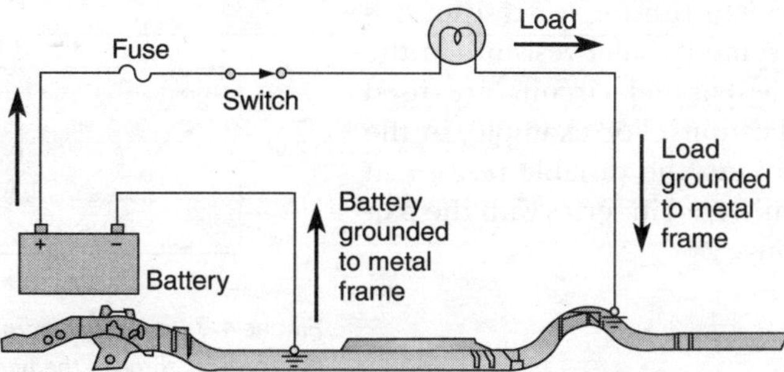

FIGURE 4-4 *In most vehicles, the metal frame, engine block, or transmission case is used as a source of ground to complete the circuit back to the battery.*

TYPES OF CIRCUITS

In a **series circuit**, the resistances are connected one after the other in the circuit, and the same current flows through all resistances (Figure 4-5). These facts may be stated about a series circuit:

1. The total resistance is the sum of all resistors in the circuit.
2. The same amount of current flows through the entire circuit.
3. Part of the source voltage is dropped across each resistor.
4. The sum of the voltage drops across each resistor equals the source voltage.

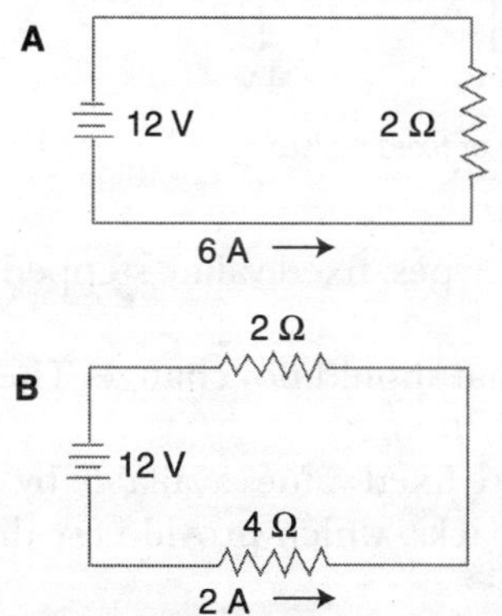

FIGURE 4-5 *In a series circuit, the same amount of current flows through the entire circuit.*

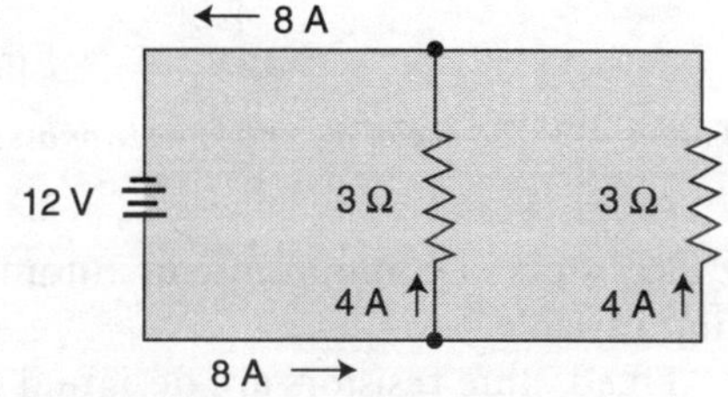

FIGURE 4-6 *A simple parallel circuit.*

In a **parallel circuit**, each resistance is connected across the circuit, and each resistance is a separate path for current flow (Figure 4-6). These facts may be stated about a parallel circuit:

1. The current flow through each resistor depends on the ohms in that resistor.
2. The total current is the sum of the current flow through each branch.
3. Full source voltage is supplied to each branch, and full source voltage is dropped across each resistor.
4. The total resistance is less than the value of the smallest resistive branch in the circuit.

In a **series-parallel circuit**, a resistor (or resistors) is connected in series with some parallel resistors in the circuit (Figure 4-7). Series-parallel circuits are used in many automotive applications. For example, in the instrument panel lamp circuit, the variable resistor in the headlamp switch is connected in series with the parallel instrument panel lamps.

FIGURE 4-7 *In a series-parallel circuit, the sum of the currents through the parallel legs must equal the current through the series part of the circuit.*

Circuit Components

Automotive electrical circuits contain a number of different types of electrical devices. The more common components are outlined in the following sections.

Resistors are used to limit current flow (and therefore voltage) in circuits where full current flow and voltage are not needed or where too much voltage may cause damage. Resistors are devices specially constructed to introduce a measured amount of electrical resistance into a circuit (Figure 4-8). In addition, some other components use resistance to produce heat and even light. An electric window defroster is a specialized type of resistor that produces heat. Electric lights are resistors that become so hot that they produce light.

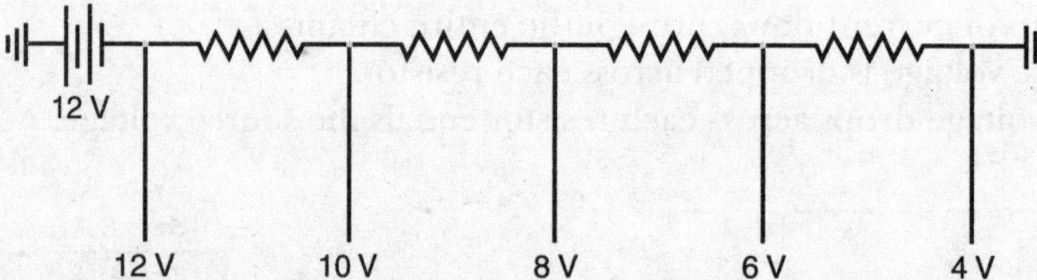

FIGURE 4-8 *The use of a stepped resistor assembly is a common application of fixed resistors.*

Resistors in common use in automotive circuits are of three types: fixed value, stepped or tapped, and variable.

Fixed value resistors are designed to have only one rating that should not change. These resistors are used to control voltage such as in an automotive ignition system.

Tapped or stepped resistors are designed to have two or more fixed values available by connecting wires to the several taps of the resistor. Heat motor resistor packs, which provide for different fan speeds, are an example of this type of resistor.

Variable resistors are designed to have a range of resistances available through two or more taps and a control. Two examples of this type of resistor are rheostats and potentiometers. **Rheostats** have two connections (Figure 4-9), one to the fixed end of a resistor and one to a sliding contact with the resistor. Turning the control moves the sliding contact away from or toward the fixed end tap, increasing or decreasing the resistance. **Potentiometers** have three connections (Figure 4-10), one at each end of the resistance and one connected to a sliding contact with the resistor. Turning the control moves the sliding contact away from one end of the resistance but toward the other end.

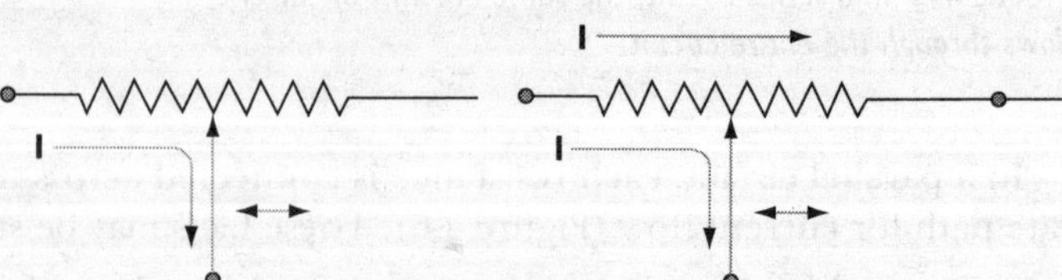

FIGURE 4-9 *A rheostat.*

FIGURE 4-10 *A potentiometer.*

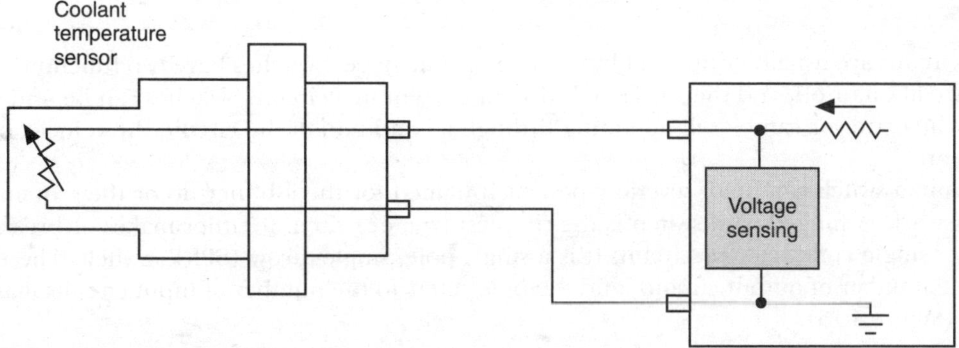

FIGURE 4-11 *A thermistor is used to measure temperature. The sensing unit measures the change in resistance and translates this into a temperature valve.*

Another type of variable resistor is the **thermistor** (Figure 4-11). This resistor is designed to change in values as its temperature changes. Although most resistors are carefully constructed to maintain their rating within a few ohms through a range of temperatures, the thermistor is designed to change its rating. Thermistors are used to provide compensating voltage in components or to determine temperature. As a temperature sender, the thermistor is connected to a voltmeter calibrated in degrees. As the temperature rises or falls, the resistance also changes. This changes the reading on the meter.

Circuit Protective Devices

When overloads or shorts in a circuit cause too much current to flow, the wiring in the circuit heats up, the insulation melts, and a fire can result unless the circuit has some kind of protective device. Fuses, fuse links, maxi-fuses, and circuit breakers are designed to provide protection from high current (Figure 4-12). These protection devices open the circuit when high current is present. As a result, the circuit no longer works, but the wiring and the components are saved from damage.

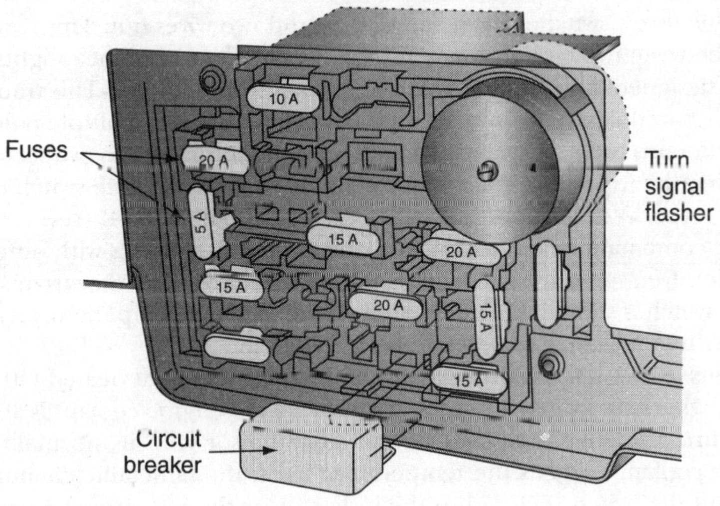

FIGURE 4-12 *A fuse panel.*

Switches

Electrical circuits are usually controlled by a switch of some type. Switches have two functions. They turn the circuit on or off, and they direct the flow of current in a circuit. Switches can be under the control of the driver or can be self-operating through a condition of the circuit, the vehicle, or the environment.

Contacts in a switch can be of several types, each named for the job they do or the sequence in which they work. A hinged-pawl switch is the simplest type of switch. It either makes or breaks the current in a single conductor or circuit. It is a single-pole, single-throw (SPST) switch. The throw refers to the number of output circuits, and the pole refers to the number of input circuits made by the switch (Figure 4-13).

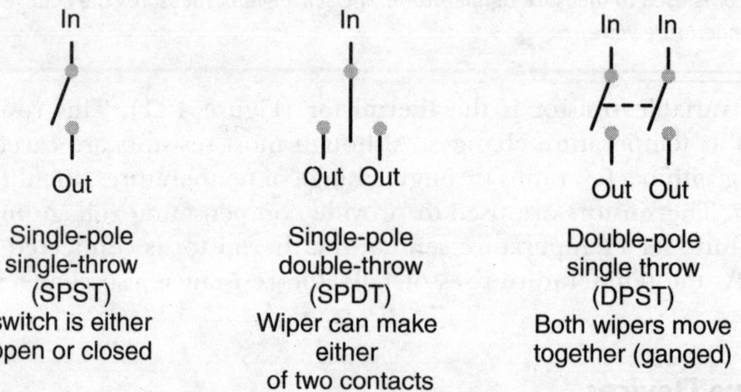

FIGURE 4-13 *Basic switches.*

Another type of SPST switch is the momentary contact switch. The spring-loaded contact on this switch keeps it from making the circuit except when pressure is being applied to the button. A horn is a switch of this type. Because the spring holds the contacts open, the switch has a further designation: normally open. In the case where the contacts are held closed except when the button is pressed, the switch is designated normally closed.

Single-pole, double-throw switches have one wire in and two wires out. This type of switch allows the driver to select between two circuits, such as high-beam or low-beam headlights.

Switches can be designed with a great number of poles and throws. The transmission neutral start switch may have two poles and six throws and is referred to as a multiple-pole, multiple-throw (MPMT) switch. It contains two movable wipers that move in unison across two sets of terminals. The dotted line shows that the wipers are mechanically linked or ganged. The switch closes a circuit to the starter in either P (park) or N (neutral) and to the back-up lights in R (reverse).

Most switches are combinations of hinged-pawl and push-pull switches with different numbers of poles and throws. However, some special switches are required to satisfy the circuits of modern automobiles. A mercury switch is sometimes used to detect motion in a component such as the one used in the engine compartment to turn on the compartment light.

A temperature-sensitive switch usually contains a bimetallic element heated either electrically or by some component where the switch is used as a sensor. When engine coolant is at or below normal operating temperature, the engine coolant temperature sensor is in its normally open condition (Figure 4-14). If the coolant exceeds the temperature limit, the bimetallic element bends the two contacts together and the switch is closed to the indicator or the instrument panel. Other applications for heat-sensitive switches are time delay switches and flashers.

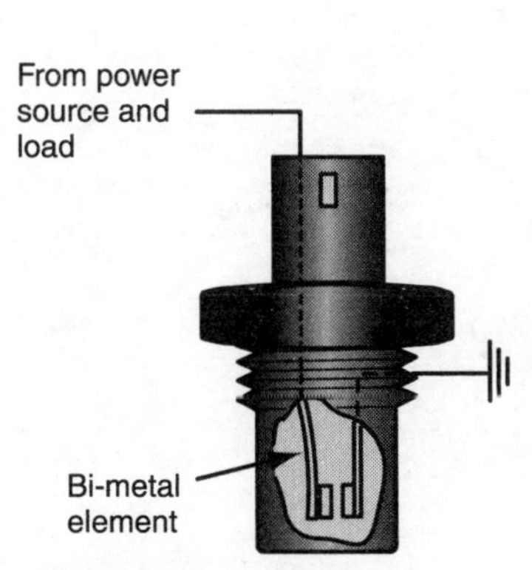

FIGURE 4-14 *A temperature-sensitive switch.*

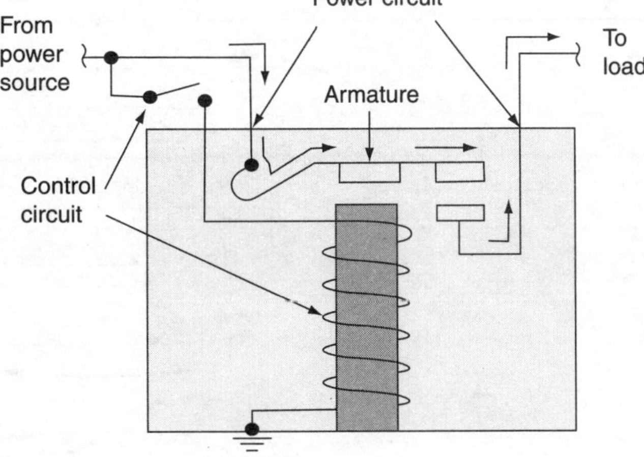

FIGURE 4-15 *A typical relay.*

Relays

A **relay** (Figure 4-15) is an electric switch that allows a small amount of current to control a much larger one. It consists of a control circuit. When the control circuit switch is open, no current flows to the coil so the windings are de-energized. When the switch is closed, the coil is energized, turning the soft iron core into an electromagnet and drawing the armature down. This closes the power circuit contacts connecting power to the load circuit. When the control switch is opened, the current stops slowing in the coil, the electromagnet disappears, and the armature is released, which breaks the power circuit contacts.

Solenoids

Solenoids are also electromagnets with movable cores used to translate electrical current flow into mechanical movement. The movement of the core causes something else to move, such as lever. They can also close electrical contacts, acting as a relay at the same time.

ELECTROMAGNETISM BASICS

Electricity and magnetism are related. One can be used to create the other. Current flowing through a wire creates a magnetic field around the wire. Moving a wire through a magnetic field creates current flow in the wire.

Many automotive components such as AC generators, ignition coils, starter solenoids, and magnetic pulse generators operate using principles of electromagnetism.

Although almost everyone has seen magnets at work, a simple review of magnetic principles is in order to ensure a clear understanding of electromagnetism.

A substance is said to be a magnet if it has the property of magnetism—the ability to attract such substances as iron, steel, nickel, or cobalt. These are called magnetic materials.

A magnet has two points of maximum attraction, one at each end of the magnet. These points are called poles, with one being designated the North pole and the other the South pole. When two magnets are brought together, opposite poles attract while similar poles repel each other.

A magnetic field, called a **field of flux**, exists around every magnet (Figure 4-16). The field consists of invisible lines along which a magnetic force acts. These lines emerge from the North pole

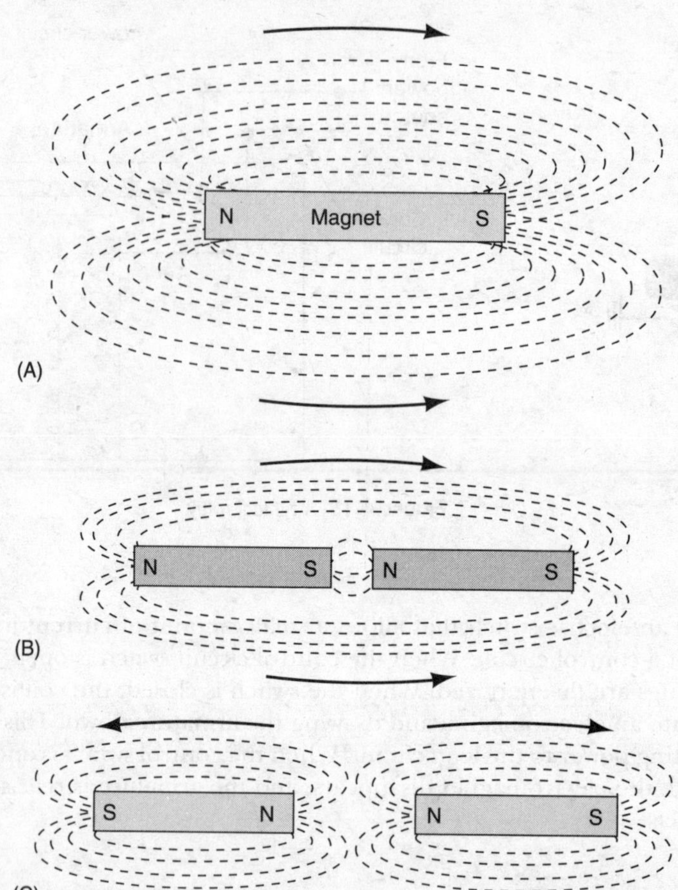

FIGURE 4-16 *Magnetic principles: (A) field of flux around a magnet, (B) unlike poles attract each other, and (C) like poles repel.*

and enter the South pole, returning to the North pole through the magnet itself. All lines of force leave the magnet at right angles to the magnet. None of the lines cross each other. All lines are complete.

Magnets can occur naturally in the form of a mineral called magnetite. Artificial magnets can also be made by inserting a bar of magnetic material inside a coil of insulated wire and passing a heavy direct current through the coil. This principle is very important in understanding certain automotive electrical components. Another way of creating a magnet is by stroking the magnetic material with a bar magnet. Both methods force the randomly arranged molecules of the magnetic material to align themselves along North and South poles.

Artificial magnets can be either temporary or permanent. Temporary magnets are usually made of soft iron. They are easy to magnetize but quickly lose their magnetism when the magnetizing force is removed. Permanent magnets are difficult to magnetize, but once magnetized they retain this property for very long periods.

Four metals (iron, steel, nickel, and cobalt) have magnetic qualities. When one of these metals is not magnetized, the molecules in the metal are randomly arranged and the magnetic strength of each molecule does not add together. If a metal is magnetized, the molecules are aligned so their magnetic strength adds together.

When current flows through a conductor, an invisible field of force surrounds the wire. This magnetic field is concentric to the conductor, and an increase in current flow results in a stronger magnetic field. The direction of the magnetic field around the conductor is determined by the direction of current flow through the conductor. If the current flow is reversed, the magnetic field is also reversed. If an iron core is placed in the center of the coil, the magnetic lines of force are strengthened because iron is a better conductor for lines of force compared to air.

The magnetic strength of an electromagnet is determined mainly by the number of turns and the current flow through the winding. To calculate the strength of an electromagnet, multiply the number of turns and the current flow through the winding. Thus, we have the formula: number of turns times amperes = ampere turns of magnetic strength.

Induced Voltage

Now that we have explained how current can be used to generate a magnetic field, it is time to examine the opposite effect of how magnetic fields can produce electricity. Consider a straight piece of conducting wire with the terminals of a voltmeter attached to both ends. If the wire is moved across a magnetic field, the voltmeter registers a small voltage reading (Figure 4-17). A voltage has been induced in the wire.

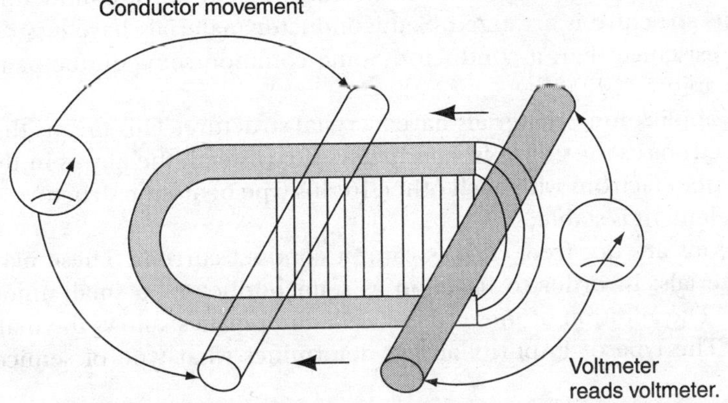

FIGURE 4-17 *Moving a conductor through a magnetic field induces a voltage in the conductor.*

It is important to remember that the conducting wire must cut across the flux lines to induce a voltage. Moving the wire parallel to the lines of flux does not induce voltage. The wire need not be the moving component in this setup. Holding the conducting wire still and moving the magnetic field at right angles to it also induces voltage in the wire.

The wire or conductor becomes a source of electricity and has a polarity or distinct positive and negative end. However, this polarity can be switched depending on the relative direction of movement between the wire and magnetic field. This is why an AC generator produces alternating current.

When voltage is induced in a conductor and the conductor is connected to a complete circuit, current flows through the circuit. This process of inducing a voltage in a conductor with a moving magnetic field is referred to as electromagnetic induction. These requirements are necessary to induce a voltage in a conductor:

1. A conductor or conductors
2. A magnetic field
3. Relative motion

During electromagnetic induction, the amount of voltage induced in the conductor is determined by these factors:

1. The strength of the magnetic field
2. The number of conductors
3. The speed of motion

BASICS OF ELECTRONICS

Computerized engine controls and other features of today's cars would not be possible if it were not for electronics. For purposes of clarity, let us define electronics as the technology of controlling electricity. Electronics has become a special technology beyond electricity. Transistors, diodes, semiconductors, integrated circuits, and solid-state devices are all considered to be part of electronics rather than just electrical devices. But keep in mind that all the basic laws of electricity apply to electronic controls.

Semiconductors

A **semiconductor** is a material or device that can function as either a conductor or an insulator, depending on how its structure is arranged. Semiconductor materials have less resistance than an insulator but more resistance than a conductor. Some common semiconductor materials include silicon (Si) and germanium (Ge).

In semiconductor applications, materials have a crystal structure. This means that their atoms do not lose and gain electrons as the atoms in conductors do. Instead, the atoms in these semiconductor materials share outer electrons with each other. In this type of atomic structure, the electrons are tightly held and the element is stable.

Because the electrons are not free, crystals cannot conduct current. These materials are called electrically inert materials. In order to function as semiconductors, a small amount of trace element must be added. The addition of these traces, called impurities, allows the material to function as a semiconductor. The type of impurity added determines what type of semiconductor will be produced.

The **diode** is the simplest semiconductor device. A diode allows current to flow in one direction but not in the opposite direction. Therefore, it can function as a switch, acting as either conductor or insulator depending on the direction of current flow.

Silicon has four valence electrons. When two pieces of silicon are joined together, the outer rings on the atoms join together, and this places eight electrons on the valence rings. This joining process between two pieces of silicon is called covalent bonding. A silicon crystal is the result of this action. When one side of a silicon crystal is mixed or doped with phosphorus, a negative-type material, an excess of electrons is formed. Doping the opposite side of the silicon crystal with boron creates a positive-type material with a lack of electrons.

If the positive polarity from a voltage source is connected to the positive side of a diode and the negative polarity is connected to the negative side of the diode, the current flows through the diode. This type of connection to a diode is called forward bias.

When the positive polarity from a voltage source is connected to the negative side of a diode and the negative polarity is connected to the positive side of the diode, the diode blocks current flow. Reverse bias is the term applied to this type of diode connection. A diode may be defined as a one-way electronic control device.

A diode connected with reverse bias is capable of blocking a certain amount of voltage. The maximum voltage that a diode blocks is called **peak inverse voltage (PIV)**. If the PIV is exceeded, the diode may break down in the reverse direction. This action ruins the diode.

A variation of the diode is the **Zener diode**. This device functions like a standard diode until a certain voltage is reached. A Zener diode is doped more heavily in the manufacturing process. This type of diode breaks down at a specific voltage in the reverse direction. For example, an 8-volt Zener diode breaks down and conducts current when an 8-volt reverse-bias voltage is supplied to the diode. If a reverse-bias voltage of 7.99 volts is supplied to the diode, it does not conduct current. A Zener diode is not damaged by a normal amount of reverse current flow.

A **transistor** is an electronic device produced by joining three sections of semiconductor materials. Like the diode, it is very useful as a switching device, functioning as either a conductor or an insulator.

A transistor is manufactured by joining three positive and/or negative materials. These positive and negative materials may be arranged as NPN or PNP. The terminals on a transistor are referred to as the emitter, base, and collector. In an NPN transistor, the emitter is negative, the base is positive, and the collector is negative (Figure 4-18).

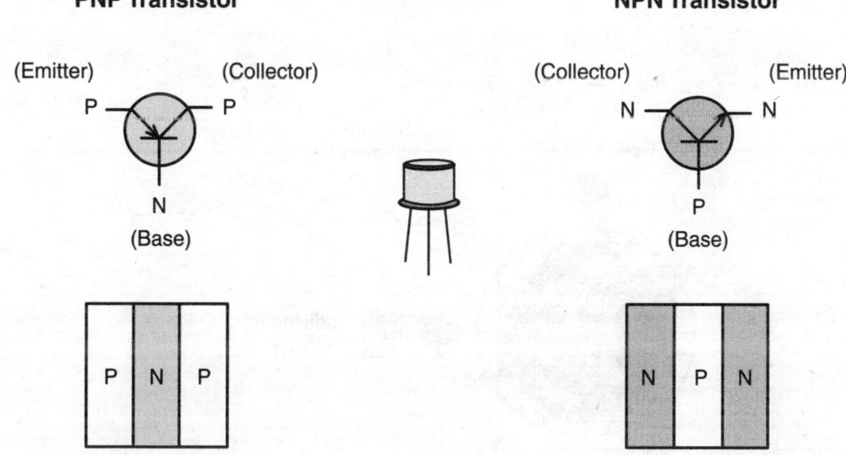

FIGURE 4-18 *NPN and PNP transistors.*

The base material is sandwiched between the emitter and the collector. The base material is much thinner than the emitter and collector materials. If positive circuit polarity is connected to the positive emitter on the PNP transistor and the negative base is connected to negative circuit polarity, the emitter base is forward biased. This type of connection results in current flow through the emitter base circuit. If the emitter base is forward biased and the collector terminal is also connected to the negative circuit polarity, a higher current flows from the emitter through the base material and out the collector terminal.

The relationship between the lower emitter base current and the higher emitter collector current is called the gain in a transistor. If a set of contacts in the base circuit is opened, current flow in the emitter base circuit is stopped. Under this condition, the current flow is also stopped in the emitter collector circuit. A very low current in the emitter base circuit may be used to switch off a much higher current in the emitter collector circuit.

The emitter base circuit of a PNP transistor is reverse biased when positive circuit polarity is connected to the negative base material and negative circuit polarity is connected to the positive emitter material. If the emitter base circuit is reverse biased, the emitter base current flow is stopped. Under this condition, the emitter collector current is also stopped.

One transistor or diode is limited in its ability to do complex tasks. However, when many semiconductors are combined into a circuit, they can perform complex functions.

An **integrated circuit (IC)** is simply a large number of diodes, transistors, and other electronic components, such as resistors and capacitors, all mounted on a single piece of semiconductor material. This type of circuit has a tremendous size advantage. It is extremely small. Circuitry that used to take up entire rooms can now fit into a pocket. The principles of semiconductor operation remain the same in integrated circuits—only the size has changed.

In the IC manufacturing process, an etching and photographic procedure is used to form thousands of components on a silicon slice (Figure 4-19). A single chip may contain more than 1 million transistors and other components. As more transistors are added to a computer chip, the computer is capable of performing more instructions per second. Currently, we have computers that handle more than 1 million instructions per second. By the end of this decade, computers will be capable of processing 20 million instructions per second. These facts indicate that computer response time and the control of output functions are increasing dramatically.

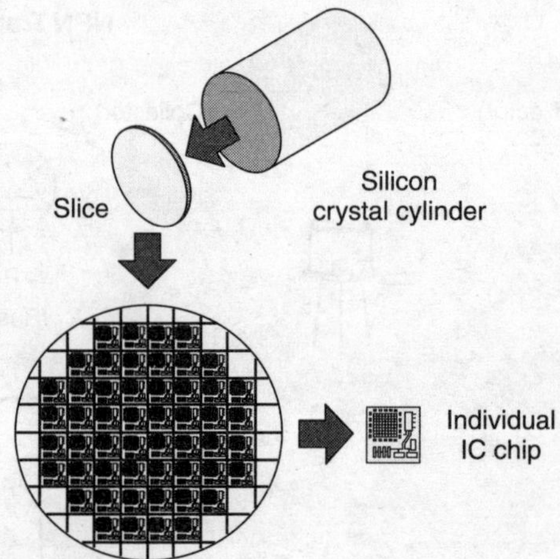

FIGURE 4-19 *An integrated circuit etched on a silicon slice.*

While the cost of electronics per vehicle has increased gradually, the price of chips has decreased consistently. Therefore, the car manufacturers can actually purchase much smarter and smaller chips for their electronic dollar. This is one reason why the number of electronic systems on cars has increased and will continue to increase.

Because of the small size of ICs, electronics are no longer confined to simple tasks such as rectifying AC generator current. Enough transistors, diodes, and other solid-state components can be installed in a car to make logic decisions and issue commands to other areas of the engine. This is the foundation of computerized control systems.

The computer has taken over many of the tasks in cars and trucks that were formerly performed by vacuum, electromechanical, or mechanical devices. When properly programmed, they can carry out explicit instructions with blinding speed and almost flawless consistency.

A typical electronic control system is made up of sensors, actuators, and related wiring that is tied to a computer.

Sensors

All sensors perform the same basic function. They detect a mechanical condition (movement or position), chemical state, or temperature condition and change it into an electrical signal that can be used by the computer to make decisions. The computer makes decisions based on information it receives from sensors. Each sensor used in a particular system has a specific job to do. Together these sensors provide enough information to help the computer form a complete picture of vehicle operation. Even though there are a variety of different sensor designs, they all fall under one of two operating categories: reference voltage sensors or voltage generating sensors.

Reference voltage (Vref) sensors provide input to the computer by modifying or controlling a constant, predetermined voltage signal (Figure 4-20). This signal, which can have a reference value from 5 volts to 9 volts, is generated and sent out to each sensor by a reference voltage regulator located inside the processor. The term processor is used to describe the actual metal box that houses the computer and its related components. Because the computer knows that a certain voltage value has been sent out, it can indirectly interpret factors like motion, temperature, and component position, based on what comes back. For example, consider the operation of the throttle position sensor (TPS). During acceleration (from idle to wide-open throttle), the computer monitors throttle plate movement based on the changing reference voltage signal returned by the TPS. (The TPS is a type of variable resistor known as a rotary potentiometer that changes circuit resistance based on throttle shaft rotation.) As TPS resistance varies, the computer is programmed to respond in a specific manner (for example, increase fuel delivery or alter spark timing) to each corresponding voltage change.

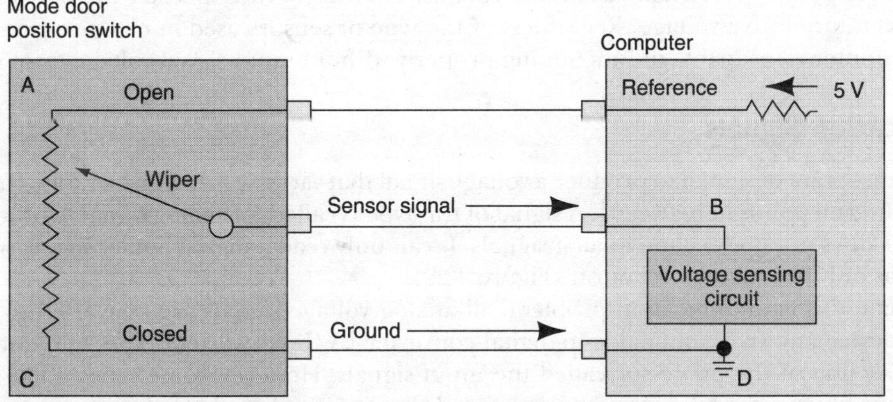

FIGURE 4-20 *A potentiometer senses voltage in response to the movement of the wiper and sends a signal back to the voltage-sensing circuit of the computer.*

Most sensors presently in use are variable resistors or potentiometers. They modify a voltage to or from the computer indicating a constantly changing status that can be calculated, compensated for, and modified. That is, most sensors simply control a voltage signal from the computer. When varying internal resistance of the sensor allows more or less voltage to ground, the computer senses a voltage change on a monitored signal line. The monitored signal line may be the output signal from the computer to the sensor (one- and two-wire sensors) or the computer may use a separate return line from the sensor to monitor voltage changes (three-wire sensors).

While most sensors are variable resistance/reference voltage, there is another category of sensors—the **voltage generating devices** (Figure 4-21). These sensors include components like the Hall

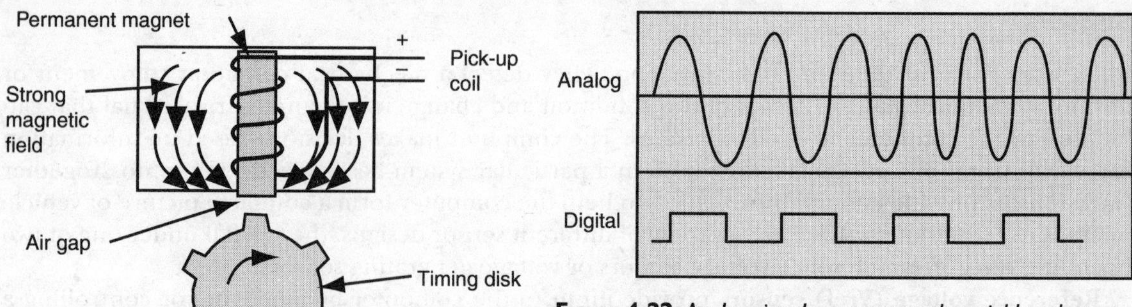

FIGURE 4-21 *A strong magnetic field is produced in the pick-up coil as the teeth align with the core. The field weakens as the teeth pass the core.*

FIGURE 4-22 *Analog signals are constantly variable, whereas digital signals are either on or off, or high and low.*

effect switch, oxygen sensor (zirconium dioxide), and knock sensor (piezoelectric), which are capable of producing their own input voltage signal. This varying voltage signal, when received by the computer, enables the computer to monitor and adjust for changes in the computerized engine control system.

In addition to variable resistors, two other commonly used reference voltage sensors are switches and thermistors. Switches provide the necessary voltage information to the computer so that vehicles can maintain the proper performance and driveability. Thermistors are special types of resistors that convert temperature into a voltage. Regardless of the type of sensors used in electronic control systems, the computer is incapable of functioning properly without input signal voltage from sensors.

Communication Signals

Most input sensors are designed to produce a voltage signal that varies within a given range (from high to low, including all points in between). A signal of this type is called an **analog** signal. Unfortunately, the computer does not understand analog signals. It can only read a **digital** binary signal, which is a signal that has only two values—on or off (Figure 4-22).

To overcome this communication problem, all analog voltage signals are converted to a digital format by a device known as an analog-to-digital converter (A/D converter). The A/D converter is located in a section of the processor called the input signals. However, some sensors like the Hall effect switch produce a digital or square wave signal that can go directly to the computer as input (Figure 4-23).

A computer's memory holds the programs and other data, such as vehicle calibrations, that the microprocessor refers to in performing calculations. To the computer, the program is a set of instructions or procedures that it must follow. Included in the program is information that tells the microprocessor when to retrieve input (based on temperature, time, etc.), how to process the input, and what to do with it once it has been processed.

Actuators

After the computer has assimilated the information and the tools used by it to process this information, it sends output signals to control devices called actuators. These actuators, which are solenoids, switches, relays, or motors, physically act or carry out a decision the computer has made.

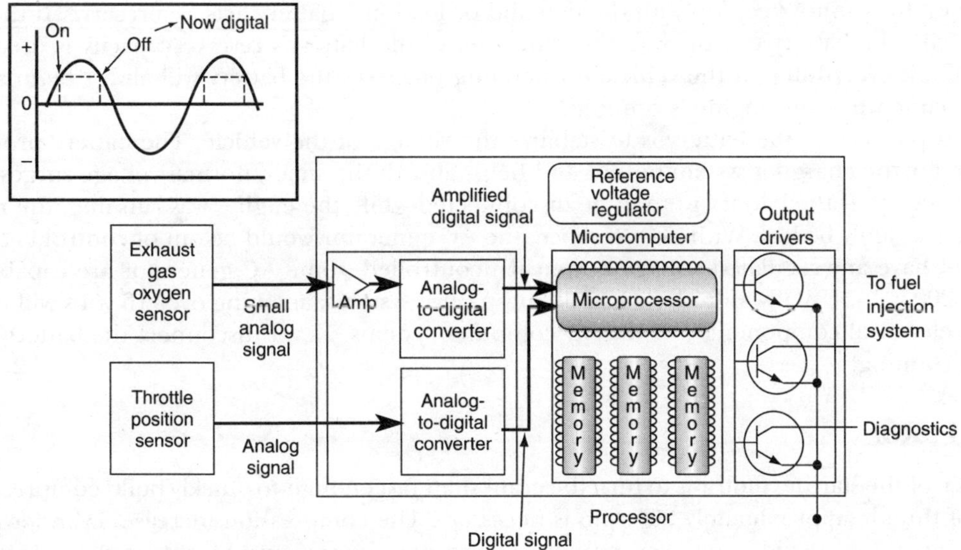

FIGURE 4-23 *The A/D converter changes analog voltage signals to digital signals that the computer can recognize.*

Actually, an **actuator** is an electromechanical device that converts an electrical current into mechanical action. This mechanical action can then be used to open and close valves, control vacuum to other components, or open and close switches. When the microcomputer receives an input signal indicating a change in one or more of the operating conditions, the microcomputer determines the best strategy for handling the conditions. The microcomputer then controls a set of actuators to achieve a desired effect or strategy goal. In order for the computer to control an actuator, it must rely on a component called an **output driver**.

Output drivers are also located in the processor (along with the input conditioners, microprocessor, and memory) and operate by the digital commands issued by the microcomputer. Basically, the output driver is nothing more than an electronic on/off switch that the computer uses to control the ground circuit of a specific actuator. Four output drivers in one component is called a quad driver.

BATTERY, STARTING, AND CHARGING SYSTEMS

Of all the electrical functions found in an automobile, the battery, starting, and charging systems are commonly grouped together in their own category. For example, when performing a diagnosis in this area, many refer to it as a battery, starting, and charging system test.

Battery

It has often been stated that the battery is the heart of the electrical system. Nothing can happen without it. The battery serves three basic purposes. The first is to crank the engine. Since energy is stored in the battery, it must provide enough power to turn the electrical starter motor. In addition, the battery must be able to supply ample voltage to power the ignition system properly in order to build adequate spark to easily start the engine during cranking in a wide range of operating conditions.

The second function of the battery is to supply voltage when the AC generator is unable to do so. When the engine is running, the primary source for electrical power is the AC generator. When the AC generator cannot keep up with the demand or load, the battery acts as a reserve. If the AC generator fails, the battery can operate the vehicle until the battery's reserve capacity is used up. Theoretically, if everything on the vehicle is operating properly, the battery will always be in some state of recharge while the engine is running.

The third purpose of the battery is to stabilize the voltage of the vehicle. The battery provides a reference for the charging system output and helps absorb the small, normal voltage surges that occasionally occur. If the battery were to be disconnected while the engine was running, the reference would suddenly be lost. With no reference, the AC generator would be out of control because it would not have any regulated voltage output. Uncontrolled, some AC generator are capable of producing 200 volts. Usually, in today's 12-volt automotive systems, anything over 16 volts will cause damage to electrical components—especially computer systems. Never disconnect the battery with the engine running!

Starting Motor

The purpose of the starting motor is to turn the crankshaft fast enough to quickly build compression. As a rule of thumb, approximately 200 rpm is necessary. The compression increases cylinder pressure and temperature to aid in quicker ignition. The starting motor must be able to deliver proper cranking speed regardless of engine or ambient temperature.

Charging System

The AC generator must provide voltage and current to maintain the proper battery charge and power all the vehicle's electrical accessories while the engine is running. When functioning properly, the AC generator is capable of maintaining enough power output to meet or exceed the vehicle's total electrical load requirements.

BATTERY CONSTRUCTION

Case

The battery case holds and protects the battery components and electrolyte (Figure 4-24). Separating walls in the case form a separate reservoir for each cell. Many batteries have a translucent plastic case that makes the electrolyte level inside the battery visible. Few batteries made today have removable cell caps. Most have sealed caps that are designed to capture much of the liquid that would otherwise have boiled out from charging. Some battery cases are too dark to see the electrolyte through. Unless the battery case is cracked or damaged where a sign of leakage is evident, there is usually no reason to suspect low electrolyte levels unless a problem caused it to boil away. Years ago, battery cases were made with a space between the floor of the battery and the bottom of the cell plates to allow sediment from the cell plates to collect. Due to the physical size restriction of the battery, the water level was close to the top of the plates. It was commonplace to add water regularly. Over a period of time, sediment from the cell plates would build up high enough on the case floor to actually come in contact with the cell plates. When this happened, the battery was soon destined to fail. Batteries are now designed using individual cell envelopes or pouches that isolate the cell plates from one another and also trap cell sediment. This allows the plates to be placed on the floor of the battery case. The cell plates can be made slightly taller and there is more room on top of the cell plates for additional water. This makes the battery low- or maintenance-free.

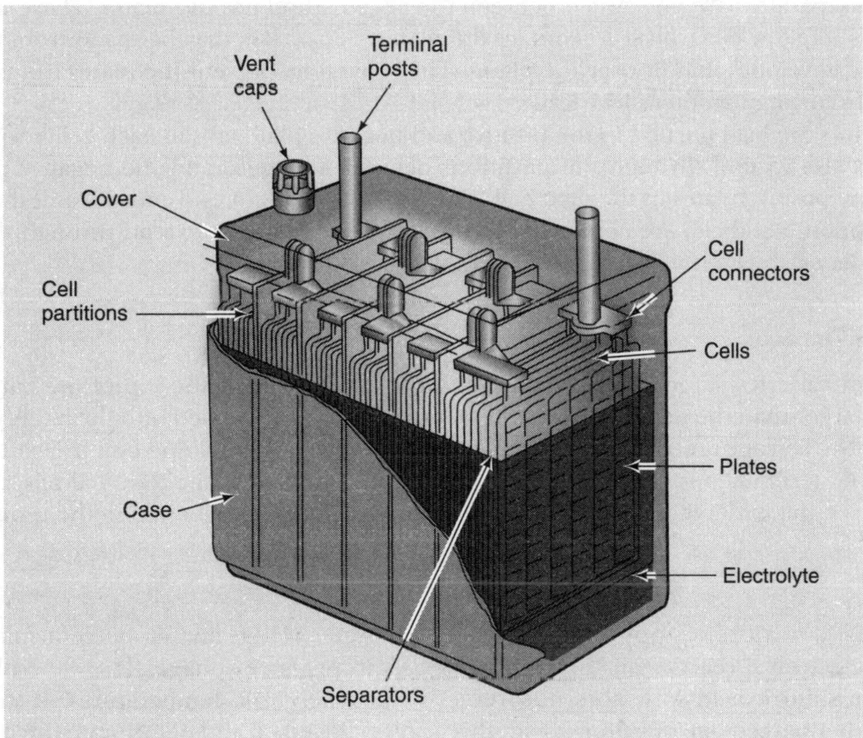

FIGURE 4-24 *Battery construction.*

Cover

The battery cover is permanently sealed to the top of the case. The cover has openings for the terminal posts and vent holes for the venting of gases. Some batteries have the terminals extending through the side of the case, and other batteries have terminals in the sides and top. Some covers have removable vent caps that may be removed to add water or test the electrolyte. These vent caps may be individual, strip-type, or box-type.

Plates

Battery plates contain a grid or coarse screen. In some batteries, the plate grids were made from lead mixed with antimony which stiffened the lead. Many batteries manufactured today have plate grids made from lead and calcium, nickel and cadmium, or strontium. The active plate materials are pasted on the grids. The material on the positive plates is lead peroxide, and the negative plate material is sponge lead. A tab on the top of each plate grid allows the plate to be connected to the cell connector.

Cell Group

A **cell group** contains a number of alternately spaced negative and positive plates. There is a negative plate positioned on both sides of each cell group and, thus, each group has an odd number of plates. For example, a cell group may have five positive plates and six negative plates.

Thin porous separators are positioned between the negative and positive plates. These separators must be porous to allow electrolyte to contact the plates. Separators may be made from fiberglass sheets or plastic envelopes that fit over the plates. The separators prevent the plates from touching each other and shorting together electrically.

Cell connectors are lead burned to the positive and negative plate tabs in each cell group. These cell connectors also extend through the partitions between the cells, and the negative plates are connected to the positive plates in the next cell. The negative plates in one end cell and the positive plates in the opposite end cell are connected to the terminal posts that extend through the top or sides of the battery.

Terminal Posts

On top-terminal batteries, large round terminal posts extend through the top of the battery. The positive post is larger than the negative post. These terminal posts are sealed into the battery cover to prevent electrolyte leakage around the posts. POS or NEG are usually stamped on the battery cover beside the proper terminal post. The battery cable ends are clamped to the terminal posts. On side-terminal batteries, the battery terminals are threaded and the cables are bolted to the terminals.

Electrolyte

The **electrolyte** is a mixture of approximately 64 percent water (H_2O) and 36 percent sulfuric acid (H_2SO_4). The electrolyte reacts with the plate materials to produce voltage. The electrolyte must contain enough sulfuric acid so it does not freeze in extremely cold temperatures. If the battery contained a higher percentage of sulfuric acid, this acid would attack and deteriorate the plate grids too quickly.

BATTERY OPERATION

If one negative and one positive plate are placed in an electrolyte solution, a chemical reaction takes place that causes approximately 2.1-volt difference between the plates. Since a 12-volt battery contains six cells, the total fully charged battery voltage is approximately 12.6 volts. When an electrical resistance such as a light bulb is connected to these two plates, the higher voltage on one plate forces current through the light to the other plate with the lower voltage. This action is called battery discharging (Figure 4-25). A battery cell with two plates will not supply a great deal of current flow. When more plates are added, the current flow capability increases.

When a voltage source such as the AC generator in the charging system is connected to the battery plates, the AC generator forces current flow in one battery plate and out of the other battery plate (Figure 4-26). This action is called battery charging. The AC generator voltage must be higher than the battery voltage to allow the AC generator to charge the battery.

A charged battery has lead peroxide (PbO_2) on the positive plates and sponge lead (Pb) on the negative plates. The electrolyte contains water (H_2O) and sulfuric acid (H_2SO_4) (Figure 4-27).

When an electrical load is connected across the battery terminals, the voltage difference between the plate materials forces current through the electrical load. As the battery discharges these chemical changes occur:

1. The H_2SO_4 breaks up in the electrolyte and the SO_4 goes to both plates where it joins with the Pb to form lead sulfate ($PbSO_4$) on both plates.
2. The O_2 on the positive plates joins with the hydrogen (H) in the electrolyte to form H_2O (Figure 4-28). The percentage of water in the electrolyte increases as the battery discharges.

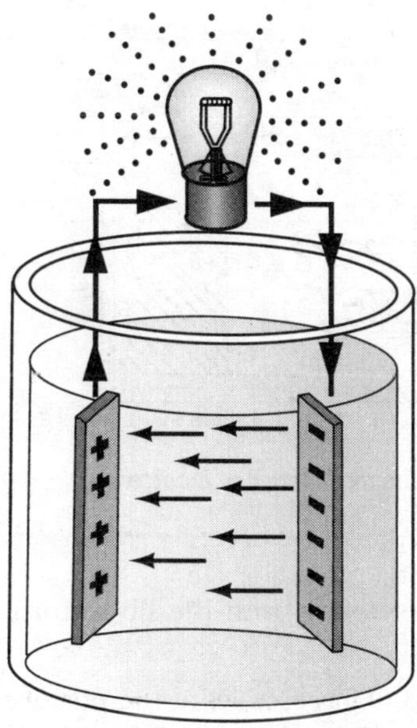

FIGURE 4-25 *Current flows from one battery plate to the other when a conductor with some electrical resistance is connected between the plates.*

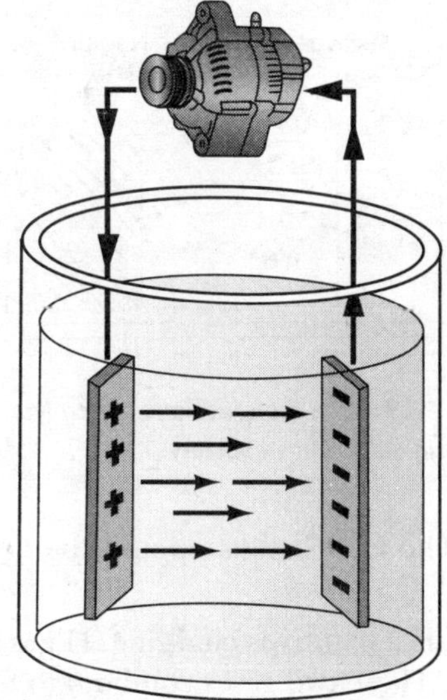

FIGURE 4-26 *When the engine is running, current flows from the alternator through the battery plates.*

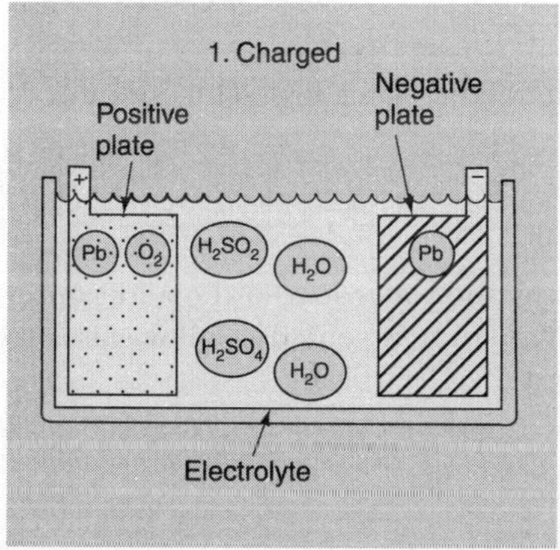

FIGURE 4-27 *Plate materials and electrolyte content in a charged battery.*

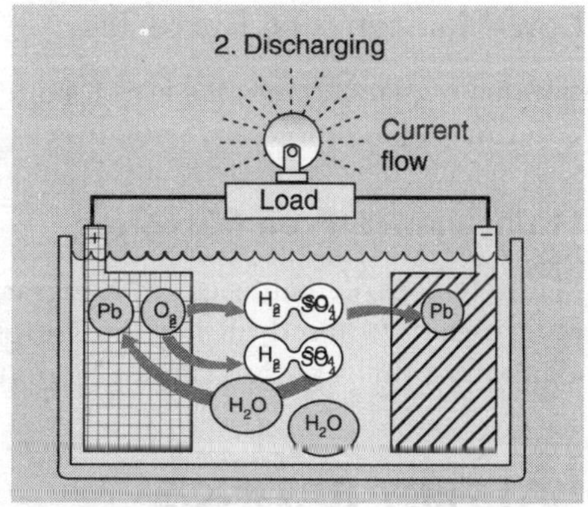

FIGURE 4-28 *Chemical action in a battery while discharging.*

In a discharged battery, both sets of plates are coated with lead sulfate ($PbSO_4$), and the electrolyte contains a high percentage of H_2O (Figure 4-29).

When a charging source such as an AC generator is charging the battery, these chemical changes occur in the battery:

1. The SO_4 comes off both plates and joins with the H in the electrolyte to form H_2SO_4 (Figure 4-30).

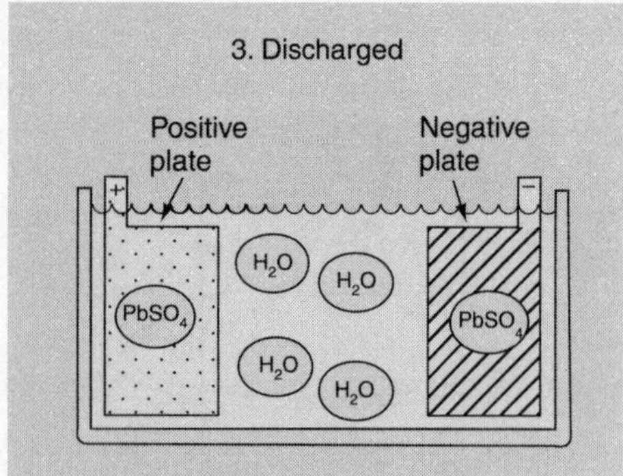

FIGURE 4-29 *Plate materials and electrolyte content in a discharged battery.*

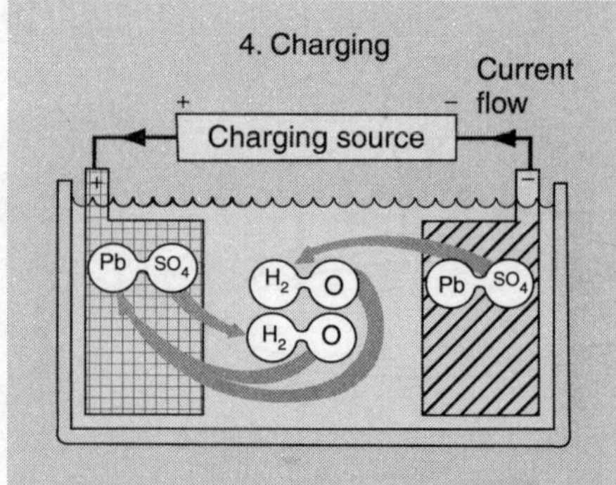

FIGURE 4-30 *Chemical action in a battery while charging.*

2. The H_2O breaks up and the O goes to the positive plates where it joins with the Pb to form PbO_2.

While a battery is charging, H gas escapes at the negative plates and O gas escapes at the positive plates. These two gases combine to form H_2O. The SO_4 is always in the electrolyte or on the plates; thus, it does not escape from the battery. Since H_2O is the only chemical that escapes from the battery, it is the only chemical that should be added to the battery.

BATTERY CLASSIFICATIONS

Low-Maintenance Batteries

Low-maintenance batteries are designed to reduce internal heat and water loss. The addition of water may be required at 15,000 miles (24,000 km).

Maintenance-Free Batteries

Maintenance-free batteries are designed to reduce internal heat and water loss so the addition of water is not required during the life of the battery. The battery cover is vented to allow gases to escape, but the vent caps cannot be removed to add water or test the electrolyte.

BATTERY RATINGS

Many different battery rating methods have been used by industry. What follows are the most common.

Cold Cranking Amperes

The Cold Cranking Amperes (CCA) rating indicates the amperes a battery will deliver at 0°F (–18°C) for 30 seconds while maintaining a voltage of at least 1.2 volts per cell or 7.2 volts in the complete battery. Many automotive batteries have a CCA rating of 350 to 600 or more.

Reserve Capacity Rating

The reserve capacity rating indicates in minutes the length of time a fully charged battery at 80°F (27°C) will deliver 25 amperes while the voltage remains above 1.75 volts per cell or 10.5 volts in the complete battery. Reserve capacity ratings are usually between 55 and 115 minutes.

Ampere-Hour Rating

The ampere-hour rating indicates the amount of current a battery will deliver for 20 hours with the voltage remaining above 1.75 volts per cell or 10.5 volts for the complete battery. If a battery delivers 5 amperes for 20 hours with the voltage above the specified value, the battery is rated at 5 × 20 = 100 ampere-hours. This is an outdated method of rating batteries and has been superseded by cold cranking amps (CCA).

Power (Watt) Rating

The watt rating is determined by multiplying the available battery voltage and the current flow delivered at 0°F (–18°C). Watt or power battery ratings are usually between 2,000 and 4,000 watts.

STARTING THE ENGINE

Any motor converts electrical energy into a rotating mechanical energy. When two like magnetic poles face each other, they tend to push away. In a motor, one of the magnetic poles is stationary in the starter's case. The other pole is fixed to a shaft that is fitted in the center of the case. The shaft is allowed to move. When the magnetic poles of the windings in the case are the same as the magnetic poles of the shaft, they push apart. This pushing causes the shaft to rotate. By connecting the shaft of the starter motor to the flywheel of the engine, the engine cranks as the shaft or armature spins.

All motors are made up of the same basic parts: a case, armature, brushes, and field windings (Figure 4-31).

Armature

A steel shaft is the basis of an armature and it runs through the center of the armature assembly. A laminated iron core is pressed onto this shaft. Heavy insulated windings are mounted in the armature core slots.

A commutator is mounted on an insulating sleeve near the front of the armature. The commutator contains a series of copper bars that are insulated from each other. The armature windings are soldered to the commutator bars. In most starting motors, four brushes are mounted in holders, and springs keep the brushes in contact with the commutator bars. In many starting motors, two of the brushes are connected to ground on the starter case, and the other two brushes are connected to the field coils.

The starter drive is mounted on splines on the back of the armature shaft. A pinion gear on the drive is pulled into mesh with the flywheel ring gear by a shift lever. Most starter drives are the overrunning clutch-type. Bushings in the starter end housings support the armature shaft.

Field Windings

Some starting motors contain four insulated field windings mounted on steel pole shoes that are bolted to the starter case. The field coils in many starting motors are connected through an insulated

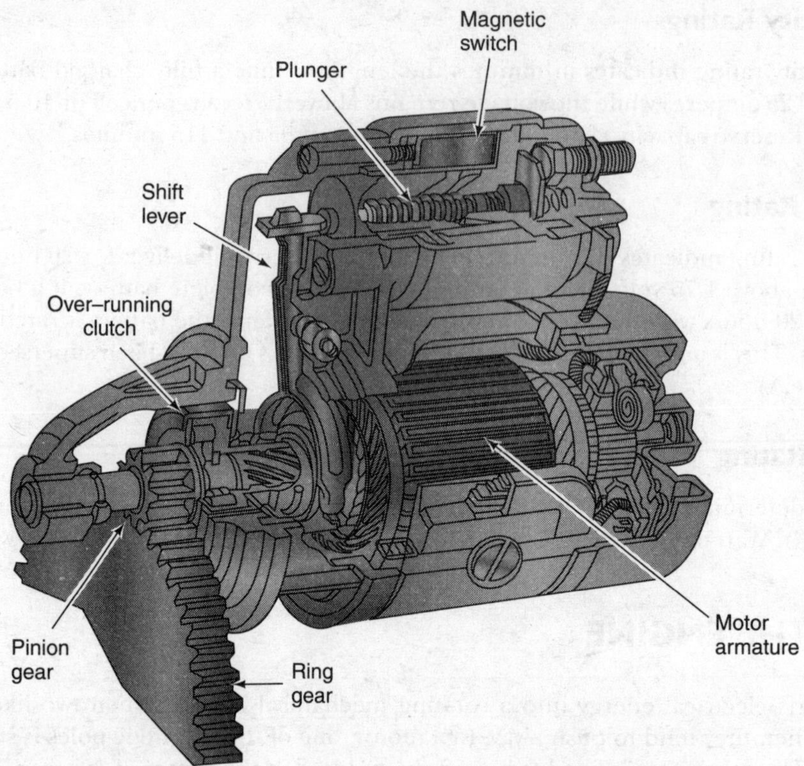

FIGURE 4-31 *Starting motor components.*

terminal in the starter case to the solenoid terminal. In some starting motors, the field windings are replaced with strong permanent magnets.

Solenoid

In many starting motors, the solenoid is mounted on the starter housing. A plunger is mounted in a bore at the center of the solenoid, and two windings surround the plunger bore. The rear of the plunger is connected to the pivoted shift lever and the lower end of this lever is mounted in the drive collar. A heavy copper disc is mounted in front of the plunger. The large starting motor terminal and the battery cable terminal are mounted in front of the heavy copper disc. A plunger return spring holds the plunger toward the rear of the starting motor and a smaller disc return spring holds the disc away from the terminals. A small terminal in the front of the solenoid is connected to the solenoid windings.

Some starting circuits are fitted with a relay or magnetic switch that completes the battery positive circuit to the starter when the ignition key is moved to the start position. These systems may or may not have a solenoid mounted to the starter.

As the contacts in a relay or solenoid open and close, some arcing may occur across the contacts. This causes voltage spikes to be present in the electrical system. Some manufacturers install clamping diodes at the solenoid and/or relay to prevent these voltage spikes.

Neutral Safety Switch Operation

In many starting motor circuits, the starter switch is part of the ignition switch. When the ignition switch is turned to the start position, voltage is supplied to the neutral safety switch. If the transmission is in neutral or park, the neutral safety switch is closed and current flows through this switch to the solenoid terminal. When the transmission is in any gear except neutral or park, the neutral safety switch is open and the starting circuit is inoperative.

The theft-deterrent computer prevents starting motor operation if someone breaks into the car—for example, if a door is forced open or a window is broken to enter the vehicle. Most theft-deterrent computers also flash the headlights and taillights and blow the horn if someone breaks into the car.

On some vehicles, the neutral safety switch is connected in series with the starter relay contacts, and this relay winding is grounded through the theft deterrent computer (Figure 4-32). When the ignition switch is turned to the start position, voltage is supplied to the starter relay contacts and the relay winding. If the vehicle has been entered with the key in the normal manner, the theft-deterrent computer provides a ground for the starter relay winding. This action provides current flow through the relay winding, which closes the relay contacts and supplies voltage to the solenoid windings.

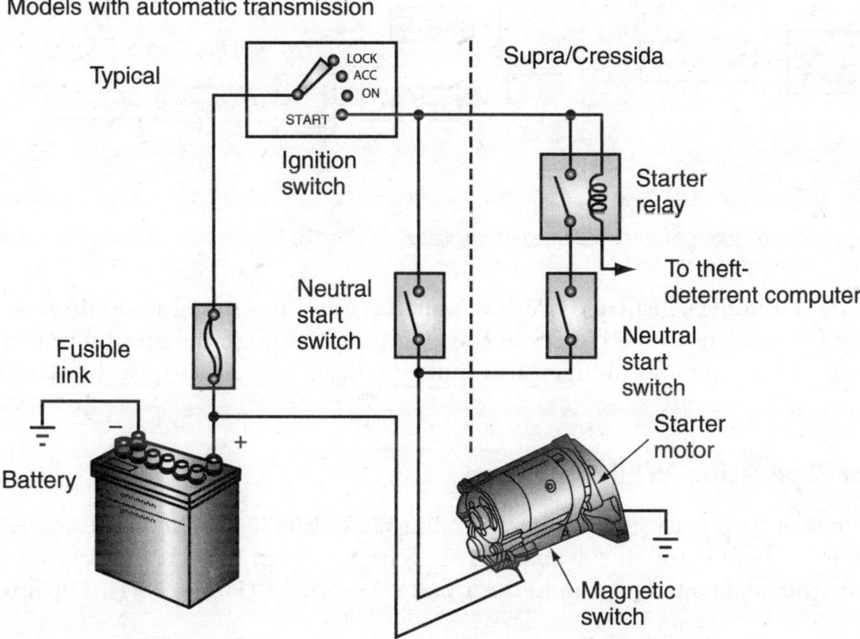

FIGURE 4-32 *Neutral safety switch, starter relay, and theft-deterrent computer circuit.*

If the vehicle is broken into by forcing a door open or breaking a window, the theft-deterrent computer does not provide a ground for the starter relay and the starting circuit is inoperative.

Starting Motor Operation While Engaging

Current flows through the solenoid terminal and through the hold-in winding to ground. Current also flows through the pull in winding and the starting motor to ground. This current flow is not high enough to operate the starting motor. However, the combined magnetic strength of both solenoid windings pulls the plunger ahead and the plunger drives the disc against the battery cable as well as the starting motor terminals. This solenoid disc action completes the circuit between the battery and the starting motor, and a very high current now flows from the battery positive cable through

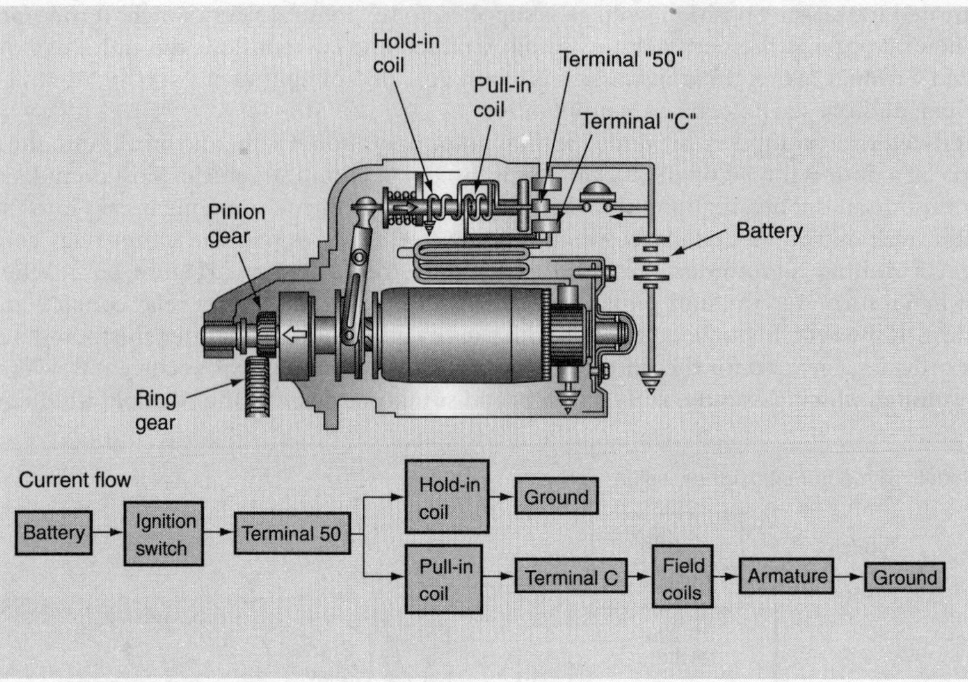

FIGURE 4-33 *Starting motor and solenoid current flow while engaging.*

the solenoid disc, field windings, insulated brushes, armature windings, and ground brushes (Figure 4-33). This current flow returns to the battery negative terminal through the ground return circuit. Forward movement of the solenoid plunger also pulls the drive into mesh with the flywheel ring gear.

Starting Motor Operation While Engaged

Since the starting motor field coils and armature windings have very low resistance, the average current flow through this circuit is 100 to 200 amperes. This high current flow creates very strong magnetic fields between the field coils and around the armature windings (Figure 4-34). The interaction

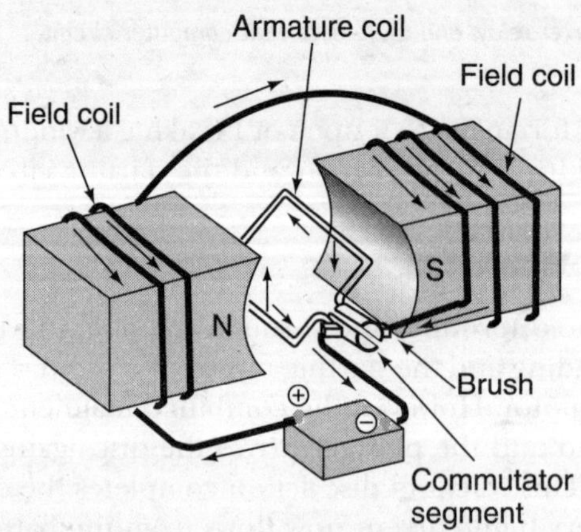

FIGURE 4-34 *Current flow through the field coils and armature windings.*

of the magnetic field between the field coils and the magnetic field around the armature windings creates a strong armature turning force to crank the engine (Figure 4-35). The starting motor is designed to deliver very high horsepower for short time periods, such as 15 seconds. Cranking the engine continually for more than 15 seconds may damage the starting motor.

Once the solenoid disc contacts the terminals, equal voltage is supplied to both ends of the solenoid pull-in winding and the current flow in this winding is stopped. Current continues to flow through the hold-in winding, and the magnetic field around this winding holds the plunger ahead (Figure 4-36).

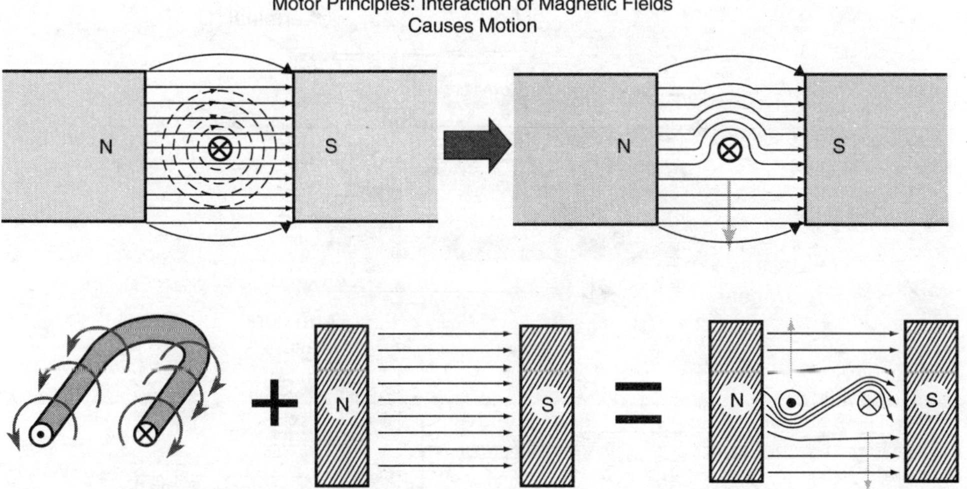

FIGURE 4-35 *Interaction of the magnetic fields between the field coils and armature windings causes the armature to rotate.*

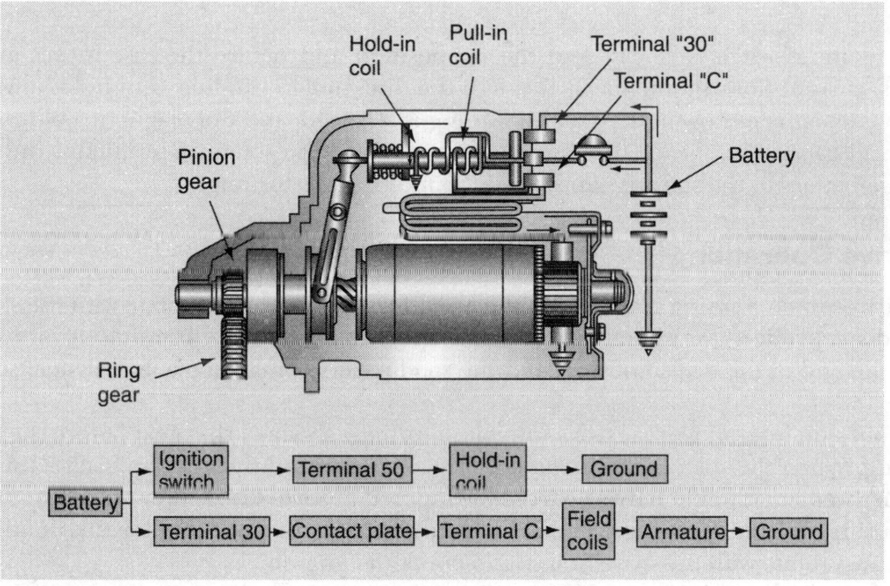

FIGURE 4-36 *Current flow while the starting motor is engaged.*

Starting Motor Operation While Disengaging

When the driver releases the ignition switch from the start to the on position, the circuit is opened between the ignition switch and the solenoid windings. When current stops flowing through the hold-in winding, the plunger spring moves the plunger rearward. This action pushes the drive out of mesh with the flywheel ring gear and allows the disc return spring to move the disc away from the solenoid terminals (Figure 4-37).

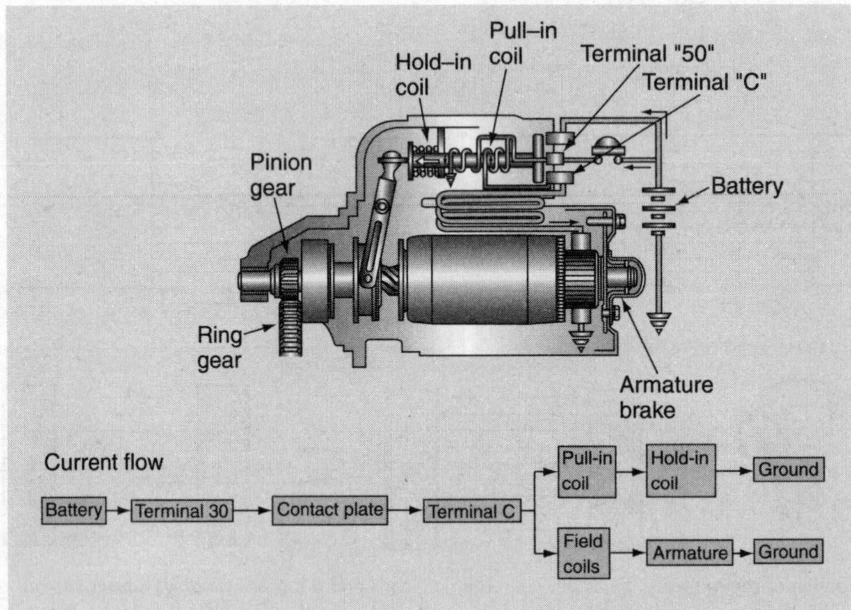

FIGURE 4-37 *Starting motor operation while disengaging.*

After the ignition switch is released to the on position and before the disc moves away from the terminals, current flows momentarily through the disc, pull-in winding, and hold-in winding to ground. However, current flow in the pull-in winding is reversed, and the magnetic fields of the two windings cancel each other. Once the disc moves away from the solenoid terminals, the circuit is open from the battery to the starting motor and the motor stops turning.

Starter Drive Operation

The starter drive clutch housing is splined to the armature shaft and must rotate with the shaft. Four spring-loaded steel rollers are mounted in tapered grooves in the drive housing. A pinion gear is mounted in the end of the drive housing, and the steel rollers contact a machined steel surface on this gear.

The solenoid shift lever moves the drive into mesh with the flywheel ring gear before the armature begins turning. When the solenoid disc contacts the terminals and the armature starts turning, the steel rollers are wedged into the narrow part of the tapered grooves where they are jammed between the drive housing and the pinion gear machined surface (Figure 4-38). Under this condition, the pinion gear must rotate with the drive housing to crank the engine.

Once the engine starts, the ring gear drives the pinion gear faster than the armature. This action moves the steel rollers against the spring tension and the rollers are now positioned in the wider part

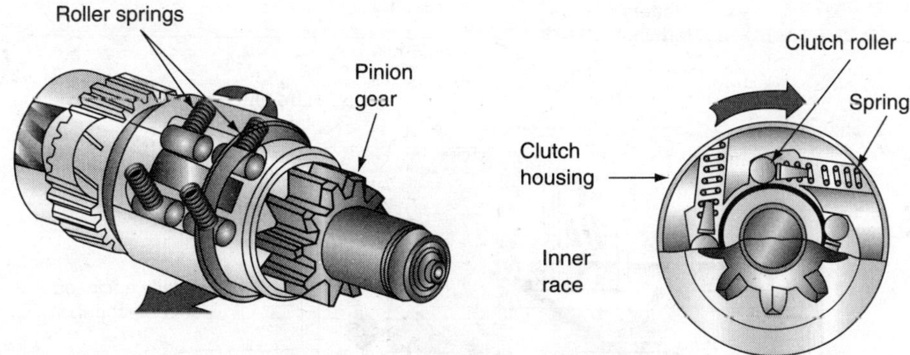

FIGURE 4-38 *Starter drive operation while cranking the engine.*

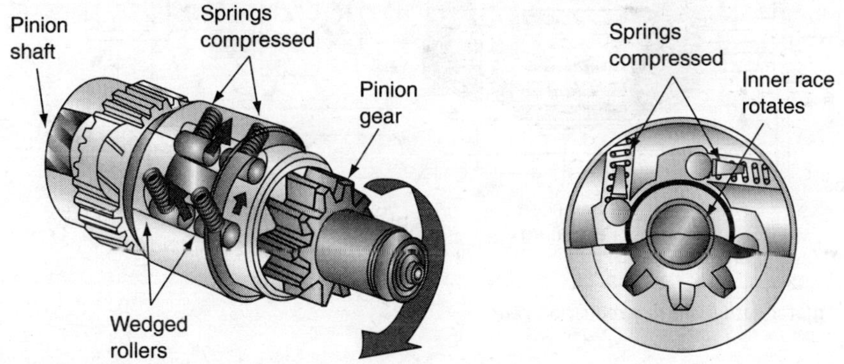

FIGURE 4-39 *Starter drive operation while overruning.*

of the tapered grooves (Figure 4-39). Under this condition, the starter drive overruns so the flywheel ring gear does not drive the armature at high speed.

This overrunning action of the drive is very important in protecting the armature from excessive speed. The average flywheel ring gear-to-pinion gear ratio is 15:1. If the drive did not overrun and the engine was running at 1,000 rpm, the armature speed would be 15,000 rpm. At this rpm, centrifugal force would throw the armature windings from their slots in the core and destroy the starting motor.

Gear Reduction Starting Motors

Many starting motors have a gear reduction between the armature and the drive. The reduction gears may be conventional or planetary (Figure 4-40). Planetary gearsets use a combination of external and internal gears. The reduction gears allow a smaller, more compact starting motor to provide the same cranking power as a larger starting motor without reduction gears.

AC GENERATORS

AC generators keep a vehicle's battery charged by sending electrical energy, which was converted from mechanical energy, to the battery. The AC generator's inner shaft is rotated by the engine via a drive belt. This inner shaft is called the rotor and is a rotating magnetic field. The rotor and its

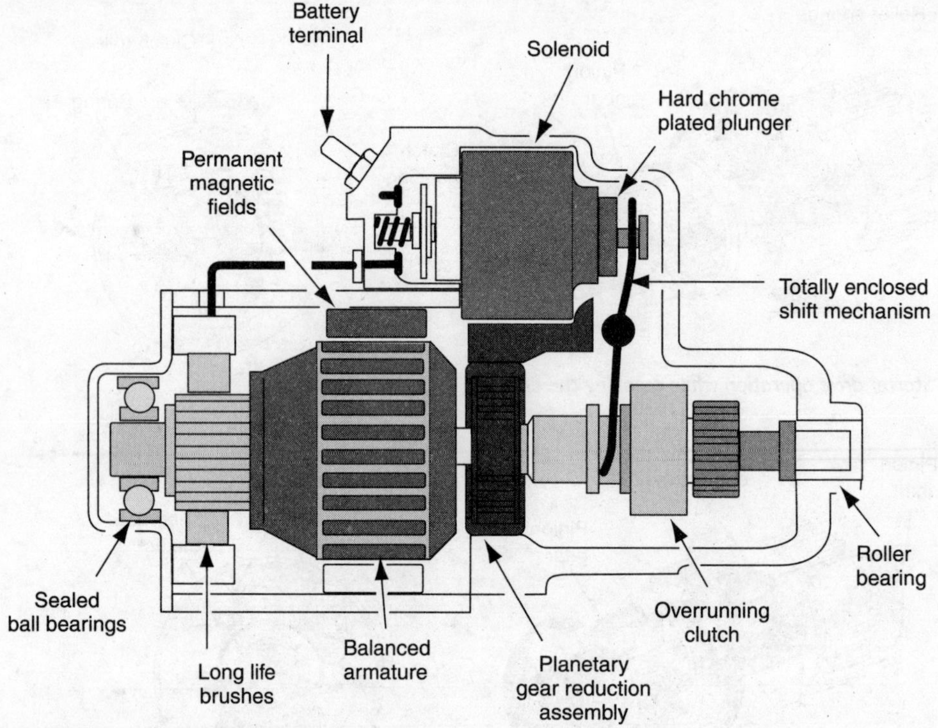

FIGURE 4-40 *Starter motor with planetary reduction gears.*

magnetic field spins inside the stator winding which are fastened to the generator case. As the magnetic field moves past the stator windings, AC voltage is induced. A rectifier circuit, comprised of several diodes, inside the generator converts the AC voltage to DC voltage before it is sent to the battery.

Rotor

A steel shaft is mounted in the center of the rotor assembly, and an insulated field winding is positioned on this shaft. Steel pole pieces with interlaced fingers are mounted over the field coil. Two insulated slip rings are positioned on the end of the rotor shaft, and the ends of the field coil are connected to the slip rings. The two slip rings are insulated from each other and from the rotor shaft. A small spring-loaded brush contacts each slip ring.

The drive end of the rotor shaft is supported on a ball bearing in the drive end housing, and the slip ring end of the shaft is mounted on a needle bearing in the slip ring end frame. A pulley is bolted or pressed on the drive end of the rotor shaft, and a cooling fan is positioned behind the pulley (Figure 4-41). The cooling fan circulates air through the AC generator to cool the internal components.

Stator and End Housings

The stator windings are mounted in a laminated iron frame, and this frame surrounds the rotor assembly. Many stators contain three windings, and the ends of these windings are connected to the diodes. The stator frame is positioned between the two end housings and through bolts extend from

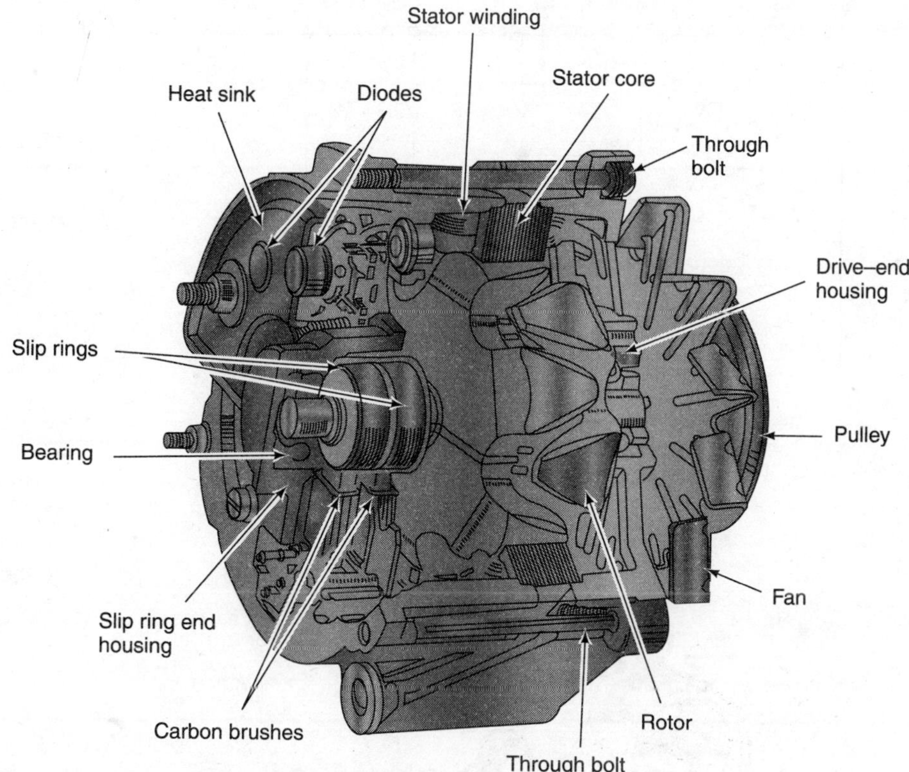

FIGURE 4-41 *Components of a typical AC generator.*

the drive end housing into the slip ring end housing to hold the assembly together. Bolt openings in the end housings allow the AC generator to be mounted on the engine.

Diodes

The purpose of diodes is to convert AC to DC. As explained earlier, a diode is an electrical one-way check valve causing current to flow in one direction only. Each winding of the stator produces a single-phase current. A three-phase current is produced with three windings. A set of diodes is used for each phase.

Many AC generators contain three negative diodes and three positive diodes (Figure 4-42). The positive diodes are mounted in an insulated heat sink to dissipate heat from the diodes. These diodes are connected to the insulated battery terminal in the end housing. Three negative diodes are connected to the end housing.

Voltage Regulators

Vehicles are equipped with integrated circuit (IC) regulators (Figure 4-43). Most IC regulators are mounted inside the AC generator or are bolted to the AC generator slip ring end housing.

The voltage regulator is always connected in the AC generator field circuit, regardless of the type of voltage regulator. The purpose of the voltage regulator is to limit the AC generator voltage to protect the electrical accessories and battery on the vehicle. If the voltage regulator allows excessive AC generator voltage, this voltage forces high current flow through the electrical accessories and battery.

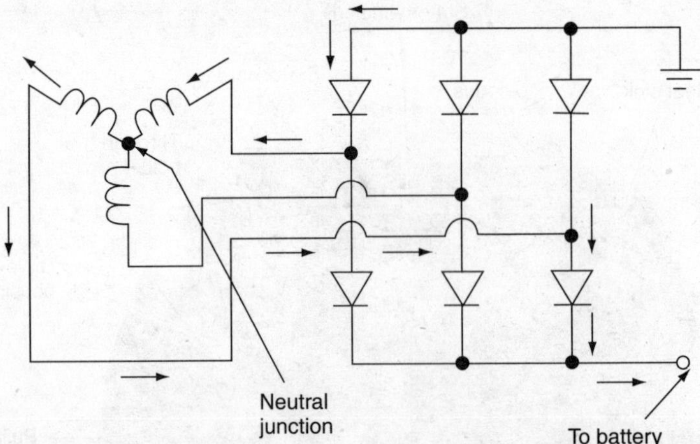

FIGURE 4-42 *A wye-wound stator wired to six diodes for rectification.*

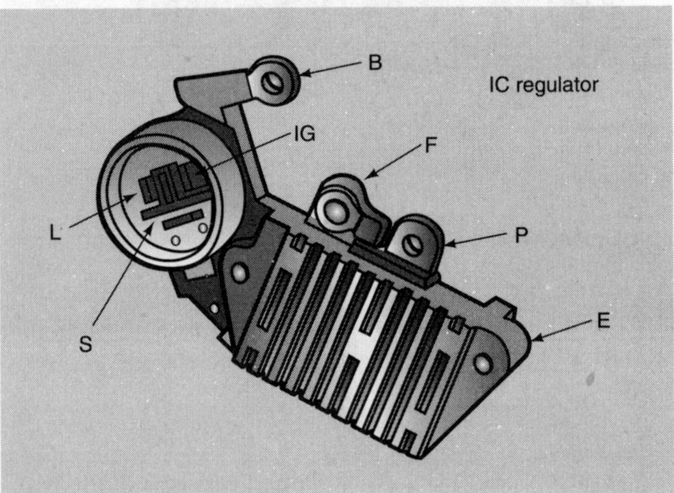

FIGURE 4-43 *Integrated circuit (IC) voltage regulators.*

This high current flow may burn out the electrical accessories and cause excessive battery gassing, which may damage the battery.

The voltage regulator controls field current through the field winding, and this action regulates the magnetic strength around the rotor. The induced voltage in the stator windings is limited by the magnetic strength of the rotor and the speed at which the rotor spins.

Voltage regulation in some vehicles is controlled by pulse width modulation of the AC generator field. In fact, an actual physical voltage regulator may not exist as part of the charging system. Instead, the charge rate is controlled by the PCM and/or a combination of processors that sense system voltage and issue an output command to the charging system, specifically the AC generator. By managing the on and off time or duty cycle of the AC generator field, a precise charge rate can be maintained and small corrections can be made quickly and accurately.

AC Generator Operation with the Ignition Switch On, Engine Stopped

When the ignition switch is turned on, current flows through the ignition switch and charge indicator light to the AC generator L terminal. From this location, the current flows through a transistor in the IC regulator to ground. Once this current flow occurs, current also flows from the battery positive terminal through the AC generator battery terminal and the field coil, slip rings, and brushes. This current flows through another transistor in the IC regulator to ground (Figure 4-44). The current flow through the field winding creates a magnetic field around the rotor, which induces voltage in the stator windings when the rotor starts turning.

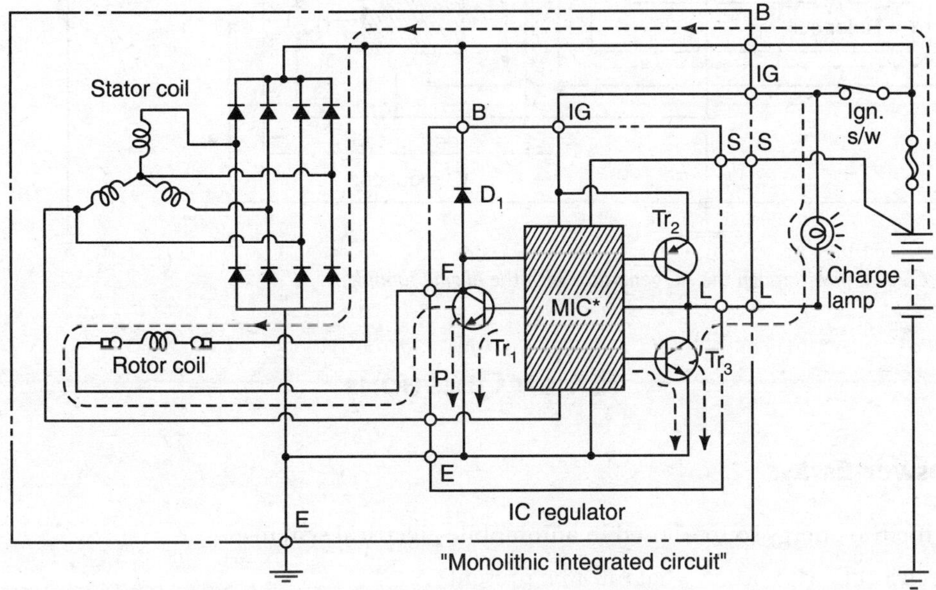

FIGURE 4-44 *Current flow through the AC generator with the ignition switch on and the engine stopped.*

AC Generator Operation with the Engine Running

When the engine starts, the rotor magnetic field induces an alternating current (AC) voltage in the stator windings. This AC voltage is changed to a direct current (DC) voltage by the diodes. Current flows from the diodes through the AC generator battery terminal to the battery and electrical accessories. This current flows through the ground return on the vehicle to the AC generator end housing and negative diodes.

Once the engine starts, equal voltage is supplied to both sides of the charge indicator light, which remains off. If the AC generator becomes defective and stops supplying current to the battery and accessories, the charge indicator light will be on with the engine running.

Some current also flows from the AC generator battery terminal through the brushes, slip rings, field winding, and IC regulator (Figure 4-45). The regulator controls this current to regulate the magnetic strength around the rotor and limit the voltage in the stator windings.

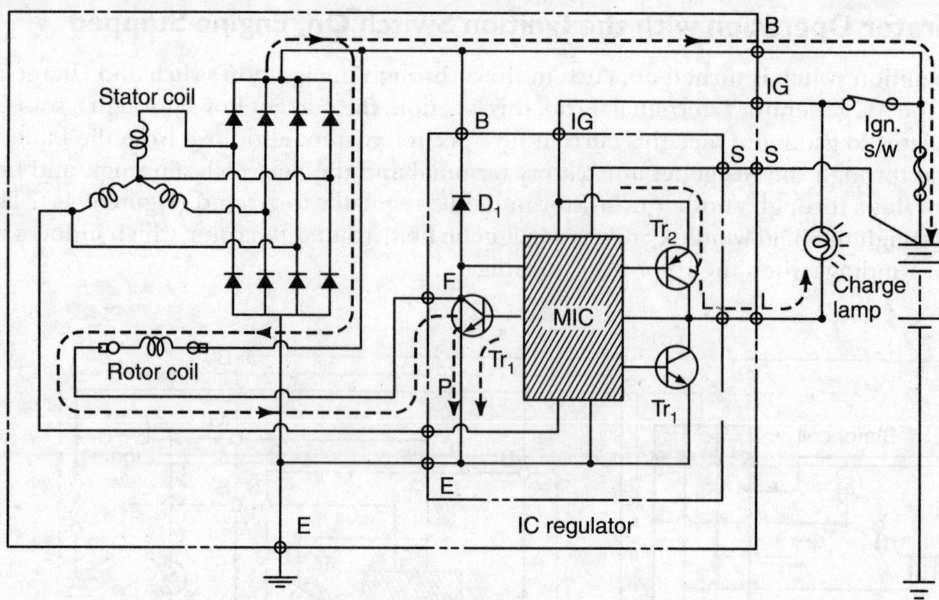

FIGURE 4-45 *Current flow through the AC generator with the engine running.*

REVIEW QUESTIONS

Short Answer Essays

1. Name the two energy sources used in automobile electrical systems.
2. For electrical flow to occur, what must be present?
3. Describe the chemical changes that occur while a battery is discharging.
4. What is the difference between voltage and current?
5. Explain the design of a starting motor armature.
6. State Ohm's Law.
7. Describe the differences between a rheostat and a potentiometer.
8. What is the difference between a fixed resistor and a variable resistor?
9. What types of sensors are typically used in an automotive computer system?
10. Explain how the voltage is induced in the AC generator stator windings, and describe the type of voltage induced.

Fill-in-the-Blanks

1. The two power or energy sources used in an automobile's electrical system are based on a ____________ ____________ and on ____________.

2. Current is measured in ____________, electrical voltage is measured in ____________, and electrical resistance is measured in ____________.

3. Many automotive battery cases are made from ______________ ______________.

4. ______________, ______________, ______________ ______________ and ______________ ______________ are used to protect circuits against current overloads.

5. ______________ control on/off and direct current flow in a circuit.

6. Many starting motors have two ______________ brushes and two ______________ brushes.

7. In an AC generator, the ends of the rotor field winding are connected to the ______________ ______________.

8. A ______________ is a material or device that can function as either a conductor or an insulator, depending on how its structure is arranged.

9. A computerized circuit depends on two types of signals: ______________ and ______________.

10. The AC generator voltage regulator is connected in the ______________ circuit.

Multiple Choice

1. *Technician A* says electrical pressure is termed voltage.
   Technician B says amperage can be described as the amount of electricity flowing in a circuit.
   Who is correct?
   A. Technician A only C. Both technicians
   B. Technician B only D. Neither technician

2. All of the following are versions of Ohms Law ***except:***
   A. $E = I \times R$ C. $R = E/I$
   B. $I = E/R$ D. $E = I/R$

3. *Technician A* says in a series circuit that the voltage is the same at all points.
   Technician B says that in a parallel circuit the amperage is the same at all points.
   Who is correct?
   A. Technician A only C. Both technicians
   B. Technician B only D. Neither technician

4. Which of the following statements are true?
   A. If current goes up and voltage stays the same, then resistance is greater.
   B. If current goes down and voltage stays the same, then resistance went down.
   C. If current goes down and voltage stays the same then resistance increased.
   D. If current goes up and voltage goes down, then resistance stayed the same.

5. *Technician A* says rheostats have two connections.
   Technician B says that potentiometers also have two connections.
   Who is correct?
   A. Technician A only C. Both technicians
   B. Technician B only D. Neither technician

6. A voltmeter is connected to the positive battery terminal and the output terminal of the AC generator.

   Technician A says this will show voltage drop from the battery positive to AC generator output.

   Technician B says this connection will show charging voltage.

   Who is correct?

A.	Technician A only	C.	Both technicians
B.	Technician B only	D.	Neither technician

7. *Technician A* says that a solenoid is an electromagnet with a fixed core.

   Technician B says a relay uses a small current to control a larger current.

   Who is correct?

A.	Technician A only	C.	Both technicians
B.	Technician B only	D.	Neither technician

8. During electromagnetic induction, the amount of current induced in the conductor is determined by all of these factors ***except:***

   A. The number of conductors

   B. The strength of the magnet

   C. Shape of the magnet

   D. Speed of motion between magnet and conductor

9. *Technician A* says that the transistor is the simplest semiconductor device.

   Technician B says that the transistor can act as an insulator or a conductor depending on the direction of current flow.

   Who is correct?

A.	Technician A only	C.	Both technicians
B.	Technician B only	D.	Neither technician

10. *Technician A* says that the thermistor is a variable resistor that changes value according to temperature.

    Technician B says a diode allows current to flow in one direction but not the other.

    Who is correct?

A.	Technician A only	C.	Both technicians
B.	Technician B only	D.	Neither technician

INTAKE AND EXHAUST SYSTEMS

5

Upon completion and review of this chapter, you should be able to:

- Describe air cleaner purpose and operation.
- Describe different types of air cleaner elements.
- Explain the purpose of a heated air inlet system.
- Explain the purpose of the exhaust crossover passage in the intake manifold on V-type engines.
- Describe the advantage of port fuel injection (PFI) in relation to intake manifold design.
- Describe how intake manifold vacuum is created and explain the relation of throttle opening to intake manifold vacuum.
- Explain the difference between tuned exhaust headers and a conventional exhaust manifold.
- Explain how carbon monoxide (CO), unburned hydrocarbons (HC), and oxides of nitrogen (NO_X) are formed during the combustion process.
- Explain a three-way catalytic converter.
- Define diesel particulate emissions.
- Explain basic turbocharger operation.

- Describe how the turbocharger boost pressure is controlled.
- Explain two ways in which the turbocharger bearings are cooled.
- Describe the results of inadequate turbocharger bearing cooling.
- List three items that cause premature turbocharger failure.
- Explain basic supercharger operation.
- Describe the difference in compression ratio in a turbocharged or supercharged engine compared to a normally aspirated engine.
- List nine components that are strengthened in a supercharged engine compared to a normally aspirated engine.

INTRODUCTION

The intake and exhaust systems are extremely important to engine operation. An air intake system must provide an adequate supply of clean air to the engine cylinders to maintain volumetric efficiency. If any component in the air intake system offers excessive air restriction, volumetric efficiency is reduced. The air cleaner element must remove all dust and abrasives from the incoming air. If the air cleaner allows any dust and abrasives to enter the engine, scoring of the cylinder walls, pistons, and piston rings will occur. In some older engines, the air intake system is responsible for maintaining air intake temperature to provide improved fuel vaporization and engine performance.

The exhaust system must deliver exhaust from the cylinder head exhaust ports to the atmosphere with a minimum amount of restriction and noise. If any exhaust system component offers excessive restriction to exhaust flow, volumetric efficiency is reduced. Exhaust leaks in any of the exhaust system components provide objectionable noise. Catalytic converters in the exhaust system are responsible for reducing tailpipe emission levels.

The Corporate Average Fuel Economy (CAFE) regulations required vehicle manufacturers to produce a greater number of small, fuel-efficient cars with small engines. In many vehicles, this shift to smaller engines resulted in a reduction in engine power and acceleration compared to the large engines of the past. However, a turbocharger or supercharger provides the best of two worlds. A turbocharger or supercharger may be used on a relatively small engine that provides adequate fuel economy when driven at normal cruising speeds. However, the turbocharger or supercharger increases engine power to provide the faster acceleration desired by the driver.

IMPORTANCE OF INTAKE AND EXHAUST SYSTEMS

An internal combustion engine requires air to operate. This air supply is drawn into the engine by the vacuum created during the intake stroke of the pistons. The air is mixed with fuel and is delivered to the combustion chambers. Controlling the flow of air and the air-fuel mixture is the job of the induction system.

Prior to the introduction of fuel injection, the induction system was quite simple. It consisted of an air cleaner housing mounted on top of the engine with a filter inside the housing (Figure 5-1). Its function was to filter dust and grit from the air being drawn into the engine. In the past, the intake manifold had to carry the atomized fuel from the carburetor all the way to the individual cylinders. If the intake manifold was cold, fuel tended to condense on the walls of the intake manifold. This condensed fuel will not burn efficiently in the engine, therefore making for cold drivability problems, reduced power, and increased fuel consumption. These problems were addressed by heating the intake manifold with heat from the exhaust. While these systems helped cold drivability, the problems were never completely resolved until the introduction of port fuel injection.

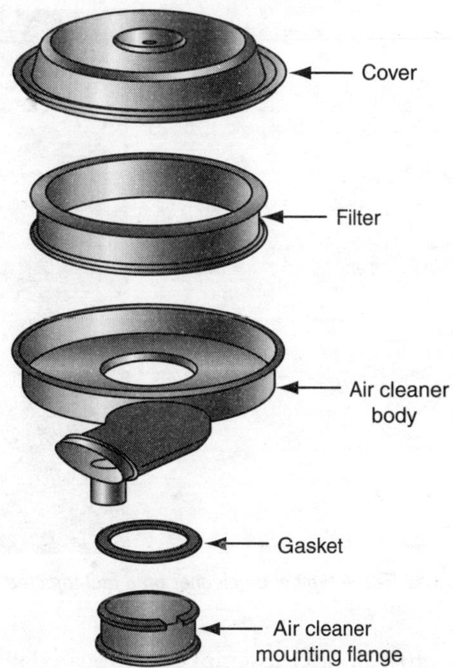

FIGURE 5-1 *An old-style air cleaner used on carbureted and TBI vehicles. These designs are too tall for the low hood height of todays's vehicles*

The air intake system on a modern fuel injected engine is more complicated. Ducts channel cool air from outside the engine compartment to the throttle plate assembly. Port fuel injection has eliminated the need for heated intake manifold systems and the design limitations of the past carburetor and throttle-body injection (TBI) systems. Intake manifold design has progressed along with fuel injection systems. Engines today use advanced intake designs that take advantage of natural pressure pulsations of the engine, called "tuning" of the intake manifold. Advanced materials such as high-temperature plastic have also been utilized to cut weight and cost. Air cleaners are located away from the top of the engine to accommodate aerodynamic body designs. These systems also measure the amount of air and its density going into the engine so the PCM can add the correct amount of fuel for a precise burn. Electronic meters measure airflow, temperature, and density. Air injection systems provide fresh air to the exhaust stream to oxidize unburned hydrocarbons in the exhaust. These components allow the air induction system to perform the following functions.

- Provide the air that the engine needs to operate
- Filter the air to protect the engine from wear
- Monitor airflow temperature and density for more efficient combustion and a reduction of hydrocarbon (HC) and carbon monoxide (CO) emissions
- Operate with the positive crankcase ventilation (PCV) system to burn the crankcase fumes in the engine
- Provide air for some air injection systems

Before each cylinder can be refilled with a fresh charge of air-fuel mixture, the cylinders must be free of the burnt gases resulting from the last four-stroke cycle. This is the primary purpose of the exhaust system. The exhaust system collects these gases, quiets exhaust noise, and carries the gases out at the rear of the vehicle.

AIR CLEANERS

The primary function of the air filter is to prevent airborne contaminants and abrasives from entering into the engine with the air-fuel mixture. Without proper filtration, these contaminants can cause serious damage and appreciably shorten engine life. All incoming air should pass through the filter element before entering the engine.

FIGURE 5-2 *A typical air cleaner on a fuel injected vehicle.*

Most air filter assemblies are located inside the air cleaner housing (Figure 5-2). In most cases, the air cleaner unit is connected to the air horn, throttle plate assembly, or manifold by an air transfer tube or duct.

The air cleaner assembly also helps muffle noise caused by the airflow through the throttle plates. The air cleaner also provides filtered air to the PCV system and provides engine compartment fire protection in the event of backfire.

Most air cleaners on fuel injected engines contain an air charge temperature and mass air flow sensors that send signals to the computer in relation to air intake temperature and quantity or mass. The computer uses this signal and other inputs to control the air-fuel mixture.

Air Cleaner Assembly and Filter Design

Older carbureted and TBI systems generally used an air cleaner mounted directly over the TBI or carburetor. In an attempt to make vehicles more aerodynamic and therefore more fuel-efficient, lower hood-lines are becoming the norm. The air cleaners have been moved to a remote location, and ducts have been run to the throttle body (Figure 5-3). All of the air that enters the engine must be filtered as dirt, and debris pulled into the engine can cause major engine damage.

Many air filters have a pleated paper element with a wire or expanded metal screen on the outside of the element to provide protection against accidental paper damage while shipping and handling. A fine mesh screen is mounted on the inside of the pleated paper. The paper element and wire screens are molded into a heat-resistant plastisol on the top and bottom of the element. This heat-resistant plastisol has large sealing beads on both sides of the element. Air filter elements are available in many different shapes and sizes to fit various air cleaners. Some pleated-paper air filter elements contain oil-wetted resin-impregnated paper to provide longer element life and improved element efficiency. Some aftermarket manufacturers have developed reusable air filters that can be cleaned and advertised to increase the amount of air drawn into the engine.

Some heavy-duty air cleaners have an oil-wetted polyurethane cover placed over the paper element. The polyurethane traps larger dirt particles, and the smaller particles pass through the polyurethane where they are caught in the paper element. The polyurethane cover may be removed, cleaned, oil-wetted, and reinstalled.

FIGURE 5-3 *Remote air cleaner assembly and Mass Air Flow meter.*

Air Filter Ducts

There are many different air cleaner designs depending on the type of fuel system and the available underhood space. Many air cleaner assemblies have a snorkel attached to the air cleaner body and the air intake at the end of the snorkel. Most air cleaner assemblies have a plastic duct connected to the snorkel, and the outer end of this duct is positioned in a cool air location such as in front of or beside the radiator (Figure 5-4). Modern air cleaners are generally designed to bring in fresh air from outside of the engine compartment. This is desirable because cold air is denser and therefore contains more oxygen than hot air from the engine compartment. A flexible coupling is positioned between the plastic duct and the snorkel. Some **air cleaner ducts** contain a large specially shaped resonator chamber that silences the airflow into the air cleaner (Figure 5-5).

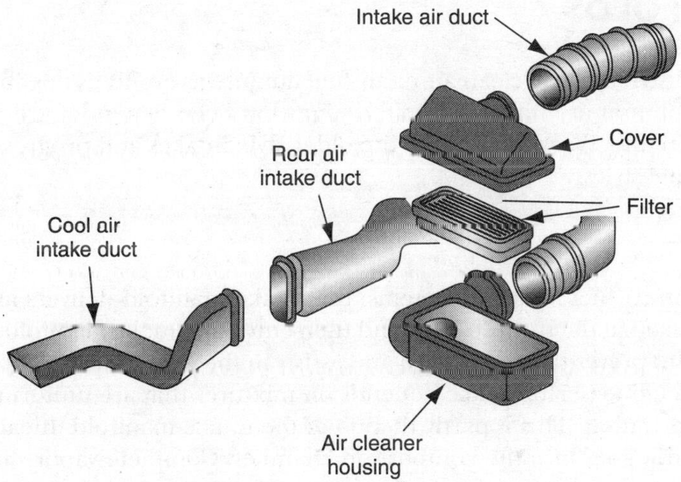

FIGURE 5-4 *Remote air cleaner and ducts.*

FIGURE 5-5 *A Helmholtz Resonator reduces engine noise.*

These air cleaner ducts are designed to reduce the amount of engine noise transmitted into the passenger compartment (Figure 5-5). Most people wonder why there are so many tubes and containers under the hood going to the air cleaner. These are often called Helmholtz resonators because they are designed to counteract what are called Helmholtz oscillations. A column of air drawn into or across a container, such as an automotive intake manifold, can produce oscillations that can result in a droning sound. These sounds occur because the air cleaner, hose, and intake have a specific frequency that will set up a vibration. (Blowing across the top of a soda pop bottle produces a similar effect.) These oscillations are always changing, due in part to the opening and closing of the intake valves and the throttle opening. The purpose of the resonator is to produce a counter-oscillation that cancels out the vibrations and therefore the sound produced.

INTAKE MANIFOLDS

The intake manifold distributes the clean air or air-fuel mixture as evenly as possible to each cylinder of the engine. The evolution of intake manifold designs has been dependent on the methods used to deliver fuel to the engine. We will start with the older style intakes and progress to the newer and more prevalent port fuel styles.

Intake Manifold Design

On throttle-body (central) fuel injection systems, the intake manifold delivers an air-fuel mixture. The air and fuel are mixed in the throttle body and then enter the intake manifold. The design of the intake manifold helps to prevent condensation and assists in the vaporization of the air-fuel mixture. Smooth and efficient engine performance depends on mixtures that are uniform in strength, quality, and degree of vaporization. This is partly the job of the intake manifold. Ideally, the fuel is completely vaporized when it goes into the combustion chamber. Complete vaporization requires high temperature, but high temperatures decrease the volumetric efficiency of the engine. Therefore, the best alternative is to deliver an air-fuel mixture that is vaporized above the point where fuel particles will be deposited on the manifold and below the point where excess heat results in power losses.

On port fuel injection systems, the intake manifold delivers only clean air to the cylinders. Fuel is introduced by the individual fuel injectors. There are many new intake manifold designs for ported gasoline fuel injection. They are often referred to as tuned intake manifolds because they have been redesigned to deliver equal amounts of airflow to each cylinder (Figure 5-6).

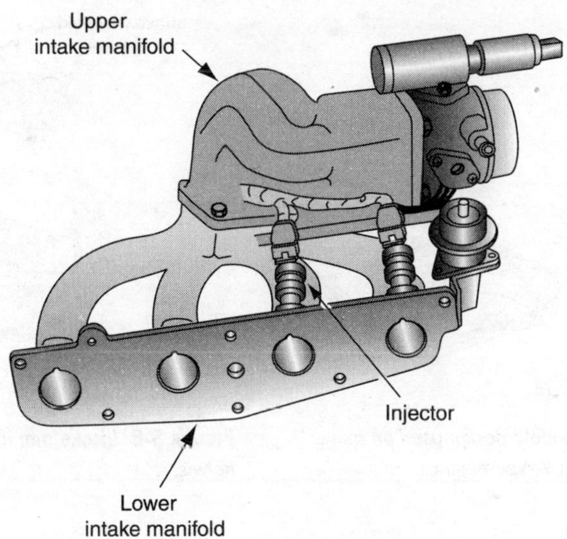

FIGURE 5-6 *This type of tuned intake manifold, used with ported fuel injection, gives a more equal amount of air to each cylinder.*

Each cylinder's intake runner tube is designed to be a certain length. All the runners for each cylinder are uniform in length as well. The effect the tubes have on incoming air causes a slight increase in velocity, which gives the air charge a type of ram effect. As air continues to enter the intake runner, a slight increase of pressure occurs. This increase takes place during the time the intake valve is closed. The intake air is packed inside the runner because it has nowhere to go. The moment the intake valve opens, the tightly packed air enters the combustion chamber with slightly more force behind it.

For years, intake manifolds were made mainly of either cast iron or aluminum. Most intake manifolds produced today leverage the advancements made in plastics and carbon-based technology. The use of this material is helpful in reducing heat-related problems. Another obvious advantage is weight reduction. The composite manifolds may also include an integral throttle body unit designed for certain applications. When performing service operations that require the removal and installation of a plastic or carbon-fiber style intake manifold, it is important to follow the manufacturer's procedures. Although tightening sequence and torque specifications are important with all intake manifolds, they are especially important with any composite-type manifold. Failure to follow these procedures will likely result in a cracked manifold or other damage.

Manufacturers are working on other fuel delivery system enhancements such as direct gasoline fuel injection that injects high-pressure gasoline directly into the combustion chamber. This will further reduce the amount of components that are made part of, or mounted to, the intake manifold.

Manifolds can be either wet or dry. **Wet intake manifolds** have coolant passages cast directly into them. **Dry intake manifolds** do not have cooling passages. Older systems, such as throttle body and carbureted vehicles, had intake manifolds with integrally cast water crossover passages that allowed coolant to warm the incoming air-fuel mixture. The absence of these systems is another advantage of port fuel injection. The intake manifold had a throttle body or carburetor mounting surface (Figure 5-7) and another mounting surface that fits against the intake port area on the cylinder head. Some intake manifolds have an upper and a lower half. The lower half of the intake manifold is bolted to the cylinder heads, and the upper half is bolted to the lower half (Figure 5-8).

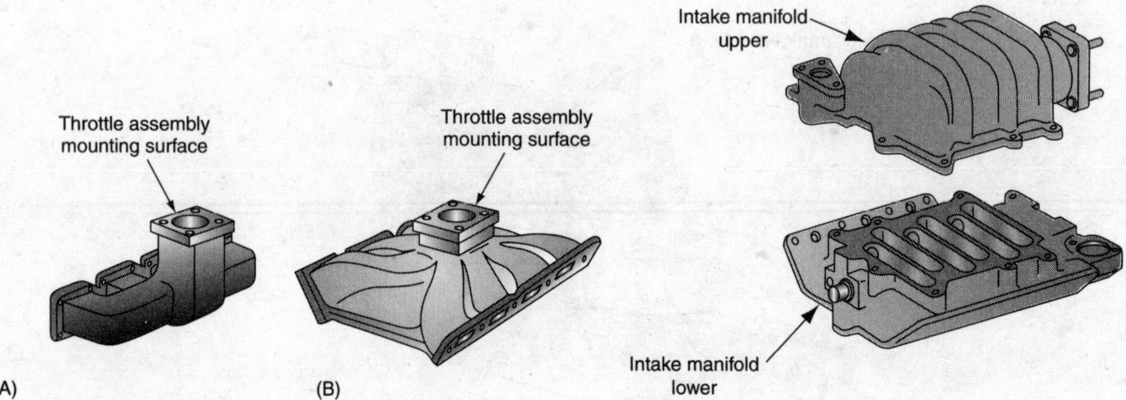

FIGURE 5-7 *(A) Typical intake manifold design used on inline engines; (B) typical design used on V-type engines.*

FIGURE 5-8 *Intake manifold—the upper and lower halves.*

On an in-line engine, the intake manifold-to-cylinder head area is a straight machined surface, whereas the intake manifold-to-cylinder head mounting surface on a V-type engine fits in the V between the cylinder heads. The intake manifold must distribute air and fuel, or air, as equally as possible to all the cylinders. Since the distance from the carburetor or TBI assembly to each cylinder is not equal, the intake manifold air passages may be designed to make this distance as equal as possible. For example, in the manifold from a four-cylinder engine, four curved air passages split off from the upper plenum and connect with passages in the lower half of the intake, which is bolted to the cylinder head (Figure 5-9). The curved passages in the upper plenum and lower half of the intake are designed with similar lengths.

A series of bolts retains the intake manifold to the cylinder head, or heads, and a gasket is positioned between these two components. All intake manifold gaskets and mounting surfaces must be in satisfactory condition to prevent air leaks into the intake manifold, which cause a lean air-fuel mixture, rough idle operation, and reduced engine performance at low speeds on a throttle body vehicle.

Intake Manifold Temperature

Intake manifold temperature is critical. If the intake manifold is too cold on TBI engines, the air fuel mixture condenses out on the manifold surfaces. Therefore, the intake manifold surface must be heated sufficiently to improve vaporization and prevent fuel condensation inside the manifold air passages.

Before today's port fuel injected engines, most intake manifolds on earlier TBI and carbureted V-type engines have an exhaust crossover passage through the intake manifold under the TBI assembly mounting surface (Figure 5-10). Exhaust flow through the crossover passage heats the intake manifold and improves fuel vaporization, especially when the engine is warming up. These systems

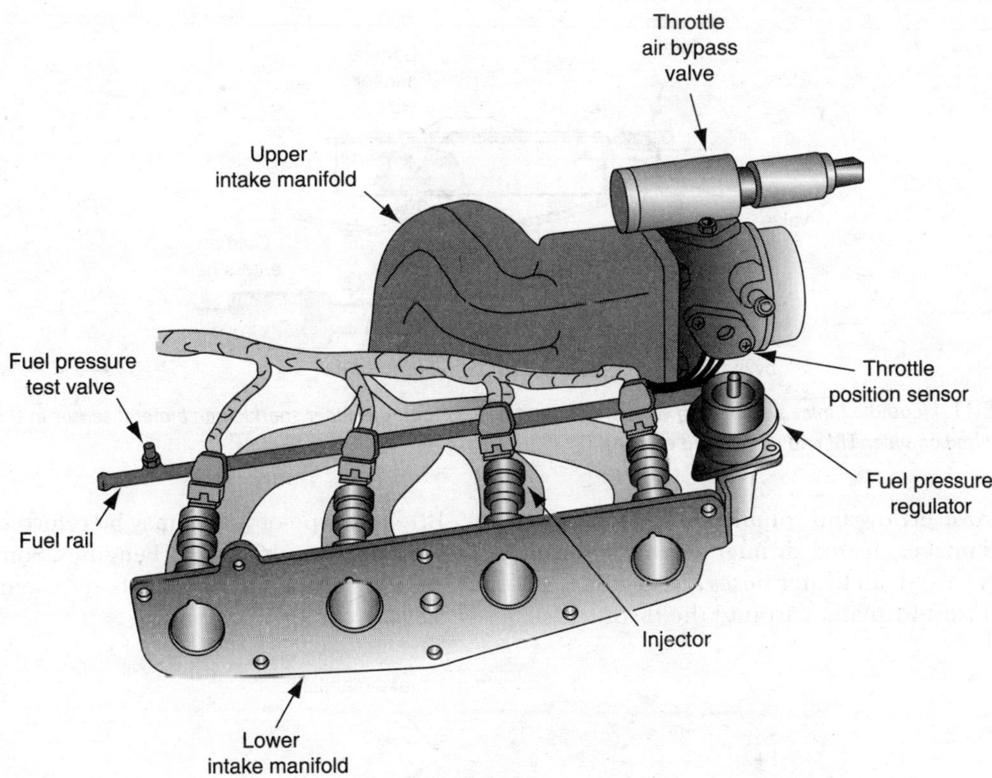

Figure 5-9 *Intake manifold from a 4-cylinder engine with curved runners in the lower half and a plenum area in the upper half.*

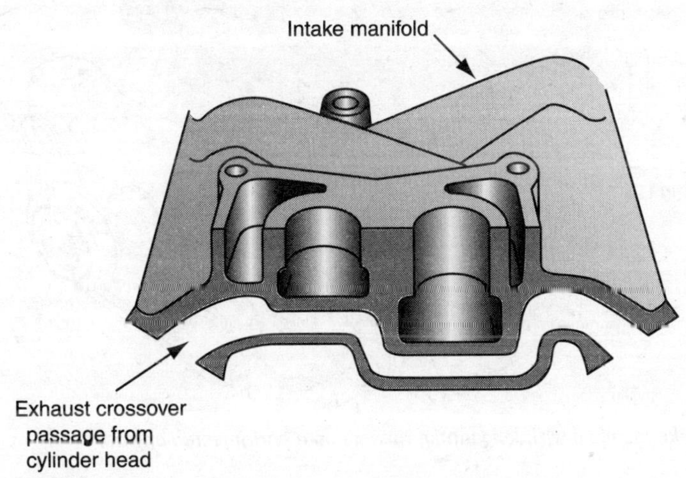

Figure 5-10 *Intake manifold from a V-8 engine with an exhaust crossover passage.*

also utilized heated air intake systems that were designed to warm the incoming air-fuel charge while the engine was cold (Figure 5-11).

On PFI engines, the intake manifold does not require as much heat because the fuel is injected at the intake ports and the manifold distributes air to the intake ports. Since manifold heating requirements are reduced on these engines, the manifold may be designed with longer curved air passages

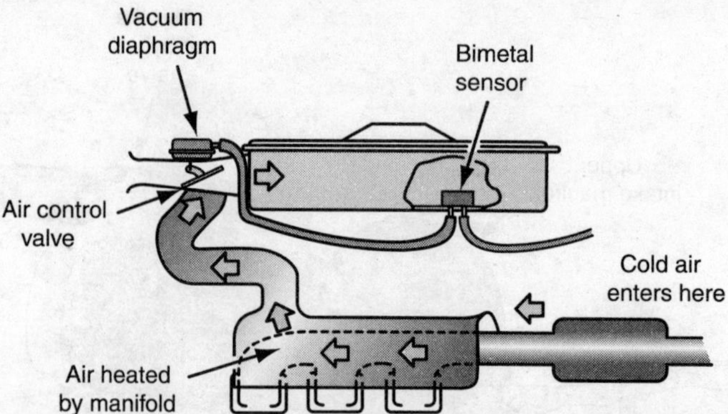

FIGURE 5-11 *Heated air inlet system with vacuumoperated door in the air cleaner snorkle and bimetal sensor in the air cleaner. Used on older TBI and carbureted vehicles.*

to improve airflow and volumetric efficiency (Figure 5-12). This type of intake may be referred to as a tuned intake. Heated air inlet systems in the air cleaner are not required on PFI engines. Some PFI engines have small heater hoses connected from the cooling system to the throttle body assembly to prevent frost formation around the throttles.

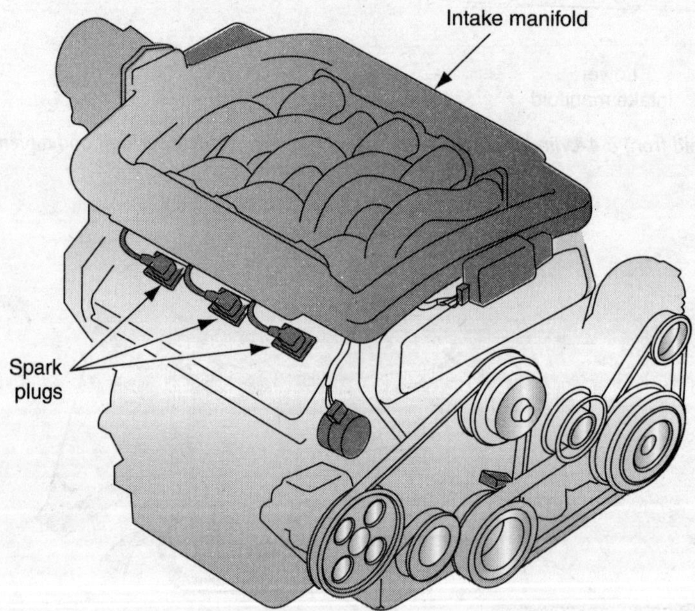

FIGURE 5-12 *Tuned intake manifold with long intake runners on a port injected engine.*

Some high-performance engines have two intake runners for each cylinder. There is a short set and a long set. Each of these sets are designed for different operating conditions—one set for low-speed, high-torque operation, and the other for high-speed operation. The switching from one set of intake runners to the next is normally controlled by the PCM. The PCM relies on input from a variety of sensors to determine the optimum time to switch from a set of runners to the other.

Intake manifolds and related intake systems contain a variety of computer input sensors on PFI, TBI, and computer-controlled carburetor systems. These sensors include the engine coolant temperature sensor (CTS), intake air temperature (IAT) sensor, mass air flow (MAF) sensor, manifold absolute pressure sensor (MAP), and knock sensor. The CTS sensor may be mounted in a coolant passage in the intake manifold. This sensor sends a signal to the computer in relation to coolant temperature. An IAT sensor is mounted in one of the airflow passages in the intake manifold. This sensor sends a signal to the computer in relation to air temperature in the intake manifold. On some engines, the IAT sensor is mounted in the air cleaner (Figure 5-13).

The MAF sensor transmits a signal to the computer in relation to the total volume of air entering the engine. This sensor is located in the air intake hose between the air cleaner and the throttle body assembly or directly in the throttle body assembly (Figure 5-14). A detailed explanation of these sensors is included later in the appropriate chapters.

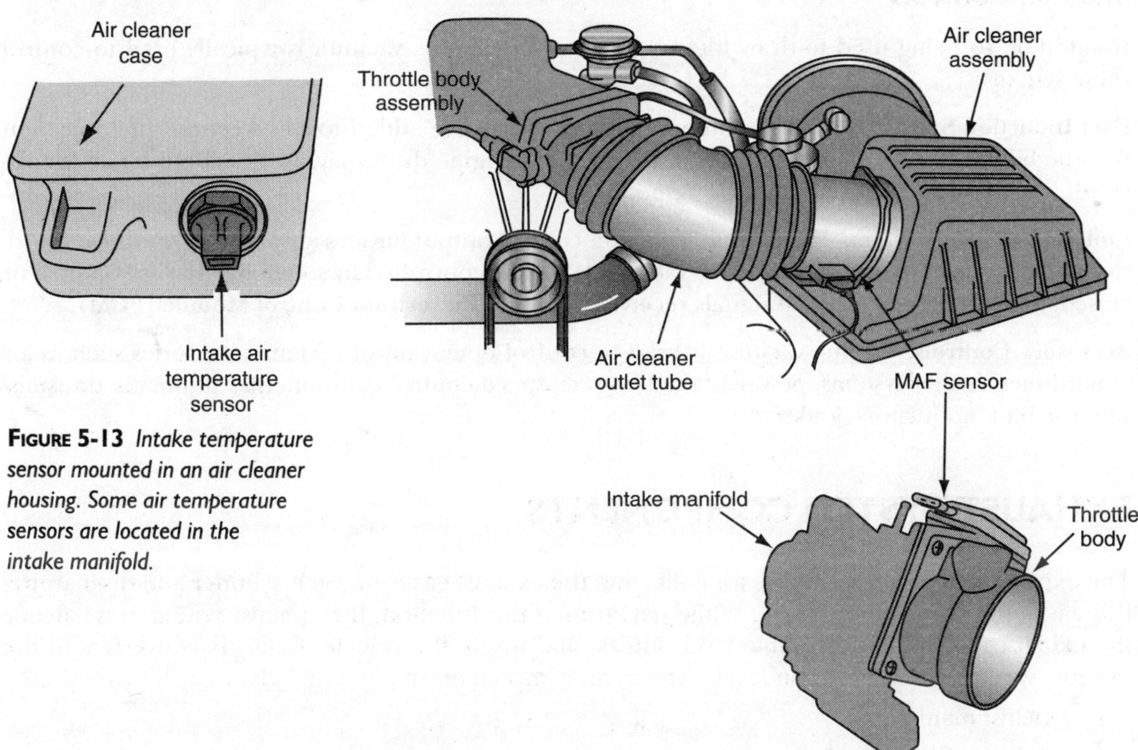

FIGURE 5-13 *Intake temperature sensor mounted in an air cleaner housing. Some air temperature sensors are located in the intake manifold.*

FIGURE 5-14 *Mass air flow (MAF) sensors.*

Vacuum Systems

The vacuum in the intake manifold is used to operate many systems, such as emission controls, brake boosters, parking brake releases, headlight doors, heater/air conditioners, and cruise controls. Vacuum is applied to these systems through a system of hoses and tubes, which can become quite elaborate.

Vacuum is measured in relation to atmospheric pressure. Atmospheric pressure is the pressure exerted on every object on earth and is caused by the weight of the surrounding air. At sea level, the pressure exerted by the atmosphere is 14.7 psi. The normal measure of vacuum is in inches of mercury (in. Hg) instead of psi. Other units of measurement for vacuum are kilopascals and bars. Normal atmospheric pressure at sea level is about 1 bar, or 100 kilopascals.

Vacuum in any four-stroke engine is created by the downward movement of the piston during the intake stroke. With the intake valve open and the piston moving downward, a partial vacuum is created within the cylinder and intake manifold. The air passing the intake valve does not move fast enough to fill the cylinder, thereby causing the lower pressure. This partial vacuum is continuous in a multi-cylinder engine since at least one cylinder is always at some stage of its intake stroke.

The amount of vacuum created is partially related to the positioning of the throttle plates. The throttle plate not only admits air or air-fuel into the intake manifold, it also helps to control the amount of vacuum available during engine operation. At closed-throttle idle, the vacuum available is usually between 15 to 22 inches. At a wide-open throttle acceleration, the vacuum can drop to zero.

Vacuum Controls

In addition to being used to draw filtered air into the engine, vacuum is typically used to control these systems.

Fuel Induction System. Certain vacuum-operated devices are added to some central fuel injection throttle bodies to ease engine startup, warm-and-cold engine driveaway, and to compensate for air-conditioner compressor load on the engine.

Emission Control System. While some emission control output devices are solenoid or linkage controlled, many operate on vacuum. This vacuum is usually controlled by solenoids that are opened or closed, depending on electrical signals received from the **Powertrain Control Module (PCM)**.

Accessory Controls. Engine vacuum is used to control operation of certain accessories such as air conditioner/heater systems, power brake boosters, speed-control components, automatic transmission vacuum modulators, and so on.

EXHAUST SYSTEM COMPONENTS

The exhaust system is responsible for collecting the exhaust gas from each cylinder and discharging this gas at the rear of the vehicle. While performing this function, the exhaust system must silence the exhaust flow to an acceptable level outside and inside the vehicle. Catalytic converters in the exhaust system reduce emission levels. The main components in a typical exhaust system are these:

1. Exhaust manifolds
2. Exhaust pipe and seal
3. Catalytic converter
4. Muffler
5. Resonator
6. Tailpipe
7. Heat shields
8. Hangers, brackets, and clamps

All the parts of the system are designed to conform to the available space of the vehicle's undercarriage and yet be a safe distance above the road.

Exhaust Manifolds

Many exhaust manifolds are made from cast iron or nodular iron. Some exhaust manifolds are made from stainless steel or heavy-gauge steel. The exhaust manifold contains an exhaust port for each exhaust port in the cylinder head, and a flat machined surface on this manifold fits against a matching surface on the exhaust port area in the cylinder head. Some exhaust manifolds have a gasket between the manifold and the cylinder head (Figure 5-15). In other applications, the machined surface fits directly against the matching surface on the cylinder head. The exhaust passages from each port in the manifold join into a common single passage before they reach the manifold flange. An exhaust pipe is connected to the exhaust manifold flange. On a V-type engine, an exhaust manifold is bolted to each cylinder head.

Exhaust system components are designed for a specific engine. The pipe diameter, component length, **catalytic converter** size, muffler size, and exhaust manifold design are engineered to provide proper exhaust flow, silencing, and emission levels on a particular engine. Exhaust headers are used in place of exhaust manifolds on some engines (Figure 5-16). Each time a power stroke occurs and an exhaust valve opens, a positive pressure occurs in the exhaust manifold. A **negative pressure** occurs in the exhaust manifolds between the positive pressure pulses, especially at lower engine speeds.

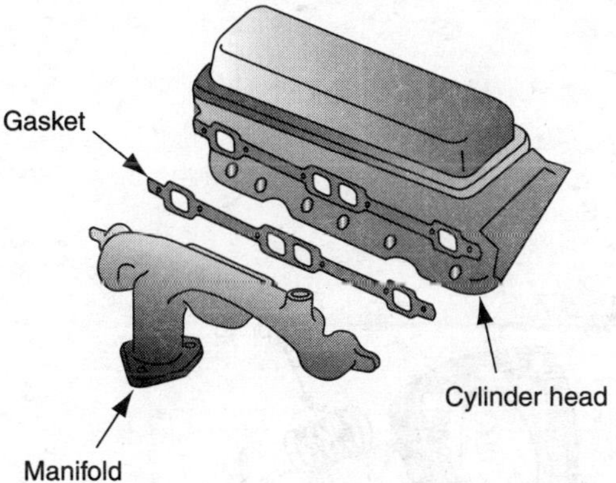

FIGURE 5-15 *Exhaust manifold and gasket.*

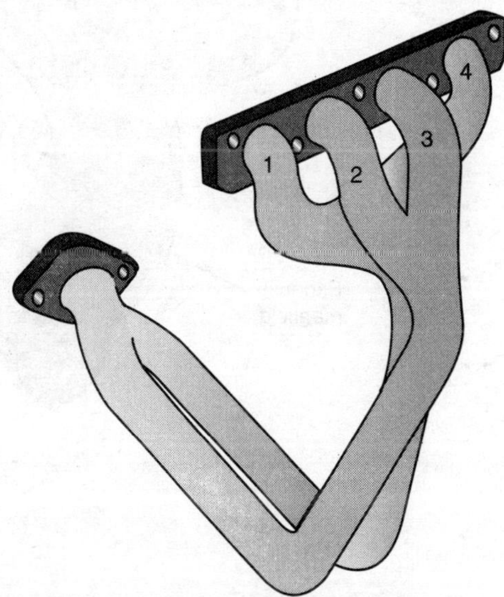

FIGURE 5-16 *Efficiency can be improved with tuned exhaust headers.*

Some **exhaust headers** are tuned so the exhaust pulses enter the exhaust manifold between the exhaust pulses from other cylinders, preventing interference between the exhaust pulses. If the exhaust pressure pulses interfere with each other, the exhaust flow is slowed, causing a decrease in volumetric efficiency. Proper exhaust manifold tuning actually creates a vacuum, which helps to draw exhaust out of the cylinders and improve volumetric efficiency. The interference between exhaust pulses is most noticeable on a V8 engine compared with a V6 or four-cylinder engine.

Exhaust Pipe and Seal

The exhaust pipe is connected from the exhaust manifold to the catalytic converter. On in-line engines, the exhaust pipe is a single pipe, but on V-type engines, the exhaust pipe is connected to each manifold flange. These two pipes are connected into a single pipe under the rear of the engine. This single pipe is then attached to the catalytic converter. Exhaust pipes may be made from stainless steel or zinc-plated steel, and some exhaust pipes are double walled. In some exhaust systems, an **intermediate pipe** is connected between the exhaust pipe and the catalytic converter. Some exhaust systems have a heavy tapered steel or steel composition sealing washer positioned between the exhaust pipe flange and the exhaust manifold flange. Other exhaust pipes have a tapered end that fits against a ball-shaped surface on the exhaust manifold flange. Bolts or studs and nuts retain the exhaust pipe to the exhaust manifold (Figure 5-17). Some V-type engines have dual exhaust systems with separate exhaust pipes and exhaust systems connected to each exhaust manifold.

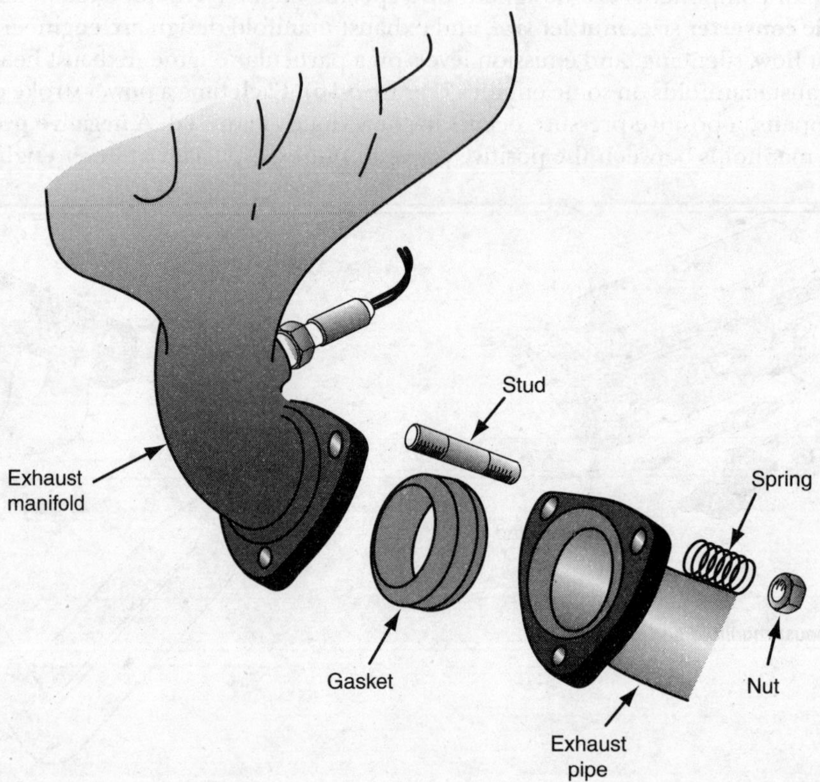

FIGURE 5-17 *Exhaust pipe retaining hardware.*

On PFI, TBI, or computer-controlled carburetor systems, the oxygen (O_2) sensor is threaded into the exhaust pipe or exhaust manifold (Figure 5-18). This sensor informs the computer if the air-fuel mixture is rich or lean.

Automotive Pollutants and Catalytic Converters

Three major automotive pollutants are carbon monoxide (CO), unburned hydrocarbons (HC), and oxides of nitrogen (NO_x). Gasoline is a hydrocarbon fuel containing hydrogen and carbon. Since the combustion process in the cylinders is never 100 percent complete, some unburned HC is left over in the exhaust. Some HC emissions occur from evaporative sources, such as gasoline tanks and carburetors.

When air and gasoline are mixed and burned in the combustion chambers, the byproducts of combustion are carbon, carbon dioxide (CO_2), CO, and water vapor. Therefore, CO is a byproduct of the combustion process.

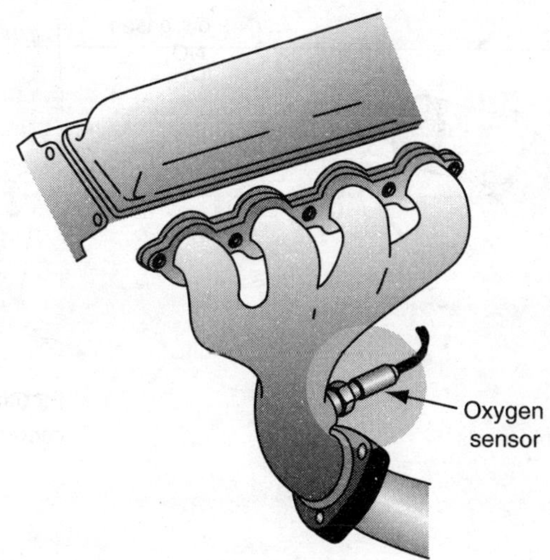

FIGURE 5-18 *Oxygen sensor location in exhaust manifold.*

Oxides of nitrogen (NO_X) are caused by high cylinder temperature. Nitrogen and oxygen are both present in air. If the combustion chamber temperatures are above 2,500°F (1,371°C), some of the oxygen and nitrogen combine to form NO_X. In the presence of sunlight, HC and NO_X join to form smog.

Catalytic converters are usually monolithic type. In a **monolithic-type catalytic converter**, the exhaust gas passes through a honeycomb ceramic block (Figure 5-19). The converter beads or ceramic block are coated with a thin coating of platinum, palladium, and rhodium and are mounted in a stainless-steel container.

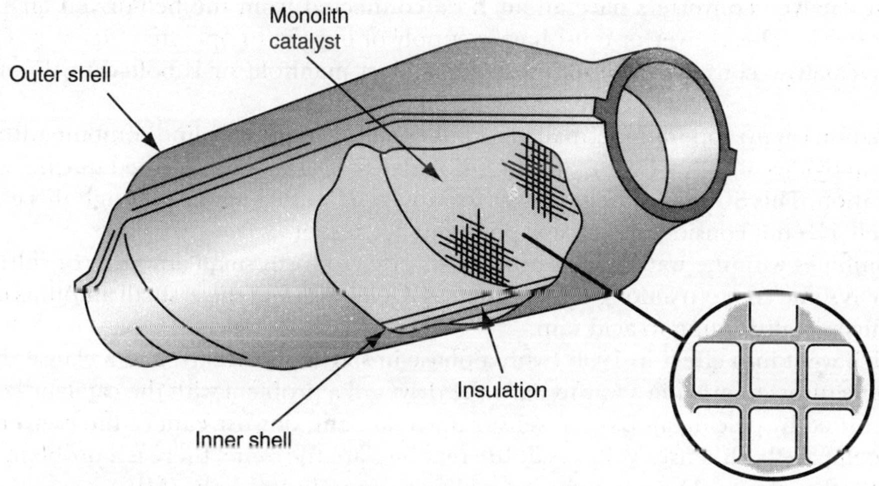

FIGURE 5-19 *Monolithic-type catalytic converter.*

In a three-way catalytic converter, the three-way converter is positioned in front of the oxidation catalyst. A three-way catalytic converter lowers NO_X emissions as well as CO and HC. The three-way catalyst reduces NO_X into nitrogen and oxygen (Figure 5-20). All modern vehicles use the three-way catalyst. Some catalytic converters contain a thermo-sensor that illuminates a light on the instrument

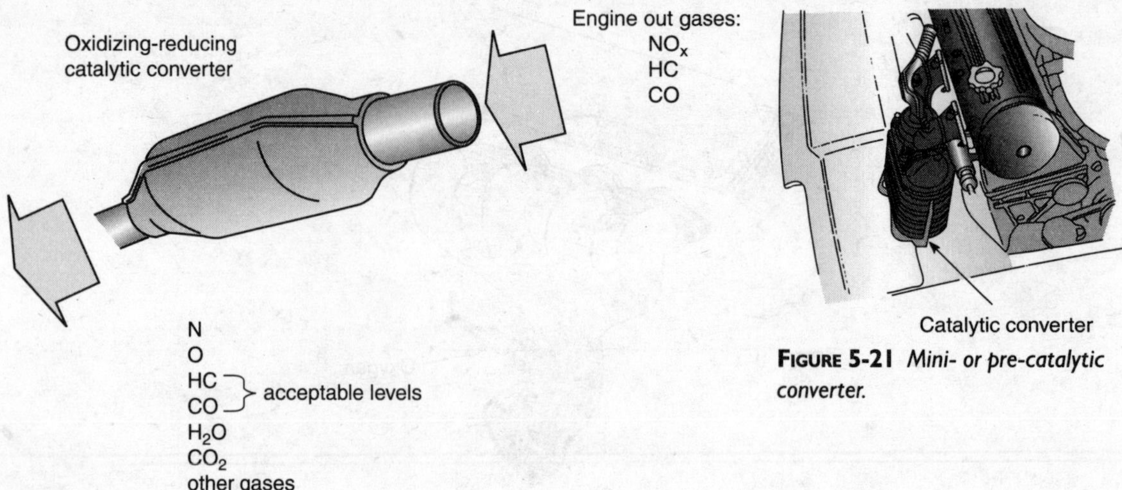

FIGURE 5-20 *A three-way catalyst.*

FIGURE 5-21 *Mini- or pre-catalytic converter.*

panel if the converter begins to overheat. Unleaded gasoline must be used in engines with catalytic converters. If leaded gasoline is used, the lead in the gasoline coats the catalyst and makes it ineffective. Under this condition, tailpipe emissions become very high. An engine that is improperly tuned causes severe overheating of the catalytic converter. Examples of improper tuning would be a rich air-fuel mixture or cylinder misfiring.

Some vehicles are equipped with a mini-catalytic converter, which provides a closecoupled converter that is either built in the exhaust manifold or is located next to it (Figure 5-21). It is primarily used to clean the exhaust during engine warmup. These converters are commonly called warmup converters or preheaters.

Some earlier catalytic converters have an air hose connected from the belt-driven air pump to the oxidation catalyst. This converter must have a supply of oxygen to operate efficiently. On some engines, a mini-catalytic converter is built into the exhaust manifold or is bolted to the manifold flange.

During oxidation catalyst operation, small amounts of sulfur in the gasoline combine with oxygen in the air to form oxides of sulfur (SO_X). Sulphur dioxide (SO_2) gas is also formed during oxidation converter operation. This SO_2 gas is the same gas produced by rotting eggs. Although this gas has an unpleasant smell, it is not considered a major pollutant at present.

The SO_X combines with the water vapor in the converter to form small amounts of sulfuric acid (H_2SO_4). There is some concern among environmental agencies about these small amounts of H_2SO_4 from many vehicles contributing to acid rain.

OBD II, which went into effect in 1996 (with a phase-in starting in 1995), had a clause that mandates the manufacturers to provide a way to warn the driver of a problem with the catalytic converter. This is accomplished by placing an oxygen sensor upstream and downstream of the converter. The computer will compare both sensor voltages. If the readings are the same, there is a problem with the converter or with the engine. This will light the malfunction indicator light (MIL).

Diesel Particulate Oxidizer Catalytic Converter

Tailpipe emissions on a diesel engine include HC, CO, and NO_X emissions, but a diesel engine also produces **particulate** emissions, which are small carbon particles. A ceramic monolith inside the diesel particulate converter reduces particulate emissions (Figure 5-22).

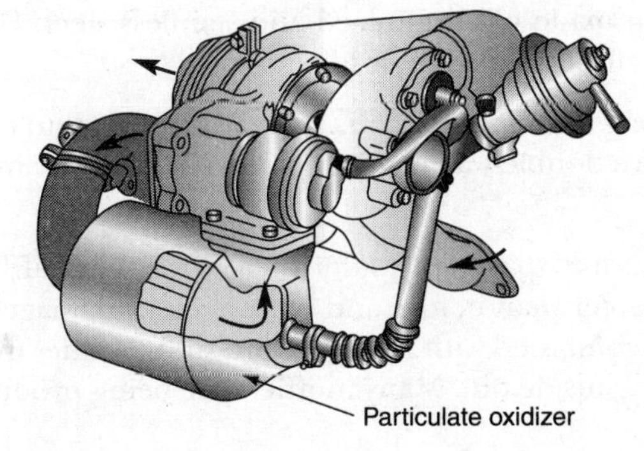

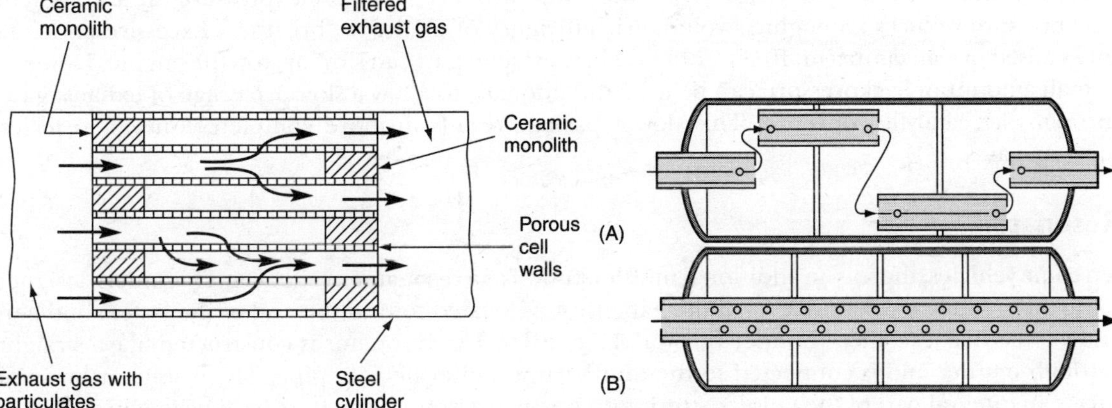

FIGURE 5-22 *Particulate catalytic converter.*

FIGURE 5-23 *(A) Reverse-flow muffler; (B) straight-through muffler.*

Some late model diesels are equipped with particulate traps that have the ability to be cleaned, called regeneration. These particulate traps are regenerated (cleaned) when the PCM adds an excess amount of fuel at certain times, causing the soot to burn off.

Mufflers

The **muffler** is an oval-shaped, or cylindrical, component made from coated and aluminized steel or stainless steel. Inlet and outlet pipes extend from the ends of the muffler. Inside the muffler, the exhaust gas flows through a series of perforated tubes and a tuning chamber to silence the exhaust. The perforated tubes inside the muffler cancel out and silence the pressure pulsations in the exhaust each time an exhaust valve opens. The muffler is located behind the catalytic converter in the exhaust system. On many vehicles, the muffler is positioned just behind the center of the vehicle, but space requirements on some vehicles demand muffler installation near the rear of the car. When the muffler is positioned near the rear of the vehicle, it runs cooler and may experience more internal condensation. Mufflers rust on the inside if excessive internal condensation occurs.

The most common type of muffler is the **reverse-flow muffler** (Figure 5-23), which changes the direction of exhaust flow inside the muffler. Some mufflers are a straight-through design in which the exhaust passes through a single perforated tube.

There have been several important changes in recent years in the design of mufflers. Most of these changes have been centered at reducing weight and emissions, improving fuel economy, and simplifying assembly. These changes include the following.

New Materials. More and more mufflers are being made of aluminized and stainless steel. Using these materials reduces the weight of the units as well as extends their life.

Double-Wall Design. Retarded engine ignition timing that is used on many small cars tends to make the exhaust pulses sharper. Many small cars now use a double-wall exhaust pipe to better contain the sound and reduce pipe ring.

Rear-Mounted Mufflers. More and more often, the only space left under the car for the muffler is at the very rear. This means that the muffler runs cooler than before and is more easily damaged by condensation in the exhaust system. This moisture, combined with nitrogen and sulfur oxides in the exhaust gas, forms acids that rot the muffler from the inside out. Many mufflers are being produced with drain holes drilled into them.

Backpressure. Even a well-designed muffler will produce some **backpressure** in the system. Backpressure reduces an engine's volumetric efficiency or ability to "breathe." Excessive backpressure caused by defects in a muffler or other exhaust system part can slow or stop the engine. However, a small amount of backpressure can be used intentionally to allow a slower passage of exhaust gases through the catalytic converter. This slower passage results in more complete conversion to less harmful gases.

Resonator

On some vehicles, there is an additional muffler known as a **resonator** or silencer. This unit is designed to further reduce the sound level of the exhaust. It is located toward the end of the system and generally looks like a smaller, rounder version of a muffler. The resonator is constructed like a straight-through muffler and is connected to the muffler by an intermediate pipe. The resonator on some cars is an integral part of the tailpipe, forming a one-piece unit. Resonators have been eliminated on nearly all late-model cars as manufacturers attempt to reduce production costs and weight.

Tailpipe

The **tailpipe** carries the flow of exhaust from the muffler to the rear of the vehicle. Some vehicles have an integral resonator in the tailpipe. This resonator is similar to a small muffler and provides additional exhaust silencing. In some exhaust systems, the resonator is clamped into the tailpipe. Tailpipes have many different bends to fit around the chassis and driveline components. All exhaust system components must be positioned away from the chassis and driveline to prevent rattling. The tailpipe usually extends under the rear bumper, and the end of this pipe is cut at an angle to deflect the exhaust downward. Chrome tailpipe extensions are available in auto parts stores. These extensions are attached to the tailpipe with lock screws.

Heat Shields, Clamps, Gaskets, and Hangers

Since exhaust system components become extremely hot, many vehicles have heat shields between some of these components and the chassis (Figure 5-24). Without the heat shields, some chassis components such as the floor pan may become hot enough to burn the padding under the floor mat.

Hangers are used to secure the exhaust system components to the chassis without transferring engine vibration to the chassis. The hanger is clamped to an exhaust system component, and a hanger bracket is bolted to the chassis (Figure 5-25). A piece of fabric-reinforced rubber between the hanger clamp and bracket prevents vibration transfer from the exhaust system to the chassis. Exhaust system clamps are bolts curved into a U-shape with two nuts that retain a bar across the U-shaped bolt.

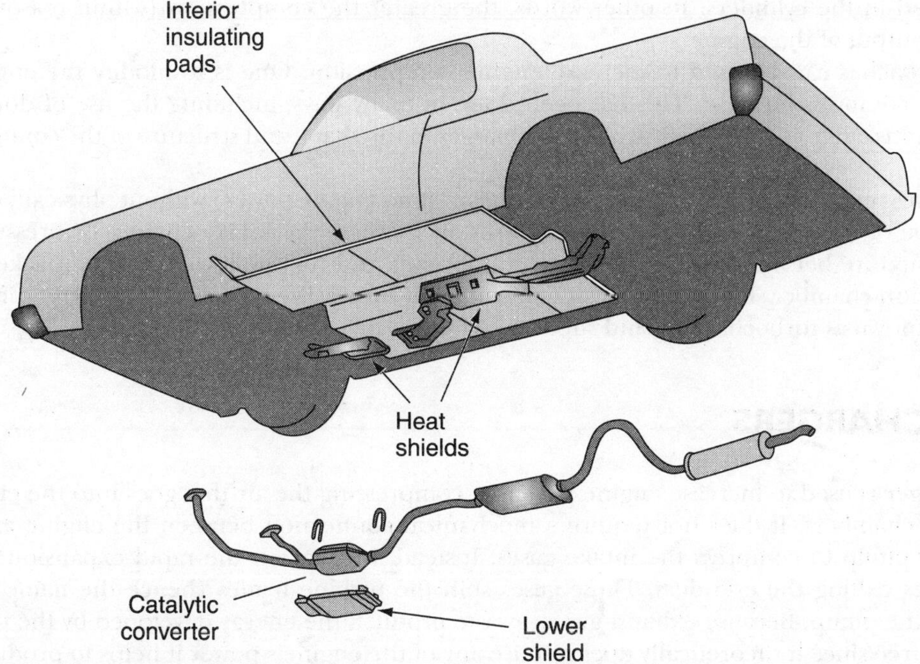

FIGURE 5-24 *Location of heat shields.*

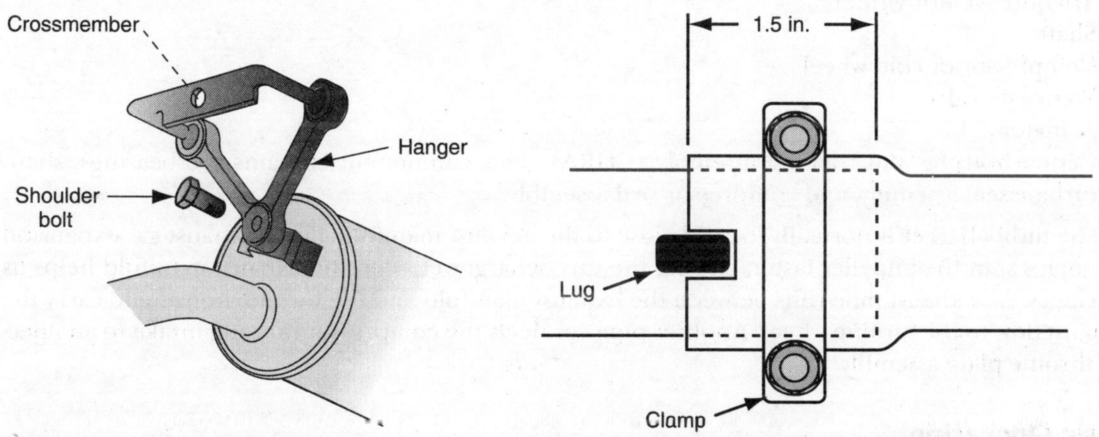

FIGURE 5-25 *Exhaust system hanger.*

FIGURE 5-26 *Exhaust pipe clamp installation.*

Exhaust system components, such as the muffler and exhaust pipe, are designed to slide over each other. These exhaust system components should overlap 1.5 to 3 inches and the clamp should be installed between the center and end of this overlap (Figure 5-26). When the clamp is tightened, the two pipes are squeezed together to prevent component movement and provide a seal between the pipes.

FORCED INDUCTION

The power generated by the internal combustion engine is directly related to the amount of air that is compressed in the cylinders. In other words, the greater the compression (within reason), the greater the output of the engine.

Two approaches can be used to increase engine compression. One is to modify the engine to increase the compression ratio. This has been done in many ways, including the use of domes or high-top pistons, altered crankshaft strokes, or changes in the shape and structure of the combustion chamber.

Another, less expensive way to increase compression (and engine power) without physically changing the shape of the combustion chamber is to simply increase the intake charge. By pressurizing the intake mixture before it enters the cylinder, more air and fuel molecules can be packed into the combustion chamber. The two processes of artificially increasing the amount of airflow into the engine are known as turbocharging and supercharging.

TURBOCHARGERS

A **turbocharger** is used to increase engine power by compressing the air that goes into the engine's combustion chambers. It does not require a mechanical connection between the engine and the pressurizing pump to compress the intake gases. Instead, it relies on the rapid expansion of hot exhaust gases exiting the cylinders. These gases spin the turbine blades (hence the name turbocharger) of the pump. Because exhaust gas is a waste product, the energy developed by the turbine is said to be free since it theoretically does not use any of the engine's power it helps to produce.

A typical turbocharger, usually called a turbo, consists of the following components (Figure 5-27):

- Turbine or hot wheel
- Shaft
- Compressor or cold wheel
- Wastegate valve
- Actuator
- Center housing and rotating assembly (CHRA). This component contains the bearings, shaft, turbine seal assembly, and compressor seal assembly.

The turbocharger is normally located close to the exhaust manifold. Since exhaust gas expansion also helps spin the impeller faster, placing the turbocharger close to the exhaust manifold helps its efficiency. An exhaust pipe runs between the exhaust manifold and the turbine housing to carry the exhaust flow to the turbine wheel. Another pipe connects the compressor housing intake to an injector throttle plate assembly.

Basic Operation

A turbocharger contains a turbine wheel and a compressor wheel mounted on a common shaft. This shaft is supported on bearings in the turbocharger housing, and both wheels contain blades. The exhaust gas from the cylinders is directed past the turbine wheel, and the force of the exhaust gas against the turbine wheel blades causes the turbine wheel and shaft to rotate. Since the compressor wheel is positioned on the opposite end of this shaft, the compressor wheel must rotate with the shaft (Figure 5-28).

The compressor wheel is mounted in the air intake and as the compressor wheel rotates, it forces air into the intake manifold. Since most turbocharged engines are port injected, the fuel is injected into the intake ports. The rotation of the compressor wheel compresses the air and fuel in the intake manifold, creating a denser air-fuel mixture. This increased intake manifold pressure forces more air-fuel mixture into the cylinders to provide increased engine power.

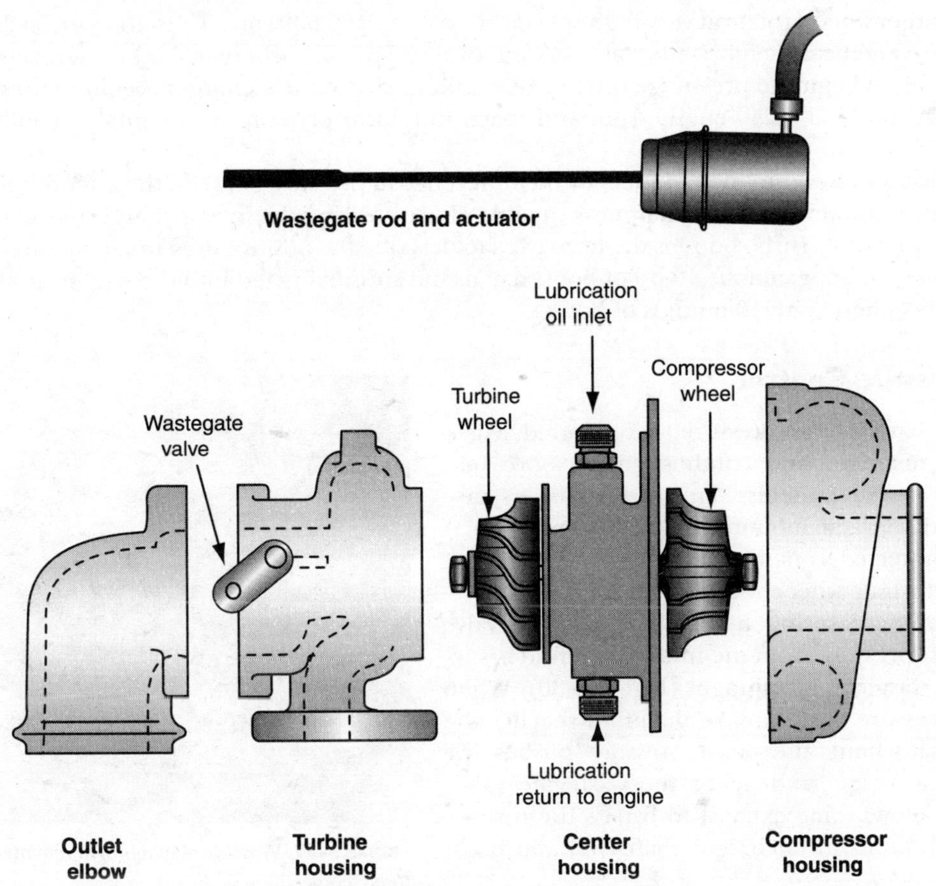

FIGURE 5-27 *Cross section of a turbocharger shows the turbine wheel, the compressor wheel, and their connecting shaft.*

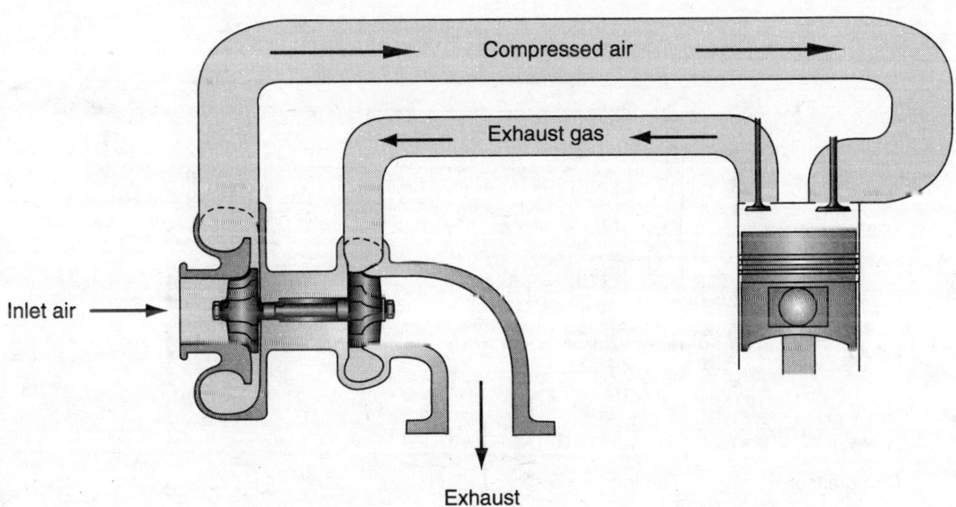

FIGURE 5-28 *Basic turbocharger with turbine and compressor wheel.*

Turbocharger wheels rotate at very high speeds in excess of 100,000 rpm. Therefore, turbocharger wheel balance and bearing lubrication are very important. The turbocharger shaft must reach a certain rpm before it begins to pressurize the intake manifold. Some turbochargers begin to pressurize the intake manifold at 1,250 engine rpm and reach full boost pressure in the intake manifold at 2,250 rpm.

Air is typically drawn into the cylinders by the difference in pressure between the atmosphere and engine vacuum. However, a turbocharger is capable of pressurizing the intake charge above normal atmospheric pressure. Turbo boost is the term used to describe the positive pressure increase created by a turbocharger. For example, 10 psi of boost means the air is being fed into the engine at 24.7 psi (14.7 psi atmospheric plus 10 pounds of boost).

Boost Pressure Control

If the turbocharger boost pressure is not limited, excessive intake manifold and combustion pressure may damage engine components. Many turbochargers have a **wastegate** diaphragm mounted on the turbocharger. A linkage is connected from this diaphragm to a wastegate valve in the turbine wheel housing (Figure 5-29).

The diaphragm spring holds the wastegate valve closed. Boost pressure from the intake manifold is supplied to the wastegate diaphragm (Figure 5-30). When the boost pressure in the intake manifold reaches the maximum safe limit, the boost pressure pushes the wastegate diaphragm and opens the wastegate valve. This action allows some exhaust to bypass the turbine wheel, which limits turbocharger shaft rpm and boost pressure.

FIGURE 5-29 *Wastegate diaphragm mounted to a turbocharger.*

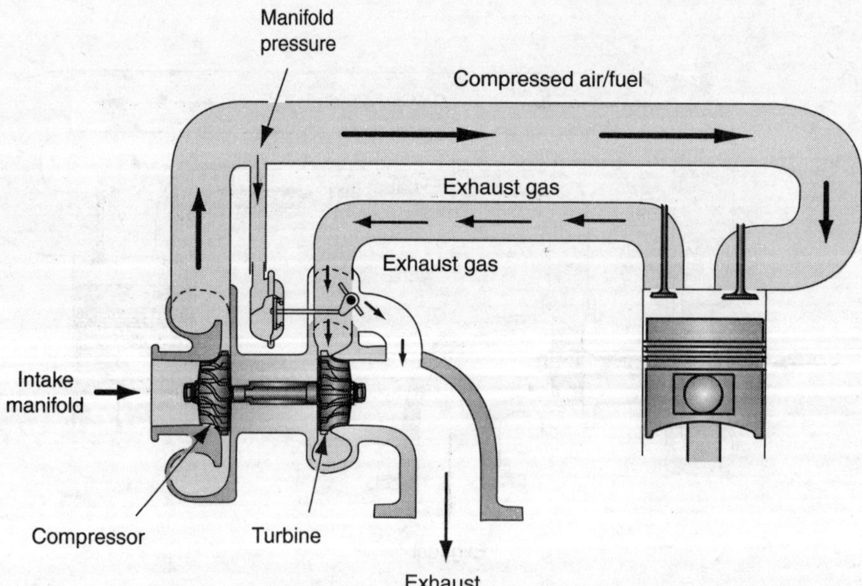

FIGURE 5-30 *A boost pressure hose is connected from the intake manifold to the wastegate diaphragm.*

On some engines, the boost pressure supplied to the wastegate diaphragm is controlled by a computer-operated solenoid. In many systems, the PCM pulses the wastegate solenoid on and off to control boost pressure. Some computers are programmed to momentarily allow a higher boost pressure on sudden acceleration to improve engine performance.

Turbocharger Cooling

Exhaust flow past the turbine wheel creates very high turbocharger temperature, especially under high engine load conditions. Many turbochargers have coolant lines connected from the turbocharger housing to the cooling system (Figure 5-31). Coolant circulation through the turbocharger housing helps to cool the bearings and shaft. Full oil pressure is supplied from the main oil gallery to the turbocharger bearings and shaft to lubricate and cool the bearings. This oil is drained from the turbocharger housing back into the crankcase. Seals on the turbocharger shaft prevent oil leaks into the compressor or turbine wheel housings. Worn turbocharger seals allow oil into the compressor or turbine wheel housings, resulting in blue smoke in the exhaust and oil consumption. Some heat is also dissipated from the turbocharger to the surrounding air.

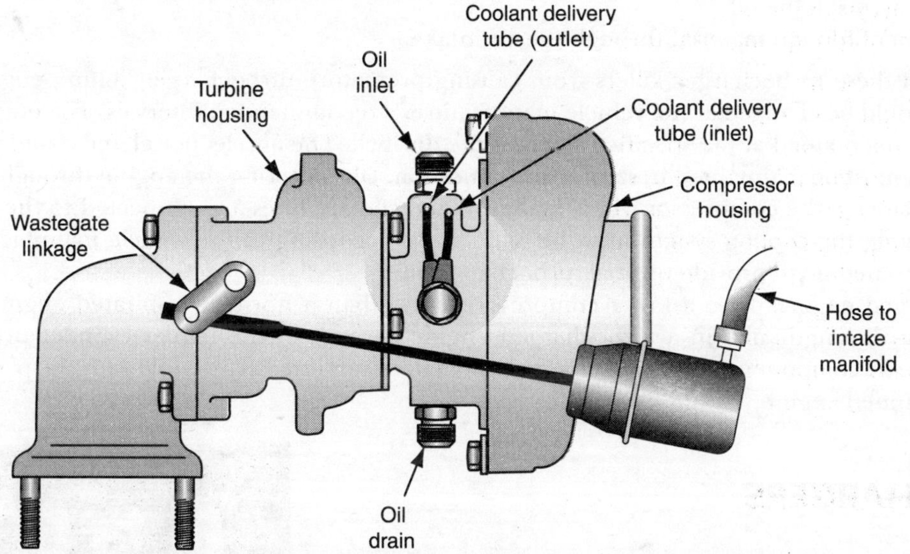

Figure 5-31 *Coolant lines connected to the turbocharger housing.*

Some turbochargers do not have coolant lines connected to the turbocharger housing. These units depend on oil and air cooling. On these units, if the engine is shut off immediately after heavy-load or high-speed operation, the oil may burn to some extent in the turbocharger bearings. When this action occurs, hard carbon particles, which destroy the turbocharger bearings, are created. The coolant circulation through the turbocharger housing lowers the bearing temperature to help prevent this problem. When turbochargers that depend on oil and air cooling have been operating at heavy load or high speed, idle the engine for at least 1 minute before shutting it off. This action will help to prevent turbocharger bearing failure.

Retarding spark timing is an often-used method of controlling detonation on turbocharged engine systems. Unfortunately, any time the ignition is permanently retarded to prevent detonation, power is lost, fuel economy suffers, and the engine tends to run hotter. Because of these trade-offs, most systems use knock-sensing devices to retard timing only when detonation is detected.

Computer-controlled devices limit the amount of boost to prevent detonation and engine damage. In fact, some turbocharging systems on computer-controlled vehicles use an electronic control unit to operate the wastegate control valve through sensor signals.

Turbo Lag

Increases in horsepower are normally evidenced by an engine's response to a quick opening of the throttle. The lack of throttle response is felt with some turbocharged systems. This delay, or turbo lag, occurs because exhaust gas requires a little time to build enough energy to spin the blower up to speed.

Turbo lag occurs when the turbocharger is unable to meet the immediate demands of the engine. This causes the power from the engine to temporarily lag behind the need.

Scheduled Maintenance

Three main turbocharger killers are:

1. Lack of oil
2. Contaminants in the oil
3. Ingestion of foreign material through the air intake

To prevent these turbocharger killers from causing premature turbocharger failure, engine oil and filters should be changed at the vehicle manufacturer's recommended intervals. The engine oil level must be maintained at the specified level on the dipstick. The air cleaner element and the air intake system must be maintained in satisfactory condition. Dirt entering the engine through an air cleaner will damage the compressor wheel blades. When coolant lines are connected to the turbocharger housing, the cooling system must be maintained according to the vehicle manufacturer's maintenance schedule to provide normal turbocharger life.

Turbocharged engines have a lower compression ratio than a normally aspirated engine, and many parts are strengthened in a turbocharged engine because of the higher cylinder pressure. Therefore, many components in a turbocharged engine are not interchangeable with the parts in a normally aspirated engine.

SUPERCHARGERS

Supercharging fascinated auto engineers even before they decided to steer with a wheel instead of a tiller. The 1906 American Chadwick had a **supercharger**. Since then many manufacturers have equipped engines with superchargers. Supercharged Dusenbergs, HispanoSuizas, and Mercedes-Benzes were giants among luxury-car marques as well as winners on the race tracks in the 1920s and 1930s. Then, after World War II, supercharging started to fade, although both Ford and American Motors sold supercharged passenger cars into the late 1950s. However, after being displaced first by larger V8 engines then by turbochargers, the supercharger started to make a comeback with 1989 models. Some automobile manufacturers are offering superchargers on performance cars as an alternative to the turbo (Figure 5-32).

FIGURE 5-32 *A supercharger installed on a V6 engine.*

Basic Design

The supercharger is belt-driven from the crankshaft by a ribbed V-belt (Figure 5-33). A shaft is connected from the pulley to one of the drive gears in the front supercharger housing, and the driven gear is meshed with the drive gear. The rotors inside the supercharger are attached to the two drive gears (Figure 5-34).

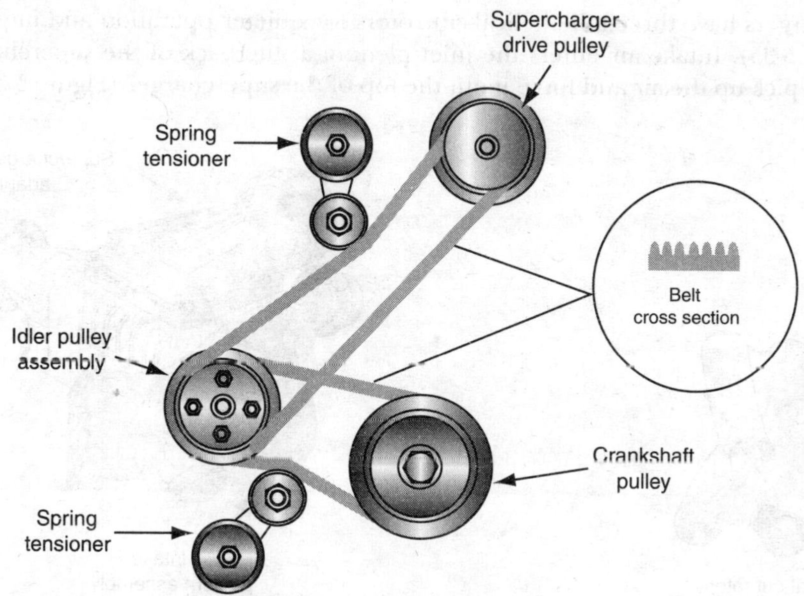

Figure 5-33 *Supercharger pulleys and drive belts.*

Figure 5-34 *Supercharger gears.*

The drive gear design prevents the rotors from touching. However, there is a very small clearance between the drive gears. In some superchargers, the rotor shafts are supported by roller bearings on the front and needle bearings on the back. During the manufacturing process, the needle bearings are permanently lubricated. The ball bearings are lubricated by a synthetic base high-speed gear oil. A plug is provided for periodic checks of the front bearing lubricant. Front bearing seals prevent lubricant loss into the supercharger housing.

Supercharger Operation

Many superchargers have three-lobe helical-cut rotors for quieter operation and improved performance (Figure 5-35). Intake air enters the inlet plenum at the back of the supercharger and the rotating blades pick up the air and force it out the top of the supercharger (Figure 5-36).

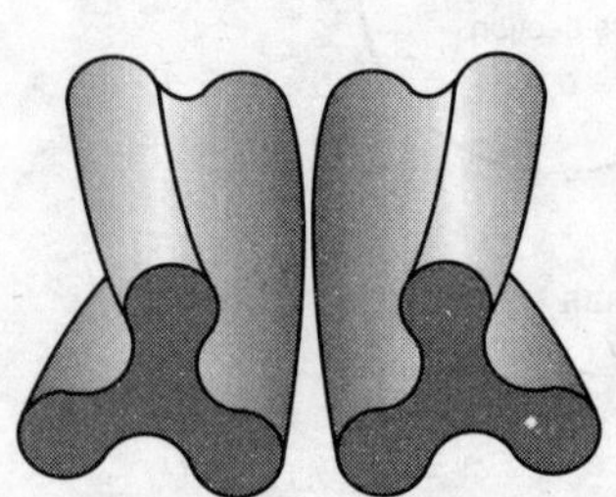

FIGURE 5-35 *Supercharger rotor design.*

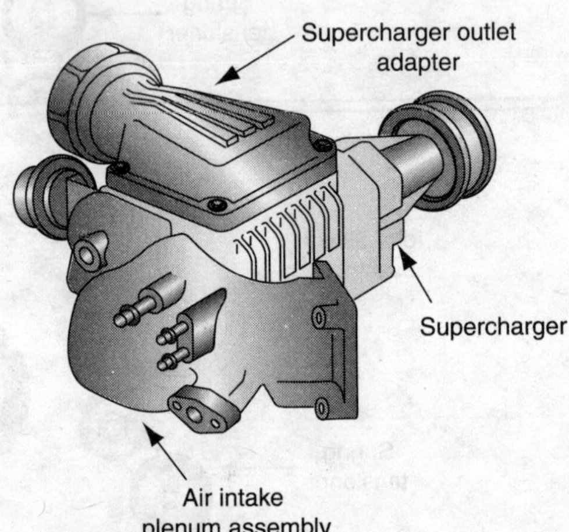

FIGURE 5-36 *Supercharger air inlet and outlet housings.*

The blades rotate in opposite directions and act like a pump as they rotate. This pumping action pulls air through the supercharger inlet and forces the air from the outlet. There is a very small clearance between the meshed rotor lobes and between the rotor lobes and the housing (Figure 5-37).

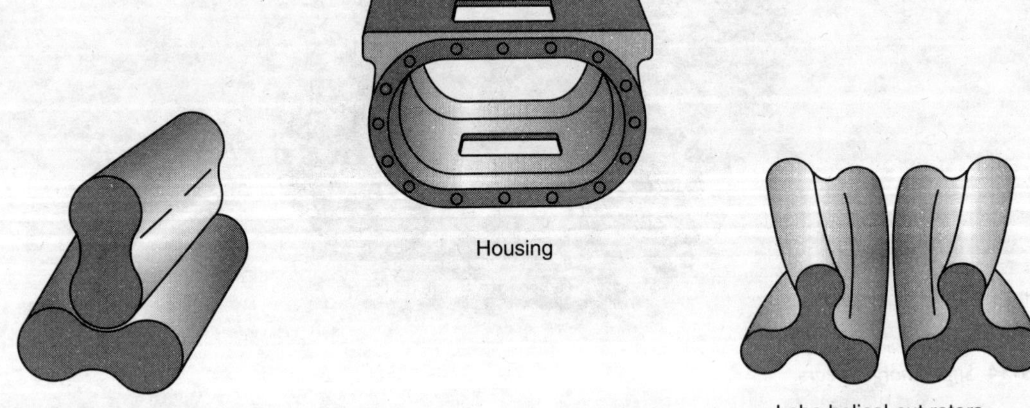

FIGURE 5-37 *Straight- and helical-cut rotors.*

Air flows through the supercharger system components in the following order:

1. Air flows through the air cleaner and mass air flow sensor into the throttle body. (The air cleaner and mass air flow sensor are not shown.)
2. Airflow enters the supercharger intake plenum.
3. From the intake plenum, the air flows into the rear of the supercharger housing (Figure 5-38).

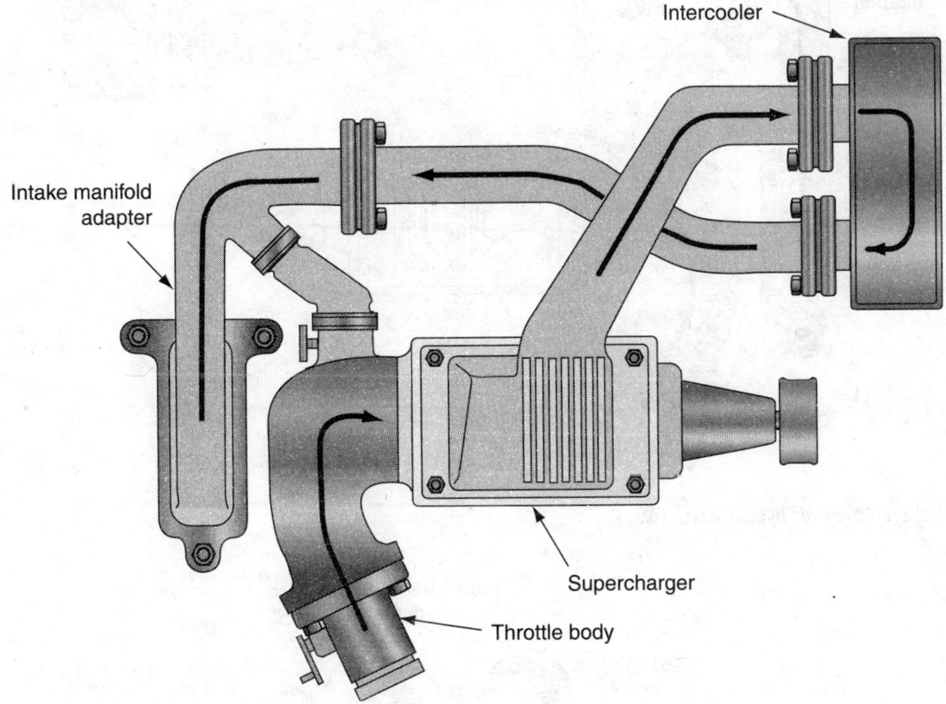

FIGURE 5-38 *Supercharger air flow.*

4. The compressed air flows from the supercharger to the intercooler inlet.
5. Air leaves the intercooler and flows into the intercooler outlet tube.
6. Air flows from the intercooler outlet tube into the intake manifold adapter.
7. Compressed, cooled air flows through the intake manifold into the engine cylinders.
8. If the engine is operating at idle or very low speeds, the supercharger is not required. Under this condition, airflow is bypassed from the supercharger through a butterfly valve to the intake manifold adapter (Figure 5-39).

The bypass butterfly valve (Figure 5-40) is operated by an air bypass actuator diaphragm as follows:

1. When manifold vacuum is 7 in. Hg or higher, the bypass butterfly valve is completely open, and a high percentage of the supercharger air is bypassed to the supercharger inlet.
2. If the manifold vacuum is 3 to 7 in. Hg, the bypass butterfly valve is partially open and some supercharger air is bypassed to the supercharger inlet while the remaining air flow is forced into the engine cylinders.
3. When the vacuum is less than 3 in. Hg, the bypass butterfly valve is closed and all the supercharger airflow is forced into the engine cylinders.

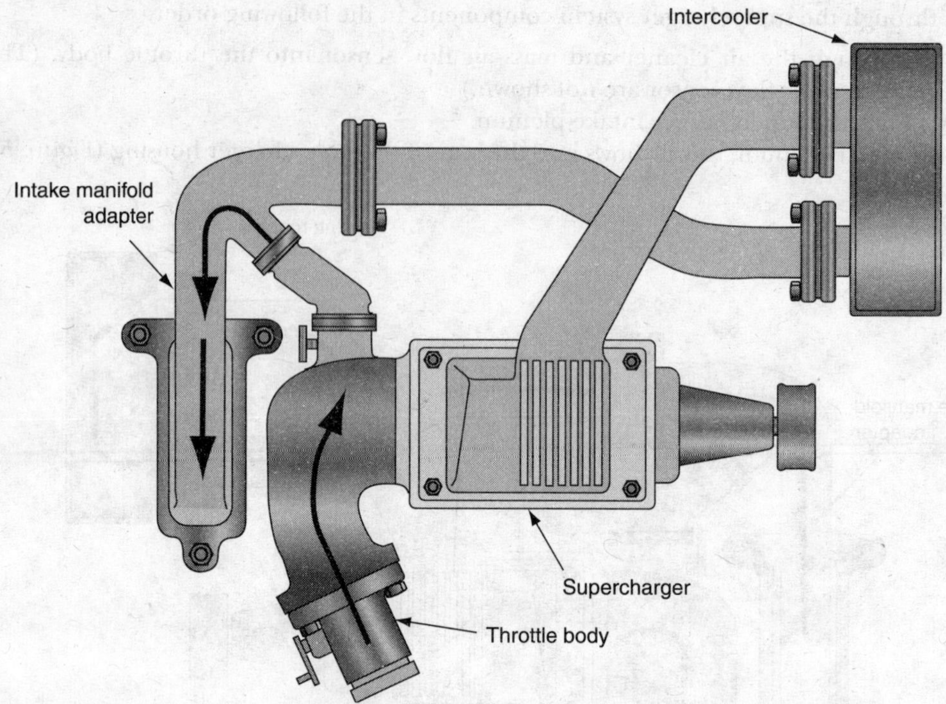

FIGURE 5-39 *Supercharger air bypass actuator.*

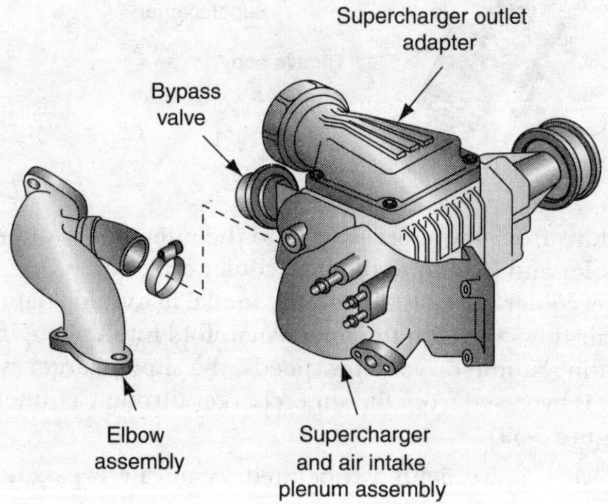

FIGURE 5-40 *Supercharger bypass hose and intake elbow.*

On some superchargers, the pulley size causes the rotors to turn at 2.6 times the engine speed. Since supercharger speed is limited by engine speed, a supercharger wastegate is not required.

Belt-driven superchargers provide instant low-speed action compared to exhaust-driven turbochargers, which may have a low-speed lag because of the brief time interval required to accelerate the turbocharger shaft. Compared to a turbocharger, a supercharger turns at much lower speed.

Friction between the air and the rotors heats the air as it flows through the supercharger. The intercooler dissipates heat from the air in the supercharger system to the atmosphere, creating a denser air charge. When the supercharger and the intercooler supply cooled, compressed air to the cylinders, engine power and performance are improved.

A Ford supercharged 3.8-L engine provides 210 hp at 4,000 rpm and 315 ft. lb. of torque at 2,600 rpm. A Ford turbocharged 3.8-L engine provides 190 hp at 4,600 rpm and 240 ft. lb. torque at 3,400 rpm. Therefore, the supercharged engine produces more horsepower and torque at a lower rpm.

The compression ratio in the supercharged 3.8-L engine is 8.2:1 compared to a normally aspirated 3.8-L engine, which has a 9.0:1 compression ratio. The following components are reinforced in the supercharged engine because of the higher cylinder pressure:

Engine block	Timing chain
Main bearings	Cylinder head
Crankshaft bearing caps	Head bolts
Crankshaft	Rocker arms
Steel crankshaft sprocket	

Supercharger Designs

While there have been a number of supercharger designs on the market over the years, the most popular is the **Roots-type**. The pair of three lobed rotor vanes in the Roots supercharger is driven by the crankshaft. The lobes force air into the intake manifold.

Of course, the key to the supercharger's operation is primarily the design of the rotors. Some Roots-type superchargers use straight-lobe rotors that result in uneven pressure pulses and, consequently, relatively high noise levels. Therefore, the supercharger used with most of today's engines uses a helical design for the two rotors. The helical design evens out the pressure pulses in the blower and reduces noise. It was found that a 60-degree helical twist works best for equalizing the inlet and outlet volumes.

Another benefit of the helical rotor design is it reduces carryback volumes—air that is carried back to the inlet side of the supercharger because of the unavoidable spaces between the meshing rotors—which represents a loss of efficiency.

The rotors are held in a proper relationship to each other by timing gears. They are supported by ball bearings in the front and needle roller bearings in the back. The needle bearings are greased for life. The ball bearings are generally lubricated by gear oil, and a plug is provided for periodic checks of the oil level at the ball bearings. The oil is a synthetic base specifically produced for high-speed use. When servicing the gear case, it is very important to keep out dirt and moisture.

To handle the higher operating temperatures imposed by supercharging, an engine oil cooler is usually built into the engine system. This water-to-oil cooler is generally mounted between the engine front cover and oil filter.

Superchargers can be enhanced with electrically operated clutches and bypass valves. These allow the same computer that controls fuel and ignition to kick the boost on and off precisely as needed. This results in far greater efficiency than a full-time supercharger.

Another popular supercharger design, especially in Europe, is the G-Lader supercharger which is based on a 1905 French design. As shown in Figure 5-41, spiral ramps in both sides of the rotor intermesh with similar ramps in the housing. Unlike most superchargers, the rotor of the G-Lader does not spin on its axis; rather, it moves around an eccentric shaft. This motion draws air in and squeezes it inward through the spiral, which compresses it, then forces it through ducts in the center into the engine. Airflow is essentially constant, so intake noise is lower than that of a Roots blower. Because there is only a slight wiping motion between the spiral and housing, wear is minimal.

A comparison of supercharger and turbocharger operations is given in Figure 5-42.

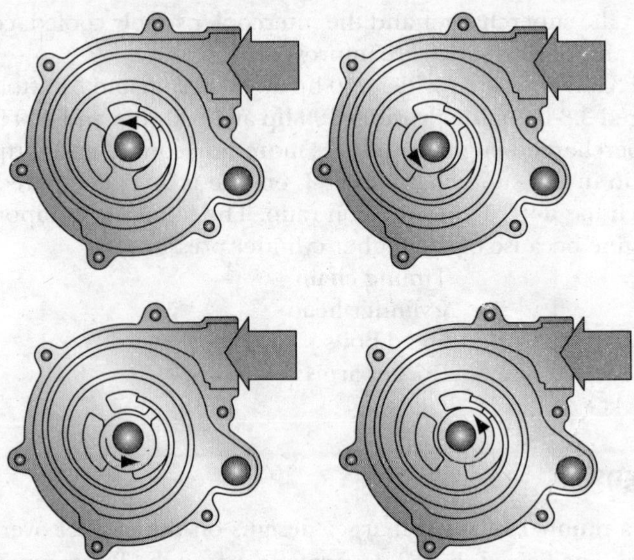

FIGURE 5-41 *Operation of a G-Lader supercharger.*

COMPARISON OF SUPERCHARGER VS TURBOCHARGER

	Supercharger	Turbocharger
Efficiency loss	Mechanical friction and power to rotate	Increased exhaust backpressure
Packaging	Belt driven	Major revisions required to package—new exhaust manifold
Lube system	Self-contained	Uses engine oil and coolant
System noise	Pressure pulsation and gear noise	High-frequency whine and wastegate
Durability	In use by OEMs; seems to be durable	In use by OEMs; improvements have been made and durability has increased
Performance	30% to 40% power increase over naturally aspirated Better low-end torque No lag—dramatic improvement in startup and passing acceleration, particularly with automatic transmission	30% to 40% power increase over naturally aspirated No loss of horsepower to operate
Temperatures	No change from naturally aspirated	Increased underhood temperatures

FIGURE 5-42 *Comparison of supercharger versus turbocharger.*

INTERCOOLERS

The **intercooler** (Figure 5-43) cools the air from a supercharger or turbocharger before it reaches the combustion chamber. Cooling the air makes it denser. Therefore, its oxygen content increases and increases the engine's power from a given boost pressure. It also lowers the temperature produced in the combustion chamber. These factors help reduce engine knock and increase engine output. Intercoolers are like radiators in that heat from the air passing through it is removed and

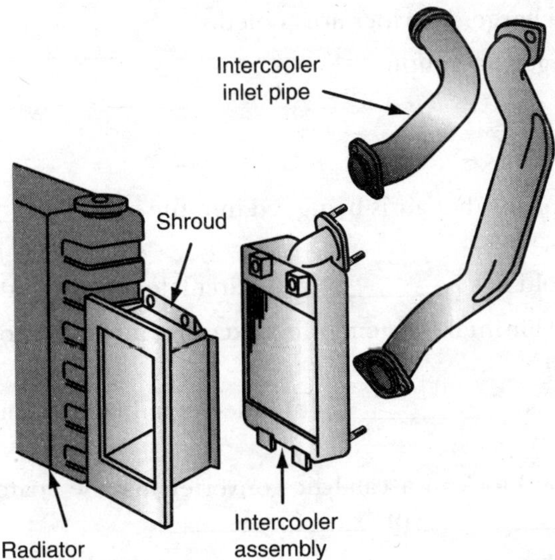

FIGURE 5-43 *A typical intercooler system.*

dissipated to the atmosphere. An air-to-air intercooler is normally located next to the conventional engine cooling radiator. Intercoolers can be air or water cooled.

Without an intercooler, the pressurized air is very hot. When this hot air is compressed during the engine's compression stroke, it will become even hotter. The hot air-fuel mixture in the cylinder may ignite on its own and at the wrong time, resulting in detonation.

A turbocharger or supercharger changes the effective compression ratio of an engine simply by packing in air that has a pressure greater than atmospheric pressure. For example, an engine that has a compression ratio of 8:1 and receives 10 pounds of boost will have an effective compression ratio of 10.5:1. This is why these boost devices increase power.

As air pressure increases, the temperature of the air also increases. The idea behind an intercooler is simply to let the turbocharger or supercharger increase the pressure of air. Then let's remove heat from the air. This allows cool, dense, high-pressure air to enter the cylinders.

REVIEW QUESTIONS

Short Answer Essays

1. List the purposes of the air cleaner on various engines.
2. Describe the effect of CAFE regulations on vehicles produced by manufacturers.
3. Describe the difference in the intake manifold of a port fuel vehicle versus one utilizing throttle body injection.
4. Describe intake manifold vacuum and how it is created.
5. Explain the operation of a three-way catalyst.
6. Explain how a turbocharger or supercharger supplies more engine power.
7. Describe basic turbocharger operation.
8. Describe how the PCM controls turbocharger boost pressure.

9. Describe how the turbocharger bearings are cooled.
10. Explain basic supercharger operation.

Fill-in-the-Blanks

1. Ten psi of turbo boost means that air is being fed into the engine at ________________ when the engine is operating at sea level.
2. A wet-type intake manifold has ________________ circulated through the manifold.
3. If any component in the air intake system offers excessive air restriction, ________________ ________________ is reduced.
4. Intake manifold vacuum is ________________ at wide-open throttle compared to the intake manifold vacuum at idle speed.
5. The honeycomb ceramic block in a catalytic converter may be coated with ________________ ________________ ________________ or ________________.
6. The exhaust flows past the ________________ wheel in a turbocharger.
7. The intake airflow is forced into the intake manifold by the ________________ wheel in a turbocharger.
8. The wastegate diaphragm is moved by ________________ pressure from the ________________ ________________.
9. A supercharger is ________________-driven from the engine.
10. Supercharger rotor speed is limited by ________________ ________________.

Multiple Choice

1. *Technician A* says that a three-way converter reduces NO_x emissions.

   Technician B says that a three-way converter oxidizes HC and CO.

   Who is correct?

   A. Technician A C. Both technicians
   B. Technician B D. Neither technician

2. *Technician A* says that a port fuel injected intake manifold can be designed for maximum efficiency since it contains only the air charge.

   Technician B says that a port fuel intake manifold needs to be heated by the exhaust manifold.

   Who is correct?

   A. Technician A C. Both technicians
   B. Technician B D. Neither technician

3. While discussing modern intake systems;

   Technician A says that they contain an EBM.

   Technician B says that they contain a CTS.

   Who is correct?

   A. Technician A C. Both technicians
   B. Technician B D. Neither technician

4. *Technician A* says that port fuel injection systems intake manifold runners are designed to be a certain length.

   Technician B says that the runners in the manifold are designed to provide a ram air effect.

   A. Technician A C. Both technicians
   B. Technician B D. Neither technician

5. *Technician A* says that the exhaust is routed past the compressor wheel of the turbocharger.

   Technician B says that the exhaust is routed past the turbine wheel.

   Who is correct?

   A. Technician A C. Both technicians
   B. Technician B D. Neither technician

6. All of the following components are part of the turbocharger ***except***

   A. turbine or hot wheel
   B. shaft
   C. waste gate valve
   D. resonator valve

7. *Technician A* says that the supercharger is belt driven.

   Technician B says that a supercharger uses a waste gate to control boost pressures.

   Who is correct?

   A. Technician A C. Both technicians
   B. Technician B D. Neither technician

8. *Technician A* says the turbocharger can utilize an intercooler.

   Technician B says that the supercharger can utilize an intercooler.

   Who is correct?

   A. Technician A C. Both technicians
   B. Technician B D. Neither technicians

9. *Technician A* says earlier TBI systems required a heated intake manifold.

   Technician B says that port fuel injection intakes do not need extra heat since the manifold only carries air.

   Who is correct?

   A. Technician A C. Both technicians
   B. Technician B D. Neither technician

10. *Technician A* says that the intake air temperature (IAT) sensor can be located in the air cleaner assembly.

    Technician B says that the IAT sensor can be located in the intake manifold.

    Who is correct?

    A. Technician A C. Both technicians
    B. Technician B D. Neither technician

INPUT SENSORS

6

Upon completion and review of this chapter, you should be able to:

- Explain the difference between analog and digital voltage signals.
- Explain binary coding as it relates to computer input signals.
- Describe the design and operation of the oxygen sensor.
- Explain the importance of the engine coolant temperature sensor signal in relation to the output control functions of the computer.
- Describe the operation of the intake air temperature sensor.
- Explain the wiring connections located on the throttle position sensor.
- Describe two types of voltage signals produced by manifold absolute pressure sensors.
- Explain the operation of three different types of mass air flow (MAF) sensors.
- Describe the operation of a knock sensor.
- Explain the purpose of the exhaust gas recirculation valve position sensor.
- Identify the output control functions affected by the vehicle speed sensor signal.

INTRODUCTION

Computer input signals must be understood in order for the technician to effectively diagnose problems as they arise. Sensors can be used to indicate mechanical movement, position, or temperature. Most sensors can be classified as voltage generating or reference voltage types. In this chapter we will look at analog and digital signals, signal conditioning, and amplification.

SENSORS

The PCM receives inputs that it checks with programmed values. Depending on the input, the computer will control the actuator(s) until the programmed results are obtained. The inputs can come from other computers, the driver, the technician, or through a variety of sensors.

Driver input signals are usually provided by momentarily applying a ground through a switch. The computer receives this signal and performs the desired functions. For example, if the driver wishes to reset the trip odometer on a digital instrument panel, a reset button is depressed. This switch provides a momentary ground that the computer receives as an input and sets the trip odometer to zero.

Switches can be used as an input for any operation that only requires a yes–no or on–off condition. Other inputs include those supplied by means of a sensor and those signals returned to the computer in the form of **feedback**. Feedback means that data concerning the effects of the computer's commands are fed back to the computer as an input signal.

If the computer sends a command signal to actuate an output device, a feedback signal may be sent back from the actuator to inform the computer that the task was performed. The feedback signal will confirm both the position of the output device and the operation of the actuator. Another form of feedback is for the computer to monitor voltage as a switch, relay, or other actuator is activated. Changing positions of an actuator should result in predictable changes in the computer's voltage sensing circuit. The computer may set a diagnostic code if it does not receive the correct feedback signal.

All sensors perform the same basic function. They detect a mechanical condition (movement or position), chemical state, or temperature condition and change it into an electrical signal that can be used by the computer to make decisions. The PCM makes decisions based on information it receives from sensors. Each sensor used in a particular system has a specific job to do (for example, monitor throttle position, vehicle speed, manifold pressure). Together these sensors provide enough information to help the computer form a complete picture of vehicle operation. Even though there are a variety of different sensor designs, they all fall under one of two operating categories: reference voltage sensors or voltage generating sensors

Reference Voltage Sensors

Reference voltage (Vref) sensors provide input to the computer by modifying or controlling a constant, predetermined voltage signal. This signal, which can have a reference value from 5 volts to 9 volts is generated and sent out to each sensor by a reference voltage regulator located inside the PCM. Because the computer knows that a certain voltage value has been sent out, it can indirectly interpret things like motion, temperature, and component position based on what comes back. For example, consider the operation of the throttle position (TP) sensor. During acceleration (from idle to wide-open throttle), the computer monitors throttle plate movement based on the changing reference voltage signal returned by the TP sensor. (The TP sensor is a type of variable resistor known as a rotary potentiometer that changes circuit resistance based on throttle shaft rotation.) As TP sensor resistance varies, the computer is programmed to respond in a specific manner (for example, increase fuel delivery or alter spark timing) to each corresponding voltage change.

Most sensors presently in use are variable resistors or potentiometers (Figure 6-1). They modify a voltage to or from the computer, indicating a constantly changing status that can be calculated, compensated for, and modified. That is, these sensors simply modify a voltage signal from the computer. When varying internal resistance of the sensor allows more or less voltage to ground, the computer senses a voltage change on a monitored signal line. The monitored signal line may be the output signal from the computer to the sensor (one-and-two-wire sensors), or the computer may use a separate return line from the sensor to monitor voltage changes (three-wire sensors).

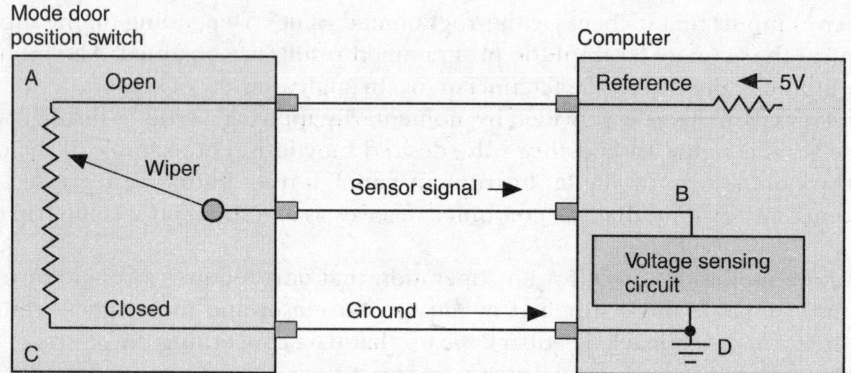

FIGURE 6-1 *A potentiometer sensor circuit measures the amount of voltage drop to determine the position of something, such as the A/C door shown in the illustration.*

Another commonly used variable resistor is a thermistor. A thermistor is a solid-state variable resistor made from a semiconductor material that changes resistance in relation to temperature changes. Thermistors are used to monitor engine coolant, intake air, and ambient temperatures. By monitoring the thermistor's resistance value, the PCM is capable of observing small changes in temperature. The PCM sends a reference voltage to the thermistor, normally 5 volts, through a fixed resistor. As the current flows through the thermistor to ground, voltage is dropped by the thermistor. A voltage sensing circuit compares the voltage sent out by the PCM to the voltage returned to the PCM and determines the voltage drop. Using its programmed values, the computer is able to translate the voltage drop into a temperature reading.

There are two basic types of thermistors: NTC and PTC. A **negative temperature coefficient (NTC)** thermistor reduces its resistance as temperature increases. This type is the most commonly used thermistor. A **positive temperature coefficient (PTC)** thermistor increases its resistance with an increase in temperature. In order to diagnose thermistors accurately, you must be able to identify the type by looking at a wiring diagram.

Wheatstone bridges (Figure 6-2) are also used as variable resistance sensors. These are typically constructed of four resistors connected in series-parallel between an input terminal and a ground terminal. Three of the resistors are kept at the same value. The fourth resistor is a sensing resistor. When all four of the resistors have the same value, the bridge is balanced and the voltage sensor will have a value of 0 volts. If the sensing resistor changes value, a change will occur in the circuit's balance. The sensing circuit will receive a voltage reading that is proportional to the amount of resistance change. If the Wheatstone bridge is used to measure temperature, temperature changes will be indicated as a change in voltage by the sensing circuit. Wheatstone bridges are also used to measure pressure **(piezoresistive)** and mechanical strain.

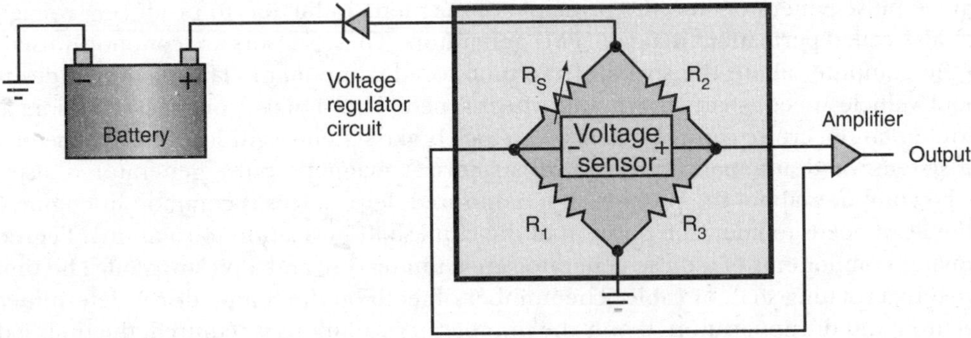

Figure 6–2 *Wheatstone bridge.*

Wheatstone bridges are one of the components used in the **manifold absolute pressure** (MAP) sensor. The MAP sensor changes resistance and therefore output voltage because of a membrane inside the sensor that is printed with piezoelectric strain gauges. The membrane responds to manifold pressure either through a hose or is attached directly to the manifold itself (Figure 6-3). A very similar sensor measures fuel tank pressure that is used by the PCM to help determine the presence of leaks in the evaporative control system (Figure 6-4). We will be discussing these sensors in more detail later.

Figure 6-3 *Typical MAP sensor.*

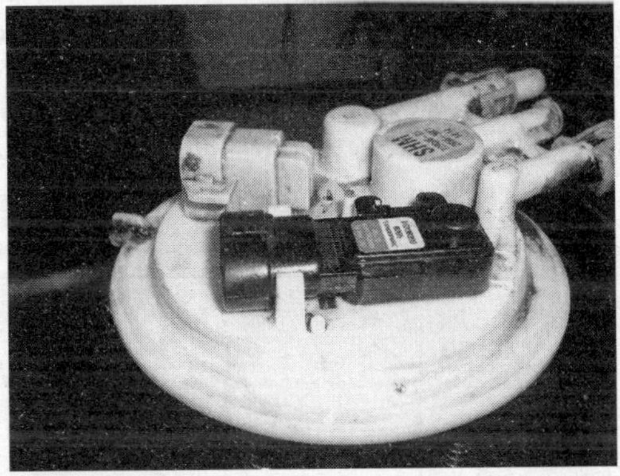

Figure 6-4 *A typical fuel tank pressure sensor. This unit is mounted on the fuel sender assembly. Author taken picture.*

In addition to variable resistors, another commonly used reference voltage sensor is a switch. By opening and closing a circuit, switches provide the necessary voltage information to the computer so that vehicles can maintain the proper performance and driveability.

Voltage Generating Sensors

While most sensors are variable resistance/reference voltage, there is another category of sensors—the voltage generating devices. These sensors include components like the magnetic pulse generators, Hall effect switches, oxygen sensors (zirconium dioxide), and knock sensors (piezo-electric) which are capable of producing their own input voltage signal. This varying voltage signal, when received by the computer, enables the computer to monitor and adjust for changes in the computerized engine control system.

Magnetic pulse generators use the principle of magnetic induction to produce a voltage signal. They are also called permanent magnet (PM) generators. These sensors are commonly used to send data to the computer about the speed of the monitored component. This data provides information about vehicle speed, shaft speed, and wheel speed. The signals from speed sensors are used for instrumentation, cruise control systems, anti-lock brake systems, ignition systems, speed-sensitive steering systems, and automatic ride control systems. A magnetic pulse generator is also used to inform the computer about the position of a monitored device. This is common in engine controls where the PCM needs to know the position of the crankshaft in relation to rotational degrees.

The major components of a pulse generator are a timing disc and a pick-up coil. The timing disc is attached to a rotating shaft or cable. The number of teeth on the timing disc is determined by the manufacturer and the application. If only the number of revolutions is required, the timing disc may have only one tooth, whereas if it is important to track quarter revolutions, the timing disc needs at least four teeth. The teeth will cause a voltage generation that is constant per revolution of the shaft. For example, a vehicle speed sensor may be designed to deliver 4,000 pulses per mile. The number of pulses per mile remains constant regardless of speed. The computer calculates how fast the vehicle is going based on the frequency of the signal. The timing disc is also known as an armature, reluctor, trigger wheel, pulse wheel, or timing core.

The pick-up coil is also known as a stator, sensor, or pole piece. It remains stationary while the timing disc rotates in front of it. The changes of magnetic lines of force generate a small voltage signal in the coil. A pick-up coil consists of a permanent magnet with fine wire wound around it.

An air gap is maintained between the timing disc and the pick-up coil. As the timing disc rotates in front of the pick-up coil, the generator sends a pulse signal (Figure 6-5). As a tooth on the timing disc aligns with the core of the pick-up coil, it repels the magnetic field. The magnetic field is forced to flow through the coil and pick-up core (Figure 6-6). When the tooth passes the core, the magnetic field is able to expand (Figure 6-7). This action is repeated every time a tooth passes the core. The moving lines of magnetic force cut across the coil windings and induce a voltage signal.

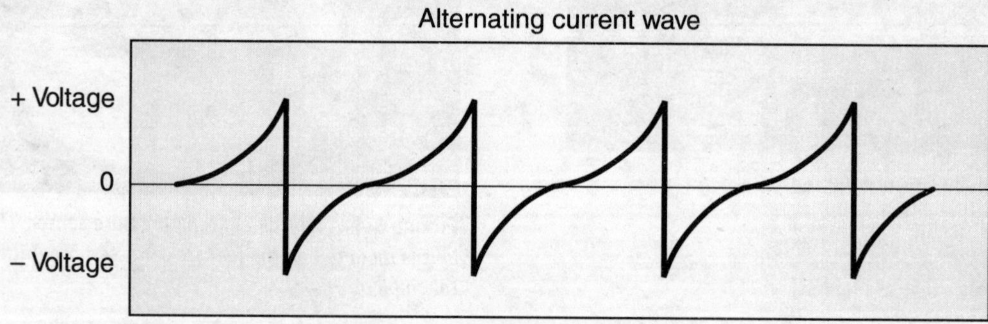

FIGURE 6-5 *Magnetic pulse generator waveform.*

When a tooth approaches the core, a positive current is produced as the magnetic field begins to concentrate around the coil. When the tooth and core align, there is no more expansion nor contraction of the magnetic field and the voltage drops to zero. When the tooth passes the core, the magnetic field expands and a negative current is produced (Figure 6-8). The resulting pulse signal is sent to the PCM.

Hall Effect Sensors

The Hall effect switch performs the same function as a magnetic pulse generator. It operates on the

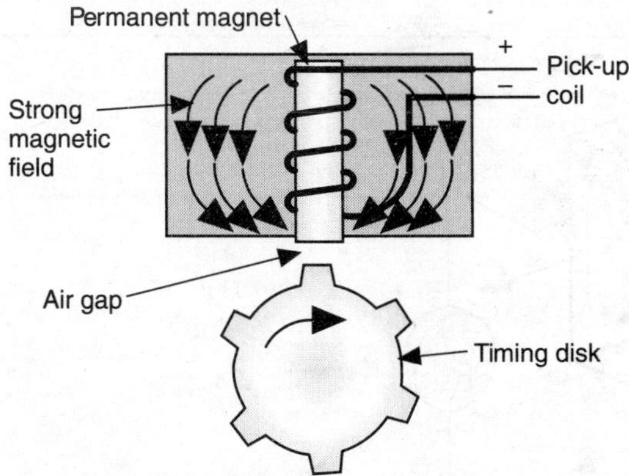

FIGURE 6-6 *A strong magnetic field is produced in the pick-up coil as the teeth align with the core.*

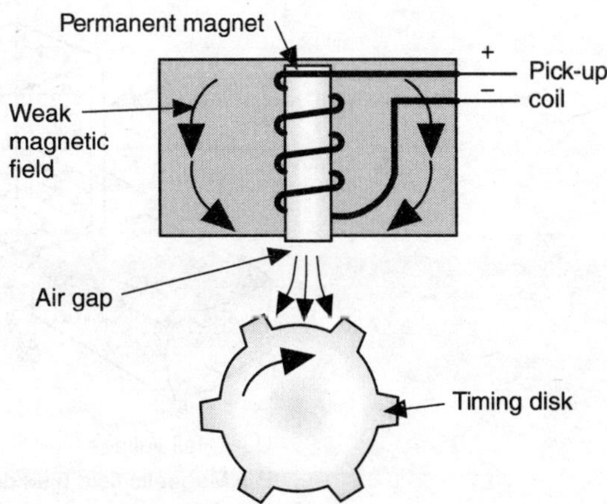

FIGURE 6-7 *The magnetic field expands and weakens as the teeth pass the core.*

principle that if a current is allowed to flow through thin conducting material that is exposed to a magnetic field, another voltage is produced (Figure 6-9).

A Hall effect switch contains a permanent magnet and a thin semiconductor layer made of Gallium arsenate crystal (Hall layer) and a shutter wheel. The Hall layer has a negative and a positive terminal connected to it. Two additional terminals located on either side of the Hall layer are used for the output circuit.

The permanent magnet is located directly across from the Hall layer so that its lines of flux will bisect at right angles to the current flow. The permanent magnet is mounted so that a small air gap is between it and the Hall layer.

A steady current is applied to the crystal of the Hall layer. This produces a signal voltage that is

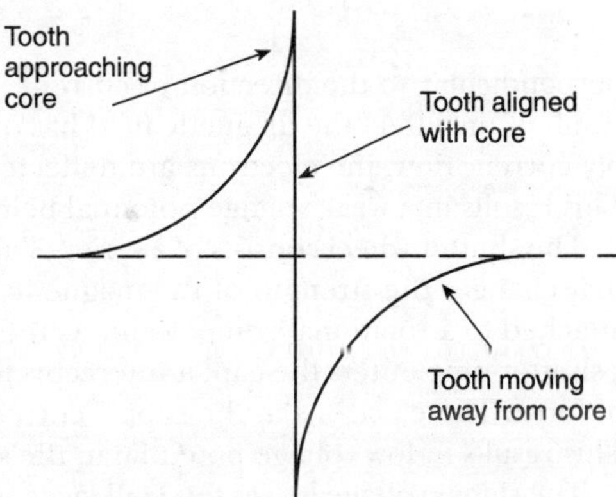

FIGURE 6-8 *Waveform produced by a magnetic pulse generator.*

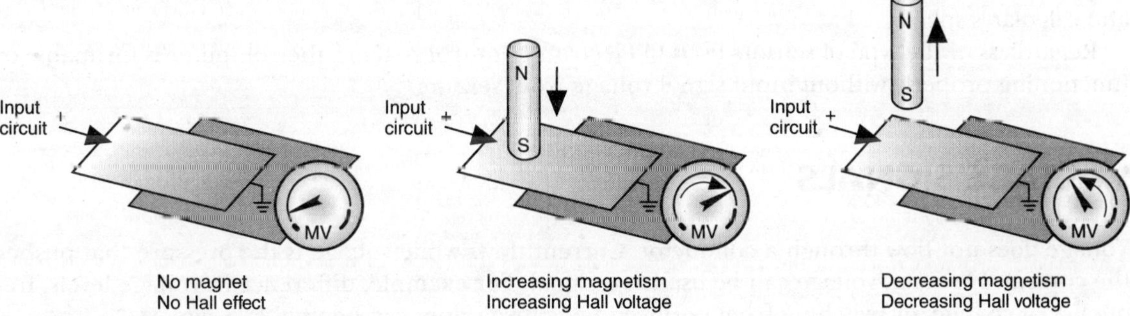

FIGURE 6-9 *Hall effect principles of voltage induction.*

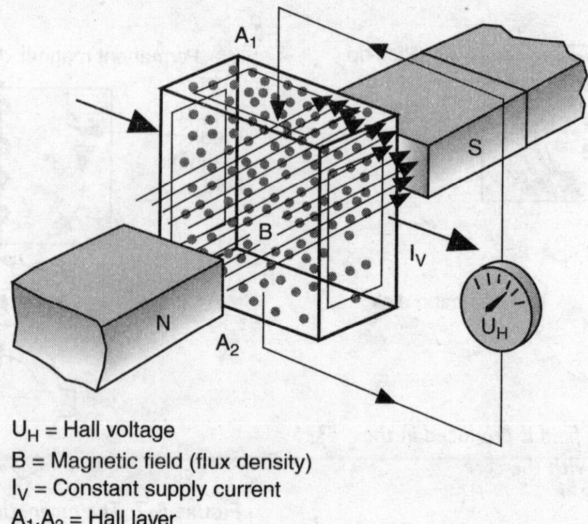

FIGURE 6-10 *The magnetic field causes the electrons from the supply current to gather at the Hall layer's negative terminal. This creates a voltage potential.*

perpendicular to the direction of current flow and magnetic flux. The signal voltage produced is a result of the effect the magnetic field has on the electrons. When the magnetic field bisects the supply current flow, the electrons are deflected toward the Hall layer negative terminal (Figure 6-10). This results in a weak voltage potential being produced in the Hall switch.

The shutter wheel consists of a series of alternating windows and vanes. It creates a magnetic shunt that changes the strength of the magnetic field from the permanent magnet. The shutter wheel is attached to a rotational component. As the wheel rotates, the vanes pass through the air gap. When a shutter vane enters the gap, it intercepts the magnetic field and shields the Hall layer from its lines of force. The electrons in the supply current are no longer disrupted and return to a normal state. This results in low voltage potential in the signal circuit of the Hall switch.

The signal voltage leaves the Hall layer as a weak analog signal. To be used by the PCM, the signal must be conditioned. It is first amplified because it is too weak to produce a desirable result. The signal is also inverted so that a low input signal is converted into a high output signal. It is then sent through a Schmitt trigger, which is a type of A/D converter, where it is digitized and conditioned into a clean square wave signal. The signal is finally sent to a switching transistor. The computer senses the turning on and off of the switching transistor to determine the frequency of the signals and calculates speed.

Regardless of the type of sensors used in electronic control systems, the computer is incapable of functioning properly without input signal voltage from sensors.

VOLTAGE SIGNALS

Voltage does not flow through a conductor. Current flows while voltage is the pressure that pushes the current. However, voltage can be used as a signal. For example, difference in voltage levels, frequency of change, or switching from positive to negative values can be used as a signal.

A computer is capable of reading voltage signals. The programs used by the PCM are "burned" into IC chips using a series of numbers. These numbers represent various combinations of voltages that the computer can understand. The voltage signals to the computer can be either analog or digital.

Analog Voltage Signals

An **analog voltage signal** is continuously variable within a certain range. When a rheostat is used to control a 5-volt bulb, the rheostat voltage may be anywhere between 0 volt and 5 volts. If the rheostat voltage is low, a small amount of current flows through the bulb to produce a dim light from the bulb. If the rheostat voltage is 5 volts, higher current flow produces increased light brilliance. As the rheostat voltage is decreased, the light becomes dimmer. This is an example of an analog voltage (Figure 6-11). Most of the sensors in an automotive computer system produce analog voltages.

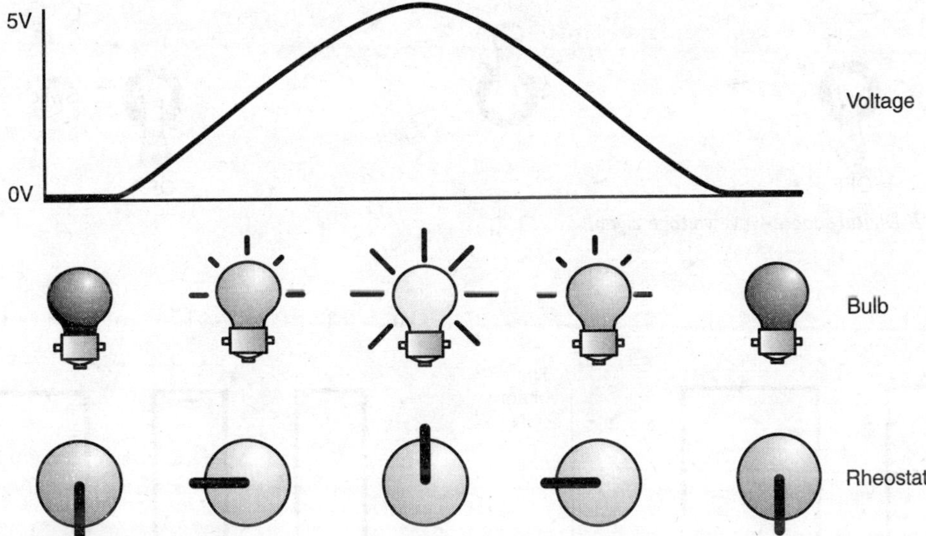

FIGURE 6-11 *Analog voltage signal.*

Digital Voltage Signal

If an ordinary on/off switch is connected to a 5-volt bulb and the switch is off, 0 volt is available at the bulb. When the switch is turned on, a 5-volt signal is sent to the bulb and the bulb is illuminated to full brilliance. If the switch is turned off, the voltage at the bulb returns to 0 volts, and the bulb goes out. The voltage signal supplied through the switch is either 0 volt or 5 volts, or we could say the voltage signal is either high or low. This type of voltage signal is referred to as a digital signal. If the switch is turned on and off rapidly, a square-wave digital voltage signal is applied from the switch to the bulb (Figure 6-12).

In an automotive computer, the microprocessor contains a large number of miniature switches that are capable of producing many digital voltage signals per second. A **digital voltage signal** is used to control various relays and components in the system. The microprocessor can vary the length of time that the digital signal is high or low for precise control (Figure 6-13)

Binary Code

We have explained that a digital signal is either high or low. A numeric value may be assigned to digital signals. For example, a low digital signal may be given a value of 0 and a high digital signal

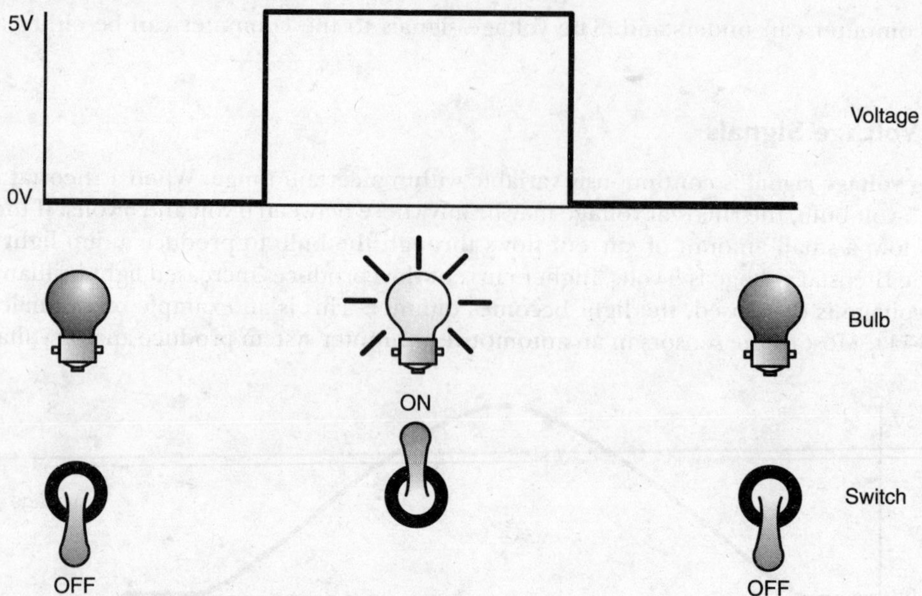

FIGURE 6-12 *Digital square-wave voltage signal.*

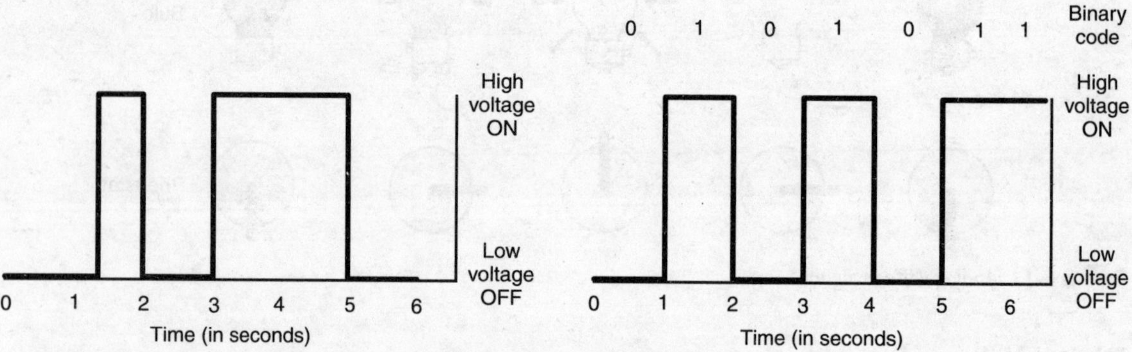

FIGURE 6-13 *Digital voltage signals with variable on time.*

FIGURE 6-14 *Applying numbers to digital voltage signals in a binary code.*

may be given a value of 1. This assignment of numeric values to digital signals is called **binary coding.** The word *binary* means two values, and in the binary coding system the two values are 0 and 1 (Figure 6-14). In an automotive computer, information is transmitted in binary code form. Conditions, numbers, and letters can be represented by a series of zeros and ones.

Many of the input sensors operate in the 0 volt to 5 volts range. The TP sensor may produce these voltages:

Closed throttle — 0 to 2 volts
Part-open throttle — 2 to 4 volts
Wide-open throttle — 4 to 5 volts

A numeric value may be assigned by the computer to each of these voltages:

0 to 2 volts — 1
2 to 4 volts — 2
4 to 5 volts — 3

INPUT CONDITIONING

Amplification

Some input sensors such as the oxygen (O_2) sensor produce a very low voltage signal of less than 1 volt. This signal also has an extremely low current flow. Therefore, this type of signal must be amplified, or increased, before it is sent to the microprocessor. This amplification is accomplished by the amplification circuit in the input conditioning chip inside the computer (Figure 6-15).

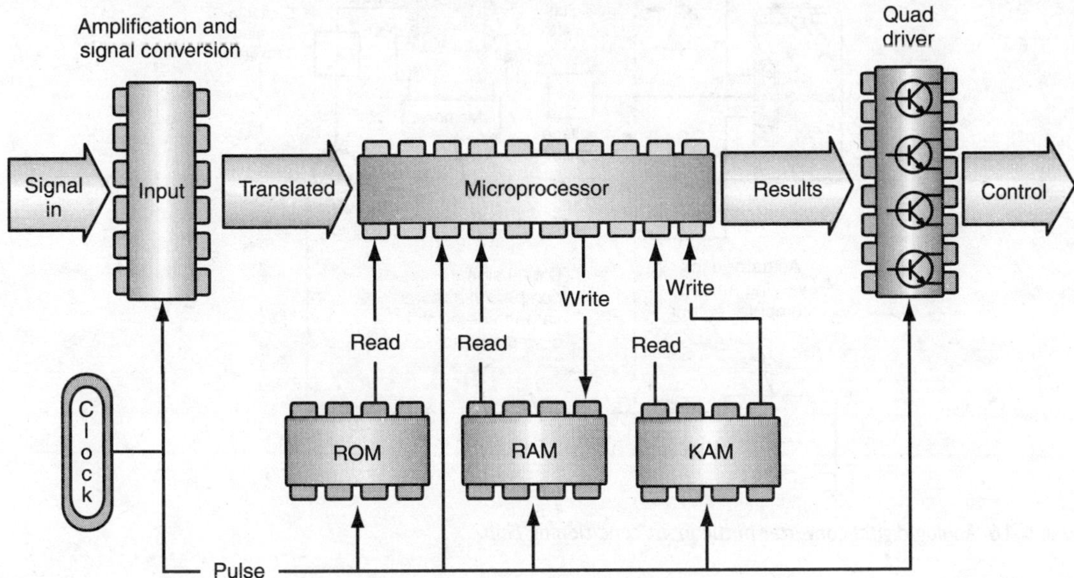

Figure 6-15 *Amplification circuit in the computer input conditioning chip.*

Analog to Digital (A/D) Conversion

Since some input sensors produce analog signals and the microprocessor operates on digital signals, something must change the sensor analog signals to digital signals. This job is done by the A/D converter in the computer input conditioning chip (Figure 6-16) and is called **analog/digital conversion.**

The A/D converter continually scans the analog input signals at regular intervals. If the A/D converter scans the TP sensor signal and finds this signal at 5 volts, the A/D converter assigns a numeric value of 3 to this specific voltage. The A/D converter then changes this numeric value to a binary code of 1 1 (Figure 6-17).

Therefore, we can understand that the A/D converter continually scans the input sensor signals and assigns numeric values to these voltages. The A/D converter then translates the numeric value to a binary code. In some automotive computers, the input conditioning chip is combined with the microprocessor.

INPUT SENSORS

Oxygen Sensor Design

The **oxygen (O_2) sensor** is threaded into the exhaust manifold or into the exhaust pipe near the engine. Some manufacturers refer to this sensor as an exhaust gas oxygen (EGO) sensor or a heated

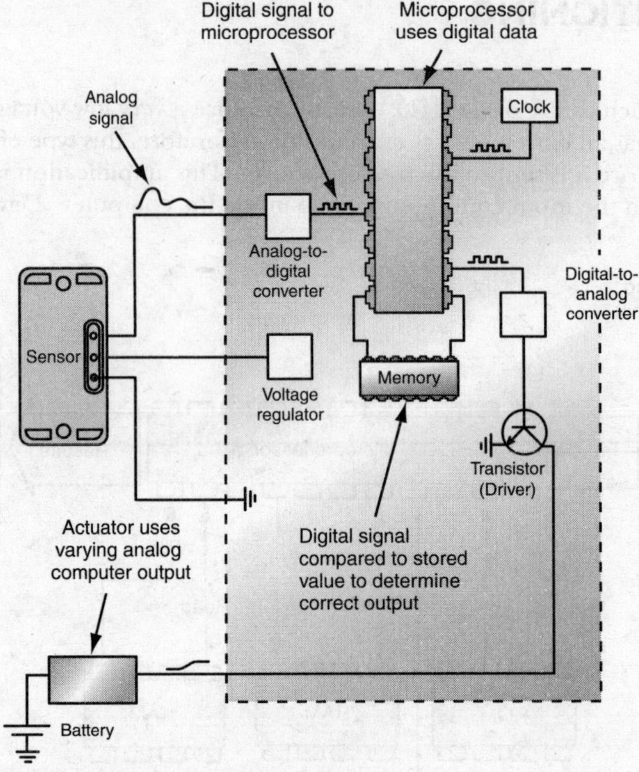

FIGURE 6-16 *Analog/digital converter in the input conditioning chip.*

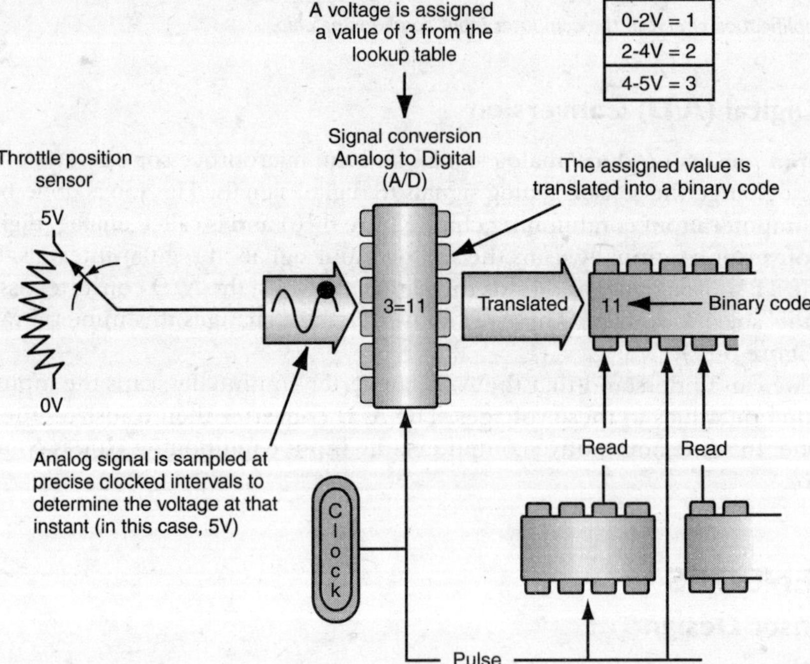

FIGURE 6-17 *The A/D converter in the computer assigns a numerical value to the input voltages and changes the numerical value to binary code.*

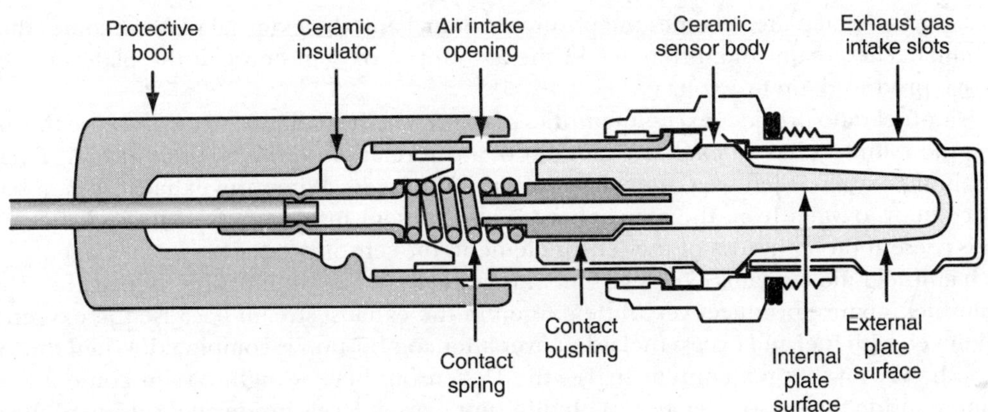

FIGURE 6-18 *Typical oxygen sensor design.*

exhaust gas oxygen (HEGO) sensor. An oxygen-sensing element in the center of the O_2 sensor is surrounded by a steel shell. The oxygen-sensing element is made from zirconia in many O_2 sensors. The steel shell has a hex-shaped area on which a socket may be installed for removal and installation purposes. Threads on the lower end of the steel shell match the threads in the exhaust pipe or manifold opening where the sensor is installed (Figure 6-18).

A steel cover or a neoprene boot is installed over the top of the sensor. On many O_2 sensors, the steel cover is loosely installed on the sensor, which allows a constant supply of oxygen from the atmosphere inside the oxygen-sensing element. If a neoprene boot is installed on the sensor, the boot has grooves cut on the inner surface to allow air inside the sensing element. In some later model O_2 sensors, the top of the sensor is tightly sealed and oxygen enters the sensor through the signal wire.

A shield covers the bottom end of the sensor that protrudes into the exhaust manifold or pipe. Flutes in this shield help to swirl the exhaust gas continually around the sensor element when the engine is running.

Some O_2 sensors have a single wire that is connected from the oxygen-sensing element to the computer, and this wire acts as a signal wire. If an O_2 sensor has two wires, the second wire is a ground wire that is connected back to the computer. Many O_2 sensors have three or four wires. The additional wires are connected to an electric heating element in the sensor. Voltage is supplied from the ignition switch to this heater when the ignition switch is on. Since the O_2 sensor does not produce a satisfactory signal until it reaches about 600°F (315°C), the internal heater provides faster sensor warmup time and helps to keep the sensor hot during prolonged idle operation. The internal O_2 sensor heater maintains higher sensor temperatures, which helps to burn deposits off the sensor. When the O_2 sensor has an internal heater, the sensor may be placed further away from the engine in the exhaust stream, thus giving engineers more flexibility in sensor location. Some O_2 sensors have four wires—a signal wire, heater wire, and two ground wires. In these four-wire sensors, the heater and the sensing element have individual ground wires. A replacement O_2 sensor must have the same number of wires as the original sensor.

Oxygen Sensor (O_2S) Operation

The zirconia oxygen sensor is used to detect the amount of oxygen in the exhaust. The oxygen sensor produces a voltage between 0 volt and 1 volt. It works by the interaction of reference oxygen and the oxygen that is in the exhaust. The zirconia is an insulator when cold and becomes a conductor at about 315°C (600°F). The internal plate surface is in contact with atmospheric oxygen, and the external plate is in contact with exhaust oxygen. At the high temperatures that the oxygen sensor operates, the internal plate becomes the positive terminal and the external plate becomes the negative terminal. The greater the difference in the amount of oxygen between the plates, the greater the voltage produced, up to 1 volt.

A lean air-fuel ratio provides excess quantities of oxygen in the exhaust stream because the mixture entering the cylinders has an excessive amount of air in relation to the amount of fuel. Therefore, air containing oxygen is left over after the combustion process. When the exhaust stream has high oxygen content, oxygen from the atmosphere is also present inside the O_2 sensor element. When oxygen is present on both sides of the sensor element, the sensor produces a low voltage.

A rich air-fuel ratio contains excessive fuel in relation to the amount of air entering the cylinders. A rich air-fuel mixture produces very little oxygen in the exhaust stream because the oxygen in the air is all mixed with fuel and excess fuel is left over after combustion is completed. When the exhaust stream with very low oxygen content strikes the O_2 sensor, there is high oxygen content from the atmosphere inside the sensor element. With different oxygen levels inside and outside of the sensor element, the sensor produces up to 1 volt. As the airfuel ratio cycles from lean to rich, the O_2 sensor voltage changes in a few milliseconds.

In a gasoline fuel system, the stoichiometric, or ideal, air-fuel mixture is 14.7:1. This indicates that for every 14.7 pounds of air entering the air intake, the carburetor or fuel injectors supply 1 pound of fuel. At the stoichiometric air-fuel ratio, combustion is most efficient and nearly all the oxygen in the air is mixed with fuel and burned in the combustion chambers. Computer-controlled carburetor or fuel injection systems always maintain the air-fuel ratio at stoichiometric under most operating conditions. As the air-fuel ratio cycles slightly rich and lean from the stoichiometric ratio, the O_2 sensor voltage cycles from high to low (Figure 6-19).

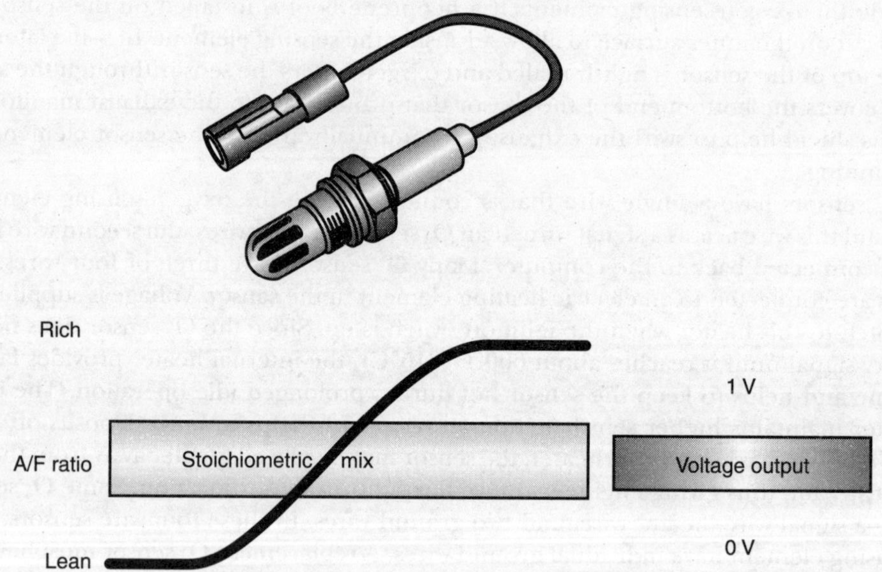

FIGURE 6-19 *Oxygen sensor voltage in relation to air-fuel ratio.*

Certain types of room temperature vulcanizing (RTV) sealant or antifreeze entering the combustion chambers will contaminate the O_2 sensor. Always use the RTV sealant recommended by the vehicle manufacturer.

Always use a digital voltmeter to check the O_2 sensor. The sensor threads should be coated with an antiseize compound prior to sensor installation or sensor removal may be difficult the next time it is necessary.

Besides the oxygen sensor's role in air-fuel ratio control, it is also important in determining the condition of the catalytic converter in OBD II vehicles. A heated oxygen sensor placed before the converter is called the pre-catalyst O_2 sensor, and another behind the converter called the postcatalyst O_2 sensor (Figure 6-20). The PCM looks at the post-catalyst O_2 compared to the precatalyst to make a determination on the condition of the catalyst. The post-converter O_2 sensor should show very little activity compared to the pre-converter O_2 sensor, since most of the oxygen would have been used to convert HC and CO inside the converter. If both O_2 sensors have the same amount of activity, then the PCM assumes that the catalyst has failed and the appropriate code is set. Many OBD II vehicles with V-type engines have a pre-catalyst O_2 sensor in each bank.

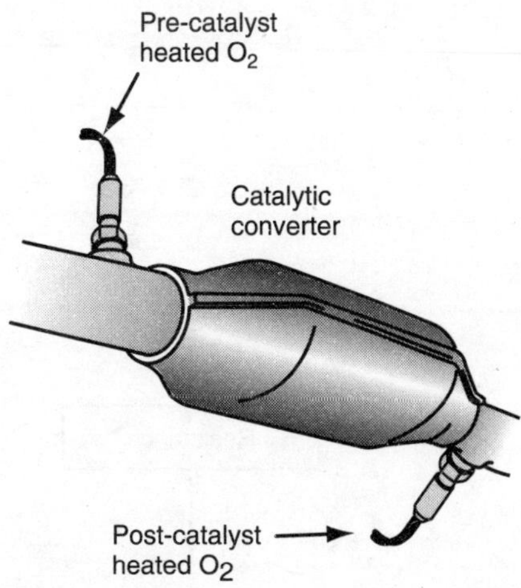

FIGURE 6-20 *Pre-catalyst and post-catalyst heated O_2 sensors.*

Titania-Type O_2 Sensor

Some vehicles are equipped with a titania-type O_2 sensor. This sensor design is similar to the zirconia-type sensor, but the sensing element is made from titania rather than zirconia (Figure 6-21).

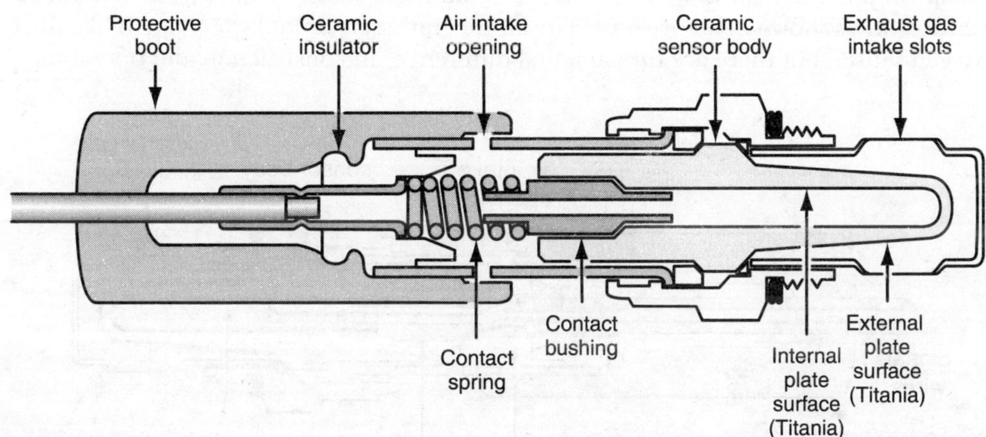

FIGURE 6-21 *Titania-type O_2 sensor.*

The titania-type sensor modifies voltage whereas the zirconia-type sensor generates voltage. The computer supplies battery voltage to the titania-type sensor, and this voltage is lowered by a resistor in the circuit. The resistance of the titania varies as the air-fuel ratio cycles from rich to lean. When the air-fuel ratio is rich, the titania resistance is low. This provides a higher voltage signal to the computer. If the air-fuel ratio is lean, the titania resistance is high and a lower voltage signal is sent to the computer (Figure 6-22).

The titania-type O_2 sensor provides a satisfactory signal almost immediately after a cold engine is started. This action provides improved air-fuel ratio control during engine warmup.

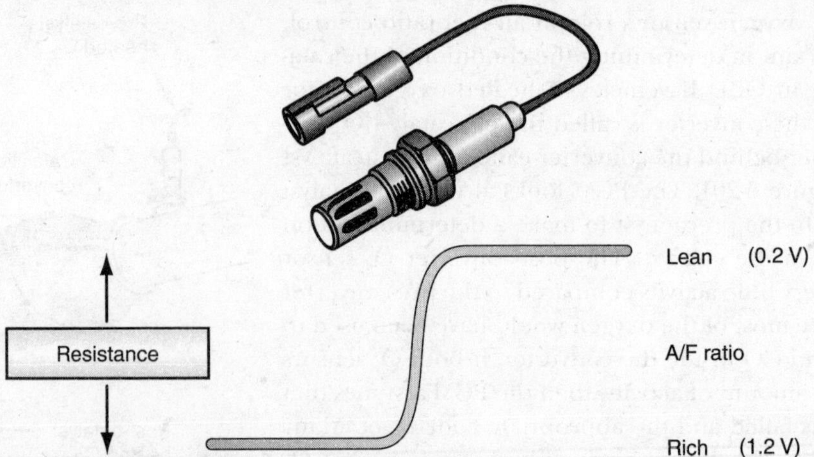

FIGURE 6-22 *Titania-type O_2 sensor resistance and voltage signal.*

Air-Fuel Ratio Sensor

The O_2 sensor has done a reliable job of indicating air-fuel ratio, but it would be advantageous to have a sensor that could indicate air-fuel ratio over a broader range. The traditional O_2 sensor has a narrow range of operation around 14.7:1. The A/F (air-fuel) sensor (Figure 6-23) can indicate from about 12:1 to 19:1 as shown in Figure 6-24. The air-fuel ratio sensor looks very much like the conventional oxygen sensor, but there are fundamental differences in construction and operation.

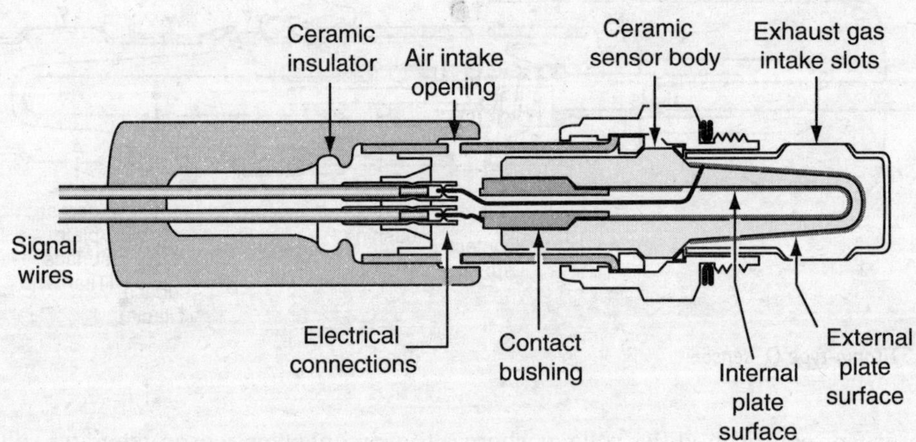

FIGURE 6-23 *The air-fuel ratio sensor is very similar to the oxygen sensor in appearance but varies in operation.*

First, the air-fuel sensor operates at 1,200°F (650°C), about twice as hot as the conventional oxygen sensor, so a heater is mandatory. Also, the A/F sensor changes amperage and voltage to indicate A/F ratio. When the mixture is lean, the current is generated in a positive direction with a voltage above 3.3 volts. When the mixture is rich, the current is generated in a negative direction with a voltage below 3.3 volts. At 14.7:1, there is no current produced. The A/F sensor does not have to toggle rich to lean in operation like the oxygen sensor. The A/F sensor can indicate not only rich and lean

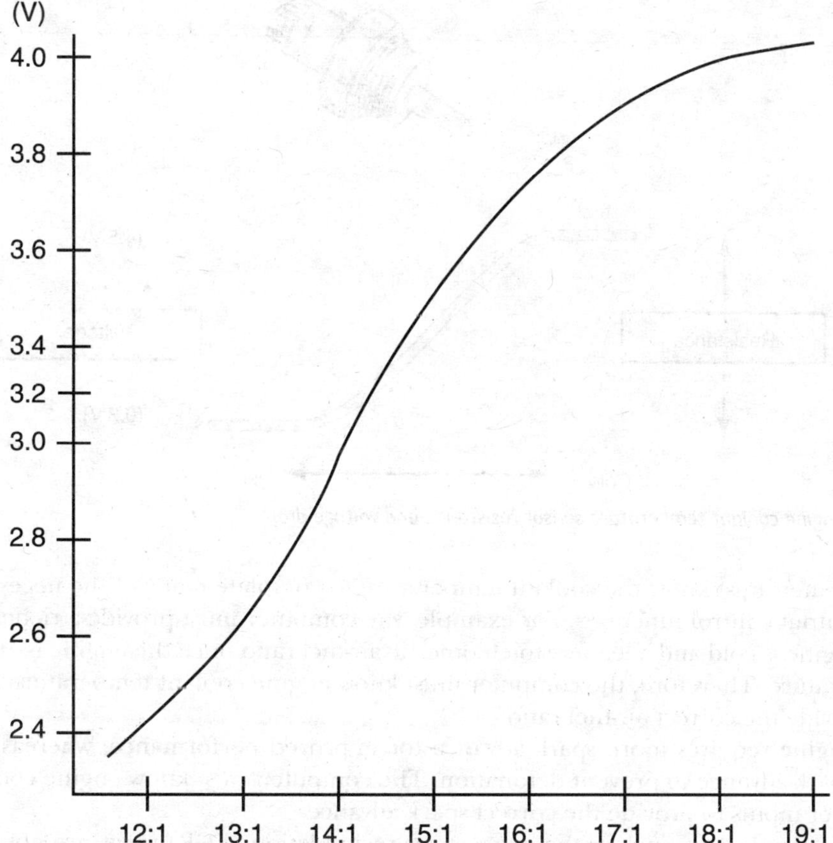

FIGURE 6-24 *A/F ratio sensor voltage and corresponding air-fuel ratio.*

like the oxygen sensor, but can indicate just how rich or lean the mixture is by varying current direction and voltage. The computer can make better decisions on fuel management since it has more accurate information. An important fact to remember is that OBD II regulations require oxygen sensors to read out between 0 volt and 1 volt, so the scan tool actually converts the signal to correspond to the conventional sensor. At this point, the only way to check an A/F sensor is with a scan tool since the signal is processed inside the PCM.

Engine Coolant Temperature (ECT) Sensor

The **engine coolant temperature (ECT) sensor** is often threaded into the intake manifold, and the lower end of the sensor is immersed in engine coolant. A typical ECT sensor contains a thermistor that provides high resistance when cold and much lower resistance at higher temperatures. A typical ECT sensor may have 269,000 Ω at –40°F (–40°C) and 1,200 Ω at 248°F (120°C). The ECT sensor has two wires connected between the sensor and the computer. One of these wires is a voltage signal wire, and the other wire provides a ground. The computer senses the voltage drop across the ECT sensor. This voltage changes in relation to the coolant temperature and sensor resistance. For example, at low coolant temperature and high sensor resistance, the voltage drop across the sensor might be 4.5 volts whereas at high coolant temperature and low sensor resistance, this voltage drop would be approximately 0.3 volt (Figure 6-25).

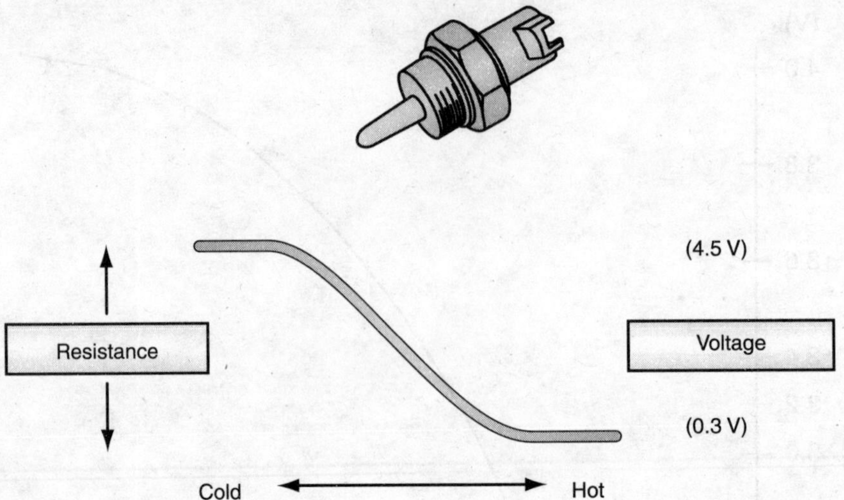

FIGURE 6-25 *Engine coolant temperature sensor resistance and voltage drop.*

The computer must know the coolant temperature to complete many of the necessary decisions regarding output control functions. For example, the computer must provide a richer air-fuel ratio when the engine is cold and a leaner stoichiometric air-fuel ratio once the engine is at normal operating temperature. Therefore, the computer must know engine coolant temperature from the ECT signal to provide the correct air-fuel ratio.

A cold engine requires more spark advance for improved performance, whereas a hot engine needs less spark advance to prevent detonation. The computer must know engine coolant temperature and other inputs to provide the correct spark advance.

Some emission devices, such as the exhaust gas recirculation (EGR) valve, are not required on a cold engine, but this valve must be operational on a hot engine under certain operating conditions. The computer uses the ECT signal and other inputs to control the EGR valve in addition to electric cooling fan operation and idle speed.

Intake Air Temperature Sensor

Some **intake air temperature (IAT) sensors** are threaded into the intake manifold and the lower end of the sensor protrudes into one of the air passages in the intake manifold. On some applications, the IAT sensor is mounted in the air cleaner and senses air intake temperature at this location. The air charge temperature sensor contains a thermistor that has ohm and voltage drop readings that are similar to the ECT sensor (Figure 6-26).

A voltage signal wire and a ground wire are connected between the air charge temperature sensor and the computer. Cold intake air is denser; therefore, a richer air-fuel ratio is required. When the IAT sensor signal indicates colder intake air temperature, the computer provides a richer air-fuel ratio.

Throttle Position (TP) Sensor

A **rotary-type throttle position (TP) sensor** contains a potentiometer with a pointer that is rotated by the throttle shaft. In computer-controlled fuel injection systems, this sensor is positioned on the end of the throttle shaft in the throttle body.

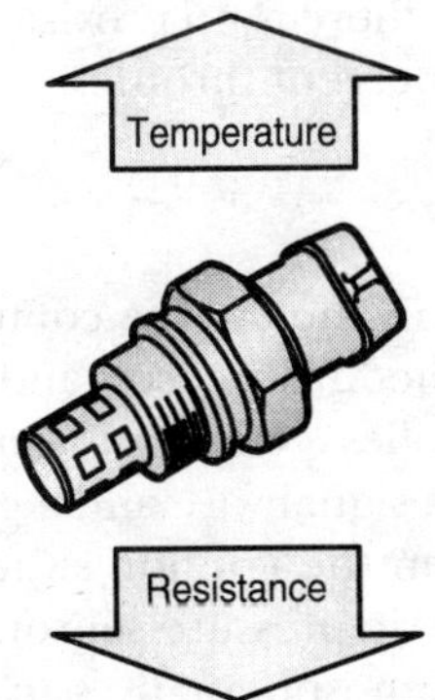

Thermistor temperature to resistance valves		
°F	°C	Ohms
210	100	185
190	90	240
160	70	450
100	38	1,800
40	4	7,500
32	0	10,000
0	-18	25,000
-40	-40	100,700

FIGURE 6-26 *Intake Air Temperature (IAT) sensor resistance and voltage drop.*

Three wires are connected from the TP sensor to the computer. When the ignition switch is on, the computer supplies a constant 5-volt reference voltage to the sensor on one of these wires. One of the other wires is a TP sensor signal wire from the sensor to the computer, and the third wire is a ground wire between these two components. Sensor ground wires are usually either black or black with a colored tracer.

A typical TP sensor has 1,000 ω with the throttle in the idle position and 4,000 ω at wide-open throttle. The voltage signal from a typical TP sensor is 0.5 volt to 1 volt at idle and 4.5 volts at wide-open throttle. This signal informs the computer regarding the exact throttle position (Figure 6-27).

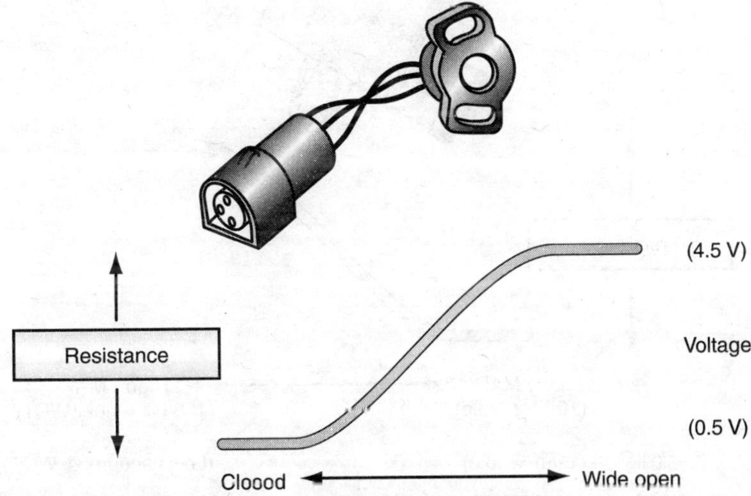

FIGURE 6-27 *Throttle position (TP) sensor resistance and voltage drop.*

The computer also knows how fast the throttle is opened from the TP sensor signal. When the engine is suddenly accelerated, a richer air-fuel ratio is required with the additional airflow into the engine. If the computer receives a TP sensor signal indicating sudden acceleration, the computer supplies the necessary richer air-fuel ratio. The computer also uses the TP sensor signal to control other outputs.

Elongated mounting holes on some TP sensors provide a sensor adjustment. When a TP sensor adjustment is necessary, the mounting bolts are loosened and the sensor is rotated until the specified signal voltage is available with the engine idling. On most TP sensors there is no provision for sensor adjustment. The lowest reading seen by the PCM is recognized as 0 percent throttle.

Manifold Absolute Pressure (MAP) Sensor

The **manifold absolute pressure (MAP) sensor** is usually mounted in the engine compartment. A hose is connected from the intake manifold to a vacuum inlet on the MAP sensor, and three wires are connected from the sensor to the computer. The computer supplies a constant 5-volt reference voltage to the sensor on one of these wires, and the other wires are a signal wire and a ground wire. These wiring connections are the same for most MAP sensors. When the ignition switch is turned on before the engine is started, many MAP sensors act as a barometric pressure sensor. Under this condition, the MAP sensor signal informs the computer regarding atmospheric pressure that varies in relation to altitude and atmospheric conditions such as the humidity. Some applications have a separate barometric pressure sensor.

There are two basic types of MAP sensor designs. Ford MAP sensors contain a pressure-sensitive disk capacitor. This type of MAP sensor changes manifold pressure to a digital voltage signal of varying frequency. The MAP sensor actually senses the difference between absolute vacuum and manifold vacuum. When the engine is idling, high intake manifold vacuum is about 18 in. Hg. Under this condition, the MAP sensor signal is approximately 109 hertz. Ford refers to this condition as low MAP because manifold pressure is low (high vacuum) (Figure 6-28).

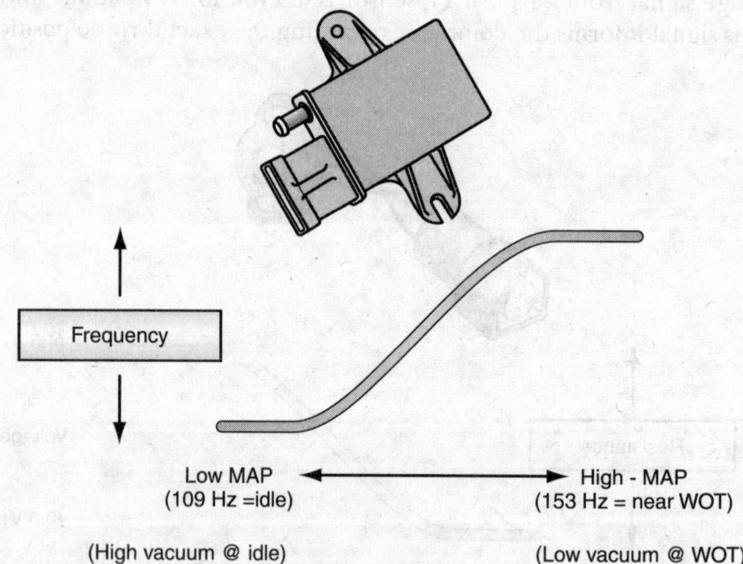

FIGURE 6-28 *Manifold absolute pressure (MAP) sensor and its voltage signal with varying frequency in response to manifold pressure.*

If the engine is operating at or near wide-open throttle, the manifold vacuum may be 2 in. Hg and the MAP sensor hertz approximates 153. This condition may be called high MAP because the manifold vacuum is closer to atmospheric pressure.

Never connect any type of voltmeter to the signal wire on a Ford MAP sensor with the ignition switch on or the MAP sensor will be damaged. Ford MAP sensor testers read the sensor hertz directly, and other Ford MAP sensor testers convert the hertz to a voltage signal.

The computer uses the MAP sensor signal to determine the engine load. When the MAP sensor signal indicates wide-open throttle, heavy load conditions, the computer provides a richer air-fuel ratio. The computer supplies a leaner air-fuel ratio if the MAP sensor signal indicates light load, moderate cruising speed conditions.

Other types of MAP sensors have a silicon piezoresistive diaphragm that reacts to pressure changes. This varying voltage signal is monitored by the PCM. These sensors have the same three wires as the Ford MAP sensors (Figure 6-29).

When the manifold vacuum stresses the silicon diaphragm, a voltage signal is sent from the sensor to the computer in relation to the amount of vacuum. On a typical MAP sensor, the signal voltage changes from 1 volt to 1.5 volts at idle to 4.5 volts at wide-open throttle. The signal voltage may be checked with a digital voltmeter on MAP sensors with a silicon diaphragm.

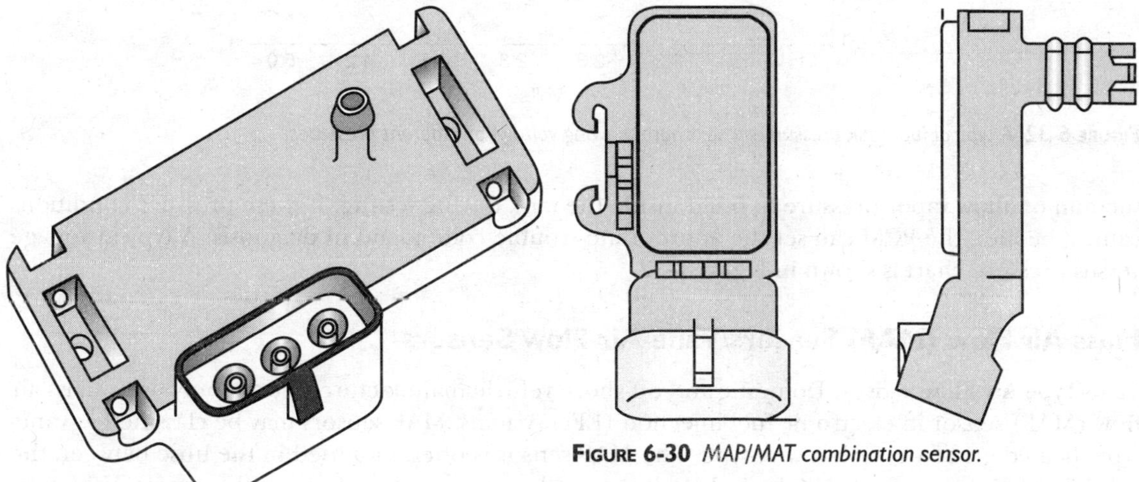

FIGURE 6-29 *Manifold absolute pressure sensor with a silicon diaphragm.*

FIGURE 6-30 *MAP/MAT combination sensor.*

Combination MAP and Manifold Air Temperature Sensors

Some manufacturers are using technological advancements to produce two-in-one sensors in order to reduce manufacturing costs. In addition, some space savings is gained with one fewer component, wire, and connector. One example of this is the Manifold Absolute Pressure/Manifold Air Temperature (MAP/MAT) sensor (Figure 6-30).

This sensor shares a common PCM power feed and ground and has two signal return wires for each sensor function. The MAP/MAT sensor provides two separate outputs critical to air-fuel optimization. These outputs include one voltage proportional to engine intake manifold pressure and one voltage output proportional to manifold air temperature.

FIGURE 6-31 *A fuel tank pressure sensor.*

The **fuel tank pressure sensor** (Figure 6-31) is closely related to the MAP sensor in operation but designed to measure very small changes between the in-tank pressure and atmospheric pressure outside the tank. The fuel tank pressure sensor allows the PCM to determine whether the evaporative emissions system (EVAP) is properly sealed. The PCM can command a

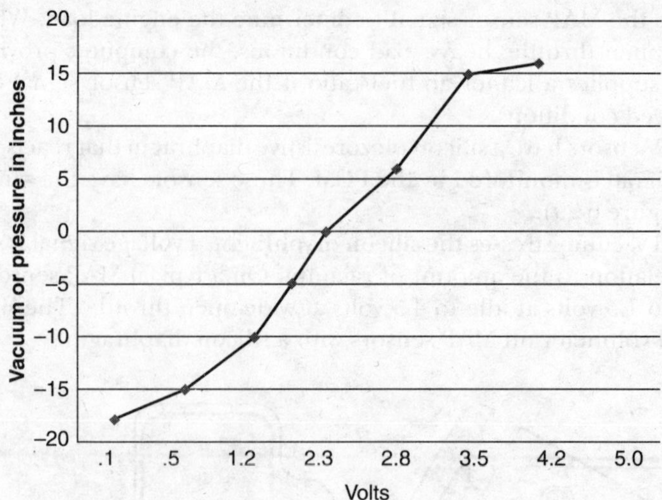

FIGURE 6-32 *A typical fuel tank pressure sensor chart showing voltage at different pressures.*

vacuum or allow vapor pressure to build inside the tank during testing. If these pressure conditions cannot be met, the PCM can set the appropriate trouble code to aid in diagnosis. A typical voltage versus pressure chart is shown in Figure 6-32.

Mass Air Flow (MAF) Sensors/Vane Air Flow Sensors

Vane-Type Air Flow Sensor. Domestic and off-shore vehicle manufacturers commonly use a mass air flow (MAF) sensor in electronic fuel injection (EFI) systems. MAF sensors may be classified as vane-type, heated grid-type, or hot wire-type. The MAF sensor is often mounted in the hose between the air cleaner and the throttle body so that all the intake air must flow through the sensor. Vane-type sensors are referred to as volume air flow meters (Figure 6-33).

In a vane-type sensor, a pivoted air measuring plate is lightly spring-loaded in the closed position. As the intake air flows through the sensor, the air measuring plate moves toward the open position. This plate movement is proportional to intake airflow (Figure 6-34).

A movable pointer is attached to the measuring plate shaft, and this pointer contacts a resistor. The movable pointer and resistor form a potentiometer, which sends a voltage signal to the powertrain control module (PCM) in relation to measuring plate movement and intake airflow. A thermistor in the airflow meter sends a signal to the PCM in relation to air intake temperature (Figure 6-35).

Heated Resistor-Type MAF Sensor. A heated resistor is mounted in the center of the air passage in some MAF sensors, and an electronic module is mounted on the side of the sensor (Figure 6-36). When the ignition switch is turned on, voltage is supplied to the module and the module sends enough current through the resistor to maintain a specific resistor temperature.

If a cold engine is accelerated suddenly, the rush of cold air tries to cool the resistor. Under this condition, the module supplies more current to maintain the resistor temperature. The module sends the increasing current signal to the PCM, and this signal is proportional to the airflow entering the engine. When the PCM receives this increasing current flow signal from the MAF module, the PCM supplies a richer air-fuel ratio to go with the additional cold airflow entering the engine. The MAF module reacts in a few milliseconds to maintain the resistor temperature. Some MAF sensors have an electric grid in place of the resistor.

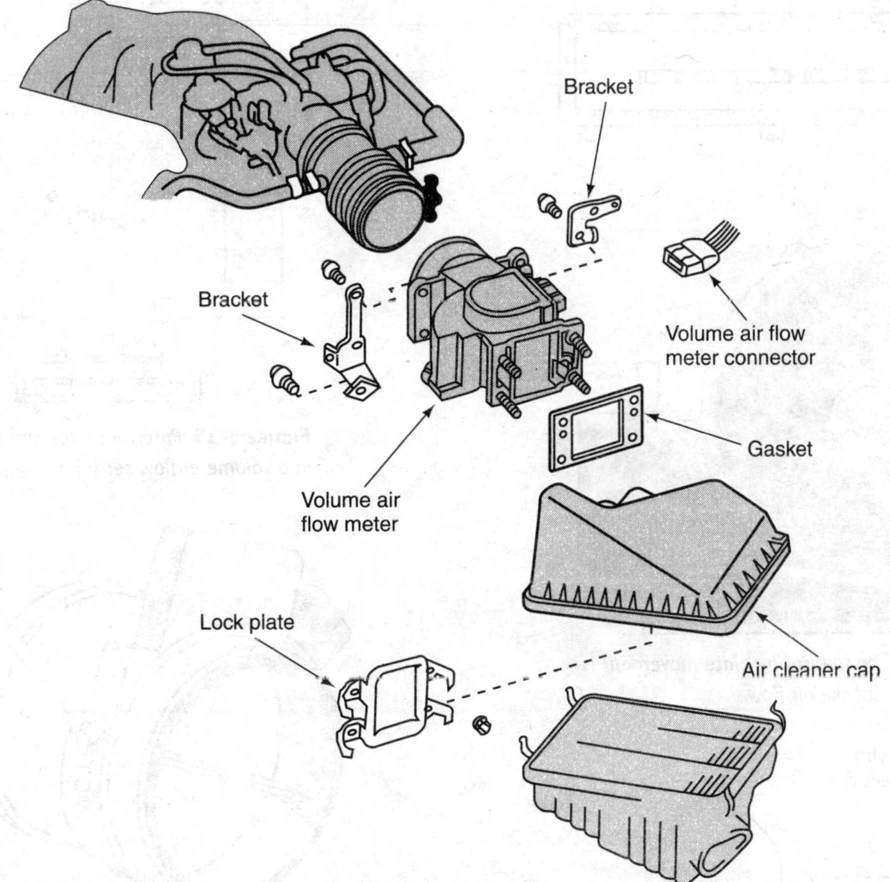

FIGURE 6-33 *A vane-type airflow sensor which may be referred to as a volume airflow meter.*

Hot Wire-Type MAF Sensor. In a hot wire-type MAF sensor, a hot wire is positioned in the airstream through the sensor, and an ambient temperature sensor wire is located beside the hot wire. This ambient temperature sensor wire senses intake air temperature, and this wire may be referred to as a cold wire (Figure 6-37).

When the ignition switch is turned on, the module in the MAF sensor sends enough current through the hot wire to maintain the temperature of this wire 392°F (200°C) above the ambient temperature sensed by the cold wire. If the engine is accelerated suddenly, the rush of cold air tries to cool the hot wire. The module immediately sends more current through the wire to maintain the wire temperature at 392°F (200°C) above the cold wire temperature. The module sends this increasing current signal to the PCM. This signal is directly proportional to the intake airflow. When this signal is received, the PCM supplies more fuel to go with the increased intake airflow, and this action maintains the exact air fuel ratio required by the engine. Some MAF sensors have a burn off relay and related circuit. When the ignition switch is turned off after the engine has been running for a specific length of time, the computer closes the burn-off relay. This relay activates a burn-off circuit in the MAF, which heats the hot wire to a very high temperature for a short time period. This action burns contaminants off the hot wire.

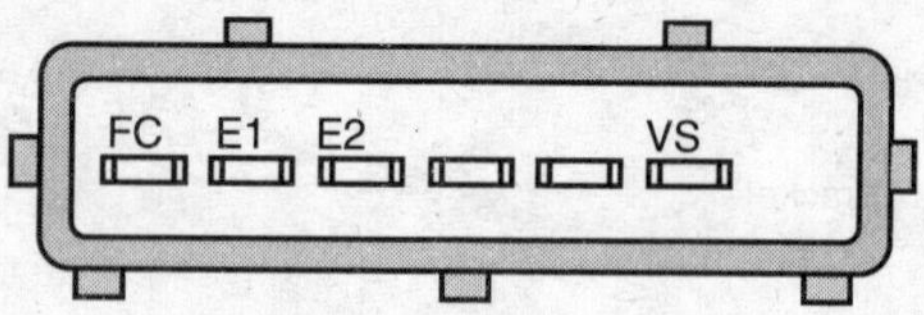

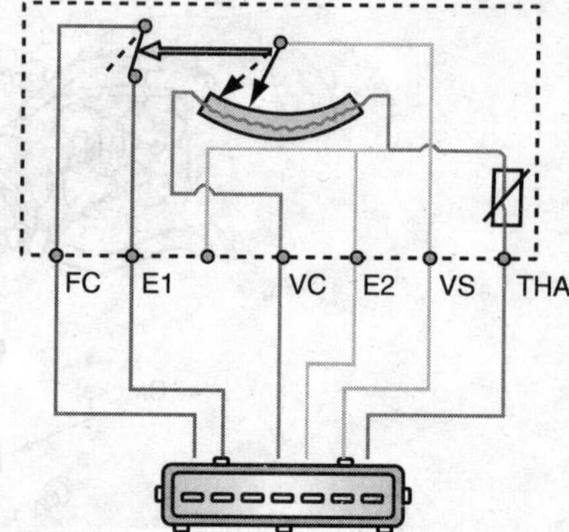

FIGURE 6-35 *Potentiometer and thermistor in a volume airflow sensor.*

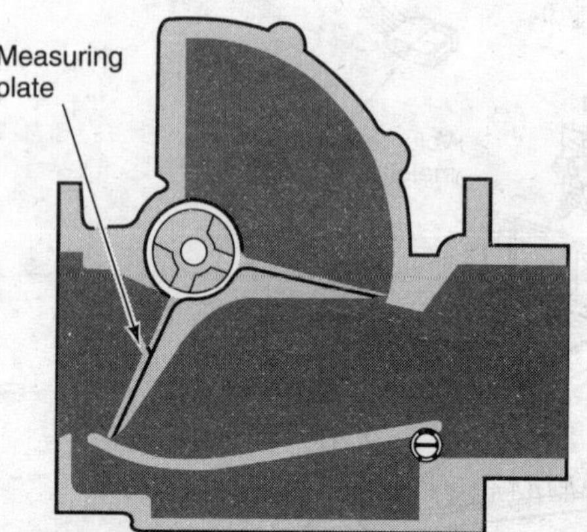

FIGURE 6-34 *The measuring plate movement is proportional to intake air flow.*

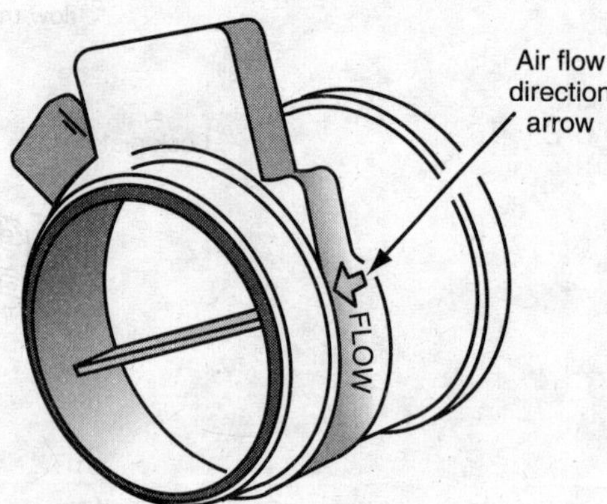

FIGURE 6-36 *Heated resistor-type MAF sensor and module.*

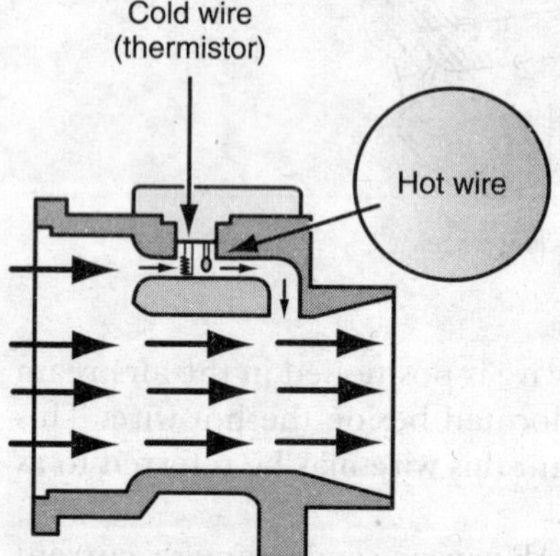

FIGURE 6-37 *Hot wire-type MAF sensor.*

Knock Sensor (KS)

The **knock sensor (KS)** is threaded into the engine block, intake manifold, or cylinder head. In some applications, the knock sensor is called a detonation sensor. Many engines now contain two knock sensors for improved detonation control. The knock sensor contains a piezoelectric sensing element that changes a vibration to a voltage signal (Figure 6-38). An internal resistor is connected in parallel with the piezoelectric sensing element.

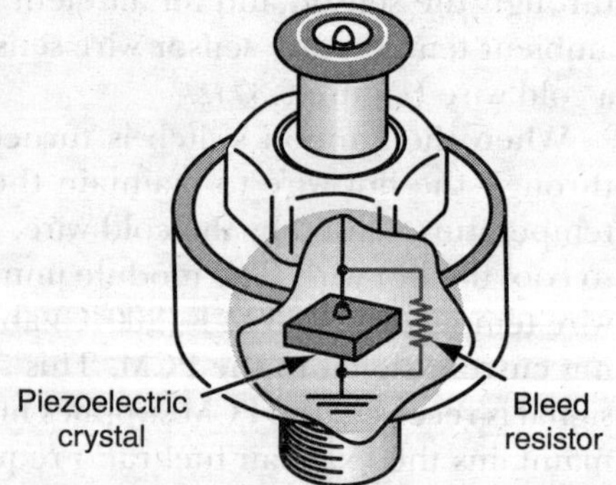

FIGURE 6-38 *Knock sensor (KS) with piezoelectric sensing device and parallel resistor.*

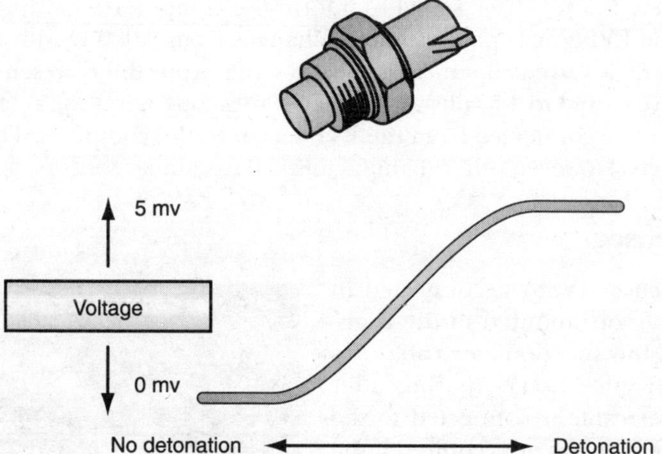

FIGURE 6-39 *Knock sensor and related voltage signal.*

When the engine detonates, a vibration is present in the engine block and cylinder head castings. The knock sensor changes this vibration to a voltage signal and sends the signal to the computer. When this signal is received, the computer reduces spark advance to eliminate the detonation. A typical knock sensor signal would be 300 millivolts (mV) to 500 mV depending on the severity of detonation (Figure 6-39).

Exhaust Gas Recirculation Valve Position (EVP) Sensor

The **exhaust gas recirculation valve position (EVP) sensor** is mounted on top of the EGR valve. A linear potentiometer is mounted in the EVP sensor, and a stem extends from this potentiometer to the top of the EGR valve. When the EGR valve opens, the potentiometer stem moves upward and a higher voltage signal is sent to the computer (Figure 6-40).

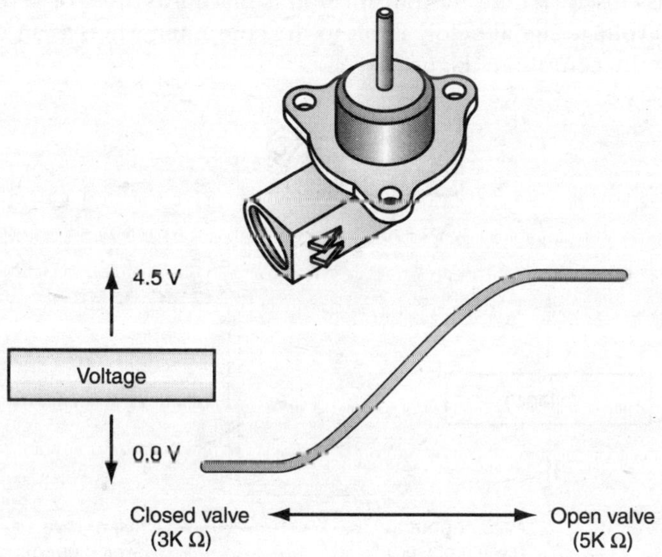

FIGURE 6-40 *EVP sensor and related voltage signal.*

The EVP sensor acts as a feedback signal to inform the computer regarding the EGR valve position. Resistance in the EVP linear potentiometer changes from 3,000 Ω with the EGR valve closed to 5,000 Ω when the EGR valve is open. The voltage signal from the EVP sensor changes from 0.8 volt with the EGR valve closed to 4.5 volts with the EGR valve open. A 5-volt reference wire, a ground wire, and a signal wire are connected from the EVP sensor to the computer. The EVP sensor is used on some Ford products. However, other manufacturers have similar sensors.

Vehicle Speed Sensor

The **vehicle speed sensor (VSS)** is connected in the speedometer cable or mounted in the transaxle opening where the speedometer cable was located previously (Figure 6-41). In the latter case, the speedometer cable is connected to the VSS. The speedometer cable is not required if the vehicle has an electronic speedometer.

FIGURE 6-41 *A VSS mounted in the tail shaft housing of a transmission.*

In some VSSs, the speedometer drive rotates a magnet inside a coil of wire. This type of sensor produces an AC voltage signal proportional to vehicle speed. In some other VSSs, a magnet with eight poles rotates past a set of reed points, and these rotating poles open the points eight times per sensor revolution. Each time the points open, a signal is sent to the computer. The computer uses the VSS signal for converter clutch lockup and cruise control operation. In some applications, the VSS is located in the speedometer head.

Neutral Drive Switch

The **neutral drive switch (NDS)** is operated by the transmission linkage. If the transmission is in park or neutral, the NDS is closed. When the transmission is placed in drive or reverse, the NDS opens. A closed NDS sends a voltage signal below 1 volt to the computer, whereas an open NDS provides a signal above 5 volts to the computer (Figure 6-42).

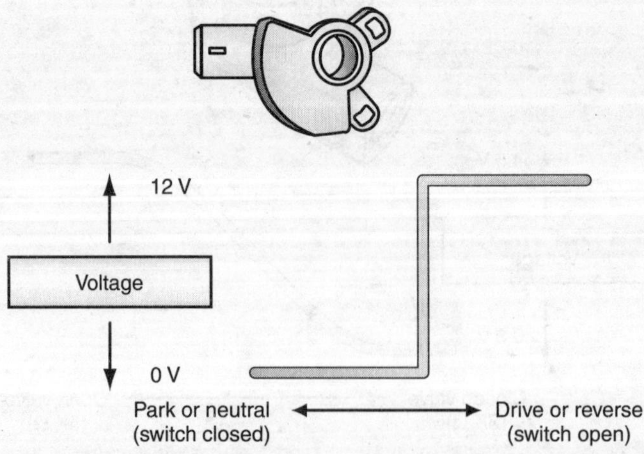

FIGURE 6-42 *Neutral-drive switch and related voltage signal.*

The NDS switch signal informs the computer regarding gear shift selector position, and the computer uses this signal to control idle speed. The NDS may be referred to as a neutral-park switch.

Brake Switch

The brake switch changes the voltage state of the computer when the brake is applied and again when it is released. This signal can be used as an input to control idle speed, EGR operation, torque converter clutch or cruise control disengagement, or to modify ignition timing.

Air-Conditioning (A/C) Demand Sensor

Air-conditioning systems are integrated into the PCM and engine management systems to signal when the compressor clutch is cycling. When closed, this pressure switch sends a voltage signal to the PCM. The PCM uses this signal to control idle speed and, on some engines, timing.

Engine Position Sensors

The engine position sensor indicates the speed of the engine and the piston's position at top dead center. This signal is used for timing control, fuel injection pulse and synchronization (if sequentially fired), and precise idle speed control. Although there are several types of sensors, all will provide a voltage signal to the PCM and change proportionately in relation to specific engine position and speed. This may be referred to as a distributor pickup coil, a crankshaft (Figure 6-43) or camshaft sensor, or a profile ignition pickup sensor. The sensor can be either a Hall effect design or variable reluctance/magnetic pulse generator type.

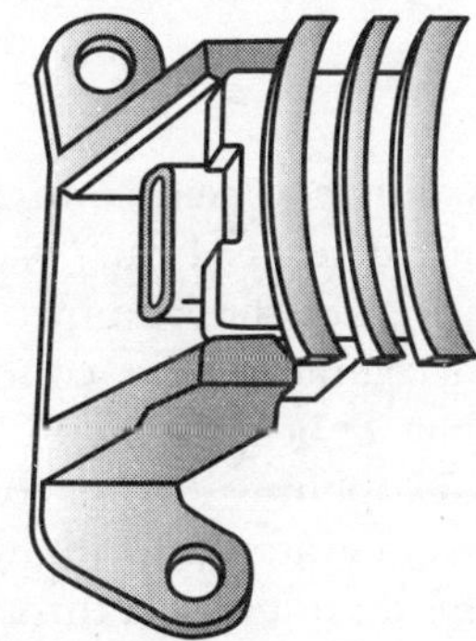

FIGURE 6-43 *A dual Hall-effect crankshaft position sensor.*

Power Steering (PS) Switch

The PS switch simply tells the PCM when there is high pressure in the power steering system due to high pump demands such as turning the steering wheel when parking. The PCM then compensates for the engine load by appropriately increasing idle speed.

System Voltage Monitor

Without proper voltage supply or adequate charging system performance, the engine management system will not operate as designed. The PCM monitors system voltage and is constantly adjusting to compensate for varying load conditions. For example, during high electrical load demands, the PCM can modify the charging system rate, fuel injector pulse width, and ignition timing as needed.

THROTTLE ACTUATOR CONTROL (TAC) SYSTEM

Throttle actuator control (TAC) is used to control the throttle opening by the PCM (Figure 6-44). The throttle is actually moved by a reversible DC electric motor that is mounted on the throttle body. Figure 6-45 shows a block diagram of a typical TAC system. The advantages of a TAC, or which some call "throttle by wire," are many. One of the best is the fact that the throttle becomes a computer output based on input from the driver. This way, the PCM can calculate the best throttle opening for the desired operation, instead of reacting to the actions of the driver directly. This also

FIGURE 6-44 *Throttle valve actuator system.*

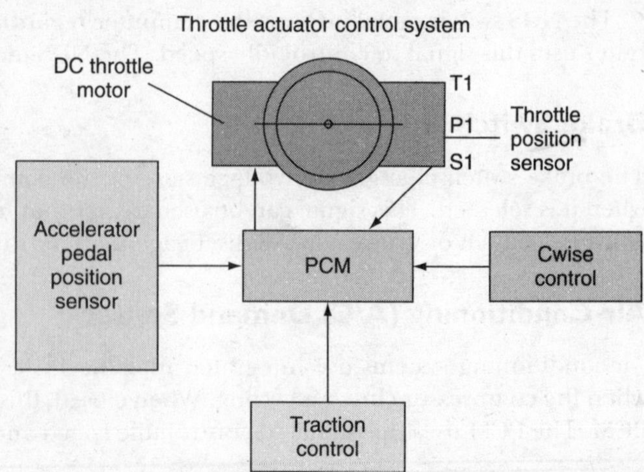

FIGURE 6-45 *Block diagram of a throttle actuator control system.*

allows for increased control for traction control systems. The PCM can "back-off' the throttle to help prevent slippage by a driver over applying the accelerator. Idle control systems are also eliminated, because the PCM controls the idle by throttle opening. Cruise control systems are also easily integrated into the design. Most of these systems do not have a throttle cable for back-up, but a few still do. Any problems that are detected result in the shutdown of the system, sometimes completely, sometimes with severely limited functionality because of safety concerns.

The **Accelerator pedal position (APP) sensor** is usually mounted on the accelerator pedal itself, as in Figure 6-46. Some vehicles that still have an accelerator cable have the sensor mounted on the throttle body. The APP sensor has three potentiometers to make sure that the signal is reliable. Figure 6-47 shows a wiring diagram for both the APP and TP sensors.

FIGURE 6-46 *The accelerator pedal position (APP) sensor is usually located on the accelerator pedal.*

The TP sensor used with this system is also backed up by using two sensors instead of one. One sensor checks the integrity of the other; if there is a discrepancy, the system is shut down. Most of these sensors are potentiometer type; however, some are Hall effect type.

Hall Effect TPS

A new style of throttle position sensor is being used that does not depend on a potentiometer. This sensor is also utilized on the TAC systems. The Hall effect TP sensor is a bit different than the shutter style used on most ignition system and crank position sensors. The Hall effect TP sensor uses two

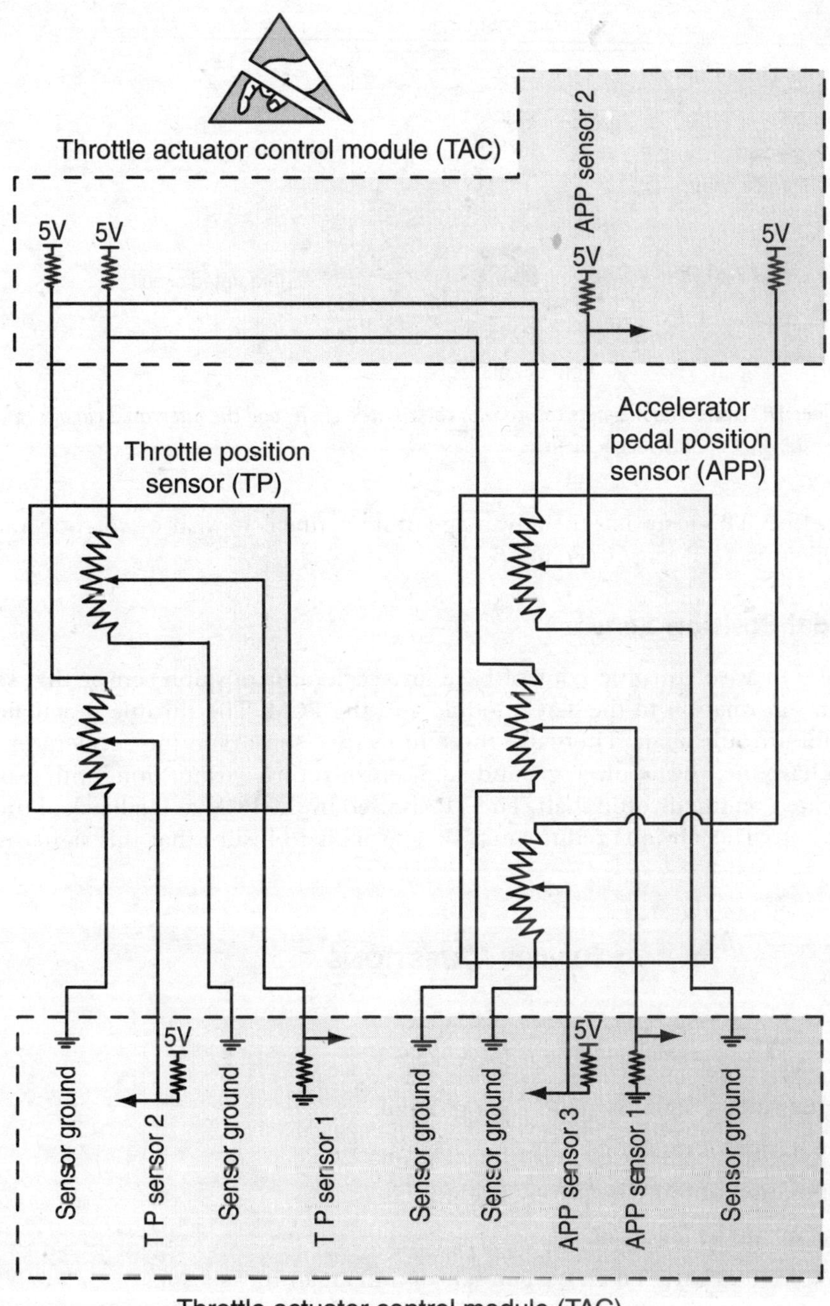

FIGURE 6-47 *Schematic for an accelerator pedal position sensor and related hardware*

magnets of opposite polarity and two **linear** Hall effect sensor-integrated circuits: Circuit A is the actual throttle position voltage, and B is used to check the integrity of circuit A. The scan tool will show a throttle valve between 10 and 24 percent at idle (depending on the desired idle speed) and a fully open throttle anywhere between 64 and 96 percent. If a failure occurs, the default value is about 16 percent throttle opening. Electrically, the output of the sensor looks much like the action of two potentiometers used previously.

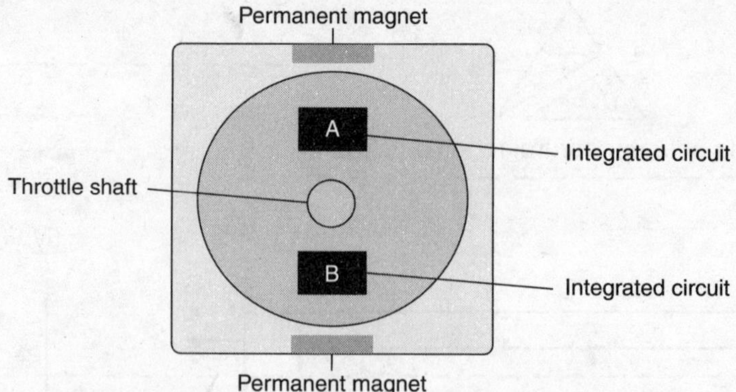

FIGURE 6-48 *A Hall effect TP sensor. The magnets rotate with the throttle shaft, and the integrated circuits measure movement by measuring the effect of the magnetic field.*

This linear Hall effect TP sensor has the advantage of no contacts to wear or corrode and is even referred to as a non-contact TP sensor (Figure 6-48).

Accelerator Pedal Position Sensor

Vehicles that use "fly by wire" throttle control have an accelerator position sensor that sends the accelerator position information to the TAC module and the PCM. The throttle is actuated by an electric motor on the throttle shaft. There are three individual sensors in the accelerator position sensor, all of which have their own power, ground, and sensor return wiring, along with two throttle position sensors located on the throttle shaft. The TPS is used by the PCM as feedback of the correct position and operation. The obvious redundancy of sensors is to insure that this signal is correct (Figure 6-47).

REVIEW QUESTIONS

Short Answer Essays

1. Compare a digital voltage signal with an analog signal.
2. Describe the operation of the knock sensor.
3. Describe the operation of the Wheatstone bridge.
4. Describe what is meant by feedback.
5. Describe the differences between an oxygen sensor and an air-fuel sensor.
6. Explain the conditions that cause an oxygen (O_2) sensor to produce high and low voltage.
7. Explain the advantage of the titania type O_2 sensor compared to the zirconia-type O_2 sensor.
8. What is meant by the term pulse width?
9. Explain the operation of a hot wire-type mass air flow (MAF) sensor.
10. Describe the voltage signals from the neutral drive switch to the computer with this switch open and closed.

Fill-in-the-Blanks

1. Most computer input sensors produce _______________ voltage signals.
2. A digital voltage signal may be called a _______________ _______________ signal.
3. The term binary means _______________ values.
4. A reference voltage sensor provides input by _______________ or _______________ a constant, predetermined voltage signal.
5. _______________ means data concerning the effects of the computer's commands are fed back to the computer as an input.
6. When the air-fuel ratio is lean, the oxygen (O_2) sensor voltage is _______________.
7. If the coolant temperature increases, the voltage drop across the engine coolant temperature (ECT) sensor _______________.
8. The three wires connected to a manifold absolute pressure (MAP) sensor are the ground wire, signal wire, and _______________ _______________ wire.
9. In a vane-type air flow sensor, the pointer on the potentiometer is connected to the _______________ _______________.
10. In some MAF sensors, the burn-off circuit is activated when the ignition switch is turned _______________.

Multiple Choice

1. *Technician A* says that an analog signal is continuously variable.

   Technician B says that a digital signal is either on or off.

   Who is correct?

   A. Technician A C. Both technicians

   B. Technician B D. Neither technician

2. *Technician A* says the TP sensor is a reference voltage sensor.

   Technician B says the oxygen sensor is a voltage generating sensor.

   Who is correct?

   A. Technician A C. Both technicians

   B. Technician B D. Neither technician

3. The signal from most sensors must be amplified and converted from:

   A. analog to digital

   B. binary to digital

   C. digital to analog

   D. voltage reference to voltage generating

4. *Technician A* says that computer feedback is information sent back to the computer to confirm that a command was carried out by an actuator.

   Technician B says feedback can also be in the form of a monitored voltage signal to a switch or relay.

   Who is correct?

   A. Technician A C. Both technicians

   B. Technician B D. Neither technician

5. *Technician A* says the pickup coil is also known as the stator.
   Technician B says the pickup coil can also be called the pole piece.
   Who is correct?
   A. Technician A C. Both technicians
   B. Technician B D. Neither technician
6. *Technician A* says the Hall effect switch contains an electro-magnet.
   Technician B says the Hall effect switch also uses a shutter wheel connected to a rotational component.
   Who is correct?
   A. Technician A C. Both technicians
   B. Technician B D. Neither technician
7. *Technician A* says that the oxygen sensor produces a high signal voltage when the exhaust is lean.
   Technician B says the oxygen sensor produces a low voltage signal when the exhaust is rich.
   Who is correct?
   A. Technician A C. Both technicians
   B. Technician B D. Neither technician
8. *Technician A* says the air-fuel ratio sensor produces below 3.3 volts in a negative direction when the exhaust is rich.
   Technician B says the air-fuel ratio sensor operates at a lower temperature than the convention oxygen sensor.
   Who is correct?
   A. Technician A C. Both technicians
   B. Technician B D. Neither technician
9. *Technician A* says the engine coolant temperature sensor (ECT) signal is used by the PCM to provide a lean mixture when the engine is cold.
   Technician B says the signal is used by the PCM to provide less spark advance on a hot engine.
   Who is correct?
   A. Technician A C. Both technicians
   B. Technician B D. Neither technician
10. *Technician A* says that the intake air temperature (IAT) sensor is a voltage generating sensor.
    Technician B says the vane-type airflow sensor is a reference voltage sensor.
    Who is correct?
    A. Technician A C. Both technicians
    B. Technician B D. Neither technician

COMPUTER OUTPUTS AND NETWORKS

7

Upon completion and review of this chapter, you should be able to:

- Describe high-side and low-side drivers.
- Explain how computer output drivers operate most output actuators.
- Describe quad drivers and output driver modules.
- Explain duty cycle.
- Explain pulse width modulation.
- Explain the output driver's role in the operation of fuel injectors.
- Describe computer control of the IAC system.
- Describe the PCM output role in the operation of the EGR valve.
- Describe computer output control of electronic spark timing.
- Provide a brief overview of electronic transmission control by the PCM.
- Describe vehicle computer networking.
- Explain a serial data bus.
- Describe UART, J1850, KWP2000, and ISO 9141 communications.
- Explain the operation of controller area networking.
- Explain two types of vehicle module wiring configurations.
- Describe peer-to-peer and master-to-slave communication.
- Examine vehicle network module function and PCM relationship.

INTRODUCTION

The modern PCM must have a host of both input and output devices in order to function. You have already studied computer inputs. In this chapter we will have an in-depth look into computer outputs and the latest in computer networking. Vehicle wiring and computer integration are undergoing a revolution by utilizing smart modules placed strategically throughout the vehicle that have the ability to communicate and make decisions. Computer networking language is dramatically changing the way vehicles communicate with scan tools and with modules on the vehicle's own serial bus.

BASIC CIRCUIT CONTROL

Any circuit can be activated in one of two basic ways: by completing the ground path, or completing the path to power. The computer takes advantage of both of these methods of activating or completing a circuit (Figure 7-1). Since the computer only knows on and off, or digital signals, ways have to be developed to allow the PCM to communicate its commands in this manner.

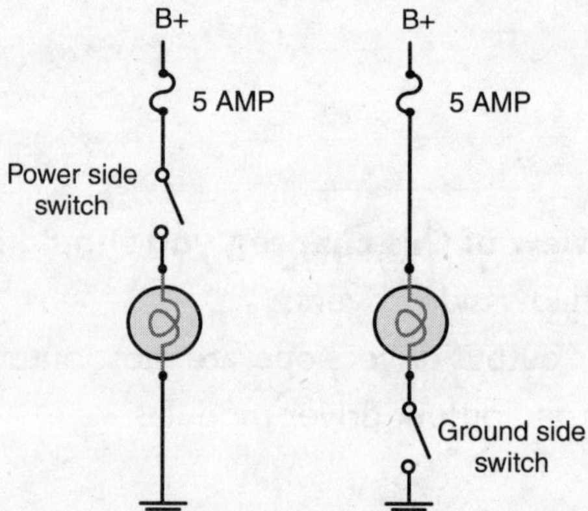

FIGURE 7-1 *A circuit can be switched from either the power or ground side.*

DRIVERS

The PCM uses transistorized switches called **drivers** to control circuits or devices. If the computer activates a component or circuit by completing a ground, it is referred to as a **low-side driver**. If the computer activates a circuit by providing power, it is referred to as a **high-side** or **feed-side driver**. Figure 7-2 shows a typical wiring diagram for the instrument cluster warning lamps that are controlled by the PCM by supplying the ground for the bulbs when the conditions are right. Notice that this particular wiring diagram does not show a simplified representation of the complex circuitry inside the PCM, but since the power is supplied continually through the fuse, a technician will know this is how the circuit works. An example of a PCM providing power to a circuit is shown in Figure 7-3. The PCM turns the fuel pump relay coil on, the relay then closes and provides power to the fuel pump. The use of a relay prevents the PCM from handling large amounts of current flow. You may notice that in Figure 7-3 that a small switch to B+ is a simplified representation of a computer driver. Some figures may show a transistor that actually represents a driver inside the PCM, as in Figure 7-4.

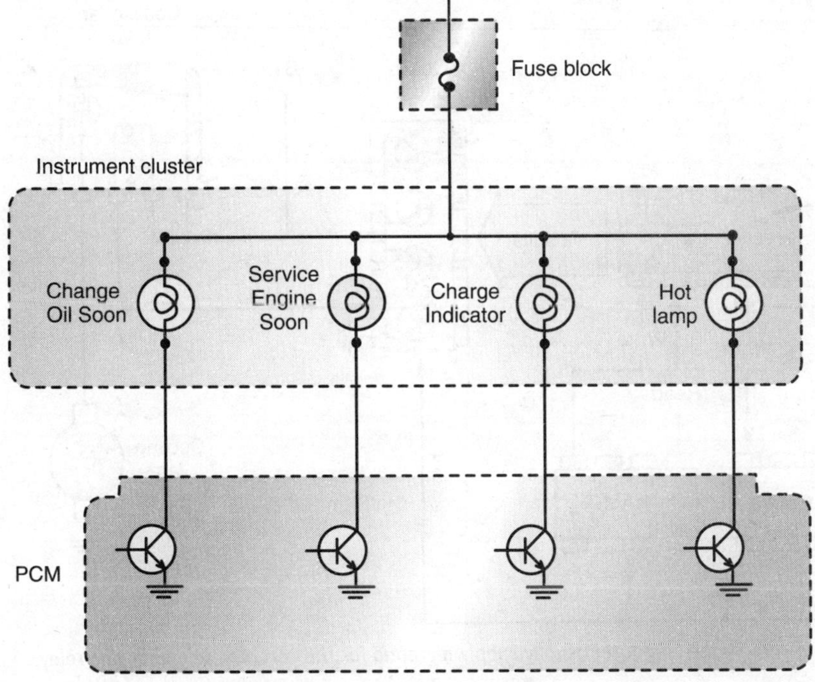

FIGURE 7-2 *These warning lamps are turned on by the PCM by supplying ground.*

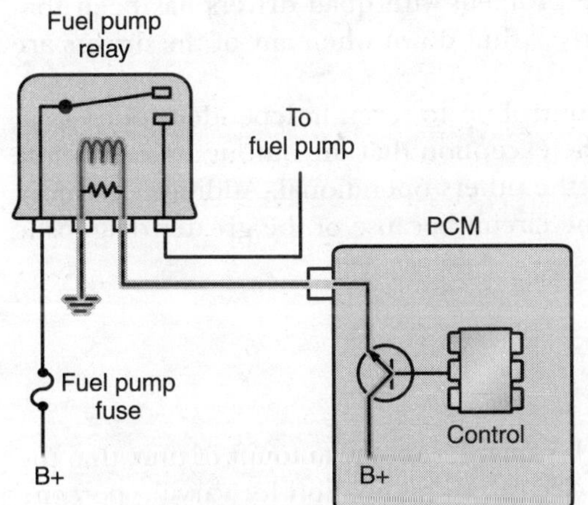

FIGURE 7-3 *This fuel pump relay coil is activated by the PCM supplying power.*

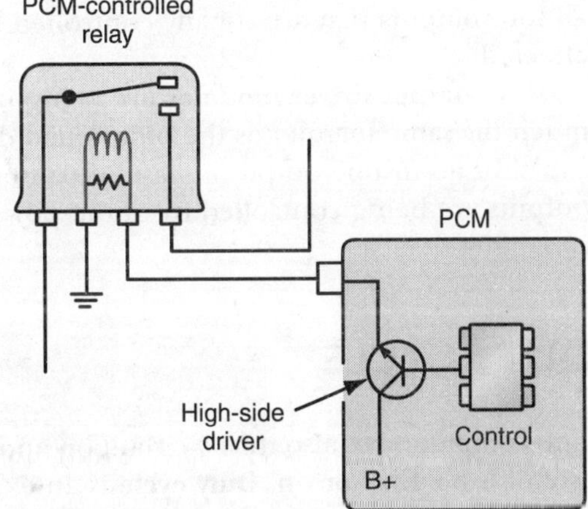

FIGURE 7-4 *A high-side driver shown as a single transistor inside the PCM.*

The computer uses **quad drivers** or **output drivers** to activate a circuit or actuator. Quad drivers are assembled into groups of four (Figure 7-5). A quad driver has four independently controllable outputs that generally operate by completing a ground to the controlled circuit. Since the early 1990s, quad drivers have had electronic circuit breakers to protect themselves in the event of over-amperage. Prior to that time, many PCMs were replaced due to the output drivers burning out. The quad drivers were damaged by components such as solenoids or relay coils shorting internally and lowering the controlled circuit resistance. With lower resistance, amperage levels climbed too high

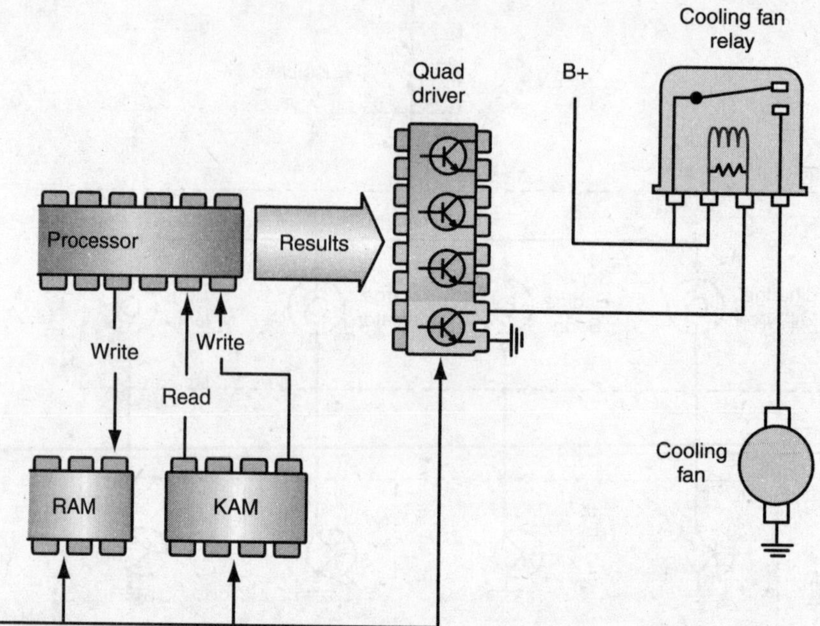

FIGURE 7-5 *Output drivers on the computer usually supply a ground for the actuator solenoids and relays.*

and damaged components. Modern quad drivers are able to set trouble codes and reset after the problem component or circuit has been replaced. The problem with quad drivers has been that all four outputs that are usually controlled by a quad driver shut down when any of the drivers are affected.

More **output driver modules** are being used which control up to seven independent outputs in much the same manner as the older quad driver, with the exception that the output driver module can shut down one output in case of trouble and leave the others operational. Additionally, more outputs are being controlled from the power sides of the circuit because of the greater diagnostic capability.

DUTY CYCLE

The computer can also turn a circuit on and off rapidly. It can also vary the amount of time that the circuit is held off or on. **Duty cycle** is an example. The circuit can be held on for varying percentages of a cycle. The cycle time remains constant as shown in Figure 7-6, Figure 7-7, and Figure 7-8. A 100-percent duty cycle would be a circuit that was on 100 percent of the time. A 0-percent duty cycle would be a circuit that was off 100 percent of the time.

PULSE WIDTH MODULATION

Another form of computer control is **pulse width modulation** (PWM). Pulse width modulation is the duration of on time, but is not connected to a specific cycle time. The on time of a pulse width modulated signal is usually measured in milliseconds (ms). The fuel injector control is a good example of pulse width modulation, but there are many uses such as lamp brightness control (Figure 7-9).

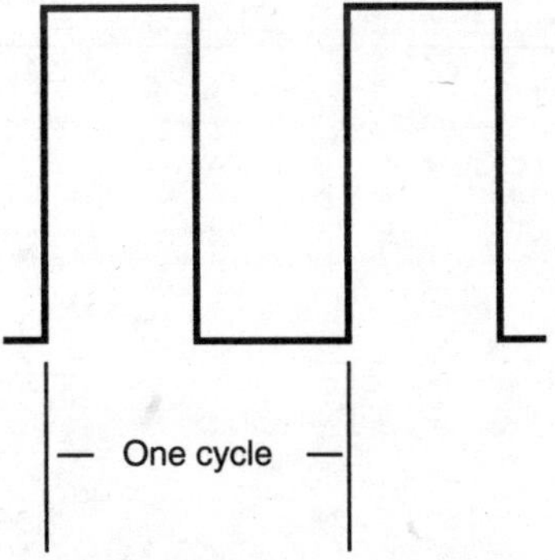

FIGURE 7-6 *One cycle of a digital signal.*

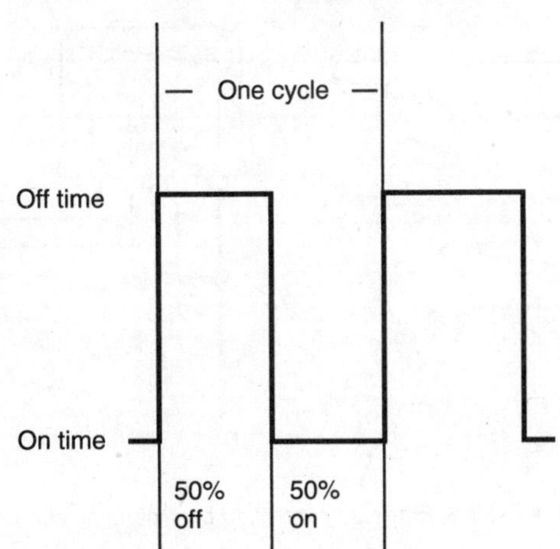

FIGURE 7-7 *A 50-percent duty cycle.*

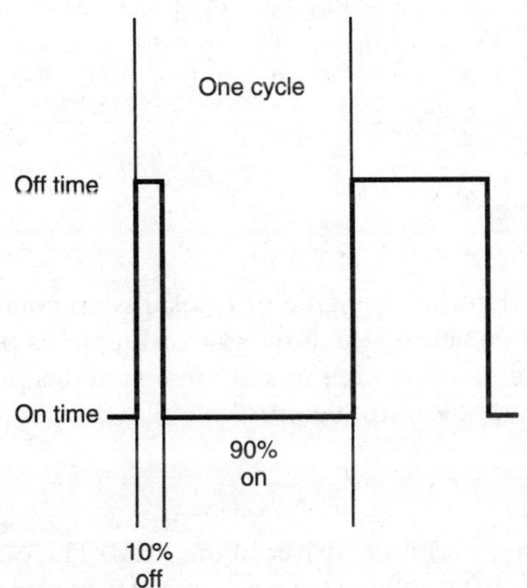

FIGURE 7-8 *A 10-percent duty cycle lasts 10 percent of a complete cycle.*

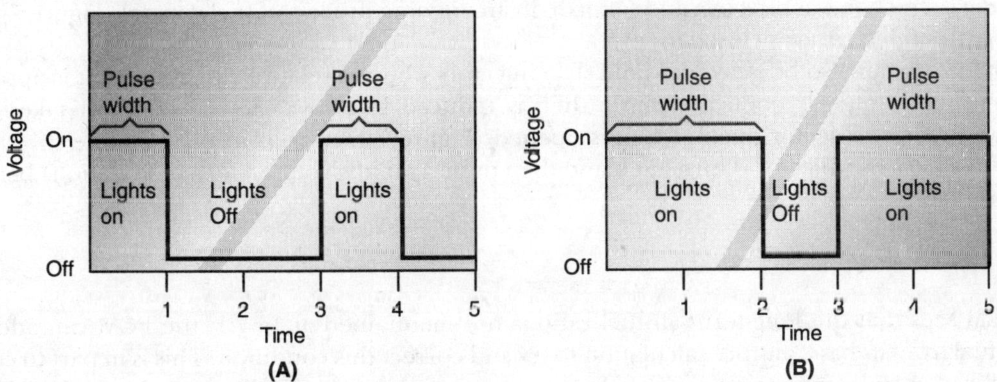

FIGURE 7-9 *Pulse width is the duration of on–off time: (A) pulse width modulation to achieve dimmer lights, (B) pulse width modulation to achieve brighter lights.*

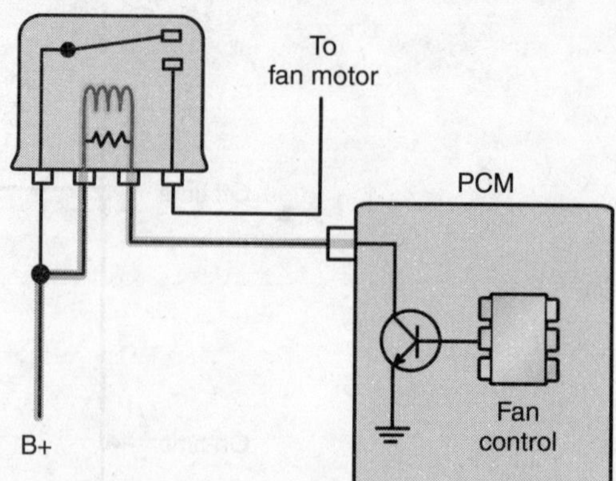

FIGURE 7-10 *A fan relay controlled by grounding the relay coil.*

Most of the devices currently in use are dash or information center displays and electromechanical devices: relays, motors, switches, and solenoids. Usually, the PCM circuit avoids controlling large amounts of current directly, such as a cooling fan. One way to control a large current with a smaller one is by using a relay. Using relays, the PCM can control such circuits as the cooling fan relay (Figure 7-10).

COMPUTER OUTPUTS

Computers all rely on inputs to determine engine or transmission conditions. The computer then processes the information and then acts on the inputs according to its programming. This information is also covered in more detail in other chapters in the text and is provided here as a brief overview during the discussion of computer output control.

Fuel Injectors

Fuel injectors are controlled by a ground-side driver in the PCM. The pulse width of the injector on time is changed based on inputs from the oxygen sensor, MAP, coolant temperature sensor, MAF, and others for optimum fuel control (Figure 7-11). The basic fuel control concept is based on the input from the oxygen sensor; the computer makes a correction and then checks the oxygen sensor to see if the correction was effective and so forth, in an ongoing process of fuel control (Figure 7-12). This process is referred to as closed loop.

Fuel injectors can also be **peak and hold**-style injectors where a relatively high current is applied to the injector to quickly open the pintle then is reduced to a lower level because it takes less current to hold the injector open after it is opened (Figure 7-13), or as in the example shown in Figure 7-14 where the injector is turned on and then pulsed rapidly (pulse width modulation) before being turned off.

Fuel Trim

If the PCM sees that the long-term air-fuel ratio is not maintained at 14.7:1, the PCM can add or subtract fuel from its basic air-fuel calculation to try and correct this condition. This is in part to compensate for wear on components as they age, or it may point to a fuel delivery problem. The pulse width of the injectors is changed to add or subtract fuel from the mixture. There are two commonly used names in relation to fuel trim. Long-term fuel trim is based on a long term trend of adding

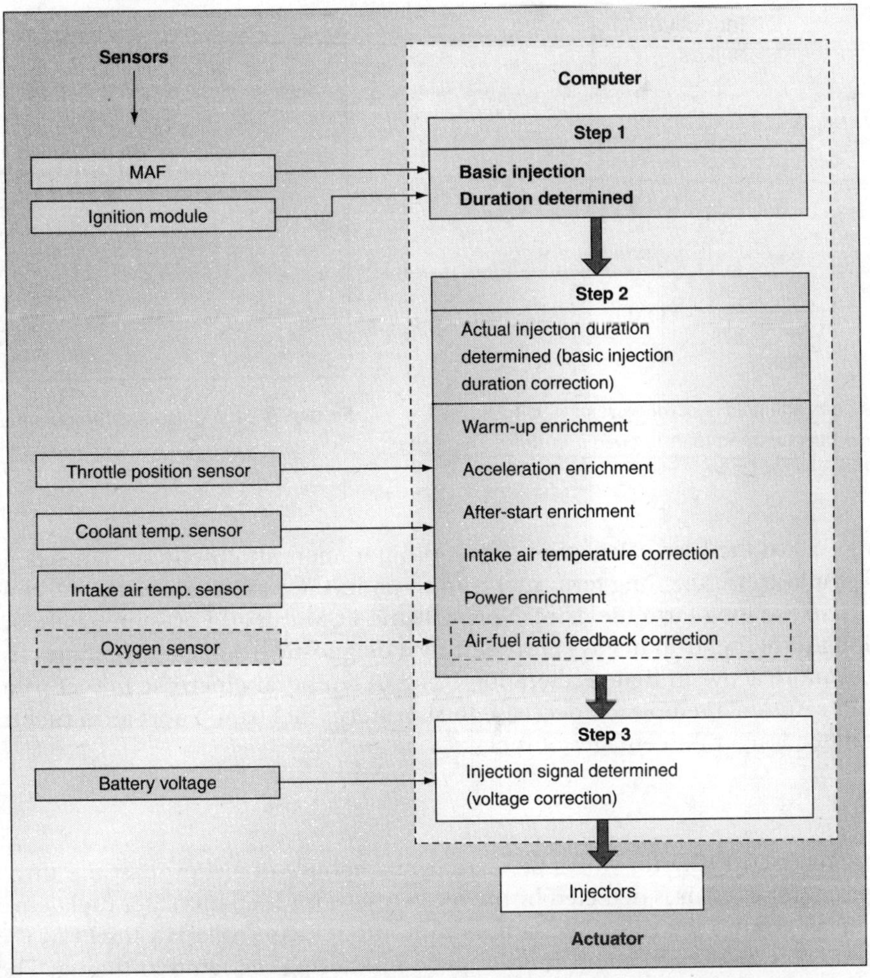

Sensors

MAF

Ignition module

Throttle position sensor

Coolant temp. sensor

Intake air temp. sensor

Oxygen sensor

Battery voltage

Computer

Step 1

Basic injection
Duration determined

Step 2

Actual injection duration determined (basic injection duration correction)

Warm-up enrichment

Acceleration enrichment

After-start enrichment

Intake air temperature correction

Power enrichment

Air-fuel ratio feedback correction

Step 3

Injection signal determined (voltage correction)

Injectors

Actuator

FIGURE 7-11 *Injector "on" time is determined by sensor inputs and the computer's programming.*

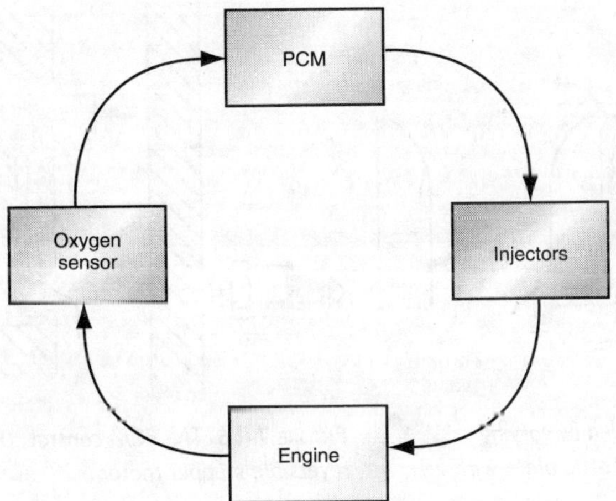

FIGURE 7-12 *The oxygen sensor reports on the amount of oxygen in the exhaust, the PCM adds or subtracts fuel as needed, then the process starts over again.*

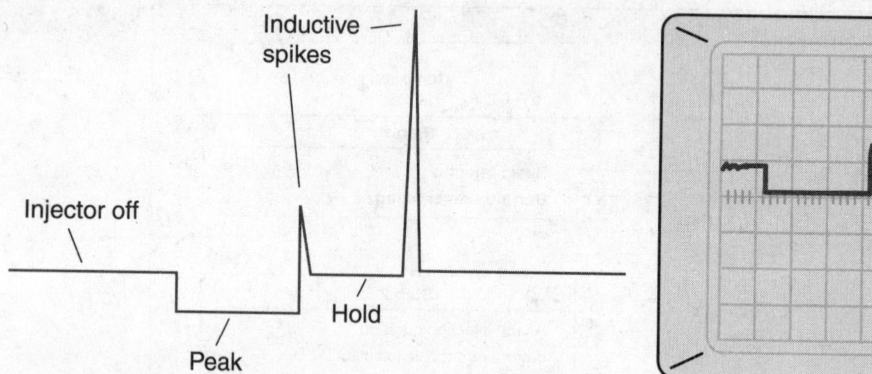

FIGURE 7-13 *A peak and hold injector waveform. It takes less energy to hold an injector open than to open it initially. The higher current opens the injector faster.*

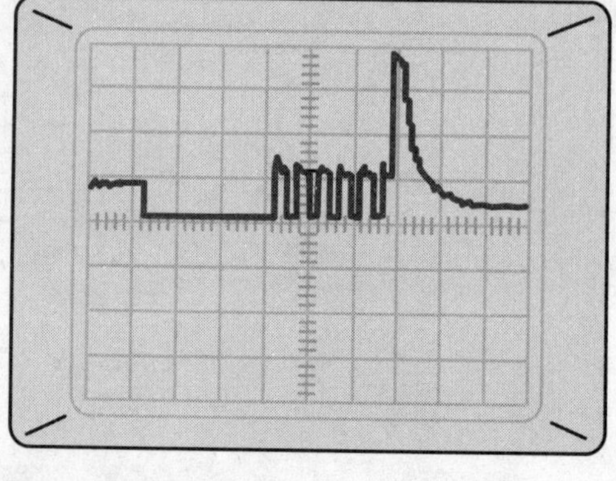

FIGURE 7-14 *A pulse width-modulated injector.*

or subtracting fuel to the base calculation that is programmed into the PCM. For example, a small vacuum leak would cause the long-term fuel trim to go in the positive direction (adding fuel) and would show up in the long-term fuel trim. Normally the PCM can add or subtract about 10 percent of the basic long-term fuel trim needs before setting a diagnostic trouble code. Short-term fuel trim, for example, is more active in that acceleration brings a temporary increase in fuel trim. Driving at low load would result in a temporary decrease in short-term fuel trim. Short-term fuel trim can add and subtract much longer percentages of fuel.

IAC

The IAC (idle air control) motor works by varying the amount of airflow past the throttle plate as shown in Figure 7-15. This air is detected by the oxygen sensor which increases fuel delivery and idle speed. The idle air control is a reversible stepper motor that is controlled by the PCM (Figure 7-16). The PCM also makes small corrections in idle speed by altering the ignition timing. The PCM uses the RPM signal as feed back for the system.

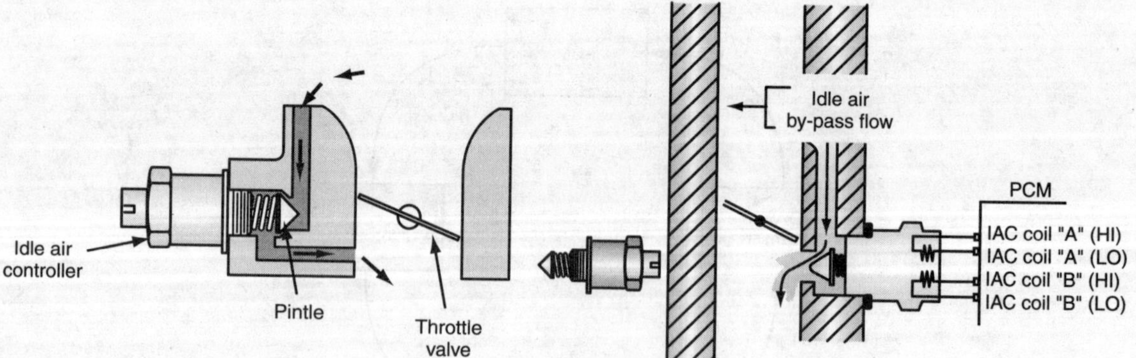

FIGURE 7-15 *The idle is controlled by varying the amount of air around the throttle plate with an IAC valve.*

FIGURE 7-16 *The PCM controls the IAC valve by using a reversible stepper motor.*

Throttle Actuator Control

On some vehicles, the throttle actuator control (TAC) system is an output from the PCM that controls cold idle speed, normal idle speed, cruise control, and traction control (Figure 7-17). Instead of an accelerator cable, a reversible DC motor is used to control the throttle operation. The output is based on information received by the PCM from the engine coolant, vehicle speed, cruise control, and traction control. The PCM also calculates engine performance information to place the throttle at the optimum location for power, fuel economy, and emissions.

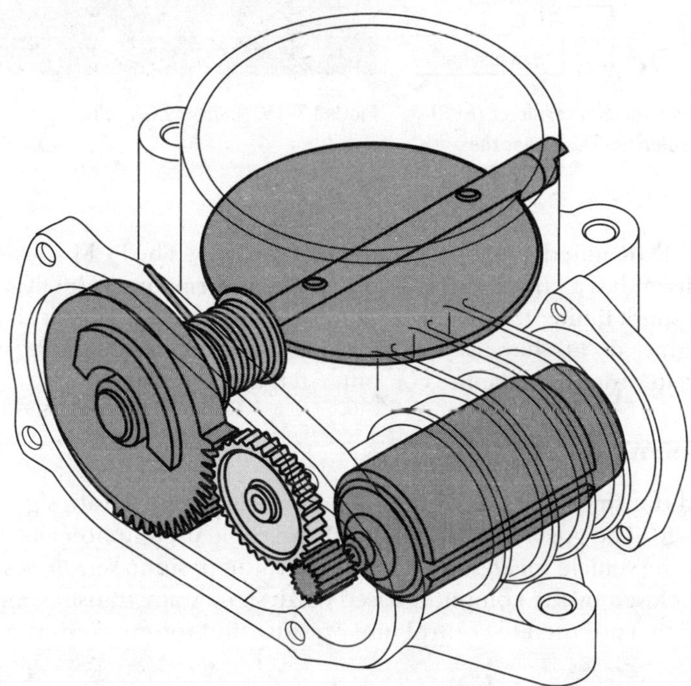

FIGURE 7-17 *A typical TAC.*

EGR

The EGR valve can be one of three basic types, linear, vacuum controlled, or digital. All EGR valves have been computer controlled for some time. An EGR valve that uses a computer-controlled duty cycle to an electronic vacuum regulator valve (EVR) is shown in (Figure 7-18). The EGR valve in Figure 7-19 is a linear EGR valve. The linear EGR valve is controlled by the PCM by pulse width modulation. The valve is a normally closed pintle opened by a solenoid. The digital EGR is comprised of three solenoids that all flow different amounts of EGR and can be opened or closed independently. The combination of open and closed solenoids permits seven different flow rates. In the case of the digital EGR valve, the solenoids are either turned on or off and are not modulated.

Electronic Spark Timing

One of the most important outputs of the PCM is the spark timing. Spark timing is one of the key elements for a successful and efficient combustion affecting both fuel economy and emissions. The PCM is equipped to make timing decisions by having all the important information needed, such as

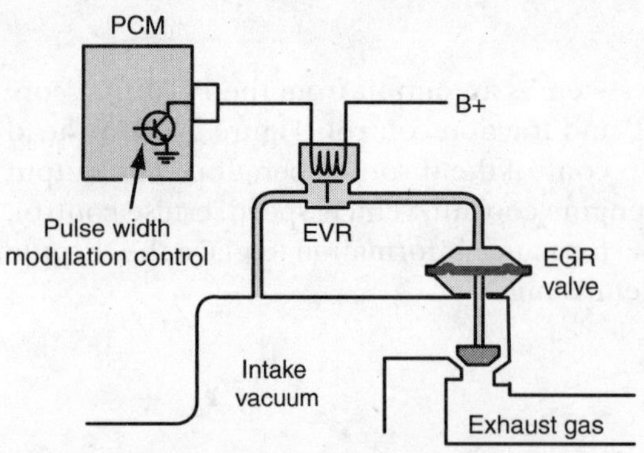

FIGURE 7-18 *The electronic vacuum regulator (EVR) is controlled by pulse modulation. This varies the vacuum applied.*

FIGURE 7-19 *A linear EGR valve.*

coolant temperature, EGR added, engine load, and mass air flow. The PCM knows if the engine starts to spark knock because it has a knock sensor to give it that information. The PCM sends a digital signal called **electronic spark timing (EST)**, to the ignition module that controls the ignition timing.

Many modern engines do not have adjustable timing. If timing is adjustable, it must be set to the proper "base" timing in order to make the computerized timing correct.

Transmission Control

Electronically shifted transmissions have several solenoids and control valves governed by the PCM, as shown in Figure 7-20. The governor and throttle valve cable used in non-electronic transmissions has been replaced by the vehicle speed sensor and the throttle position sensor, respectively. Shift solenoids are opened or closed by the computer based on design. Many transmissions have pulse width modulated solenoids that are used to control line pressure and torque converter clutch apply.

COMPUTER NETWORKING

Computer networking is a way for individual modules to share information between themselves. An example of this would be the anti-lock brake module. The PCM and the ABS computer both need vehicle speed information. Rather than using two individual sensors and the associated wiring or using one sensor and running individual wiring to both computers, it would be much easier for the PCM and the ABS computer to share information over the **serial data bus**. Imagine a network where many individual modules share information with each other as needed. Serial data is digitally encoded information that computers can share together. On your home personal computer, this is much like sharing information on an office intranet or worldwide over the Internet. Late-model vehicles have their own network of computers, or modules (Figure 7-21). Some modules still stand alone, some are capable of communicating and working with each other, and others take commands from another module as commands. Networking shares information and results in cutting down the number of connectors and the length of wiring, in addition to the added bonus of increased reliability while reducing costs.

Networking smaller, more specialized modules is more cost effective than using one or two centralized complex modules. The smaller, less complex modules can be added according to option

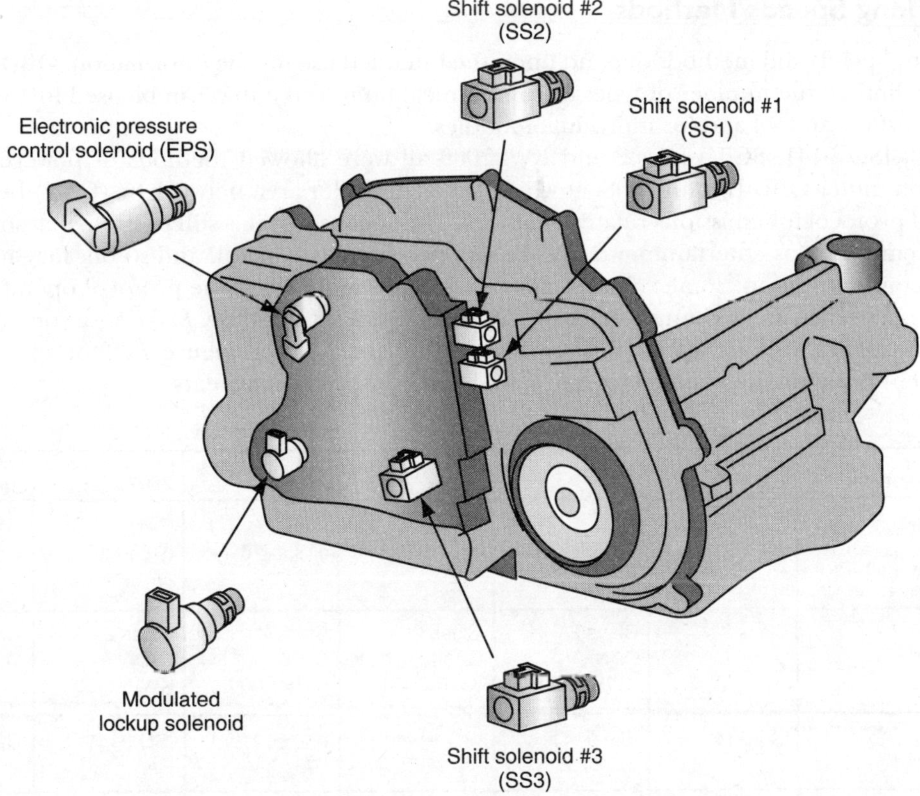

FIGURE 7-20 *Some of the electronically controlled actuators for an automatic transmission.*

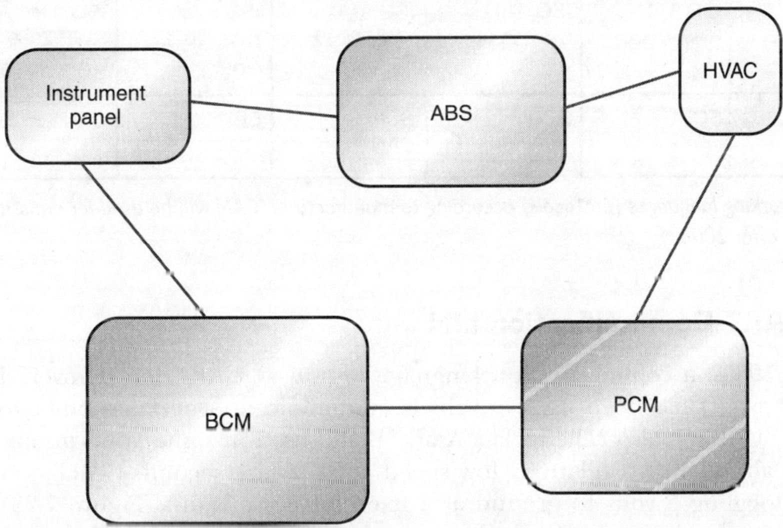

FIGURE 7-21 *Networked modules share information with each other over the serial data bus.*

content. An example would be a power window control module. Obviously, if the vehicle did not have power windows, this module would not be needed.

Networking Speeds/Methods

Networking speeds and methods depend upon the intended use for the information. OBD II regulations have limited the number of types of communication to three that can be used for connection to a diagnostic scan tool and/or individual modules.

Class B, ISO 9141, SCP, Class 2, and KWP2000 all were allowed methods of powertrain communication under OBD II until 2008, at which time controller area network or (CAN) became the mandated protocol for emissions-related modules. This means that it is still possible that some of the other systems, such as entertainment, HVAC, security, stability control, and so on, may have other forms of communication. Some vehicles can and do have more than one protocol operating at the same time, especially since changes are happening so rapidly at this time. Make sure you understand the system you are working with before performing repairs. Look at Figure 7-22 for an example of the different programming languages that have been in use in recent years.

Manufacturer	2003	2004	2005	2006	2007	2008 AND Beyond
Chrysler	ISO 9141-2 J1850-10.4	CAN J1850-10.4	CAN J1850-10.4	CAN J1850-10.4	CAN J1850-10.4	CAN
GM	Class 2	Class 2 CAN KWP 2000	Class 2 CAN KWP 2000	Class 2 CAN KWP 2000	Class 2 CAN KWP 2000	CAN
Honda	ISO 9141	ISO 9141	ISO 9141	ISO 9141 CAN	ISO 9141 CAN	CAN
Toyota	ISO 9141	CAN ISO 9141	CAN ISO 9141	CAN	CAN	CAN
VW/Audi	ISO 9141 KWP 2000	ISO 9141 KWP 2000	ISO 9141 KWP 2000 CAN	ISO 9141 KWP 2000 CAN	ISO 9141 KWP 2000 CAN	CAN
Ford	SCP	SCP	SCP CAN	SCP CAN	CAN	CAN

FIGURE 7-22 *Networking languages (protocols) according to manufacturer. CAN will be used for emission module communication exclusively after 2008.*

Class A or UART Communication/LIN

Since the early 1980s, a communication language known as UART for (Universal Asynchronous Receive and Transmit) has been used in vehicle communication between on-board modules and diagnostic tools. UART is also called Class A and is still used in some applications as a communication protocol although it is relatively low speed at 8192 bits/second. UART accomplishes communication by toggling 5 volts to ground at a fixed bit pulse width (Figure 7-23). LIN or Local Interconnect Network is a low-speed supplemental data base that uses UART communication along with up to 15 slave modules.

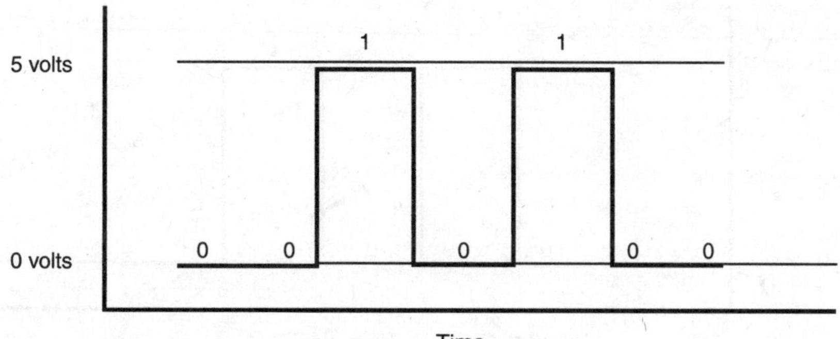

FIGURE 7-23 *UART communication is based on a fixed bit pulse width.*

Class B/J1850/SCP

With a speed of 10,400 bits/second, Class B (also called J1850) communication is faster than UART. Ford has been using a Class B communication standard they call SCP for Standard Corporate Protocol along with an ISO 9141 network which will be discussed later. Modules that are configured on the SCP allow communication between individual modules in addition to interfacing with a scan tool. GM's Class B communication is called Class 2. Class 2 communications are different than UART in that instead of toggling a voltage from high to low and using 5 volts, it toggles a voltage from 0 to 7 volts, and the signal can be sent in long or short pulse widths (Figure 7-24).

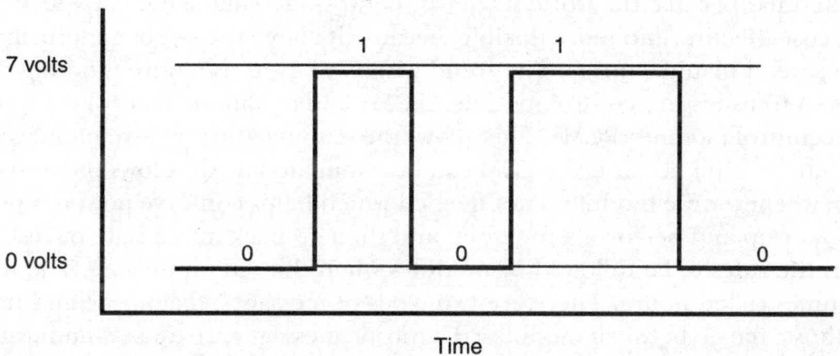

FIGURE 7-24 *Class 2 communication has different pulse times.*

ISO 9141/KWP2000

ISO 9141 is similar to UART in that it is a bit-by-bit-style communication method instead of a pulse width communication, and instead of working on 5 volts and 0 volts, it works on 12 volts and 0 volt (Figure 7-25). ISO 9141 requires a scan tool that asks a module for the information needed and the module responds. Some Ford vehicles use ISO 9141 for communication with the **Electronic Crash Sensor (ECS)** in addition to the Class B SCP described earlier. DaimlerChrysler and the Asian automakers have used ISO 9141 on many vehicles. ISO 9141 is not a communication language in the sense that it links separate modules, but is used to allow a scan tool to communicate with a module and is used for diagnostics only. When the vehicle network is operating in normal mode, it may be using different communication rates and methods. European automakers are using KWP2000 (Key

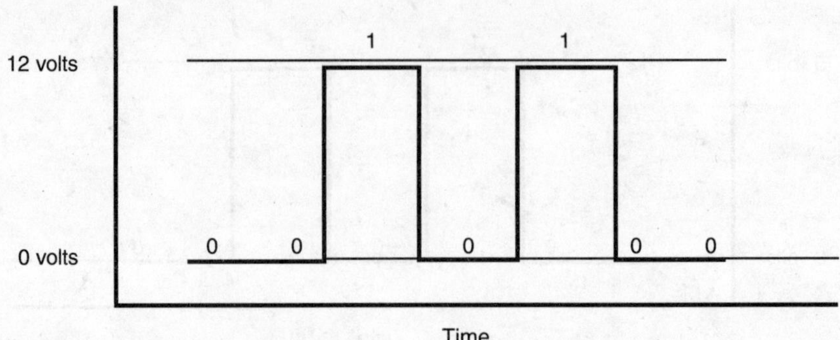

FIGURE 7-25 *ISO communication.*

Word Protocol 2000) that is similar to the Japanese ISO 9141 in that it is used for diagnostics only, but can be used to connect a scan tool to more than one module.

Controller Area Network, or CAN J2284/ISO 15765-4

Starting in 2008, the only communication standard that can be used for emissions-related modules is **CAN (Controller Area Network)** but was used by many manufacturers sooner.

CAN is a universal communication method or "language" used that allows sharing of technology around the world. CAN was developed by Bosch in 1984 for the automotive industry and was first used on some Mercedes Benz models in the early nineties. Since then, CAN has found its way on many devices and has became the world leader in networking languages. CAN technology is faster, more reliable, cost-effective, and more flexible, because it allows the use of generic modules that are available from several manufacturers. The trend with CAN is to use more modules, for example, a vehicle may use a transmission control module (TCM) and an engine control computer in place of the powertrain control module (PCM). This allows the manufacturer to save money on vehicles that use a manual transmission because the TCM can be eliminated. CAN allows the individual modules to power down whenever the module is not needed which helps conserve power. A module can wait for a signal, power up and perform a function, and then go back into a state of rest. The CAN language contains the rules to be followed by modules when they communicate. The individual modules are sometimes called nodes. There are two types of messages: diagnostic and normal. Normal messages are those that go between modules; diagnostic messages are those communicated to a scan tool. Each CAN message contains the following information:

- A signal that informs the other modules that a message is following
- The priority of the following message is communicated. A low priority message will have to wait on a higher priority message.
- The size of the message
- Checks for message reliability
- Other modules acknowledge the message

Each module in CAN receives every communication, but only the messages with the correct heading are responded to by the module. Each module also sends out a periodic message telling the other modules that it is online. If a module fails to "check in" with the other modules, a trouble code is set. There are defaults that can be used for most modules if they fail to prevent the entire system from going down in the event that one of the modules should fail.

CAN currently has some commonly used versions referred to "speeds" or "classes," although there are no hard-and-fast rules that bind designers to a particular speed.

- Class A is a low-speed language that runs at speeds up to 10.4 Kbps. This could be used for such items as a driver-operated switch.
- Class B or CAN-B, a medium-speed language that can be a single wire. Its use for large amounts of information speed is not an issue. It can communicate at speeds up to 83 Kbps.
- Class C or CAN C, referred to as high-speed CAN than can run as fast as 1 Mbps. This data bus is used for "real time" engine performance, anti-lock brake, and active suspension control. The wiring for CAN C is a twisted pair to help prevent electrical interference. The bus wires are connected by a termination resistor at the end which helps to prevent 'reflected' messages coming over the bus.

Figure 7-26 shows a typical high-speed CAN electrical signal. The 'idle' voltage is about 2.5 volts. The modules look for the difference in voltage levels between CAN+ and CAN–. The positive voltage goes to about 3.5 volts and the negative down to 1.3 volts.

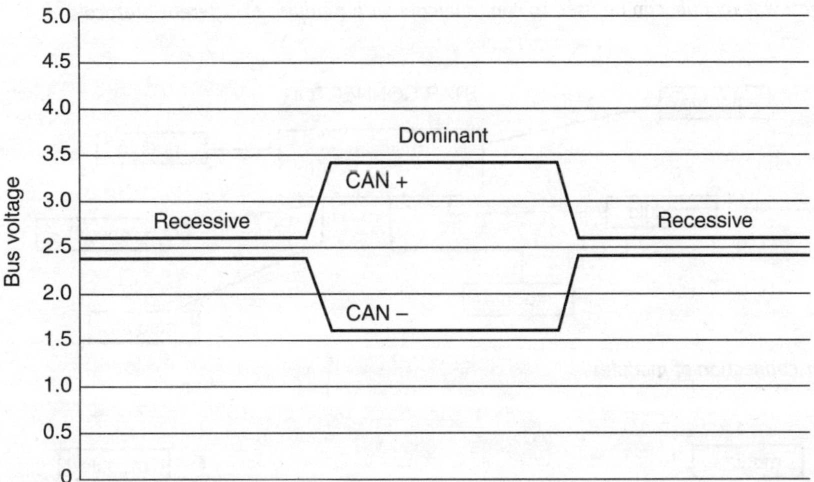

FIGURE 7-26 *CAN-C high speed messages are transmitted as a voltage differential.*

As stated above, the CAN communication standard relates only to emission-control modules, so some vehicles will use CAN along with a 'gateway' module to communicate with other protocols as shown in Figure 7-27. The gateway module can translate and share serial data over the other busses and diagnostic scan tools as well. The LIN modules are low priority, low-speed body control devices that do not need sophisticated communications.

Network Wiring

There are two primary ways to wire the serial bus in a vehicle network; **star** and **loop**. The star network is shown in Figure 7-28. The star network uses star connectors as junction blocks to join the serial bus. In the loop network (Figure 7-29), the modules are connected in series. The advantage of the loop network is that there has to be two opens to affect the network (Figure 7-30). It only takes one open to affect the star network, but only the module on the affected line goes down (Figure 7-31).

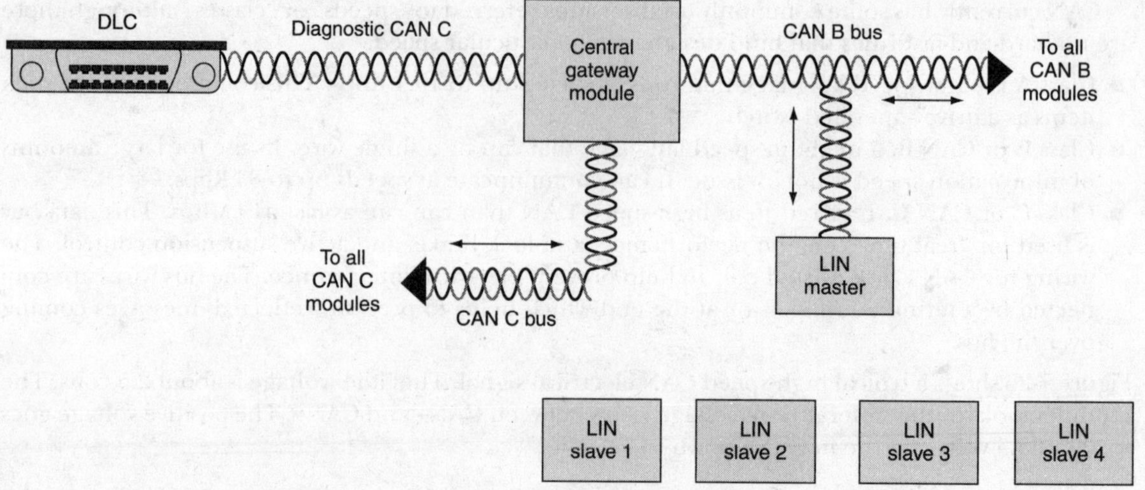

FIGURE 7-27 *A gateway module can be used to communicate with modules of different protocols.*

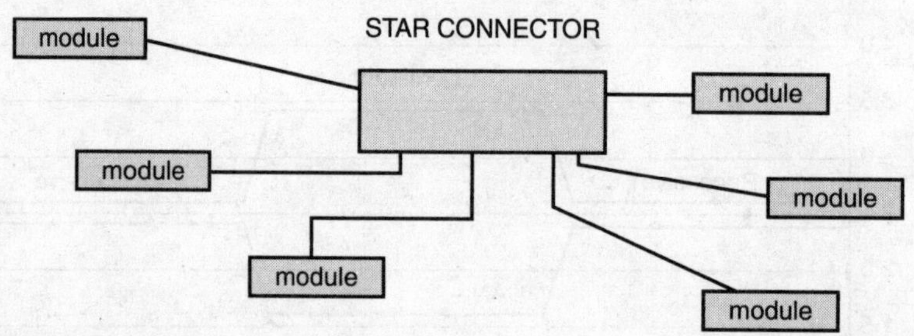

FIGURE 7-28 *Star connection of modules.*

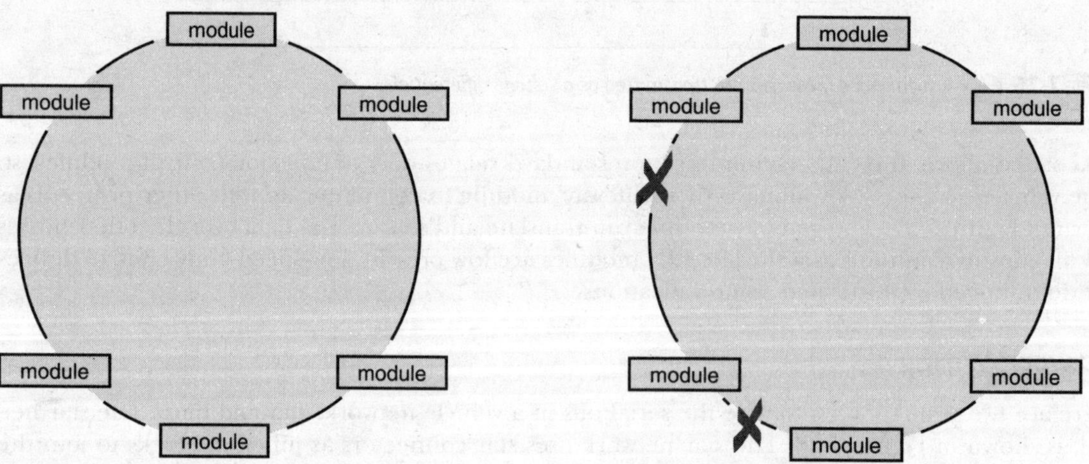

FIGURE 7-29 *Loop network connections of modules.*

FIGURE 7-30 *Two faults are resumed to isolate a module from the loop network.*

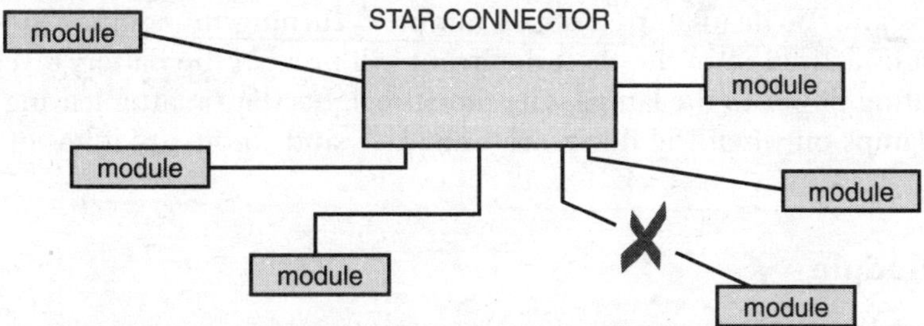

FIGURE 7-31 *One fault will isolate a module on a star-style network, but only one module is affected.*

Peer-to-Peer and Master-to-Slave Communication

Some modules on the serial bus can initiate communication with other modules on the serial data bus. These modules are called **masters**. Some modules are referred to as **slaves**. Slaves just listen to instruction from the master and relay confirmation that instructions have been carried out (Figure 7-32).

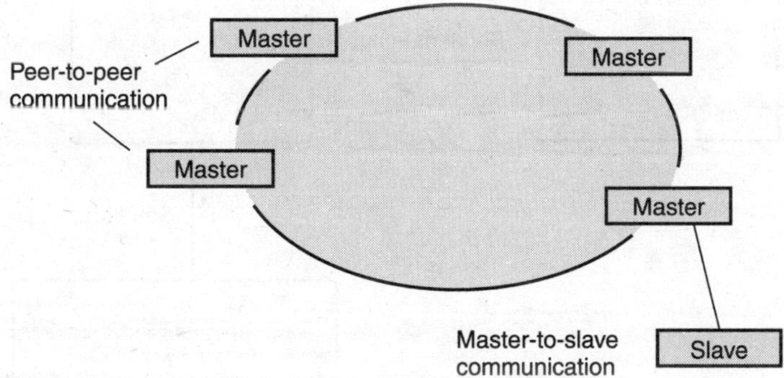

FIGURE 7-32 *Peer-to-peer and master-to-slave communication slaves cannot initiate communication on the serial bus.*

Modules of the Vehicle Network

We will look at some of the more common computer modules in recent use. The use of modules can allow for **customization** of the module's function. This section will give you an idea of how the modules work together and why they are used. As a note, most of the various body control modules have to be reprogrammed when replaced in order to function properly. Some modules have to be asked for their information that is collected and used to reprogram the replacement module. Once again, there is vast variety in the number, placement, naming, and use of various body control modules, and technologies are changing rapidly. This explanation of body control modules does not cover every available make and function, but tries to familiarize you with the vehicle networking concept. Make sure that you have the factory service information available to you to actually begin diagnosis of these systems.

Lighting Control Module

For this example we will look at the function of the lighting control module from Ford. This **lighting control module (LCM)** takes care of the warning chimes, interior and exterior lighting, and theft deterrent. The lighting control module has a battery saver function that will disrupt power to the courtesy lamps and/or headlamps after 10 minutes. Turning the ignition switch to the run or accessory position or activation of the theft deterrent will prevent the battery saver by disabling the timers and reinstating power to the lamps. The time the lights stay on after leaving the vehicle, turning the courtesy lamps on when the doors are unlocked, and so on, are a few of the customizable functions.

Driver Door Module

The **driver door module (DMM)**-controlled functions include the power windows, power door locks, remote keyless entry, and others depending on the make and model of the vehicle. See Figure 7-33 for a block diagram example of module operation for a typical GM product. The DDM receives a signal from the driver to open the passenger window. The DDM sends a serial message over the network to all the modules that the window is to be rolled down. Since it is addressed only to the **front passenger door module (FPDM)**, it reads the message and then rolls the window down.

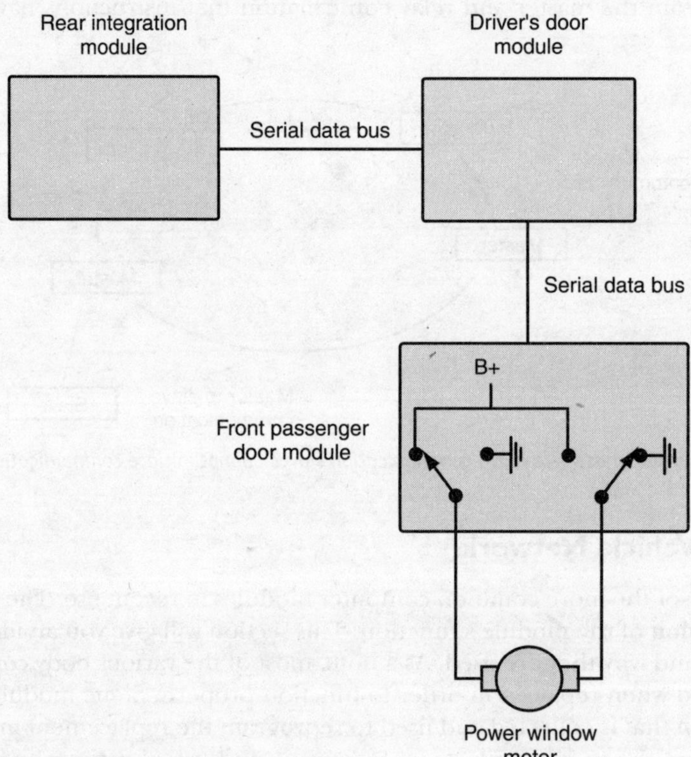

FIGURE 7-33 *Interaction of rear integration module, driver's door module, and front passenger door module of a typical GM product.*

The FPDM is a slave module that can receive messages and send acknowledgment that a command has been executed but it has no access to the main serial bus. You may notice that the FPDM has the ability to provide either power or ground for the circuit to operate.

Heating and Air Conditioning

The electronic heating and air conditioning system has been in vehicles for some time. In order to provide the most efficient and comfortable climate control, these systems have also moved towards integration into the body control system (Figure 7-34). The system described originated on a Ford product, but most manufacturer systems are similar. The climate control assembly is used to input the desired temperature, which is sent to the **electronic automatic temperature control (EATC)** module. The EATC then knows what course of action to take based on the **ambient air temperature sensor**, the **in-car temperature sensor**, and the **A/C sunload temperature sensor**. The temperature sensors report directly to the EATC, and the A/C compressor clutch is controlled from the PCM based on evaporator discharge temperatures by way of an evaporator temperature sensor. The PCM also has the last word on whether the A/C will be allowed to operate when the EATC requests; for instance, if the engine temperature is too high, the PCM may prevent A/C clutch operation. The EATC automatically controls the temperature control actuator, the outlet position, and blower motor settings. The temperature sensors and sunload sensor give the EATC a basis for action. For example, if the difference in the inside and outside temperatures is great, then the EATC knows that the temperature control door will need to be moved as far as possible to heat after the engine has reached operation temperature. If the selected vehicle temperature is close to the outside air temperature, then the blower speed may be set to low, and very little regulation of heating and cooling may be required.

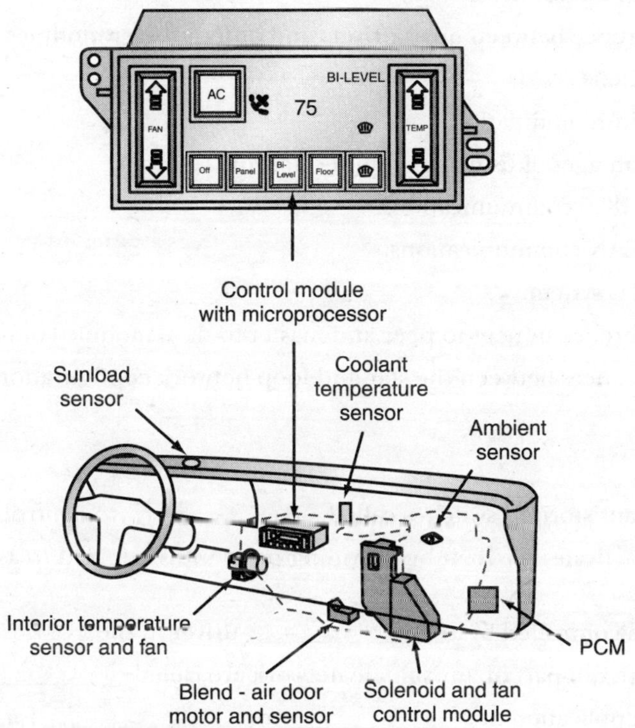

FIGURE 7-34 *Typical automatic air-conditioning system components.*

Anti-Theft Systems

Ford uses an anti-theft system called PATS, for passive anti-theft system, or SecuriLock® uses a specially encoded key that must be programmed into the system. There is a PATS transceiver module located inside the steering column that reads the key's identification and sends it to the PCM. If there is a problem with the system, the theft indicator will either stay on steady or flash rapidly.

Daimler/Chrysler uses a system called **VTSS**, for **vehicle theft security system**. The system uses a **BCM**, or **body control module**. The BCM communicates with the **power door module (PDM)**, which also has the keyless entry receiver functions. The BCM receives inputs from the door lock and door-ajar switches and the ignition switch. The BCM is programmed to interpret a vehicle break-in or activation of the "panic button" and will flash the headlamps and blow the horn in short intervals.

Standalone Modules

Some modules that are not part of any vehicle network are called **standalone modules**. An example would be found in some vehicles' sunroof control. There are a set of switches connected to a module whose sole purpose is the control of the sunroof function.

Review Questions

Short Answer Essays

1. Describe high-side output drivers.
2. Explain the difference between quad drivers and output driver modules.
3. Describe duty cycle.
4. Describe pulse width modulation.
5. Describe the advantages of using a computer network.
6. Briefly describe J1850 communications.
7. Briefly describe CAN communications.
8. Describe the EATC system.
9. Describe the difference in peer-to peer and master-to-slave module communication.
10. Explain the differences between the star and loop network configurations.

Fill-in-the-Blank

1. The PCM uses transistorized switches called ____________ to control circuits or devices.
2. If the computer activates a circuit by providing power, it is referred to as a ____________ or ____________.
3. Fuel injectors are controlled by a ____________ driver in the PCM.
4. Some modules are not part of any vehicle network are called ____________.
5. Duty cycle is the application of ____________ or ____________ for a percentage of a fixed cycle.
6. ____________ is the oldest and slowest type of vehicle computer communication.
7. Vehicle modules communicate with each other over a ____________.
8. Recently, the Japanese have been using ____________ for scan tool diagnostic communication.

9. Class 2 is the GM name for ______________ communication.
10. Ford calls their J1850 communication ______________.

Multiple Choice

1. *Technician A* says that a circuit can be turned on by switching power to the circuit.
   Technician B says a circuit can be switched on by supplying ground to the circuit.
   Who is correct?
   A. Technician A C. Both technicians
   B. Technician B D. Neither technician

2. *Technician A* says a low-side driver switches power to activate a device.
   Technician B says an output driver can control up to five devices independently.
   Who is correct?
   A. Technician A C. Both technicians
   B. Technician B D. Neither technician

3. *Technician A* says a quad-driver has four independently controlled outputs.
   Technician B says that modern quad-drivers do not have a self-resetting circuit breaker in case a controlled device is shorted.
   Who is correct?
   A. Technician A C. Both technicians
   B. Technician B D. Neither technician

4. *Technician A* says that Ford's J1850 standard of communication is called DLP.
   Technician B says that GM's J1850 standard of communication is called Class 2.
   Who is correct?
   A. Technician A C. Both technicians
   B. Technician B D. Neither technician

5. *Technician A* says that duty cycle is a percentage of time in a fixed cycle that a device is on.
   Technician B says that a 50 percent duty cycle means that the device was on for 1/2 second.
   Who is correct?
   A. Technician A C. Both technicians
   B. Technician B D. Neither technician

6. While discussing pulse width modulation (PWM),
   Technician A says that pulse width is measured in a length of time, not a percentage of a cycle.
   Technician B says that the cooling fan relay is usually controlled by the PCM through PWM.
   Who is correct?
   A. Technician A C. Both technicians
   B. Technician B D. Neither technician

7. *Technician A* says that long-term fuel trim is constantly changing for driving conditions.
   Technician B says that the PCM can add or subtract about 10 percent of the base fuel trim before setting a trouble code.

Who is correct?

A. Technician A C. Both technicians

B. Technician B D. Neither technician

8. *Technician A* says that governors and throttle valve cables used in earlier transmissions have largely been replaced by the vehicle speed sensor and TP sensor in modern, electrically shifted transmissions.

   Technician B says that pulse width modulated solenoids also control line pressure.

   Who is correct?

   A. Technician A C. Both technicians

   B. Technician B D. Neither technician

9. *Technician A* says the communications protocol called UART has been around since the early 1980s.

   Technician B says CAN is the standard for all emissions-related modules starting in 2010.

   Who is correct?

   A. Technician A C. Both technicians

   B. Technician B D. Neither technician

10. All CAN protocol messages contain all of the following information ***except***:

    A. The size of the message

    B. Message reliability

    C. Other modules acknowledge the message

    D. The speed of the message

ON-BOARD DIAGNOSTIC (OBD II) AND COMPUTER SYSTEMS

8

Upon completion and review of this chapter, you should be able to:

- Explain the reasons for On-Board Diagnostics (OBD) II.
- Describe the primary provisions of OBD II.
- Explain the requirements to illuminate the malfunction indicator light (MIL) in an OBD II system.
- Briefly describe the monitored systems in an OBD II system.
- Describe the main hardware differences between an OBD II system and other systems.
- Explain the advantage of an EEPROM compared to a PROM.
- Describe an OBD II warm-up cycle.
- Explain trip and drive cycle in an OBD II system.
- Describe how engine misfire is detected in an OBD II system.
- Describe the differences between a type A and type B misfire.
- Describe the purpose of having two oxygen sensors in an exhaust system.
- List five mandates in OBD II.
- Briefly describe what the comprehensive component monitor looks at.

- Describe briefly the design of a microprocessor chip and state the basic purpose of this chip.
- Explain briefly how the microprocessor stores and retrieves information.
- Describe the purpose of random access memory (RAM).
- Explain the terms volatile and nonvolatile memory.
- Describe the purpose of read only memory (ROM).

INTRODUCTION

Technological advances are being made every year to keep pace with more stringent emission laws and consumer demands. These advancements include computer-controlled engine systems that help provide more power, better performance, lower emissions, and better fuel economy. From one year to the next, changes are common among all manufacturers. Because of this, it would be impossible to memorize all engine control systems and test procedures on every vehicle ever built. It is essential to verify the VIN when performing any service on the vehicle and always use the appropriate service manual. Subtle changes in components or system design can cause changes in diagnostic procedures. Costly mistakes have been made failing to verify the vehicle information before the diagnosis or repair begins. The on-board diagnostic capabilities found in vehicles equipped with computerized engine controls provide the technician with a greater troubleshooting advantage. Once the technician understands the vehicle's operating system and testing routines, the computer can be used to reveal the source of most performance problems. A typical engine control system is shown in Figure 8-1.

The On-Board Diagnostic II (OBD II) systems were developed in response to the federal government's and the state of California's emission control system monitoring standards for all automotive manufacturers. The main goal of OBD II was to detect when engine or system wear or when component failure caused exhaust emissions to increase by 50 percent or more. Additionally, monitoring and protecting the catalytic converter is one of the major priorities of an OBD II system. OBD II also called for standard service procedures without the use of dedicated special tools. To accomplish these goals, manufacturers needed to change many aspects of their electronic engine control systems. According to the guidelines of OBD II, all vehicles must have:

- A universal diagnostic test connector, known as the data link connector (DLC), with dedicated pin assignments.
- A standard location for the DLC. It must be under the dash on the driver's side of the vehicle and must be visible (SAE standard J1962).
- A standard list of diagnostic trouble codes (DTCs) (SAEs standard J2012).
- A standard communication protocol (SAE standard J1850). (CAN after 2008.)
- The use of common scan tools on all vehicle makes and modes (SAE standard J1979).
- Common diagnostic test modes (SAE standard J2190).
- Vehicle identification must be automatically transmitted to the scan tool.
- Stored trouble codes must be able to be cleared from the computer's memory with the scan tool.
- The ability to record and store in memory a freeze frame of the operating conditions that existed when a fault occurred.

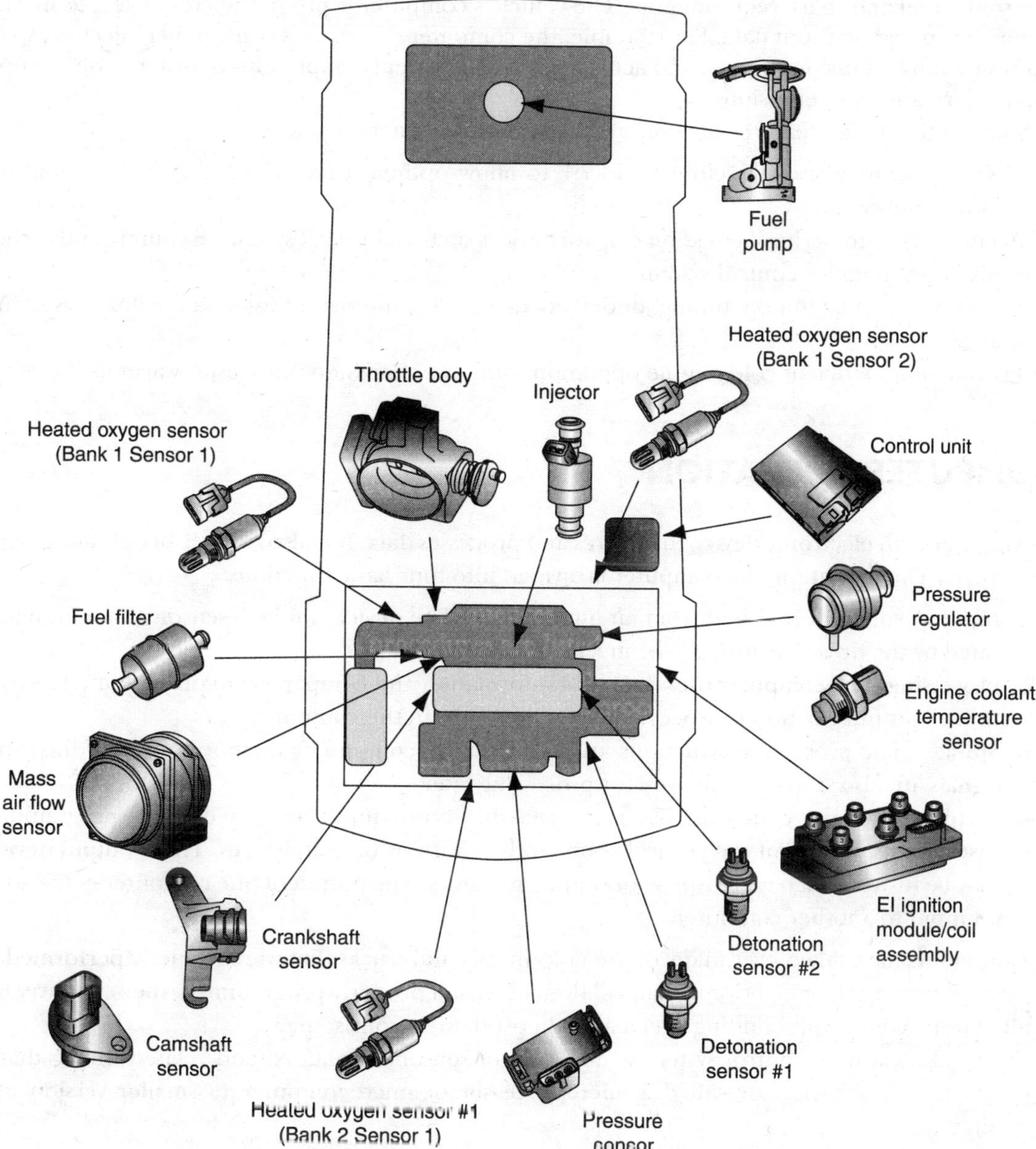

Figure 8-1 *Components of a typical engine control system.*

- The ability to store a code whenever something goes wrong and affects exhaust emissions.
- A standard glossary of terms, acronyms, and definitions must be used for all components in the electronic control systems (SAE standard J1930).

System Functions

Most electronic engine control systems work in a similar way regardless of the manufacturer. All systems require multiple input signals to indicate engine load, speed, and engine temperatures used to determine fuel and spark requirements. The vehicle's computer is programmed to execute specific commands based on input data. For example, the computer commands control fuel injectors, spark ignition timing, emission devices, and actuators or other system components in order to obtain optimal performance and emissions.

Some of the design features of computerized engine management are:

- Maintain air-fuel ratios as close to 14.7:1 to allow optimal catalytic converter operation and improve fuel economy.
- Accurately control critical emission control devices such as the EGR system, air pump, and carbon canister/evaporative control system.
- Precisely control ignition timing under all driving conditions adjusted for climate and fuel grade.
- Provide more efficient cold engine operation with lower emissions and faster warmups.

COMPUTER OPERATION

A computer is an electronic device that stores and processes data. It is also capable of operating other computers. The operation of a computer is divided into four basic functions:

1. Input: A voltage signal sent from an input device. The device can be a sensor or a button activated by the driver, technician, or mechanical part.
2. Processing: The computer uses the input information and compares it to programmed instructions. This information is processed by logic circuits in the computer.
3. Storage: The program instructions are stored in the computer's memory. Some of the input signals are also stored in memory for processing later.
4. Output: After the computer has processed the sensor input and checked its programmed instructions, it will put out control commands to various output devices. These output devices may be instrument panel displays or output actuators. The output of one computer may also be an input to another computer.

Computers have taken over many of the tasks in cars and trucks that were formerly performed by vacuum, mechanical, or electromechanical devices. When properly programmed, they can carry out explicit instructions with blinding speed and almost flawless consistency.

A typical electronic control system is made up of sensors, actuators, and related wiring that is tied into a central processor called a **microprocessor** or microcomputer (a smaller version of a computer).

The central processing unit (CPU) is the brain of a computer. The CPU is constructed of thousands of transistors that are placed on a small chip. The CPU brings information into and out of the computer's memory. The input information is processed in the CPU and checked against the program in the computer's memory. The CPU also checks the memory for any other information regarding programmed parameters. The information obtained by the CPU can be altered according to the instructions of the program. The CPU may be ordered to make logic decisions on the information received. Once these decisions or calculations are made, the CPU sends out commands to make the required corrections or adjustments to the system being controlled (Figure 8-2).

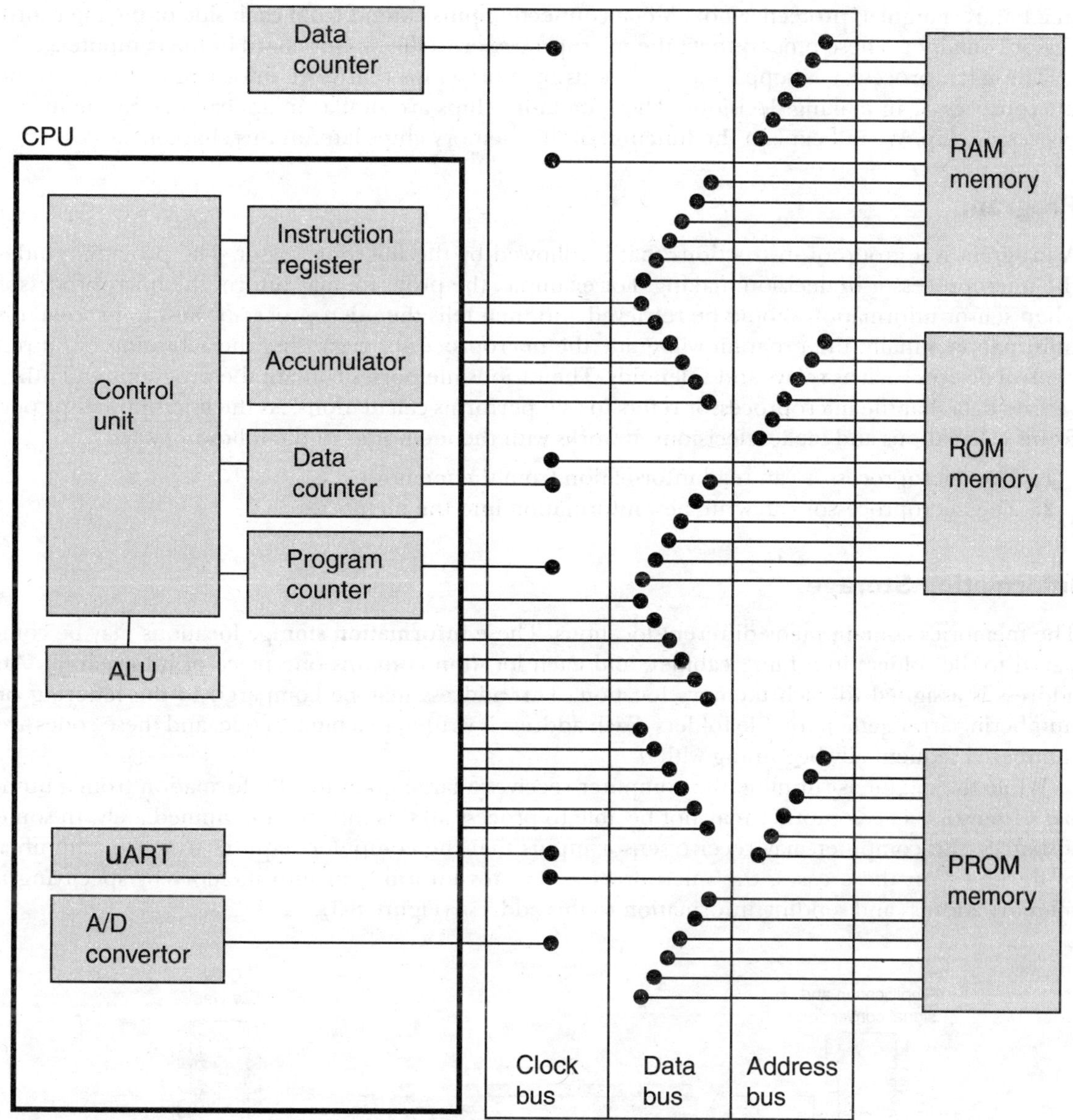

FIGURE 8-2 *Major components of a computer and its CPU.*

MICROPROCESSORS

Design

The microprocessor is the calculating and decision-making chip in a computer. Thousands of miniature transistors and diodes are contained in the microprocessor. These transistors act as electronic switches that are either on or off. The components in the microprocessor are etched on an integrated circuit (IC) that is small enough to fit on a fingertip. The silicon chip containing the IC is mounted in a flat, rectangular, protective box. Metal connecting pins extend from each side of the microprocessor container. These pins connect the microprocessor to the circuit board in the computer.

The microprocessor is supported by various memory chips that store information and help the microprocessor in making decisions. These memory chips are similar in appearance to the microprocessor chip. We will explain the function of the memory chips later in this chapter.

Program

A program is a group of instructions that is followed by the microprocessor. The program guides the microprocessor in decision making. For example, the program may inform the microprocessor when sensor information should be retrieved and then tells the microprocessor how to process this information. Finally, the program will guide the microprocessor regarding the activation of output control devices such as relays and solenoids. The various memories contain the programs and other vehicle data that the microprocessor refers to as it performs calculations. As the microprocessor performs calculations and makes decisions, it works with the memories in the following ways:

1. The microprocessor can read information from the memories.
2. The microprocessor can write new information into the memories.

Information Storage

The memories contain many different locations. These **information storage** locations may be compared to file folders in a filing cabinet, and each location contains one piece of information. An address is assigned to each memory location. This address may be compared to the lettering or numbering arrangement on file folders. Each address is written in a binary code, and these codes are numbered sequentially beginning with 0.

While the engine is running, the computer receives a large quantity of information from a number of sensors. The computer may not be able to process all this information immediately. In some instances, the computer may receive sensor inputs that the computer requires to make a number of decisions. In these cases, the microprocessor writes information into memory by specifying a memory address and sending information to this address (Figure 8-3).

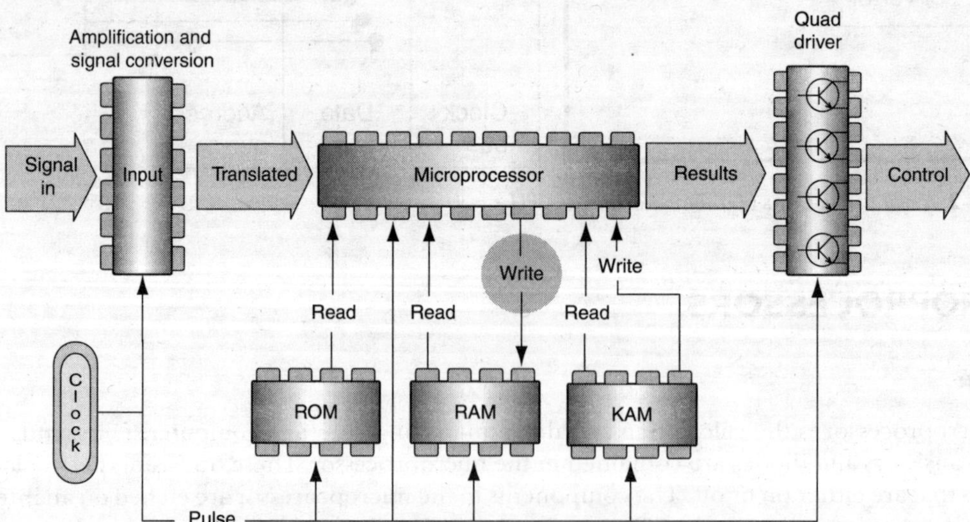

FIGURE 8-3 *Information storage.*

Information Retrieval

When stored information is required, the microprocessor specifies the stored information address and requests the information. This is known as **information retrieval**. When stored information is requested from a specific address, the memory sends a copy of this information to the microprocessor. However, the original stored information is still retained in the memory address.

The memories store information regarding the ideal air-fuel ratios for various operating conditions. The sensors inform the computer about the engine and vehicle operating conditions. The microprocessor reads the ideal air-fuel ratio information from memory and compares this information with the sensor inputs. After this comparison, the microprocessor makes the necessary decision and operates the injectors to provide the exact air-fuel ratio required by the engine.

TYPES OF COMPUTER MEMORIES

A computer's memory holds the programs and other data, such as vehicle calibrations, that the microprocessor refers to in performing calculations. To the CPU, the program is a set of instructions or procedures that it must follow. Included in the program is information that tells the microprocessor when to retrieve input (based on temperature, time, and so on), how to process the input, and what to do with it once it has been processed. The microprocessor works with memory in two ways: it can read information from memory or change information in memory by writing in or storing new information.

Random Access Memory

Information that requires temporary storage is sent from the microprocessor to the **random access memory** (**RAM**). The information stored in the RAM is subject to change. Since the sensor input information changes frequently in relation to various operating conditions, this information is stored in the RAM (Figure 8-4). The microprocessor may write the results of calculations and other changeable data into the RAM. The microprocessor can write information into the RAM, read information from the RAM, and erase RAM information.

The term *random access* indicates that the microprocessor can retrieve information from any RAM address in any order. If the RAM has a volatile memory, each time the ignition switch is turned off, the information stored in the RAM is erased. RAMs may also be designed with a nonvolatile memory. This type of RAM retains information when the ignition switch is turned off. If the RAM has a volatile memory, new information will be written into the RAM when the engine is restarted.

Read Only Memory

The microprocessor can read information from the **read only memory** (**ROM**), but information cannot be written into the ROM by the microprocessor, and the microprocessor cannot erase ROM information (Figure 8-5). During the chip manufacturing process, information is programmed into the ROM. This information is not erased even if the battery terminals are disconnected.

The ROM contains look-up tables that contain information about how a vehicle should perform. For example, the look-up table would contain the ideal manifold vacuum under various engine operating conditions. The microprocessor compares the sensor inputs to the ideal vacuum in this table. If the sensor inputs indicate that the actual manifold vacuum is different from the ideal vacuum in look-up tables, the microprocessor will take some appropriate action.

The ROM also contains calibration tables regarding specific engine, transaxle or transmission, and differential specifications.

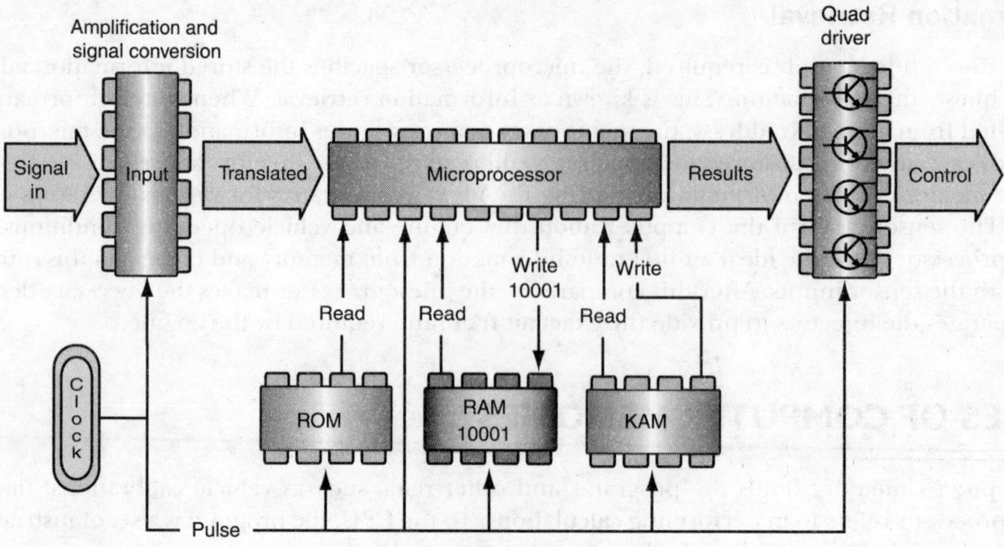

FIGURE 8-4 *Random access memory (RAM).*

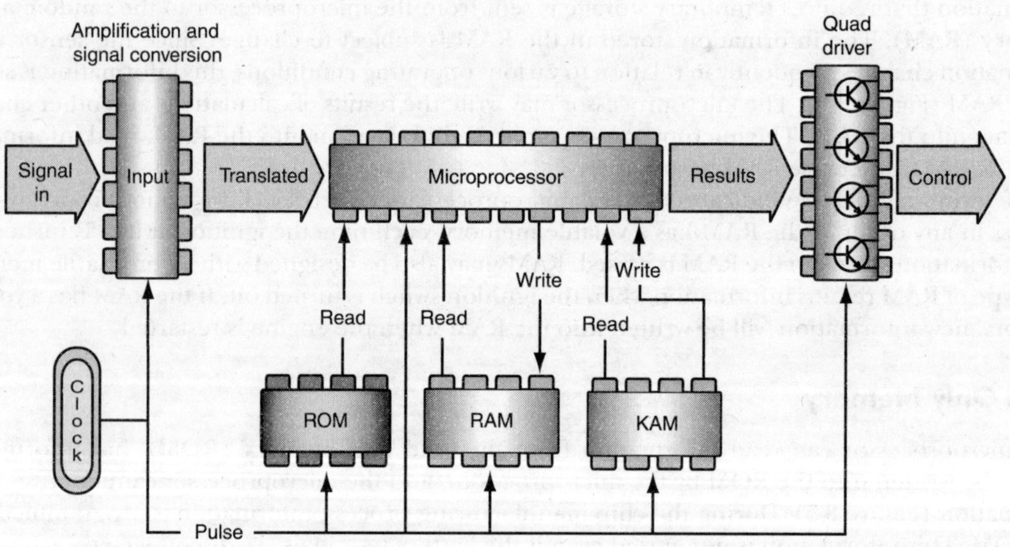

FIGURE 8-5 *Read only memory (ROM).*

Programmable Read Only Memory (PROM)

OBD I General Motors computers have a removable **programmable read only memory (PROM)**, which is serviced separately from the computer. The PROM contains specific programs such as the spark advance program, which is designed for the specific requirements of each vehicle. For example, this spark advance program varies with different transmissions or rear axle ratios.

OBD II computers are equipped with an **electronically erasable programmable read only memory (EEPROM)**. This type of memory chip may be reprogrammed easily by the manufacturer, and these are not chips usually serviced separately from the computer.

If an OBD II computer is replaced, the operating instructions for the vehicle must be programmed into the computer before use. The replacement PCM is much like a new personal computer that has to have software installed before use. Information stored in the PCM has to be tailored to the exact vehicle being serviced according to the VIN number. This programmed is called **flashing** the PCM. The elimination of the replaceable PROM chip was part of the OBD II legislation to prevent the use of aftermarket high-performance PROMs. There is an advantage to not using the replaceable PROM in that many updates for engine performance concerns can be performed during service by changing the **calibration** of the PCM without the need of having replacement parts. This calibration change is called **reflashing** the PCM. When servicing OBD II vehicles, always check for service bulletins that will alert the technician to any available service updates, including reflashing information.

Keep Alive Memory

The **keep alive memory (KAM)** has characteristics similar to the RAM. For example, the microprocessor can read and write information to and from the KAM and it can erase KAM information (Figure 8-6). However, the KAM retains information when the ignition switch is turned off. When the battery power is disconnected from the computer, the KAM memory is erased. The KAM is used for adaptive strategies that are explained under the next heading.

ADAPTIVE STRATEGY

Operation

If a computer has **adaptive strategy** capabilities, the computer can actually learn from past experience. For example, the normal voltage input range from a throttle position sensor (TPS) may be 0.6 volt to 4.5 volts. If a worn TPS sends a 0.3-volt signal to the computer, the microprocessor interprets this signal as an indication of component wear. The microprocessor stores this altered calibration in the KAM. The microprocessor now refers to this new calibration during calculations; thus, normal engine performance is maintained. If a sensor output is erratic or considerably out of range, the computer may ignore this input. When a computer has adaptive strategy, a short learning period is necessary:

1. after the battery has been disconnected.
2. when a computer system component has been replaced or disconnected.
3. on a new vehicle.

During this learning period, the engine may surge, idle fast, or have a loss of power. The average learning period lasts for 5 miles of driving.

Most adaptive strategies have two parts: **short-term fuel trim (Short-term FT)** and **long-term fuel trim (Long-term FT)**. Short-term strategies are those immediately enacted by the computer to overcome a change in operation. These changes are temporary. Long-term strategies are based on the feedback about the short-term strategies. These changes are more permanent. To understand how

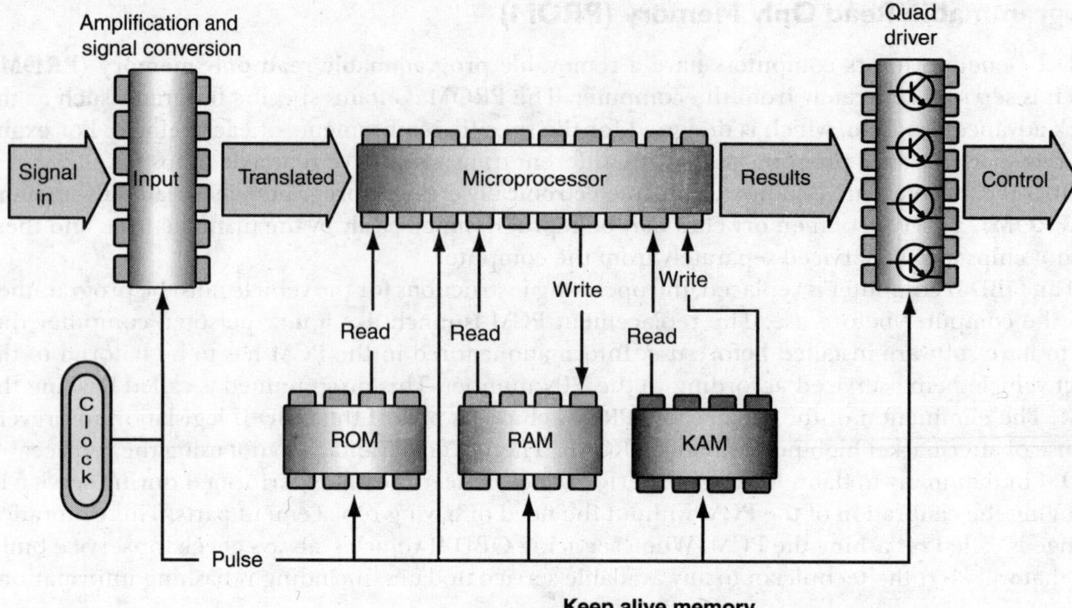

FIGURE 8-6 *Keep alive memory (KAM).*

a computer adapts itself to certain conditions, you must understand the differences between short-term fuel trim (adaptive) memory and long-term fuel trim (adaptive) memory.

Short-term changes are not saved in the computer's memory. All changes to the fuel system happen immediately and occur in direct response to the O_2 sensor and/or other sensors. These changes are also designed to keep the O_2 sensor switching at its middle point.

Long-term changes are saved in the computer's memory. These stored values are used the next time the engine is operated in a similar situation and under similar conditions. Long-term changes are triggered to keep all short-term strategies within particular parameters. These strategies are not based on the activity of the O_2 sensor, rather, they are based on the results of the O_2 sensor.

OBD II INTRODUCTION AND IMPLEMENTATION

The OBD II systems must illuminate the malfunction indicator lamp (MIL) (Figure 8-7) if the vehicle conditions would allow emissions to exceed 1.5 times the allowable standard for that model year based on a Federal Test Procedure (FTP). When a component or strategy failure allows emissions to exceed this level, the MIL is illuminated to inform the driver of a problem, and a diagnostic trouble code is stored in the powertrain control module (PCM).

Besides enhancements to the computer's capacities, some additional hardware is required to monitor the emissions performance closely enough to fulfill the tighter constraints and beyond merely keeping track of component failures. In most cases, this hardware consists of an additional

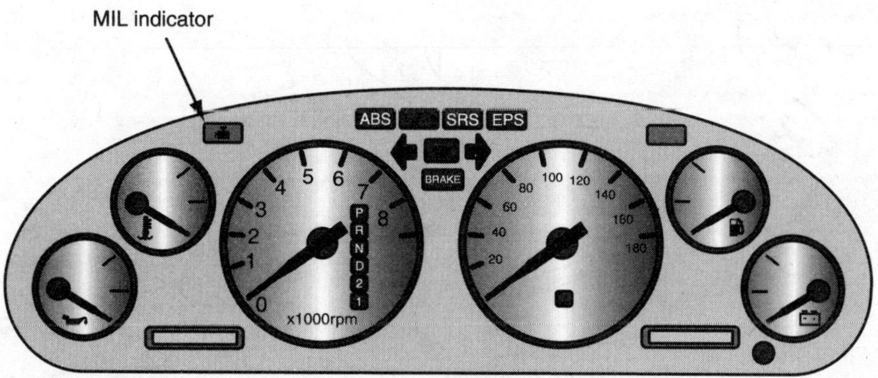

FIGURE 8-7 *A standard MIL.*

heated oxygen sensor down the exhaust stream from the catalytic converter (Figure 8-8); upgraded specific connectors and components to last the mandated 100,000 miles or 10 years; in some cases, a more precise crankshaft or camshaft position sensor (to detect misfires); and a new standardized 16-pin DLC.

The following is an outline of the development of computerized engine control systems leading to OBD II compliance for the domestic manufacturers:

Chrysler

1981–1983	Lean burn computer
1983–1987	Logic module/power module system
1988–1989	Single-module engine controller
1990–1995	Single-board engine controller
1995–	OBD II

Ford

1978–1979	EEC I
1979	EEC II
1980–1984	EEC III
1980–1991	MCU
1984–1995	EEC IV
1994–	EEC V (OBD II)

General Motors

1975–1979	Cadillac EFI
1980	C-4
1981–1990	CCC (Carburetor controls)
1982–1996	EFI/PFI
1994–1996	OBD II Phase In
1996–	OBD II

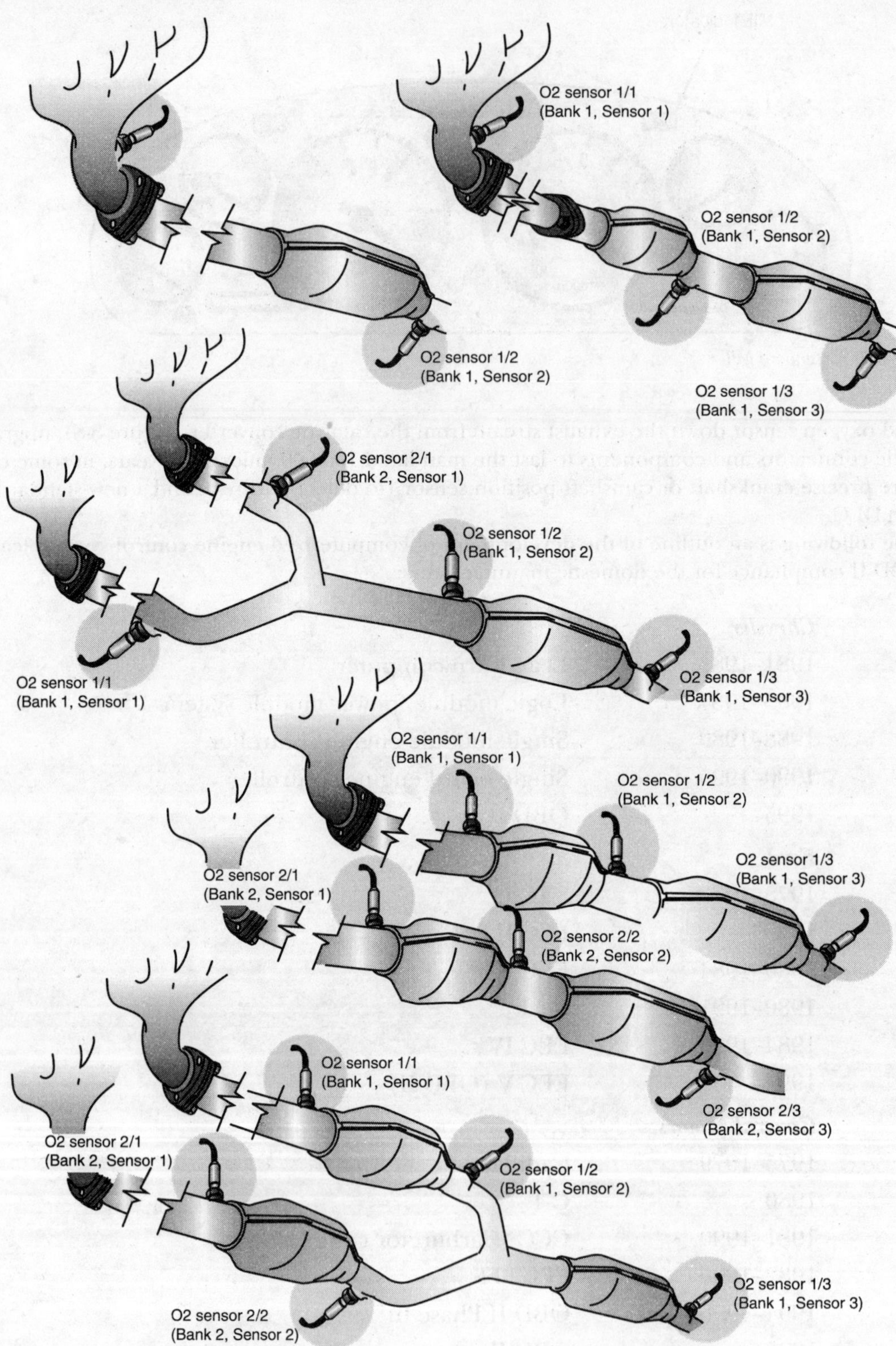

FIGURE 8-8 *Oxygen sensor identification.*

Vehicle manufacturers installed OBD II systems on some 1994 models. For example, Ford installed their EEC V system on the 3.8L Mustang and the 4.6L Thunderbird and Cougar. In 1995, the OBD II system was also installed on Lincoln Town Cars and Continentals, Grand Marquis, Crown Victorias, Rangers, and Windstars. Since OBD II systems were not mandated until 1996, some of the 1994 and 1995 OBD II systems are partial systems that do not have all of the monitors required for a complete OBD II system.

The EEC V system hardware includes the PCM, sensors, switches, actuators, solenoids, wires, terminals, and the constant control relay module. The software is the program in the PCM that the PCM uses to control the outputs. The major difference between EEC V with OBD II and previous systems is the software containing the monitoring strategies inside the PCM.

The main hardware difference in the EEC V system is the addition of a downstream **heated oxygen sensor** (HO_2S) mounted downstream from the catalytic converter. The conventional HO_2S is mounted in the exhaust manifold. The HO_2S are identified by their position in relation to the number one cylinder and their location relative to the converters. Sensors on the same side of the vehicle as the number one cylinder have a 1 prefix, and sensors mounted downstream from the converter have a 2 suffix (Figure 8-9).

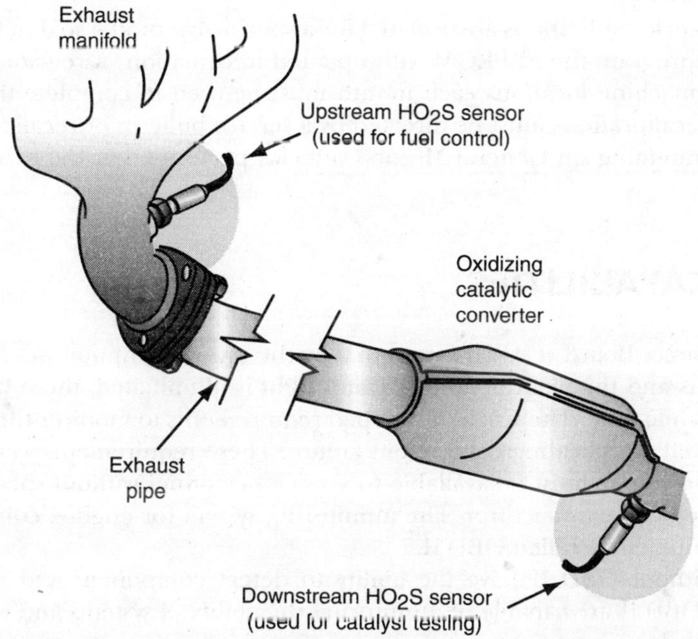

Figure 8-9 *OBD II system with heated oxygen sensors in the exhaust manifold and after the catalytic converter (pre- and post-catalyst).*

The EEC V PCM has 104 terminals compared to the previous 60 terminals on the EEC IV PCM (Figure 8-10). The additional terminals are required for the extra inputs and outputs in the EEC V system with OBD II. The EEC V PCM has smaller diameter pins and the wires have thinner high-temperature insulation, which allows more wires to occupy the same space. Some of the PCM terminals are goldplated, and the connectors on the HO_2S and throttle position sensor have improved seals to keep out dirt and moisture.

Instead of a fixed, unalterable programmable read only memory (PROM), the PCMs are equipped with an electronically erasable programmable read only memory (EEPROM) to store a large amount

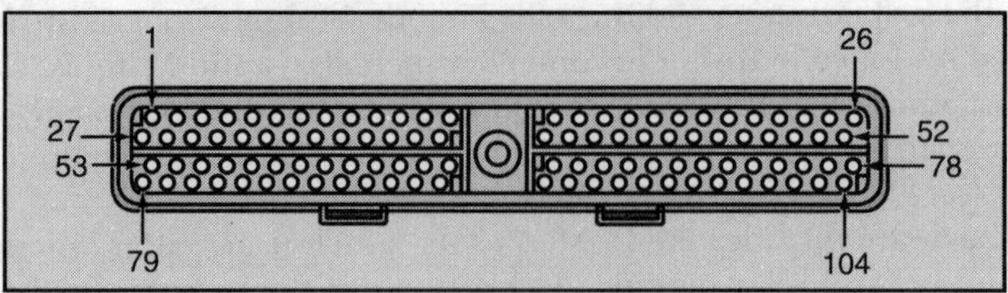

FIGURE 8-10 *EEC V PCM wiring terminal with 104 terminal pins.*

of information. The EEPROM is soldered into the PCM and is not replaceable. The EEPROM stores data without the need for a continuing source of electrical power.

The EEPROM is an integrated circuit that contains the program used by the PCM to provide powertrain control. It is possible to erase and reprogram the EEPROM without removing this chip from the computer. When a modification to the PCM operating strategy is required, it is no longer necessary to replace the PCM. The EEPROM may be reprogrammed through the DLC using the Service Bay Diagnostic System (SBDS).

For example, if the vehicle calibrations are updated for a specific car model sold in California, the SBDS may be used to reprogram the EEPROM with updated information. A red-colored CD-ROM that is sent to all SBDS machine locations each month must be used to complete the reprogramming procedure. PCM recalibrations must be directed by a service bulletin or recall letter. Another example is "flash" programming on General Motors' vehicles performed at the dealership with a Tech-2 scanner.

MONITORING CAPABILITIES

The California Air Resources Board (CARB) found that by the time a computer or emission system component failure occurs and the malfunction indicator light is illuminated, the vehicle emissions have been excessive for some time. The CARB developed requirements to monitor the performance of emission systems, as well as indicating component failure. These requirements were accepted by the EPA. The monitoring results must be available to service personnel without special test equipment marketed by the vehicle manufacturer. The monitoring system for engine, computer system, and emission system equipment is called OBD II.

Computer systems without OBD II have the ability to detect component and system failure. Computer systems with OBD II are capable of monitoring the ability of systems and components to maintain low emission levels.

Computer systems with OBD II capabilities are similar to previous systems except for the monitoring systems and the monitoring strategies in the PCM, which are extensive. New refinements are frequently incorporated into the PCM and other system components as improved technology is developed. Monitors included in OBD II are:

1. Catalyst efficiency monitor
2. Engine misfire monitor
3. Fuel system monitor
4. Heated exhaust gas oxygen sensor monitor
5. Exhaust gas recirculation monitor
6. Evaporative system monitor
7. Secondary air injection monitor

8. Thermostat monitor
9. PCV monitor
10. Heated Catalyst (if used)
11. Comprehensive component monitor

OBD II systems will perform certain tests on various subsystems of the engine management system. OBD II is designed to turn on the MIL when the vehicle has any failure that could potentially cause the vehicle to exceed its designed emission standard by a factor of 1.5. The system does that by the use of a monitor. If one or more monitored systems are out limit, then the MIL turns on to indicate a problem. The various monitors are:

Catalyst Efficiency Monitor

OBD II vehicles use a minimum of two oxygen sensors (O_2S) as a **catalyst efficiency monitor**. One of these is used for feedback to the PCM for fuel control, and the other, located at the rear of the catalytic converter, gives an indication of the efficiency of the converter. If the converter is operating properly, the signal from the pre-catalyst O_2 will have oscillations, while the post-catalyst O_2 will be relatively flat (Figure 8-11). Once the signal from the rear sensor approaches that of the front sensor, the MIL comes on and a DTC is set.

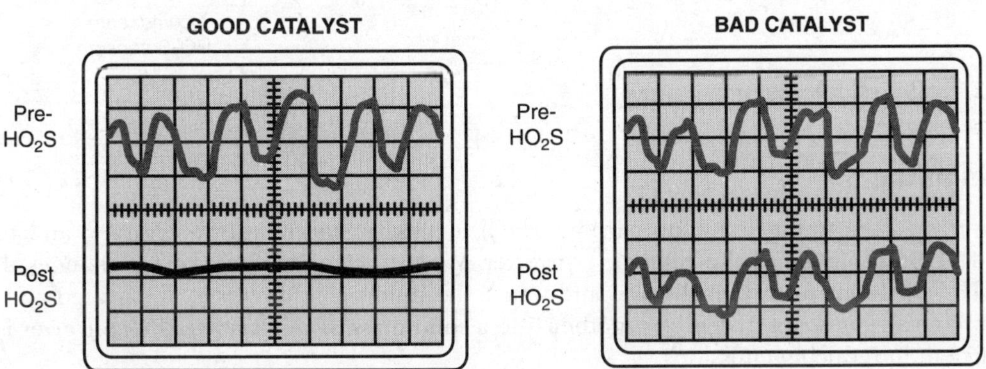

FIGURE 8-11 *Oxygen sensor signals for a good and bad catalytic converter.*

The downstream HO_2Ss have additional protection to prevent the collection of condensation on the ceramic. The internal heater is not turned on until the engine coolant temperature (ECT) sensor signal indicates a warmed up engine. This action prevents cracking of the ceramic. Goldplated pins and sockets are used in the HO_2Ss, and the downstream and upstream sensors have different wiring harness connectors.

A catalytic converter stores oxygen during lean engine operation and gives up this stored oxygen during rich operation to burn up excessive hydrocarbons. Catalytic converter efficiency is measured by monitoring the oxygen storage capacity of the converter during closed-loop operation.

When the catalytic converter is storing oxygen properly, the downstream HO_2Ss provide low-frequency voltage signals. If the catalytic converter is not storing oxygen properly, the voltage signal frequency increases on the downstream HO_2Ss until the frequency of the downstream HO_2Ss approaches the frequency of the upstream HO_2Ss (Figure 8-12). When the downstream HO_2Ss voltage signals reach a certain frequency, a DTC is set in the PCM memory. If the fault occurs on three drive cycles, the MIL light is illuminated.

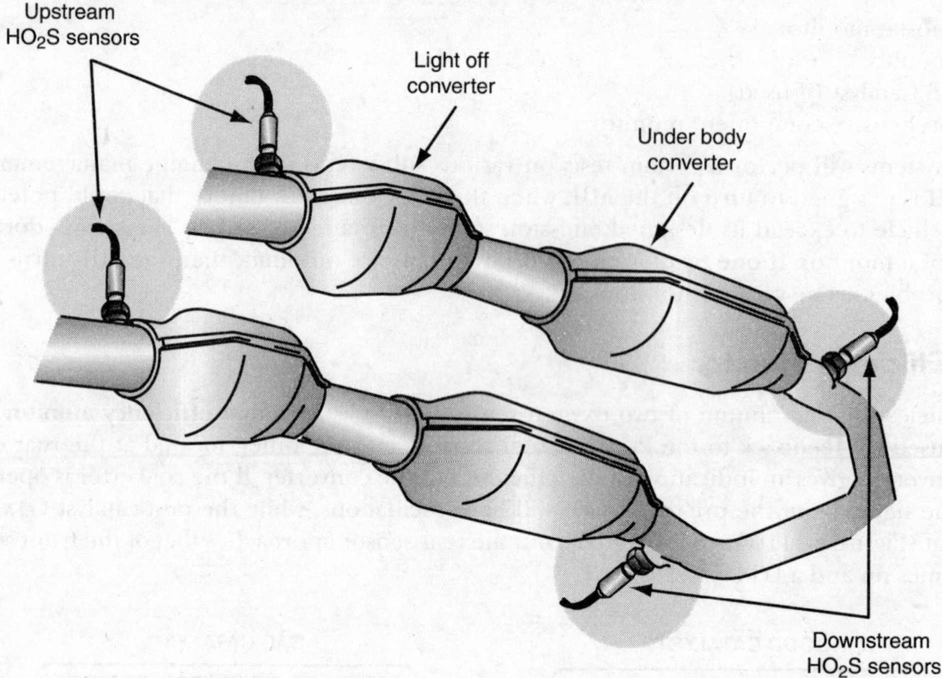

FIGURE 8-12 *Catalyst efficiency monitoring system.*

Misfire Monitor

If a cylinder misfires, unburned hydrocarbons (HC) are exhausted from the cylinder, and these excessive HC emissions enter the catalytic converter. When the catalytic converter changes these excessive HC emissions to carbon dioxide and water, the catalytic converter is overheated and the honeycomb in the converter may melt together into a solid mass. If this occurs, the converter is no longer efficient in reducing emissions.

Cylinder misfire monitoring requires measuring the contribution of each cylinder to engine power. The misfire monitoring system uses a highly accurate crankshaft angle measurement to measure the crankshaft acceleration each time a cylinder fires. A high data rate crankshaft sensor is required for this function (Figure 8-13). The PCM monitors the crankshaft acceleration time for each cylinder firing. If a cylinder is contributing normal power, a specific crankshaft acceleration time occurs. When a cylinder misfires, the cylinder does not contribute to engine power, and crankshaft acceleration for that cylinder is slowed.

Most OBD II systems allow a random misfire rate of about 2 percent before a misfire is flagged as a fault. It is important to note that this monitor only looks at the speed of acceleration of the crankshaft during a cylinder's firing stroke. It cannot determine if the problem is fuel-, ignition-, or mechanical-related. Misfire is categorized as type A or type B. **Type A misfire** could cause immediate catalyst damage. **Type B misfire** could cause emissions of 1.5 times the design standard and could cause an inspection/maintenance (I/M) failure. When there is a type A misfire, the MIL will flash. If there is a type B misfire, the MIL will turn on but will not flash.

The misfire monitoring sequence includes an adaptive feature compensating for variations in engine characteristics caused by manufacturing tolerances and component wear (Figure 8-14). It also has the adaptive capability to allow vibration at different engine speeds and loads. When an individual cylinder's contribution to engine speed falls below a certain threshold, the misfire monitoring sequence calculates the vibration, tolerance, and load factors before setting a misfire code.

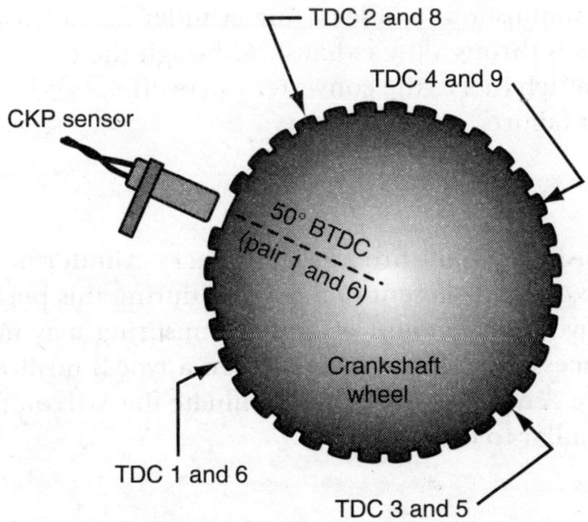

FIGURE 8-13 *High data rate crankshaft sensor used for misfire detection.*

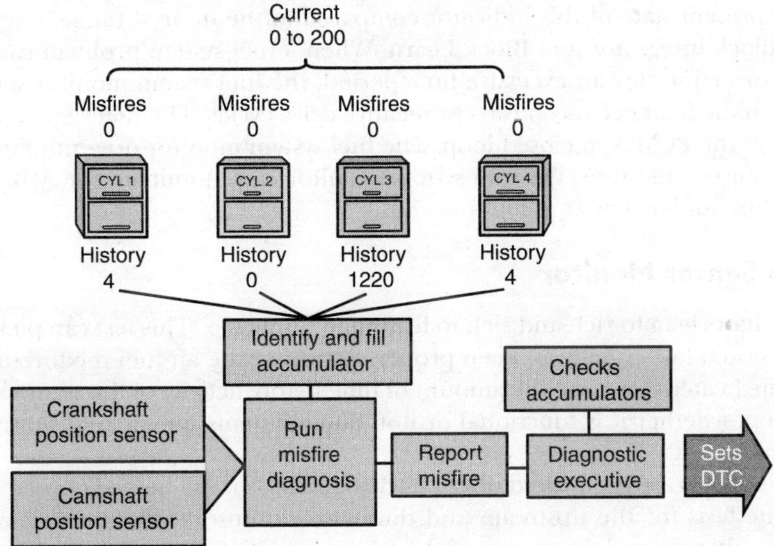

FIGURE 8-14 *Engine misfire file system.*

Type A Misfires

Type A and type B engine misfires are detected by the misfire monitor. When detecting a type A misfire, the monitor checks cylinder misfiring over a 200-rpm period. If cylinder misfires are between 2 percent and 20 percent, the monitor considers the misfiring to be excessive. Under this condition, the PCM may shut off the fuel to the misfiring cylinder or cylinders to limit catalytic converter heat. The PCM may turn off two injectors at the same time on misfiring cylinders. When the engine is operating under heavy load, the PCM will not turn off the injectors on misfiring cylinders.

If the misfire monitor detects a type A cylinder misfire and the PCM does not shut off the injector or injectors, the MIL light begins flashing. When the misfire monitor detects a type A cylinder misfire and the PCM shuts off an injector or injectors, the MIL is illuminated continually.

A misfire means a lack of combustion in at least one cylinder for at least one combustion event. A misfire pumps unburned fuels through the exhaust. Although the converter can handle an occasional sample of raw fuel, too much fuel to the converter can overheat and destroy it. A type A misfire sets a trouble code on the first failure.

Type B Misfires

To detect a type B cylinder misfire, the misfire monitor checks cylinder misfiring over a 1,000-rpm period. If cylinder misfiring exceeds 2 percent to 3 percent during this period, the monitor considers the misfiring to be excessive. This amount of cylinder misfiring may not overheat the catalytic converter but it may cause excessive emission levels. When a type B misfire is detected, a pending DTC is set in the PCM memory. A type B misfire can illuminate the MIL on the second non-consecutive failure if conditions are similar to the first.

Fuel System Monitoring

The **fuel system monitor** checks short-term fuel trim (Short-term FT) and long-term fuel trim (Long-term FT) while the PCM is operating in closed loop. Fuel trim is similar to idle air control in that the system looks at the present state of this indicator compared to the desired range. On GM vehicles, this was known as Block Integrator and Block Learn. When a fuel system problem causes the PCM to make fuel trim corrections for an excessive time period, the fuel system monitor sets a DTC and illuminates the MIL if the fault occurs on two consecutive drive cycles. The fuel system monitor operates continually when the PCM is in closed loop. The fuel system monitor does not involve any new hardware. Like the misfire monitor, the fuel system monitor can illuminate the MIL on a second non-consecutive failure under similar conditions.

Heated Oxygen Sensor Monitor

The system also monitors lean to rich and rich to lean time responses. This test can pick up a lazy O_2 sensor that cannot switch fast enough to keep proper control of the air-fuel mixture in the system. These sensors are the heated type, and the amount of time before activity of the sensor signal is present is an indication of whether it is functional or not. Some systems use current flow to indicate if the heater is working or not.

All of the system's HO_2Ss are monitored once per drive cycle, but the heated oxygen sensor monitor provides separate tests for the upstream and downstream sensors. The heated oxygen sensor monitor checks the voltage signal frequency of the upstream HO_2S. Excessive time between signal voltage frequency indicates a faulty sensor. At certain times, the heated oxygen sensor monitor varies the fuel delivery and checks for HO_2S's response. A slow response in the sensor voltage signal frequency indicates a faulty sensor. The sensor signal is also monitored for excessive voltage.

The heated oxygen sensor monitor also checks the frequency of the rear HO_2S sensor signals and checks these sensor signals for excessively high voltage. If the monitor does not detect signal voltage frequency within a specific range, the rear HO_2Ss are considered faulty. The heated oxygen sensor monitor will command the PCM to vary the air-fuel ratio to check the rear HO_2S response.

On many V-type engines, there are two primary or upstream O_2 sensors, one for each cylinder bank. These individual sensors report the air-fuel mixture and combustion for the cylinders on that side of the engine.

EGR System Monitoring

The exhaust gas recirculation (EGR) monitors use several different strategies to determine if the system is operating properly. Some monitor the temperature within the EGR passages. A high temperature indicates that exhaust gas is present. Other systems look at the manifold absolute pressure (MAP) signal, energize the EGR valve, and look for corresponding change in vacuum levels.

The EGR system may contain a delta pressure feedback EGR (DPFE) sensor. An orifice is located under the EGR valve, and small exhaust pressure hoses are connected from each side of this orifice to the DPFE sensor. During the EGR monitor, the PCM first checks the DPFE signal. If this sensor signal is within the normal range, the monitor proceeds with the tests.

With the engine idling and the EGR valve closed, the PCM checks for pressure difference at the two pressure hoses connected to the DPFE sensor. When the EGR valve is closed and there is no EGR flow, the pressure should be the same at both pipes. If the pressure is different at these two hoses, the EGR valve is stuck open.

The PCM commands the EGR valve to open and then checks the pressure at the two exhaust hoses connected to the DPFE sensor. With the EGR valve open and EGR flow through the orifice, there should be higher pressure at the upstream hose than at the downstream hose (Figure 8-15).

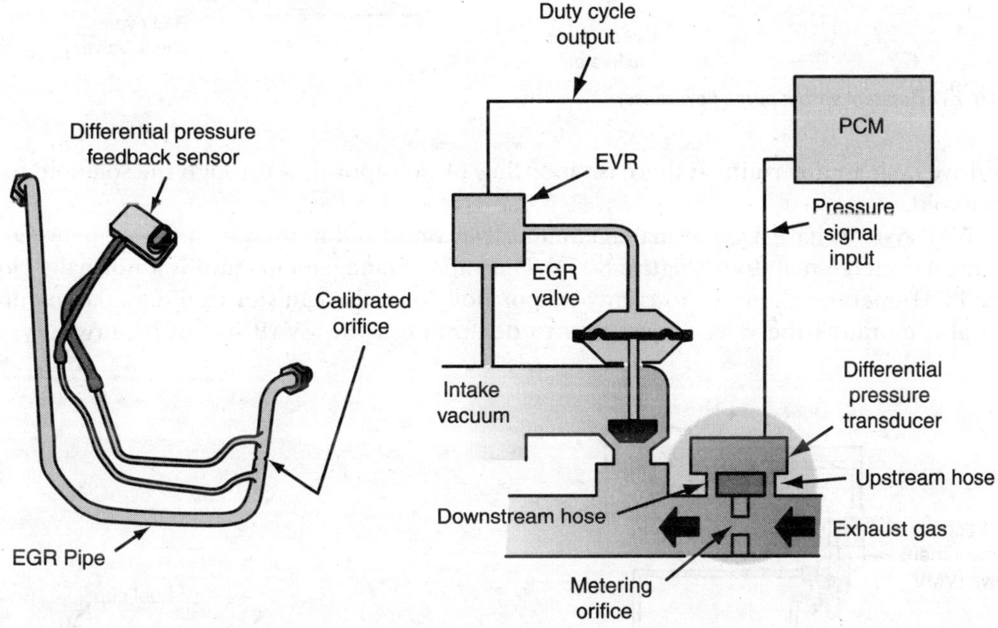

FIGURE 8-15 *EGR system with a delta pressure feedback sensor.*

The PCM checks the EGR flow by checking the DPFE signal value against an expected DPFE value for the engine operating conditions at steady throttle within a specific rpm range. If a fault is detected in any of the EGR monitor tests, a DTC is set in the PCM memory. If the fault occurs during two consecutive drive cycles, the MIL is illuminated. The EGR monitor operates once per OBD II trip.

Evaporative (EVAP) Emission System Monitor (Non-Enhanced)

In addition to the various components and failures that could affect the tailpipe emissions on a vehicle, OBD II monitors the evaporative systems as well. The system tests the ability of the fuel tank to hold pressure and of the purge system to vent the gas fumes from the charcoal canister.

Some EVAP systems have a purge flow sensor (PFS) connected to the vacuum hose between the canister purge solenoid and the intake manifold (Figure 8-16). The PCM monitors the PFS signal

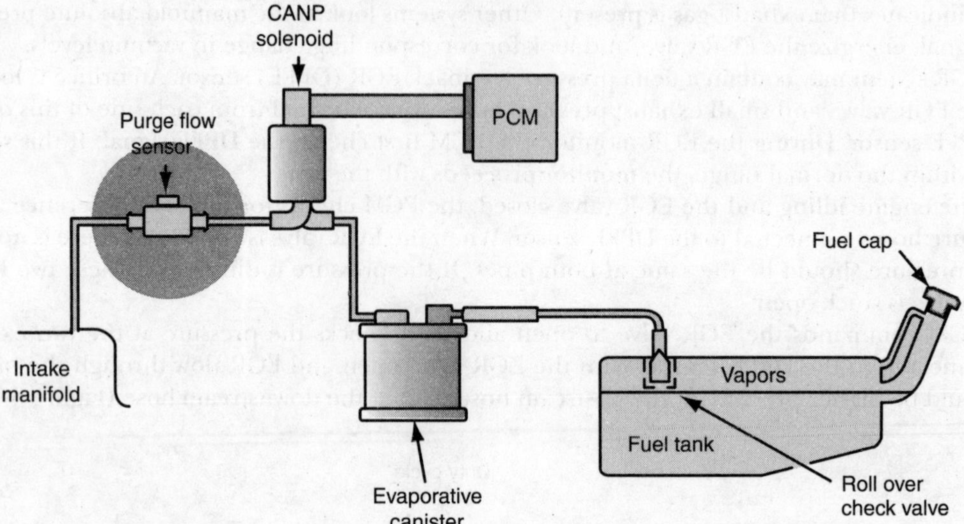

FIGURE 8-16 *EVAP system with a purge flow sensor.*

once per drive cycle to determine if there is vapor flow or no vapor flow through the solenoid to the intake manifold.

Other EVAP systems have a vapor management valve connected in the vacuum hose between the canister and the intake manifold (Figure 8-17). The vapor management valve is a normally closed valve. The PCM operates the valve to control vapor flow from the canister to the intake manifold. The PCM also monitors the valve's operation to determine if the EVAP system is purging vapors properly.

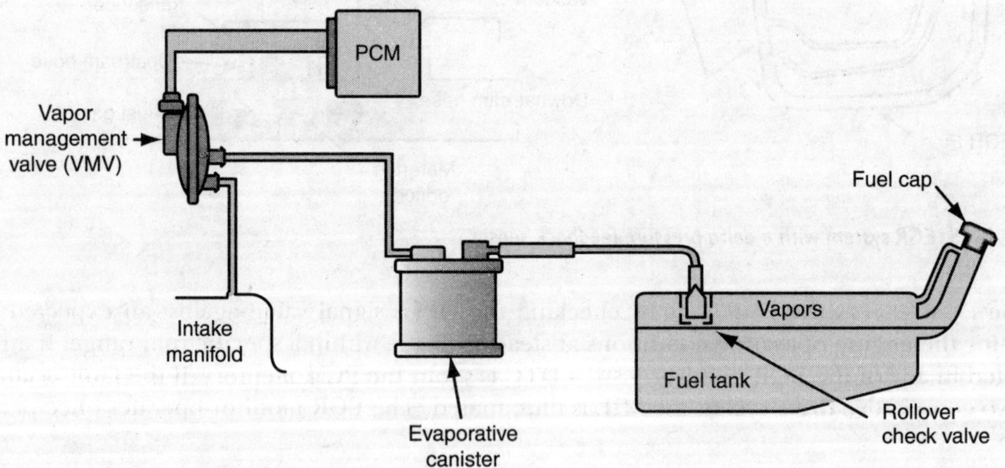

FIGURE 8-17 *EVAP system with vapor management valve.*

Enhanced EVAP system

Since 1996, enhanced EVAP system vehicles have an enhanced evaporative system monitor (Figure 8-18). This system detects leaks and restrictions in the EVAP system. A newly designed fuel tank filler

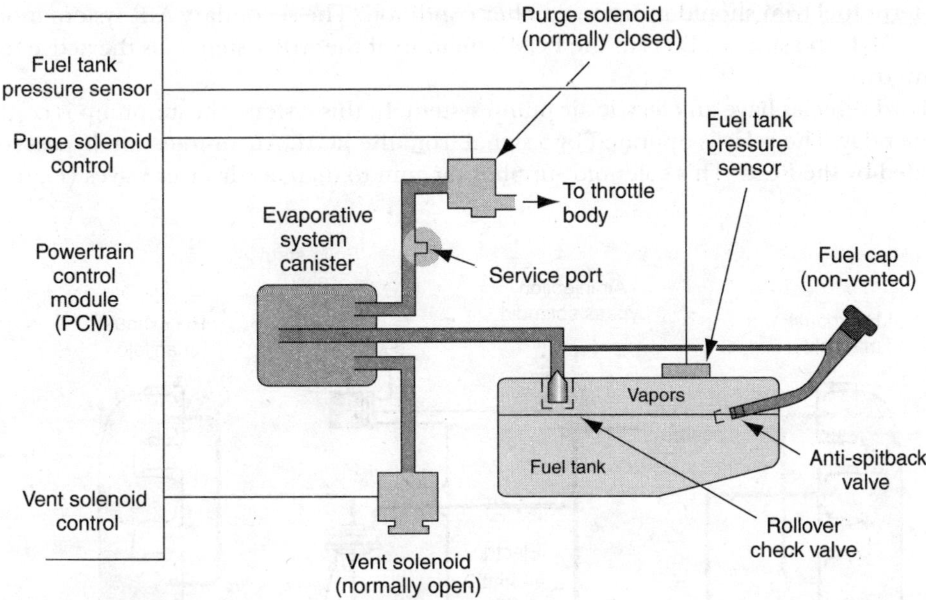

FIGURE 8-18 *An enhanced EVAP system.*

cap is used on this system. In these enhanced systems, an evaporative system leak or a missing fuel tank cap will cause the MIL to turn on. This enhanced system has to be able to detect leaks as small as .020 in diameter. In order to accomplish this, the system uses a fuel tank pressure sensor, a vent solenoid, and a purge solenoid. These three devices allow the PCM to run pressure and vacuum checks for leaks in the system. (We will cover these systems in more detail later in the book.) A new fuel cap that was easier to install was added to prevent setting a code from a loose fuel cap. Some vehicles can also illuminate a "check fuel cap" if the cap is loose. Additionally, since 1998, vehicles have to capture refueling vapors in a system called on-board refueling vapor recovery (ORVR). The ORVR is not monitored by OBD II.

SECONDARY AIR INJECTION (AIR) SYSTEM MONITOR

The AIR system operation can be verified by turning the AIR system on to inject air upstream of the oxygen sensor while monitoring its signal. Many designs inject air into the exhaust manifold when the engine is in open loop. This extra air helps heat the converter for proper operation.

In some vehicles, the AIR system is monitored with passive and active tests. During the passive test, the voltage of the pre-catalyst HO_2S is monitored from startup to closed-loop operation. The AIR pump is normally on during this time. Once the HO_2S is warm enough to produce a voltage signal, the voltage should be low if the AIR pump is delivering air to the exhaust manifold. The secondary AIR monitor will indicate a pass if the HO_2S voltage is low at this time. The passive test also looks for a higher HO_2S voltage when the AIR flow to the exhaust manifold is turned off by the PCM. When the AIR system passes the passive test, no further testing is done. If the AIR system fails the passive test or if the test is inconclusive, the AIR monitor in the PCM proceeds with the active test.

During the active test, the PCM cycles the AIR flow to the exhaust manifold on and off during closed-loop operation and monitors the pre-catalyst HO_2S voltage and the short-term fuel trim value. When the AIR flow to the exhaust manifold is turned on, the sensor's voltage should decrease and the short-term fuel trim should indicate a richer condition. The secondary AIR system monitor illuminates the MIL and stores a DTC in the PCM's memory if the AIR system fails the active test on two consecutive trips.

Some Ford vehicles have an electric air pump system. In this system, the air pump is controlled by a solid-state relay. The relay is operated by a signal from the PCM. An air-injection bypass solenoid is also operated by the PCM. This solenoid supplies vacuum to dual air diverter valves (Figure 8-19).

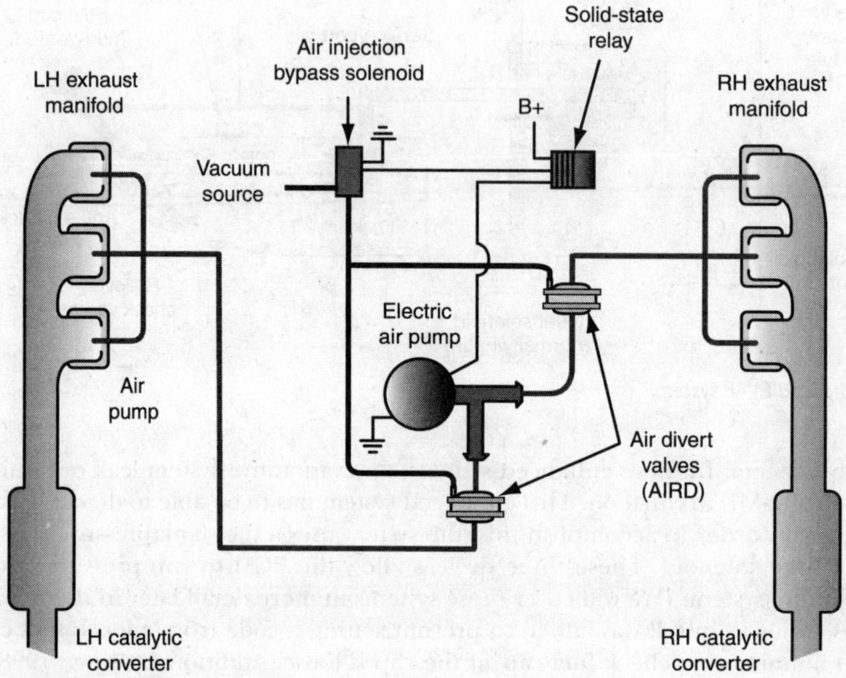

FIGURE 8-19 *An electric air pump system.*

When the engine is started, the PCM signals the relay to start the air pump. This module supplies the high current required for air pump operation. The air pump may provide a 10-second delay in pump operation after the engine is started. The PCM also energizes the air-injection bypass solenoid. When this solenoid is energized, it supplies vacuum to the dual air diverter valves. This action opens the normally closed air diverter valves. Air from the pump is now delivered to the exhaust manifold. The purpose of the air pump is to oxidize HC and CO in the exhaust manifolds from 20 to 120 seconds after the engine has started and until the catalytic converter is working properly. The length of time the air pump is operating depends on the temperature of the engine. Once the catalyst is warmed up, the PCM signals the relay to shut down the air pump. The PCM also de-energizes the air injection bypass solenoid which allows the air diverter valves to close.

The PCM monitors the relay and the air pump to determine if secondary air is present. This PCM monitor for the air pump system functions once per drive cycle. When a malfunction occurs in the air pump system on two consecutive drive cycles, a DTC is stored and the MIL is turned on. If the malfunction corrects itself, the MIL is turned off after three consecutive drive cycles in which the fault is not present.

Thermostat Monitor

One of the newer monitors to appear is the thermostat monitor, which was added in 2002. Since vehicles cause more pollution when they are cold, not to mention the fact that the vehicle may not get hot enough to boil off unburned fuel and water from the oil in the crankcase. A timer is set when the engine is started after a period of sitting to cool down. The PCM faces the intake air temperature (IAT) sensor when the vehicle is started and decides how long it should take for the coolant to reach normal operating temperature. If it does not reach this temperature, the PCM will set a code on the second consecutive occurrence (Type B code).

PCV Monitor

The PCV system monitor was phased in starting in 2002 and required for vehicles built after the 2004 model year. This monitor has the ability to monitor PCV hoses for disconnection. GM has built their PCV into the intake manifold. Since this eliminated the hoses, it also eliminated the need for a separate system. Ford's strategy for the monitor was to make the hoses large enough that the vehicle would not run with the PCV hoses disconnected.

Heated Catalyst

Very few vehicles have a heated catalyst to help keep cold start emissions low. The catalytic converter is heated electrically in this system. Most manufacturers opted to use the secondary air system to accomplish this task. If the vehicle has a heated catalyst, it has to be monitored.

Comprehensive Monitor

The system looks at any electronic input that could affect emissions. The strategy is to look for opens and shorts or input signal values that are out of the normal range. It also looks to see if the actuators have their intended effect on the system and to monitor other abnormalities.

The **comprehensive component monitor** (CCM) uses two strategies to monitor inputs and two strategies to monitor outputs. One strategy for monitoring inputs involves checking certain inputs for electrical defects and out-of-range values by checking the input signals at the analog-to-digital converter. The input signals monitored in this way are (Figure 8-20):

1. Rear HO_2S inputs
2. HO_2S inputs
3. Mass air flow sensor
4. Manual lever position sensor
5. Throttle position sensor
6. Engine coolant temperature sensor
7. Intake air temperature sensor

The CCM checks frequency signal inputs by performing rationality checks. During a rationality check, the monitor uses other sensor readings and calculations to determine if a sensor reading is proper for the present conditions. The CCM checks these inputs with rationality checks:

1. Crankshaft position sensor
2. Output shaft speed sensor
3. Ignition diagnostic monitor
4. Camshaft position sensor
5. Vehicle speed sensor

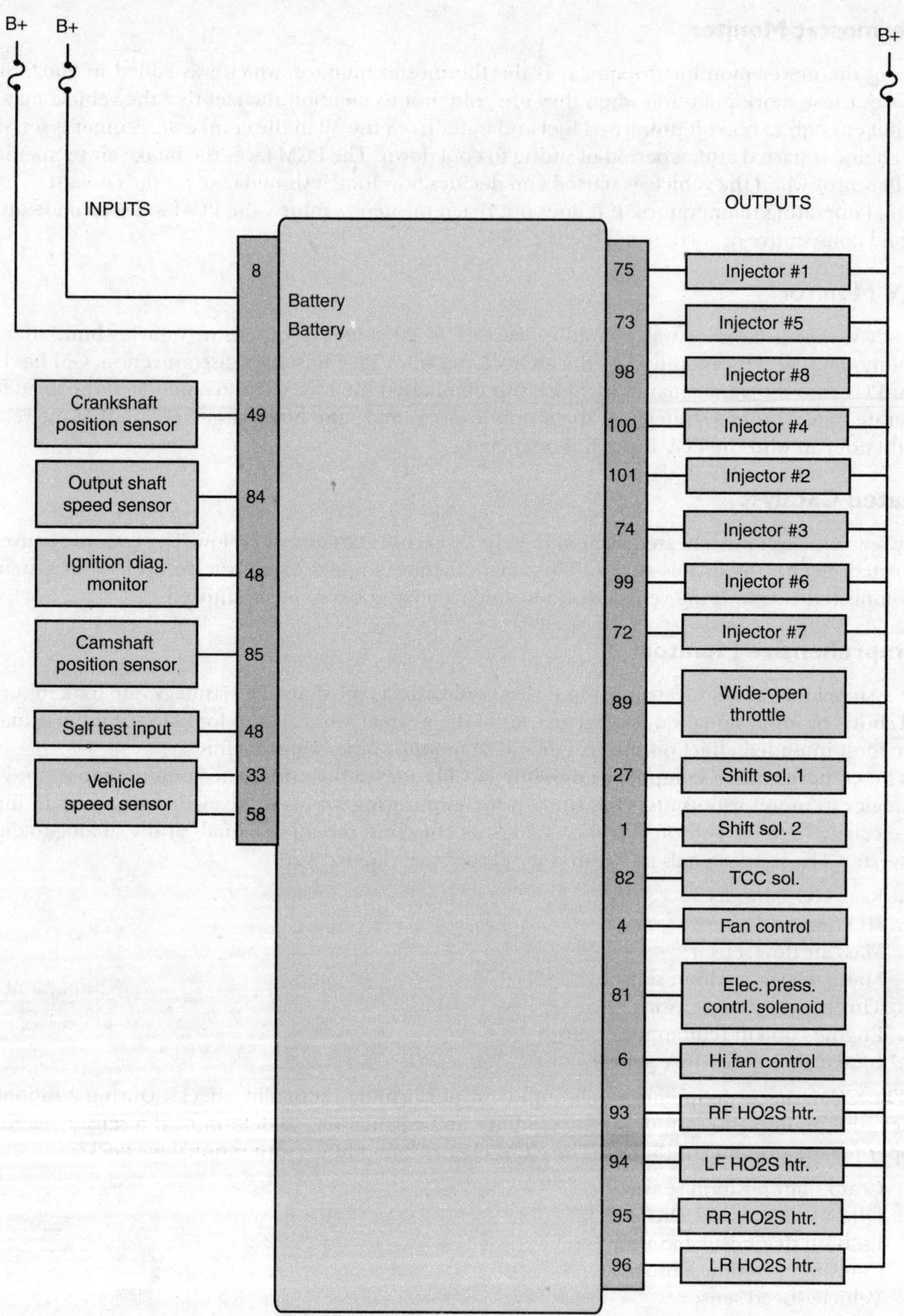

FIGURE 8-20 *EEC V system components.*

The PCM output that controls the idle air control motor is monitored by checking the idle speed demanded by the inputs against the closed-loop idle speed correction supplied by the PCM to the idle air control (IAC) motor.

The output state monitor in the CCM checks most of the outputs by monitoring the voltage of each output solenoid, relay, or actuator at the output driver in the PCM. If the output is off, this voltage should be high. This voltage is pulled low when the output is on.

Monitored outputs include:

1. Wide-open throttle A/C cutoff
2. Shift solenoid 1
3. Shift solenoid 2
4. Torque converter clutch solenoid
5. HO_2S heaters
6. High fan control
7. Fan control
8. Electronic pressure control solenoid

SYSTEM READINESS MODE

All OBD II scan tools include a readiness function showing all of the monitoring sequences on the vehicle and the status of each, complete or incomplete. If vehicle travel time, operating conditions, or other parameters were insufficient for a monitoring sequence to complete a test, the scanner will indicate which monitoring sequence is not yet complete.

Warm Up Cycle

OBD II standards define a warm-up cycle as a period of vehicle operation, after the engine had been turned off, in which the coolant rises by at least 40°F and reaches at least 160°F. Most DTCs are automatically erased after 40 warm-up cycles if the fault is not detected during that time. Some manufacturers retain erased DTCs in a flagged condition. This can be useful if the technician notices a pattern of component failure, all of which may be related to a single intermittent cause like low fuel pressure.

OBD II TRIP

The OBD II **trip** consists of an engine start following an engine off period, with enough vehicle travel to allow for a monitor to complete.

The definition of a trip depends on the monitor involved. For instance, the fuel system monitor will run once the following criteria are met:

- closed loop
- coolant temperature between 20 and 257°F
- intake air temperature between 20 and 293°F
- mass air flow between 1 and 500 grams per second
- barometric pressure is greater than 10.7 psi
- engine speed between 400 and 5,700 rpm
- vehicle speed less than 80 mph
- manifold absolute pressure between 2.2 and 12.3 psi

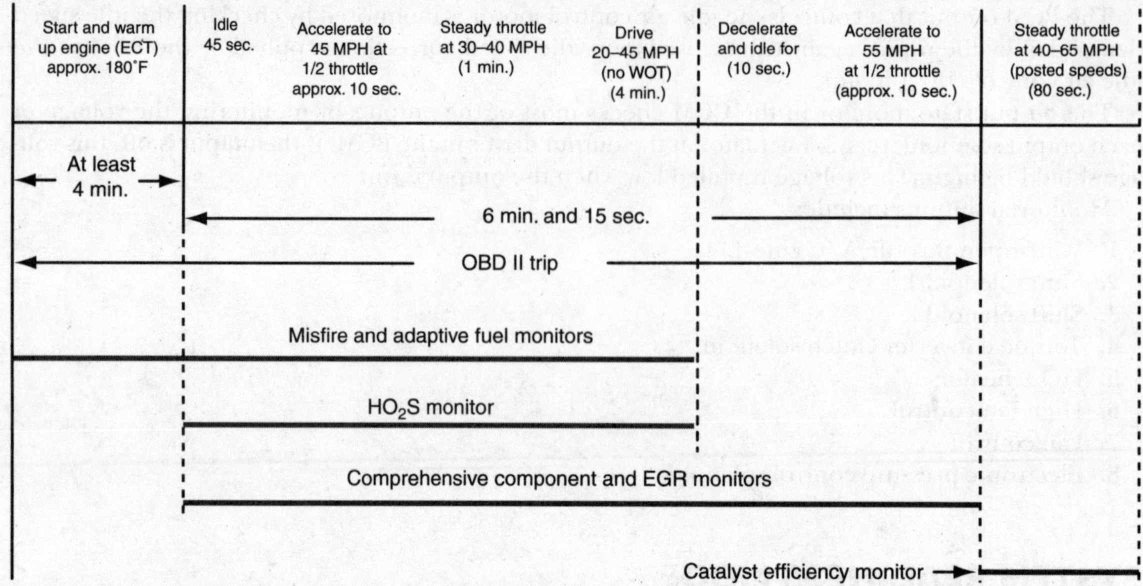

FIGURE 8-21 *Chart showing different trips for various monitors.*

Every vehicle may have a slightly different set of criteria; this is just an example. The monitor will run once when this criteria is met while driving (Figure 8-21).

DRIVE CYCLE

An OBD II **drive cycle** (Figure 8-22) consists of an engine start and vehicle operation that brings the vehicle into closed loop and includes whatever specific operating conditions are necessary either to initiate and complete a specific monitoring sequence or to verify a symptom or verify a repair. A monitoring sequence is an operational strategy designed to test the operation of a specific system, function, or component.

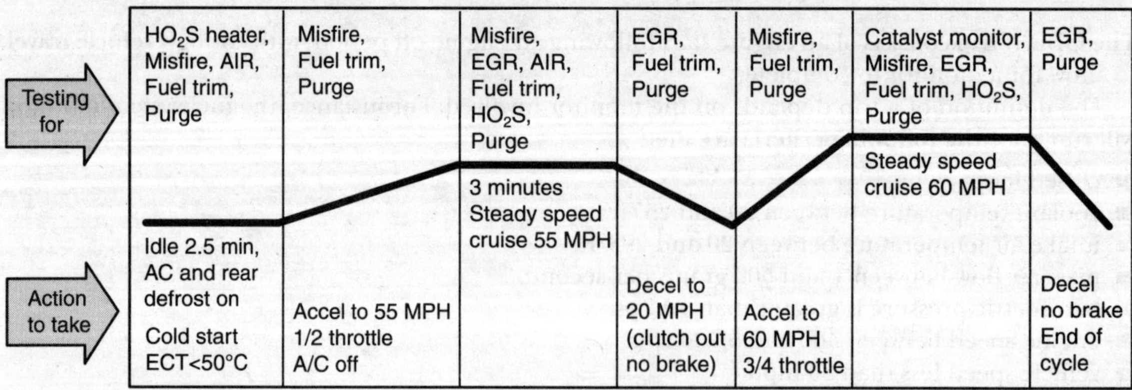

FIGURE 8-22 *An OBD drive cycle.*

A minimum drive cycle is from engine startup and vehicle operation until after the PCM enters closed loop. To complete a drive cycle, all trip monitors must be completed. The catalyst monitor must be completed after the other monitors in a drive cycle. A steady throttle opening between 40 to 60 mph (64 to 96 kph) for 80 seconds is required to complete the catalyst efficiency monitor.

FORD'S ELECTRONIC ENGINE CONTROL V (EEC V) SYSTEM

One of the most electronically advanced Ford production vehicles is the Lincoln Continental. The EEC V application, which consists of the PCM and ten other modules, uses a DLC as the universal link to system diagnosis. The major difference on this vehicle is that the modules communicate (Figure 8-23) with each other through the use of one twisted pair of wires called the MCN (multiplexing communications network). This network is accessible through the DLC.

The DLC pin designations dictated by the SAE J1962 document allow for some flexibility between vehicle manufacturers. While certain pin assignments must remain uniform, the use of the ISO

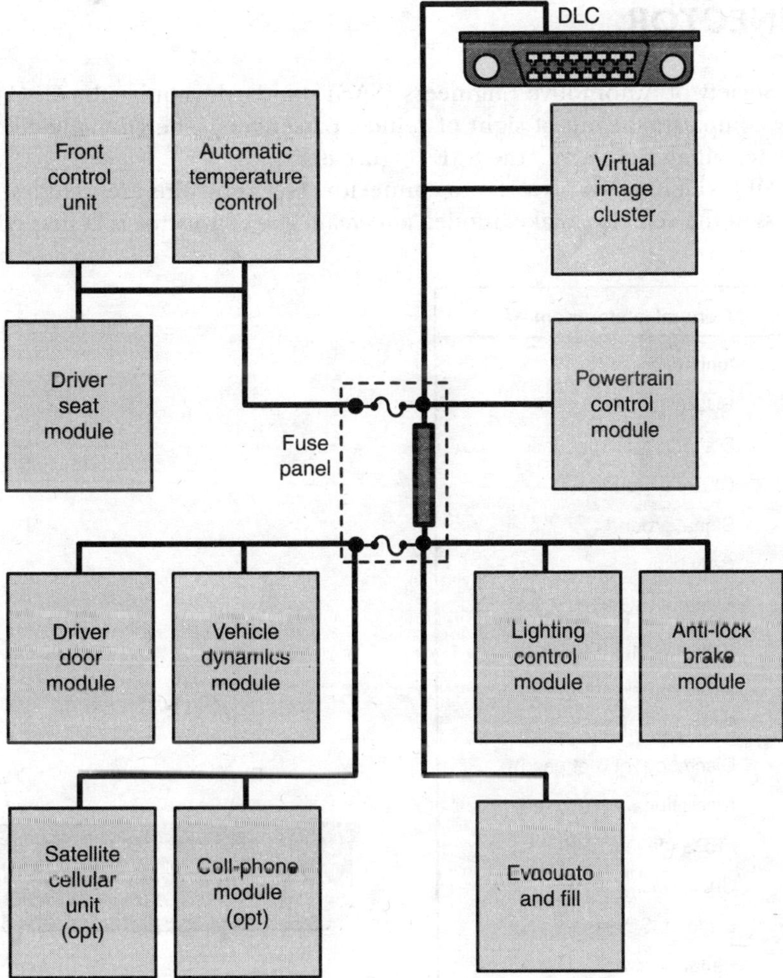

FIGURE 8-23 *The multiplex communication network circuit on a Lincoln Continental.*

protocol is up to the manufacturer. Ford chose to designate pin numbers two and ten to communicate OBD II and Standard Corporate Protocol (SCP) information to their New Generation STAR (NGS) tester (Figure 8-24).

On the EEC V, the standard corporate protocol (SCP) data links are the carrier for the MCN. If there is a problem with one of the modules in the system, a technician can monitor the module that controls the component or system. The technician can also control the actuators through bidirectional communications between the scan tool and the module being tested. This enables the technician to view PIDs (parameter identifications) related to the component he has commanded to turn on through the scan tool.

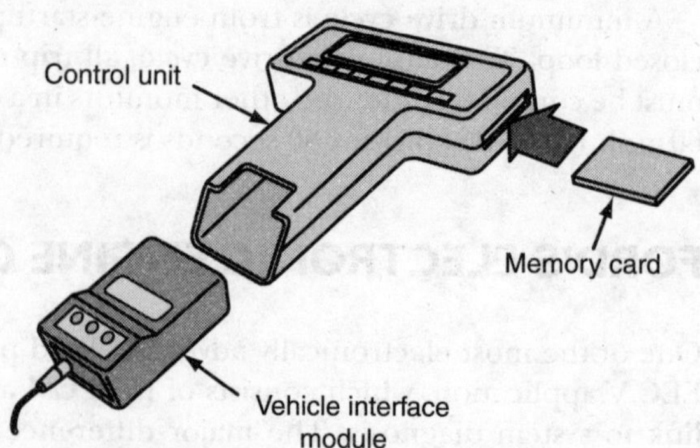

FIGURE 8-24 *Ford's new generation STAR tester.*

TEST CONNECTOR

OBD II and the Society of Automotive Engineers (SAE) standards require the DLC to be mounted in the passenger compartment out of sight of vehicle passengers. The DLC must be a 16-terminal connector with 9 terminals defined by the SAE (Figure 8-25).

The standard DLC (Figure 8-26) is a 16-pin connector. The same pins are used for the same information, regardless of the vehicle's make, model, and year. The connector is D-shaped and has guide

Cavity	General assignment
1	Ignition control
2	BUS (+) SCP
3	Discretionary (not used)
4	Chassis ground
5	Signal ground
6	CAN high
7	K line of ISO 9141
8	Discretionary (not used)
9	Discretionary (not used)
10	BUS (–) SCP
11	Discretionary (not used)
12	Discretionary (not used)
13	FEPS (flash EEPROM)
14	CAN low
15	L line of ISO 9141
16	Battery power

FIGURE 8-25 *DLC terminal identification.*

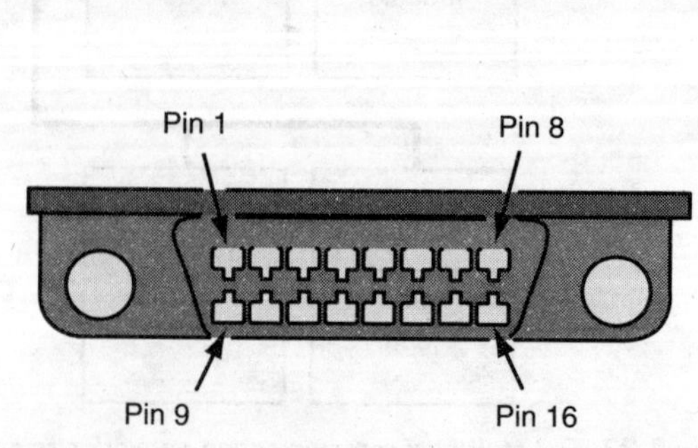

FIGURE 8-26 *A 16-pin DLC.*

keys that allow the scan tool to be installed only one way. Using a standard connector design and by designating the pins allows data retrieval with any scan tool designed for OBD II. Some European vehicles meet OBD II standards by providing the designated DLC along with their own connector for their own scan tool.

The DLC is designed only for scan tool use. You cannot jump across any of the terminals to display codes on an instrument panel or other indicator lamp. The MIL is only used to inform the driver that the vehicle should be serviced soon. It also informs a technician that the computer has set a trouble code.

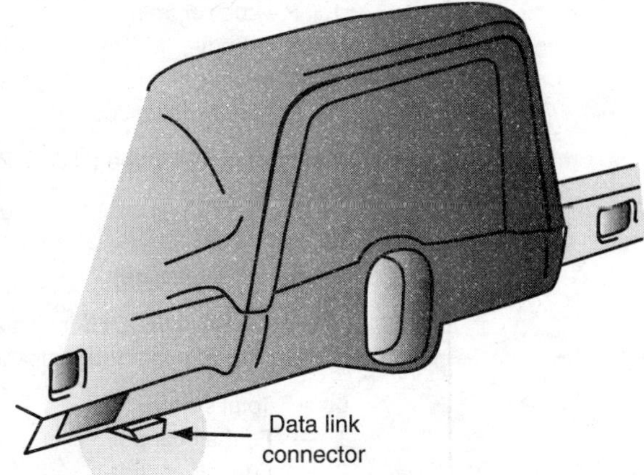

FIGURE 8-27 *Designated location for the DLC.*

The DLC must be easily accessible while sitting in the driver's seat (Figure 8-27). All DLCs must be located somewhere between the left end of the instrument panel and a position 300 millimeters to the right of the center. The DLC cannot be hidden behind panels and must be accessible without tools. Any generic scan tool can be connected to the DLC and can access the diagnostic data stream.

The connector pins are arranged in two rows and are numbered consecutively. Seven of the sixteen pins have been assigned by the OBD II standard. The remaining nine pins can be used by the individual manufacturers to meet their needs and desires.

MALFUNCTION INDICATOR LAMP OPERATION

An OBD II system continuously monitors the entire emissions system, switches on a MIL if something goes wrong, and stores a fault code in the PCM when it detects a problem. The codes are well defined and can lead a technician to the problem. A scan tool must be used to access and interpret emission-related DTCs regardless of the make and model of the vehicle (Figure 8-28).

Many of the trouble codes from an OBD II system will mean the same thing regardless of manufacturer. However, some of the codes will pertain only to a particular system or will mean something different with each system. The DTC is a five-character code with both letters and numbers (Figure 8-29). This is called the alphanumeric system. The first character of the code is a letter. This defines the system where the code was set. Currently, there are three possible first character codes: B for body, C for chassis, and P for powertrain. The U-codes are designated for use as a network problem codes.

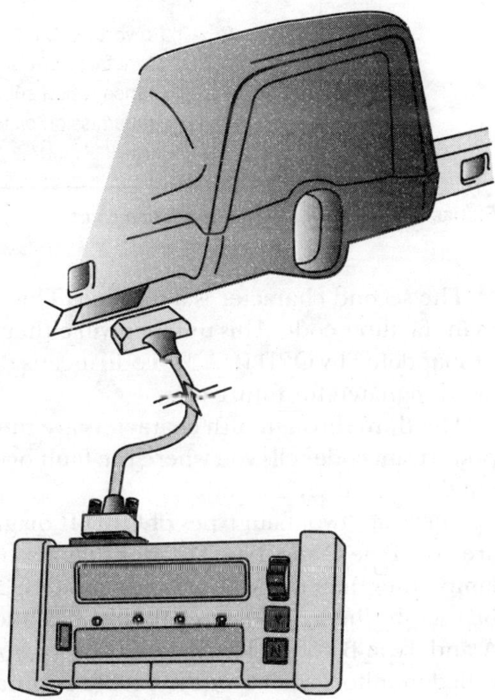

FIGURE 8-28 *Scan tool connected to the DLC.*

The SAE J2012 standards specify that all DTCs will have a five-digit alphanumeric numering and lettering system. The following prefixes indicate the general area to which the DTC belongs:

1. P — power train
2. B — body
3. C — chassis
4. U — network codes

The first number in the DTC indicates who is responsible for the DTC definition.

1. 0 — SAE
2. 1 — manufacturer

The third digit in the DTC indicates the subgroup to which the DTC belongs. The possible subgroups are:

0 — Total system
1 — Fuel-air control
2 — Fuel-air control
3 — Ignition system misfire
4 — Auxiliary emission controls
5 — Idle speed control
6 — PCM and I/O
7 — Transmission
8 — Non-EEC powertrain

The fourth and fifth digits indicate the specific area where the trouble exists. Code P1711 has this interpretation:

P — Powertrain DTC
1 — Manufacturer-defined code
7 — Transmission subgroup
11 — Transmission oil temperature (TOT) sensor and related circuit

FIGURE 8-29 *OBD II DTC interpretation chart.*

The second character is a number. This defines the code as being a mandated code or a special manufacturer code. This number will either be a 0, 1, 2, or 3. A 0 code means that the fault is defined or mandated by OBD II. A "1" code means that the code is manufacturer specific. Codes of "2" or "3" are designated for future use.

The third through fifth characters are numbers. These describe the fault. The third character of a powertrain code tells you where the fault occurred. The remaining two characters describe the exact condition that set the code.

There are two main types of OBD II diagnostic trouble codes (DTCs), Type A and Type B. There are also Type C and Type D codes that are not emissions related. The Type C codes can illuminate a lamp other than the MIL on some models; Type D codes do not usually illuminate any lamp but can be used by the technician to aid troubleshooting. In this discussion, we will be concerned with Type A and Type B codes. In the OBD II monitors that were previously discussed, the vehicle runs tests called monitors whenever the **enable criteria** for the test is correct. A Type A DTC will illuminate the MIL on the first failure and indicates a catalyst-damaging misfire. Type B codes are "pending" on the first failure, and a MIL is illuminated on the second *consecutive* failure unless the pending DTC is for fuel trim or misfire. The fuel trim and misfire codes can be set on a second *non-consecutive* failure. Additionally, the catalyst monitor must fail *three consecutive* tests before illuminating the MIL.

For misfire and fuel monitors, if the fault does not occur on three consecutive drive cycles under similar conditions, the MIL is turned off. The system defines similar conditions as:

1. Engine speed within 375 rpm compared to when the fault was detected
2. Engine load within 10 percent compared to when the fault was detected
3. Engine warmup state or coolant temperature must match the temperature when the fault was detected

For the catalyst efficiency, HO_2S, EGR, and comprehensive component monitors, the MIL is turned off if the same fault does not reappear for three consecutive drive cycles. When the fault is no longer present and the MIL is turned off, the DTC is erased after 40 engine warmup cycles. A technician may use a scan tester to erase DTCs immediately.

A pending DTC is a code representing a fault that has occurred but that has not occurred enough times to illuminate the MIL. Some scan testers are capable of reading pending DTCs with the continuous DTCs.

TEST MODES

All OBD II systems have the same basic test modes. These test modes must be accessible with an OBD II scan tool. Mode 1 is the **parameter identification (PID)** mode. It allows access to certain data values, analog and digital inputs and outputs, calculated values, and system status information. Some of the PID values will be manufacturer specific, while others are common to all vehicles.

Mode 2 is the freezeframe data access mode. This mode permits access to emission-related data values from specific generic PIDs. These values represent the operating conditions at the time the fault was recognized and logged into memory as a DTC. Once a DTC and a set of freezeframe data are stored in memory, they will stay in memory even if other emission-related DTCs are stored. The number of these sets of freezeframes that can be stored are limited.

There is one type of failure that is an exception to this rule—misfire. Fuel system misfires will overwrite any other type of data except for other fuel system misfire data. This data can only be removed with a scan tool. When a scan tool is used to erase a DTC, it automatically erases all freezeframe data associated with the events that lead to that DTC.

Mode 3 permits scan tools to obtain stored DTCs. The information is transmitted from the PCM to the scan tool following an OBD II Mode 3 request. Either the DTC, its descriptive text, or both will be displayed on the scan tool.

The PCM reset mode, Mode 4, allows the scan tool to clear all emission-related diagnostic information from its memory. Once the PCM has been reset, the PCM stores an inspection maintenance readiness code until all OBD II system monitors or components have been tested to satisfy an OBD trip cycle without any other faults occurring. Specific conditions must be met before the requirements for a trip are satisfied.

Mode 5 is the oxygen sensor monitoring test. This mode gives the oxygen sensor fault limits and the actual oxygen sensor outputs during the test cycle. The test cycle includes specific operating conditions that must be met to complete the test. This information helps determine the effectiveness of the catalytic converter.

Mode 6 is the on-board test of non-continuously monitored systems. The PCM will indicate the pass/fail status of each monitored system in one trip. Using this mode, the technician can determine that the monitor has run and passed or failed without having the system fail twice and set the MIL. The systems that are monitored include:

- Thermostat
- Evaporative system
- EGR system
- Secondary AIR system
- Catalyst
- Oxygen sensor heater
- Oxygen sensor
- PCV system
- Heated catalyst

Mode 7 is the monitoring of test results for continuously monitored systems. A two-trip DTC may be displayed here after the first failure as a pending code, but the information may not be accurate until confirmed by another failure. If the vehicle shows a failure here after one trip, the technician should make sure that the vehicle is okay before returning it to the customer.

Mode 8 is the request for control of an on-board system test or component. In this mode, the technician can use the scan tool to control the PCM to test a system and its related components. Presently, Mode 8 is most commonly used for testing of the EVAP system. The EVAP leak test is conducted in this mode because the PCM has set conditions to enable the technician to test the EVAP system for leaks.

Mode 9 (if supported) allows the PCM to identify:

- The vehicle's identification number (VIN)
- The PCM's calibration ID and calibration verification.

This information can be used by the technician to see if the latest calibration has been programmed into the PCM.

SNAPSHOTS

The primary purpose of OBD II is to make the diagnosis of emissions and driveability problems simple and uniform in the future. No longer will it be necessary to learn entirely new systems from each manufacturer. The basic plan is to allow technicians to diagnose any vehicle with the same diagnostic tools. Manufacturers can introduce special diagnostic tools or capacities for their own systems providing that standard scan tools along with DMMs and lab scopes can analyze the system. These special tools can have additional capabilities beyond those given in the standards. One of the mandated capabilities is the **freezeframe** or **snapshot** feature. This is the ability of the system to record data from all of its sensors and actuators at a time when the system turns the MIL on. GM expanded this capability to include "failure reports" which do the same thing as the snapshot but also includes any fault stored in memory, not just those related to the emissions-related circuits.

The basic advantage of the snapshot feature is the ability to look at the existing conditions when a code was set. This will be especially valuable for diagnosing intermittent problems. Whenever a code is set, a record of all related activities will be stored in memory. This allows the technician to look at the action of sensors and actuators when the code was set. This helps identify the cause of the problem.

REVIEW QUESTIONS

Short Answer Essays

1. Describe the main hardware differences between an OBD II system and other systems.
2. Explain the advantage of a flash EEPROM compared to a PROM.
3. Describe an OBD II warmup cycle.
4. Explain trip and drive cycle in an OBD II system.
5. Describe how engine misfire is detected in an OBD II system.
6. Describe the differences between an A misfire and a B misfire.
7. Describe the purpose of having two oxygen sensors in an exhaust system.
8. List five things that were mandated by OBD II.
9. Briefly describe what the comprehensive component monitor looks at.
10. Describe briefly five of the monitors in an OBD II system.

Fill-in-the-Blanks

1. The main goal of OBD II was to detect when engine wear or component failure caused exhaust emissions to increase by ______________ percent or more.
2. OBD II regulations required that all vehicles produced after ______________ be equipped with these new systems. However, some manufacturers started to equip their vehicles with this equipment in ______________.
3. In order to meet the requirements for misfire detection in some cases, a new more precise position sensor was needed.
4. The downstream HO_2S monitors ______________ efficiency.
5. Type B engine misfires are excessive if the misfiring exceeds ______________ to percent in a(n) ______________ rpm period.
6. The ______________ monitor system checks the action of the canister purge system.
7. The ______________ monitor system has a(n) ______________ and ______________ test to check the efficiency of the air injection system.
8. The fuel monitor checks ______________ ______________ fuel trim and ______________ fuel trim.
9. OBD stands for ______________ ______________ ______________.
10. In an OBD II system, the MIL is illuminated if the emission levels exceed ______________ times the standard for that model year.

Multiple Choice

1. While discussing OBD II vehicles,
Technician A says OBD II vehicles must have a universal test connector (DLC).
Technician B says that the DLC must be under the dash on the drivers' side.
Who is correct?
A. Technician A C. Both technicians
B. Technician B D. Neither technician

2. While discussing a computerized engine control system,
Technician A says its job is to maintain air-fuel ratio as close to 14.7:1 as possible.
Technician B says it must accurately provide ignition timing under all driving conditions.
Who is correct?
A. Technician A C. Both technicians
B. Technician B D. Neither technician

3. All of the following are parts of a computer's operation ***except***:
A. Input C. Processing
B. Determination D. Output

4. *Technician A* says the computer memory that can be written into by the PCM is RAM.
Technician B says non-volatile RAM is erased when the ignition is switched off.
Who is correct?
A. Technician A C. Both technicians
B. Technician B D. Neither technician

5. *Technician A* says a short-learning period may be necessary on a vehicle with adaptive strategy after the battery is disconnected.
Technician B says that the learning period is also needed after some computer system parts are replaced.
Who is correct?
A. Technician A C. Both technicians
B. Technician B D. Neither technician

6. *Technician A* says that computer systems **without** OBD II have the ability to be capable of monitoring the ability of systems and components to maintain low emissions.
Technician B says that computer systems **with** OBD II are capable of only detecting component and system failure.
Who is correct?
A. Technician A C. Both technicians
B. Technician B D. Neither technician

7. *Technician A* says that the misfire monitor is designed to prevent catalytic converter damage by excessive amounts of NO_X.
Technician B says the misfire monitor uses a highly accurate crankshaft sensor to detect engine misfires.

Who is correct?

A. Technician A C. Both technicians
B. Technician B D. Neither technician

8. *Technician A* says to complete a warm-up cycle the engine temperature must reach at least 160°F.
Technician B says the engine must be shut down long enough that the coolant must rise at least 40 degrees to complete a warm-up cycle.
Who is correct?

A. Technician A C. Both technicians
B. Technician B D. Neither technician

9. All of the following are mandates of OBD II ***except:***
A. A data link connector (DLC) with dedicated pin assignments
B. A standard list of diagnostic trouble codes
C. Vehicle identification number (VIN) must be automatically transmitted to the scan tool
D. Stored vehicle codes must be erased by disconnecting the battery.

10. While discussing the EEPROM, on OBD II systems
Technician A says the EEPROM must be programmed (flashed) whenever the PCM is replaced.
Technician B says the PCM can be reprogrammed (re-flashed) whenever necessary if dictated by a service bulletins or procedures.
Who is correct?

A. Technician A C. Both technicians
B. Technician B D. Neither technician

9 FUEL SYSTEMS

Upon completion and review of this chapter, you should be able to:

- Describe the four performance characteristics of gasoline.
- Describe the various types of gasoline and additives.
- Describe the different alternative fuels, including diesel.
- Explain the principles of operation of a fuel injection system. List the advantages of fuel injection.
- Explain the differences between throttle body and port injection systems.
- Describe the difference between a sequential fuel injection (SFI) system and a multiport fuel injection (MFI) system.
- Explain the design and function of major electronic fuel injection (EFI) components.
- Describe fuel tank design and mounting on the vehicle.
- Describe a fuel tank filler and filler cap design.
- Describe three different types of fuel lines.
- Explain five different types of fuel line fittings.
- Describe the different fuel filter designs and mountings.

- Describe the operation of an electric fuel pump, including the operation of the relief valve and check valve.
- Describe the purpose of the inertia switch in a fuel pump circuit.
- Explain the purpose of the oil pressure switch that is connected in parallel with some fuel pump relays.
- Explain the operation of Direct Fuel Injection.

INTRODUCTION

This chapter focuses on an engine system that has been and is being modified year after year to meet the fuel economy and emissions demands of the government in addition to the engine performance demands of the public. In order for an engine to be efficient, it must receive the correct amount of fuel mixed with the correct amount of air. Providing this is the purpose of the carburetion, fuel injection, and fuel delivery systems. The basics of these systems is covered in this chapter. More detailed *coverage* of fuel injection systems is covered in later chapters of this book.

Before any discussion on fuel systems can take place, the properties of the most commonly used fuel in automobiles, gasoline, must be studied. This chapter takes a look at the composition and qualities of gasoline as well as the other alternate fuels being used by some engines.

Fuel injection systems have replaced carburetion in all late-model passenger cars and light trucks manufactured since the early 1990s.

Fuel injection involves spraying or injecting fuel directly into the engine's intake manifold (Figure 9-1). Fuel injection, especially when it is electronically controlled, has several major advantages over carbureted systems. These include improved driveability under all conditions, improved fuel control and economy, decreased exhaust emissions, and an increase in engine efficiency and power.

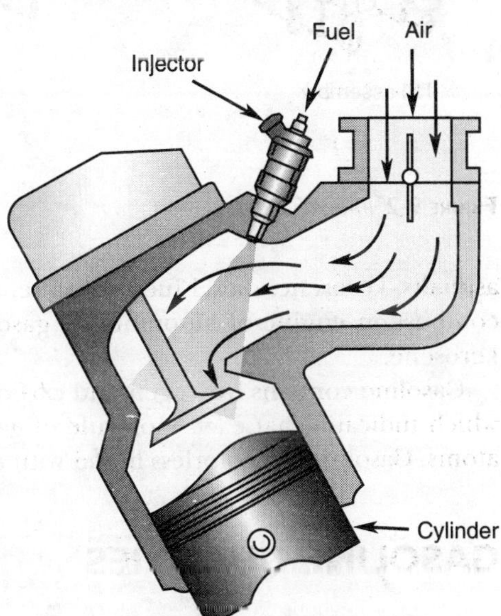

FIGURE 9-1 *In a port fuel injection system, air and fuel are mixed in the intake manifold runners very close to the intake valve(s) of the combustion chamber.*

The automobile's fuel system is both simple and complicated. It is simple in the systems that transfer fuel to the engine and complex in the fuel injection system that mixes fuel with air in the correct amounts and proportion to meet all needs of the engine. The basic parts of the fuel delivery system include the fuel tank, fuel lines, filters, and pumps (Figure 9-2).

GASOLINE COMPOSITION

Crude oil, as removed from the earth, is a mixture of hydrocarbon compounds ranging from gases to heavy tars and waxes. The crude oil can be refined into products such as lubricating oils, greases,

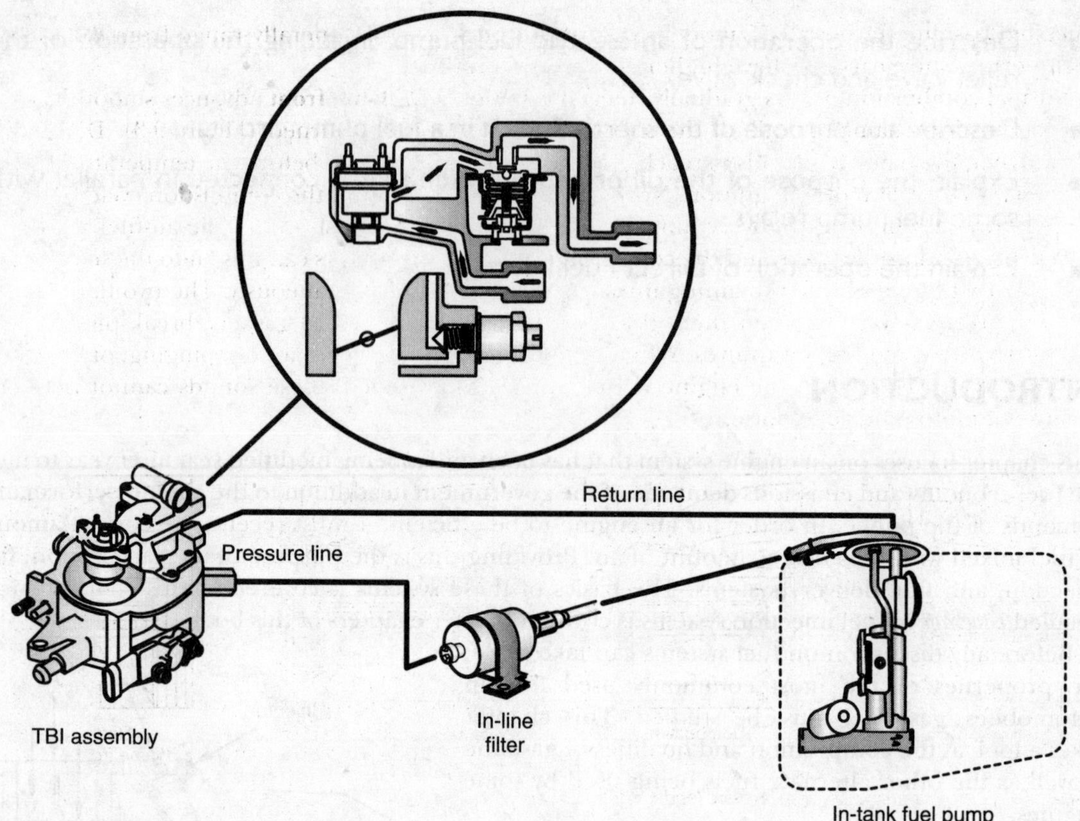

FIGURE 9-2 *In-line fuel filter.*

asphalts, kerosene, diesel fuel, gasoline, and natural gas. Before its widespread use in the internal combustion engine of automobiles, gasoline was an unwanted byproduct of refining for oils and kerosene.

Gasoline contains hydrogen and carbon molecules. The chemical symbol for this liquid is C_8H_{15}, which indicates that each molecule of gasoline contains eight carbon atoms and fifteen hydrogen atoms. Gasoline is a colorless liquid with excellent **vaporization** capabilities.

GASOLINE QUALITIES

Many of the performance characteristics of gasoline can be controlled in refining and blending to provide proper engine function and vehicle driveability. The major factors affecting fuel performance are antiknock quality, volatility, sulfur content, and deposit control.

Antiknock Quality

Two important factors affect the power and efficiency of a gasoline engine—compression ratio and **detonation**. The higher the compression ratio, the greater the engine's power output and efficiency. The better the efficiency, the less fuel consumed to produce a given power output. To have a high compression ratio requires an engine of greater structural integrity. Due to the use of low-octane unleaded gasoline in post-1975 models, compression ratios now generally range from 8:1 to 10:1. High performance cars may have higher compression ratios.

Normal combustion occurs gradually in each cylinder. The **flame front** advances smoothly across the combustion chamber until all the air-fuel mixture has been burned (Figure 9-3). Detonation occurs when the flame front fails to reach a pocket of air-fuel mixture before the temperature in that area reaches the point of self-ignition. Normal burning at the start of the combustion cycle raises the temperature and pressure of everything inside the cylinder. The last part of the air-fuel mixture is both heated and pressurized, and the combustion of those two factors can raise it to the self-ignition point. At that moment, the remaining mixture burns almost instantaneously. The two flame fronts create a pressure wave between them that can destroy cylinder head gaskets, break piston rings, and burn pistons and exhaust valves. When detonation occurs, a hammering, pinging, or knocking sound is heard. But, when the engine is operating at high speed, these sounds cannot be heard because of motor and road noise.

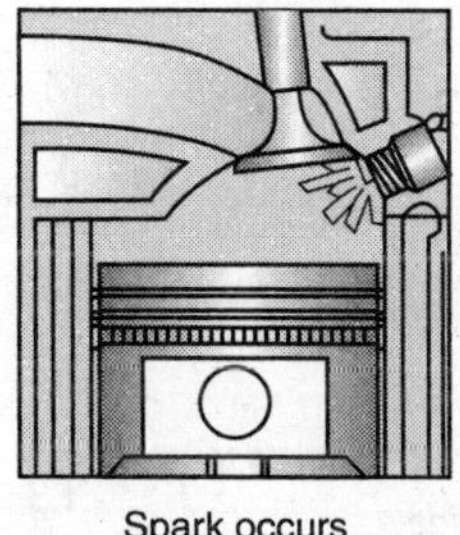

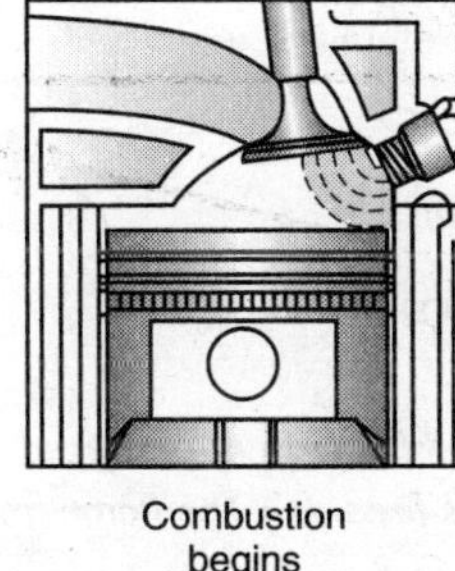

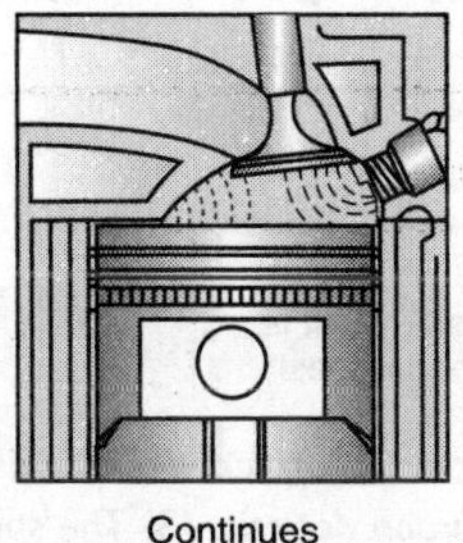

FIGURE 9-3 *The stages of combustion that lead to detonation.*

Pre-ignition is another term used to describe abnormal combustion. Pre-ignition is the term used to describe the igniting of fuel prematurely by a hot spot in the combustion chamber, such as a glowing piece of carbon (Figure 9-4). With pre-ignition, the fuel is ignited before the spark, resulting in power loss and possible engine damage.

An **octane number** or rating was developed by the petroleum industry so the **anti-knock** quality of a gasoline could be rated. The octane number is a measure of the fuel's tendency not to produce knock in an engine. The higher the octane number, the lesser the tendency to knock. By itself, the antiknock rating has nothing to do with fuel economy or engine efficiency.

Two commonly used methods for determining the octane number of motor gasoline are the motor octane number (MON) method and the research octane number (RON) method. Both use a laboratory single-cylinder engine equipped with a variable head and knock meter to indicate knock intensity. The test sample is used as fuel, and the engine compression ratio and air-fuel mixture are adjusted to develop a specified knock intensity. There are two primary standard reference fuels, isooctane and heptane. Isooctane does not knock in an engine but is not used in gasoline because of its expense. Heptane knocks severely in an engine. Isooctane has an octane number of 100. Heptane has an octane number of zero.

A fuel of unknown octane value is run in the special test engine and the severity of knock is measured. Various proportions of heptane and isooctane are run in the test engine to duplicate the severity of the knock of the fuel being tested. When the knock caused by the heptane-isooctane mixture is identical to the test fuel, the octane number is established by the percentage of isooctane in the mixture. For example, if 85 percent isooctane and 15 percent heptane produce the same severity of knock as the fuel in question, the fuel is assigned an octane number of 85.

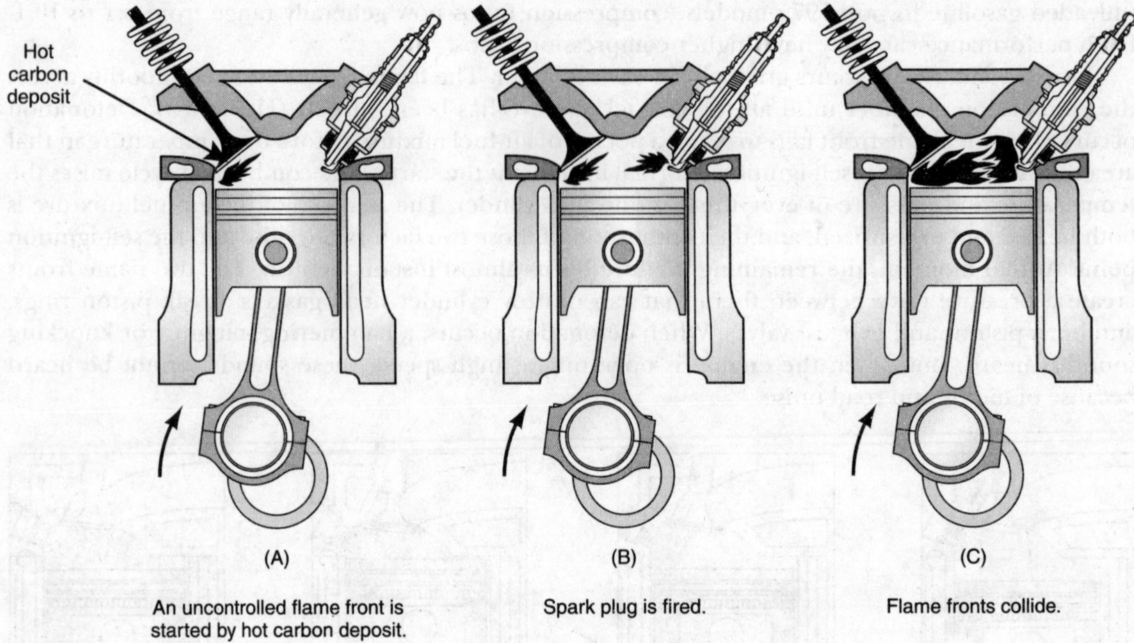

FIGURE 9-4 *The preignition process is started when an uncontrolled flame front is started too soon. (A) An uncontrolled flame front is started by a hot carbon deposit. (B) The spark plug is fired. (C) The flame fronts collide.*

The octane rating required by law and the one displayed on gasoline pumps is the Anti-knock Index (AKI) and is actually an average of the motor octane and research octane numbers. This formula is commonly found on the gasoline pumps at service stations and indicates the method used to establish a particular octane rating. This method actually uses an average of the two numbers. The formula is R + M/2 or RM/2, meaning research plus motor divided by two.

Factors that affect knock include:

- Lean Fuel Mixture. A lean mixture burns slower than a rich mixture. The heat of combustion is higher which promotes the tendency for unburned fuel in front of the spark-ignition flame to detonate.
- Overadvanced Ignition Timing. Advancing the ignition timing induces knock. Slowing ignition timing suppresses knock.
- Compression Ratio. Compression ratio affects knock because cylinder pressures are increased with the increase in compression ratio.
- Valve Timing. Valve timing that fills the cylinder with more air-fuel mixture promotes higher cylinder pressures, increasing the chances for detonation.
- Turbocharging. Turbocharging or supercharging forces additional fuel and air into the cylinder. This induces higher cylinder pressures and promotes knock.
- Coolant Temperature. Hotspots in the cylinder or combustion chamber due to inefficient cooling or a damaged cooling system raise combustion chamber temperatures and promote knock.
- Cylinder-to-Cylinder Distribution. If an engine has poor distribution of the air-fuel mixture from cylinder to cylinder, the leaner cylinders could promote knock.
- Excessive Carbon Deposits. The accumulation of carbon deposits on the piston, valves, and combustion chamber causes poor heat transfer from the combustion chamber. Carbon accumulation also artificially increases the compression ratio. Both conditions cause knock.

- Air Inlet Temperature. The higher the air temperature when it enters the cylinder, the greater the tendency to knock.
- Combustion Chamber Shape. The optimum combustion chamber shape for reduced knocking is hemispherical with a spark plug located in the center (Figure 9-5). This hemi-head allows for faster combustion, allowing less time for detonation to occur ahead of the flame front.
- Octane Number. Only when an engine is designed and adjusted to take advantage of the higher octane gasoline can the value of the fuel be obtained. Most modern engines are designed to operate efficiently with regular grade gasoline and do not require a high-octane premium grade.

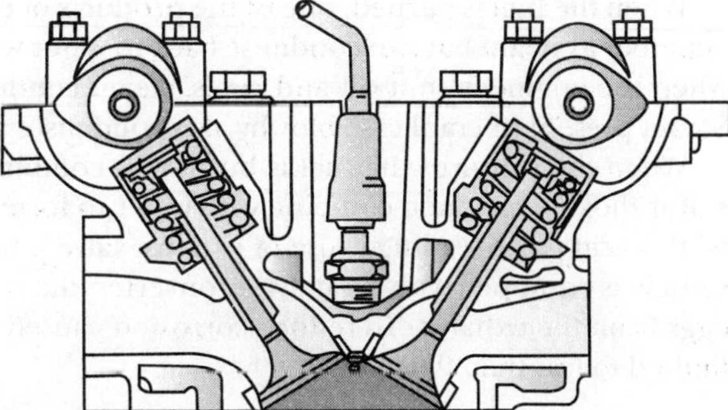

FIGURE 9-5 *Cross section of a hemispherical combustion chamber.*

Volatility

Liquid gasoline will not burn. The fuel must vaporize prior to entering the combustion chamber. Various types and grades of fuel have different rates of volatility. Volatility is the fuel's ability to change from a liquid to a vapor. Typically, gasoline is blended for a certain region or climate several times a year. Volatility that is too high can cause hot weather driveability and emission problems as well as vapor lock. Volatility that is too low can cause cold weather starting problems including slow warm-ups, as well as a buildup of deposits in the combustion chamber, crankcase, and on the spark plugs. To ensure complete combustion, complete vaporization must occur. The volatility of gasoline affects the following performance characteristics or driving conditions.

Cold Starting and Warmup. A fuel can cause hard starting, hesitation, and stumbling during warmup if it does not vaporize readily. A fuel that vaporizes too easily in hot weather can form vapor bubbles in the fuel line and fuel pump, resulting in vapor lock or loss of performance.

Temperature. Because a highly volatile fuel vaporizes at a lower temperature than a less volatile fuel, winter grade gasoline is more volatile than summer grade gasoline.

Altitude. Gasoline vaporizes more easily at high altitudes. Therefore, volatility is controlled in blending according to the elevation of the place where fuel is sold.

Crankcase Oil Dilution. A fuel must vaporize well to prevent diluting the crankcase oil with liquid fuel. If parts of the gasoline do not vaporize, droplets of liquid break down the oil film on the cylinder wall, causing scuffing or scoring. The liquid eventually enters the crankcase oil and results in the formation of sludge, gum, and varnish accumulation as well as decreasing the lubrication properties of the oil.

Driveability. Poor vaporization can also affect the distribution of fuel from cylinder to cylinder since vaporized fuel travels farther and faster in the manifold.

Sulfur Content

Gasoline can contain some of the sulfur present in the crude oil. Sulfur content is reduced at the refinery to limit the amount of corrosion in the engine and exhaust system.

When the fuel is burned, one of the products of combustion is water. Water leaves the combustion chamber as steam but can condense back to water when passing through a cool exhaust system. Also, when the engine is shut off and cools, steam condenses back to a liquid and forms water droplets. Steam present in crankcase blowby also condenses to water.

When the sulfur in the fuel is burned, it combines with the oxygen to form sulfur dioxide. This sulfur dioxide can then combine with water to form highly corrosive sulfuric acid. Corrosion caused by this acid is the leading cause of exhaust valve pitting and exhaust system deterioration. When the vehicle is equipped with a catalytic converter, the sulfur dioxide can cause a noxious odor of rotten eggs from the exhaust. To reduce corrosion caused by sulfuric acid, the sulfur content in gasoline is limited to less than 0.01 percent.

Deposit Control

Several additives are put in gasoline to control harmful deposits, including gum or oxidation inhibitors, detergents, metal deactivators, and rust inhibitors.

BASIC FUEL ADDITIVES

At one time, all a gasoline-producing company had to do to produce their product was pump the crude from the ground, run it through the refinery to separate it, dump in a couple of grams of lead per gallon, and deliver the finished product to the service station. Of course, automobiles were much simpler then and what they burned was not very critical. As long as gasoline vaporized easily and did not cause the low compression engines to knock, everything was fine.

For many years, lead compounds such as tetraethyl lead (TEL) and tetramethyl lead (TML) were added to gasoline to improve its octane ratings. However, since the mid-1970s, vehicles have been designed to run on unleaded gasoline only. Leaded fuels are no longer available as automotive fuels. The main reason for the change to unleaded gasoline was to provide a fuel for cars with special antipollution devices—catalytic converters. These systems must have unleaded fuel in order to work properly.

Because of the deactivating or poisoning effect lead has on catalytic converters, gasolines are limited to a lead content of 0.06 gram per gallon. Since TEL or TML is not added to unleaded gasolines, the required octane number is obtained by blending compounds of the required octane quality. Methylcylopentadienyl manganese tricarbonyl (MMT) is a catalyst-compatible octane improver. Vehicles with catalytic converters are labeled at both the fuel gauge and fuel filler “Unleaded Fuel Only.”

Times have changed. Today, refiners are under constant pressure to ensure that their product passes a series of rigorous tests for seasonal volatility, minimum octane, existent gum, and oxidation stability as well as add the correct deicers and detergents to make the product competitive in a price-sensitive marketplace. Gasoline additives, primarily used in unleaded gasolines, have different properties and a variety of uses.

- Anti-Icing or Deicer. Isopropyl alcohol is added seasonally to gasoline as an anti-icing agent to prevent gas line freeze-up in cold climates.
- Metal Deactivators and Rust Inhibitors. These additives are used to inhibit reactions between the fuel and the metals in the fuel system that can form abrasive and filterplugging substances.
- Gum or Oxidation Inhibitors. Some gasolines contain aromatic amines and phenols to prevent formation of gum and varnish. During storage, harmful gum deposits can form due to the reaction of some gasoline components with each other and with oxygen. Oxidation inhibitors are added

to promote gasoline stability. They help control gum, deposit formation, and staleness. Stale gasoline becomes cloudy and smells like paint thinner.

- Detergents. The use of detergent additives in gasoline has been the subject of some public confusion. Detergent additives are designed to do only what their name implies—clean certain critical components inside the engine. They do not affect octane.
- Ethanol. By far the most widely used gasoline additive today is **ethanol**, or grain alcohol. Ethanol's value as an octane enhancer becomes more apparent when considered in the context of the government-mandated phasedown of tetraethyl lead. Blending 10 percent ethanol into gasoline is seen as a comparatively inexpensive octane booster that results in an increase of 2.5 to 3 road octane points. In addition to octane enhancement, ethanol blending keeps the fuel injectors clean due to detergent additive packages found in most of the ethanol marketed. It also inhibits fuel system and injection corrosion due to additive packages and decreases carbon monoxide emissions at the tailpipe due to the higher oxygen content of blended fuel. Ethanol as a motor fuel has been explored for some time. The problem with unblended ethanol is that it burns slower than gasoline and is not as volatile. One solution has been found in the use of a fuel called E-85, which is being produced in some areas of the country for use in specially equipped vehicles. E-85 is a mixture of 15 percent gasoline and 85 percent ethanol. The vehicles have a sensor built into the fuel system to detect the amount of ethanol in the fuel tank. The PCM is programmed to change the operating characteristics of the engine to accept the fuel. The gasoline is added to aid volatility of the fuel, needed especially for good cold starting. So far, E-85 is only available in some states in the Midwest, but with rising fuel prices and the concern over fuel importation, E-85 may become a viable alternative. The ethanol can be produced from a renewable resource such as corn.
- Methanol. Methanol is the lightest and simplest of the alcohols and is also known as wood alcohol. It can be distilled from coal but most of what is used today is derived from natural gas. Many automakers continue to warn motorists about using a fuel that contains more than 10 percent methanol and co-solvents by volume. Methanol is recognized as being far more corrosive to fuel system components than ethanol, and it is this corrosion that has automakers concerned.

ALTERNATIVE FUELS

Tighter federal, state, and local emissions regulations have led to a search for an alternative fuel. Many factors are considered when determining the viability of an alternative fuel, including emissions, cost, fuel availability, fuel consumption, safety, engine life, fueling facilities, weight and space requirements of fuel tanks, and the range of a fully fueled vehicle. Currently, the major competing alternative fuels include ethanol, methanol, propane, and natural gas. Diesel fuel has been in use for many years, and its properties are included in this section.

Ethanol and methanol were presented earlier under other gasoline additives. Propane is a petroleum-based pressurized fuel used as a liquid. It is a constituent of natural gas. Natural gas comes in two forms: **compressed natural gas** (**CNG**) and liquefied natural gas (LNG).

LP-Gas

LP-gas is a byproduct of crude oil refining, and it is also found in natural gas wells. Fuel grade LP-gas is almost pure propane with a little butane and propylene usually present. Because of its high propane content, many people simply refer to LP-gas as propane.

Propane burns clean in the engine and can be precisely controlled. Because it vaporizes at atmospheric temperatures and pressures, it does not puddle in the intake manifold. This means it emits less hydrocarbons and carbon monoxide. Emission controls on the engine can be simpler. Cold starting is easy, down to much below zero. At normal cold temperatures, the propane engine fires easily and produces power without surge or stumble. Propane has a higher octane rating than gasoline and can be utilized in an engine with a higher compression ratio. However, power loss is about 5 percent due to lower volumetric efficiency.

One of the most noticeable differences between propane and gasoline is that propane is a dry fuel. It enters the engine as vapor. Gasoline, on the other hand, enters the engine as tiny droplets of liquid whether it flows through a carburetor or is sprayed in through a fuel injector.

The propane fuel system is a completely closed system that contains a supply of pressurized LP-gas. Since the fuel is already under pressure, no fuel pump is needed. From the pressurized fuel tanks, the fuel flows to a vacuum filter fuel lock. This serves as a filter and a control allowing fuel to flow to the engine. Fuel flows to a converter or heat exchanger where it changes from a liquid to a gas. When the propane flows through the converter, it expands as it changes into a gas. The carburetor mixes gaseous propane with the gaseous air. Airflow into the engine is controlled by a butterfly valve in the venturi. Mixture is controlled by a fuel **metering** valve operated by a diaphragm which is controlled by intake manifold pressure. The idle system is an air bleed similar to a gasoline engine. In fact, except for the fact that the propane carburetor does not require a fuel bowl, the two carburetor types are basically the same.

Natural Gas

Vehicles have been designed with gasoline/CNG, diesel/CNG, and dedicated CNG engine applications. Compressed natural gas (CNG) (Figure 9-6) vehicles offer several advantages over gasoline.

- The fuel costs less.
- It is the cleanest alternative fuel, generating up to 99 percent less carbon monoxide than gasoline, no particulates, almost no sulfur dioxide, and 85 percent less reactive hydrocarbons than gasoline.
- Natural gas vehicles are safer. The fuel tanks used for CNG are aluminum or steel cylinders with walls that are 1/2- to 3/4-inch thick. They can withstand severe crash tests, direct gunfire, dynamite explosions, and burning beyond any standard sheet metal gasoline tank. Because it is lighter than air, natural gas dissipates quickly. It also has a higher ignition temperature.
- It generally reduces vehicle maintenance since it burns cleanly. Oil changes may not be needed before 12,000 miles, and spark plugs could last longer.
- Natural gas is abundant and readily available in the United States.

The chief disadvantage of CNG at present is its nonavailability to most users. Fuel facilities are needed in greater numbers than are currently in existence due to the relatively shorter range of CNG vehicles. The space taken by the CNG cylinders and their weight, about 300 pounds, would also be considered disadvantages in most applications.

Diesel Fuel

Diesel fuel is also made from petroleum. At the refinery, the petroleum is separated into three major components: gasoline, middle distillates, and all remaining substances. Diesel fuel comes from the middle distillate group, which has properties and characteristics different from gasoline.

The shape of the fuel spray, turbulence in the combustion chamber, beginning and duration of injection, and the chemical properties of the diesel fuel all affect the power output of the diesel engine. The significant chemical properties of diesel fuel are described briefly in the following.

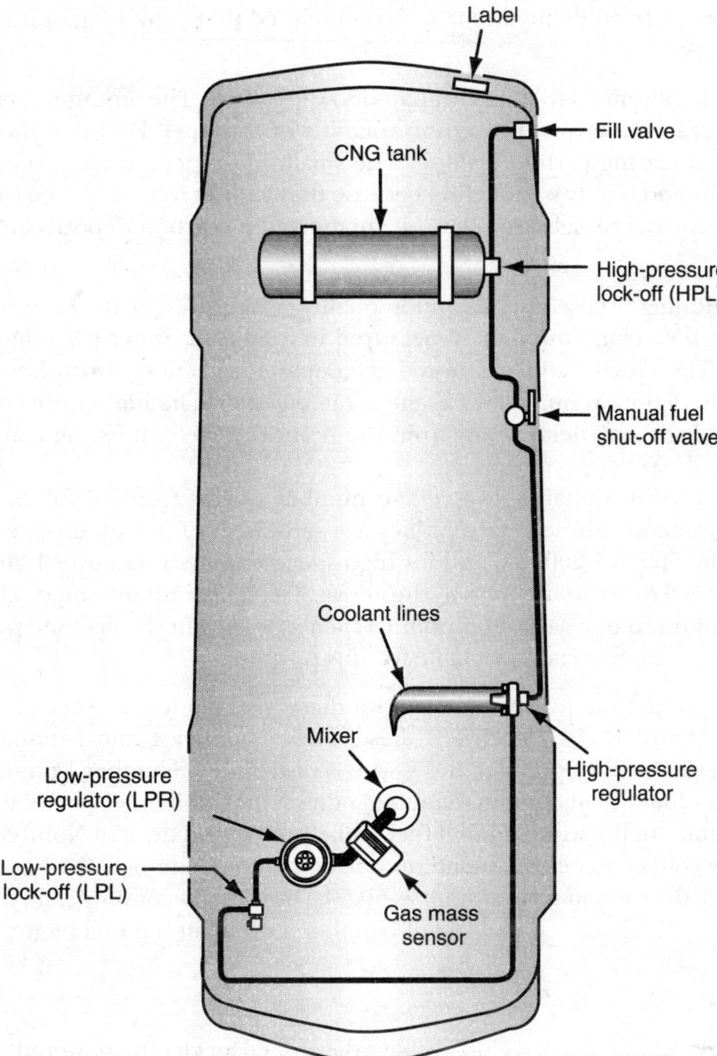

FIGURE 9-6 *CNG system components.*

Viscosity. The viscosity of diesel fuel varies with temperature. The viscosity of diesel fuel directly affects the spray pattern of the fuel into the combustion chamber. Fuel with a high viscosity produces large droplets that are hard to burn. Fuel with a low viscosity sprays in a fine, easily burned mist. However, if the viscosity is too low it does not adequately lubricate and cool the injection pump and nozzles.

Wax Appearance Point and Pour Point. Temperature affects diesel fuel more than it affects gasoline. This is because diesel fuels contain **paraffin**. As temperatures drop past a certain point, wax crystals begin to form in the fuel. The point where the wax crystals appear is the wax appearance point (WAP) or cloud point. The better the quality of the fuel, the lower the WAP. As temperatures drop, the wax crystals grow larger and restrict the flow of fuel through the filters and lines. Eventually, the fuel, which may still be liquid, stops flowing because the wax crystals plug a filter or line. As the temperature continues to drop, the fuel reaches a point where it solidifies and no longer flows. This is called the pour point. In cold climates it is recommended that a low-temperature pour point fuel be used.

Volatility. Gasoline is extremely volatile compared to diesel fuel. The amount of carbon residue left by diesel fuel depends on the quality and the volatility of that fuel. Fuel that has a low volatility is much more prone to leaving carbon residue. The small, high-speed diesels found in automobiles require a high-quality and highly volatile fuel because they cannot tolerate excessive carbon deposits. Large, low-speed industrial diesels are relatively unaffected by carbon deposits and can run on low-quality fuel.

Cetane Number or Rating. Diesel fuel's ignition quality is measured by the **cetane** rating. Much like the octane number, the cetane number is measured in a single-cylinder test engine with a variable compression ratio. The diesel fuel to be tested is compared to cetane, a colorless, liquid hydrocarbon that has excellent ignition qualities. Cetane is rated at 100. The higher the cetane number, the shorter the ignition lag time (delay time) from the point the fuel enters the combustion chamber until it ignites.

In fuels that are readily available, the cetane number ranges from 40 to 55, with values of 40 to 50 being most common. These cetane values are satisfactory for medium-speed engines whose rated speeds are from 500 to 1,200 rpm and for high-speed engines rated over 1,200 rpm. Low-speed engines rated below 500 rpm can use fuels in the above 30 cetane number range. The cetane number improves with the addition of certain compounds such as ethyl nitrate, acetone peroxide, and amyl nitrate. Amyl nitrate is commercially available for this purpose.

Diesel Fuel Grades. Minimum quality standards for diesel fuel grades have been set by the American Society for Testing Materials. Two grades of diesel fuels, Number 1 and Number 2, are available. Number 2 diesel fuel is the most popular and is widely distributed. Number 1 diesel fuel is less dense than Number 2 with a lower heat content. Number 1 diesel fuel is blended with Number 2 to improve starting in cold weather. In the winter, diesel fuel is likely to be a mixture of Number 1 and Number 2 fuels. In moderately cold climates, the blend may be 90 percent Number 2 to 10 percent Number 1. In very cold climates, the ratio may be as high as 50:50. Diesel fuel economy can be expected to drop off during the winter months due to the use of Number 1 diesel in the fuel blend.

Electric Vehicles

Almost all automobile manufacturers globally have developed an electric powered vehicle. Electronic vehicles, or EVs, are powered by electric motors with energy stored in battery packs (up to 26 batteries). The primary advantage of EVs is a reduction in emissions and noise levels. The EV can travel about 50 to 70 miles before needing a recharge. Driving conditions, temperature, and load can affect how long the vehicle can be driven. It may take up to 10 hours to completely recharge a battery. One of the biggest disadvantages to the EV is the driving range, although research continues to evolve to extend the range. Currently, new technology includes regenerative braking and high-efficiency accessories in addition to permanent magnet electric drive motors. Disadvantages include the high cost of replacement batteries and the dangers of high operating voltage.

Hybrid Electric Vehicles

Hybrid vehicles use two sources of power, a small internal combustion engine that provides the main source of vehicle power, plus a high-voltage electric motor that serves to assist the internal combustion engine during acceleration (Figure 9-7). The high-voltage components such as the control unit and 144-volt battery module are located in the rear of the vehicle. The internal combustion engine, the

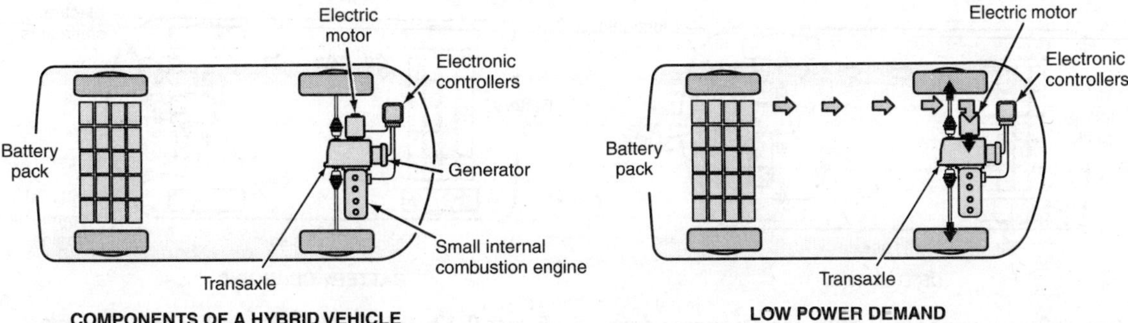

FIGURE 9-7 *Main components of a hybrid vehicle.*

FIGURE 9-8 *During low power demand, the battery pack can provide power to allow the electric motor to move the vehicle.*

electric motor, and the transmission are located in the front of the vehicle. The electric motor is situated between the engine and transmission (Figure 9-8).

The high-voltage DC motor also serves as a starter for the internal combustion engine and as a generator to recharge the 144-volt battery through the internal combustion engine and through regenerative braking (Figure 9-9). If power demand is low, such as in stop-and-go city traffic, the electric motor can be used alone to power the wheels. Conventional 12-volt electrical circuits and a 12-volt battery are supplied with current through the main battery with a voltage reduction DC/DC converter.

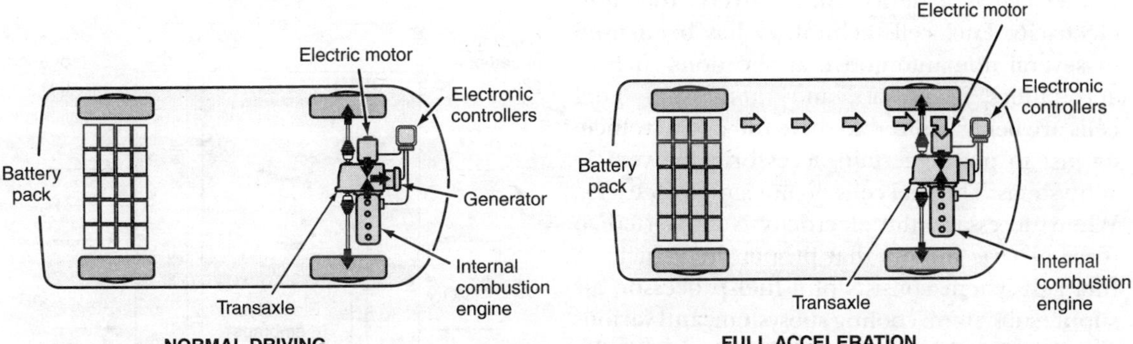

FIGURE 9-9 *During normal driving, the internal combustion engine provides power and recharges the battery.*

FIGURE 9-10 *Both electric motor and gas engine power the vehicle on acceleration.*

The hybrid system also uses a battery condition module and a motor control module working together to prevent under or overcharging of the main battery by turning off either the electric assist when the battery is undercharged, or regenerative braking if the battery is in danger of overcharge. If there is a low battery state of charge or a problem in the electric motor, a conventional starter is used to start the internal combustion engine (Figure 9-10 and Figure 9-11).

When the vehicle comes to a stop, the main engine can be shut down to improve fuel economy if the engine is warm (Figure 9-12), the electrical demands are low, and the outside temperature is above about 40°F. The engine will automatically restart when safe to do so as determined by transmission selection, brake, and clutch pedal action. Since the electric motor is connected directly

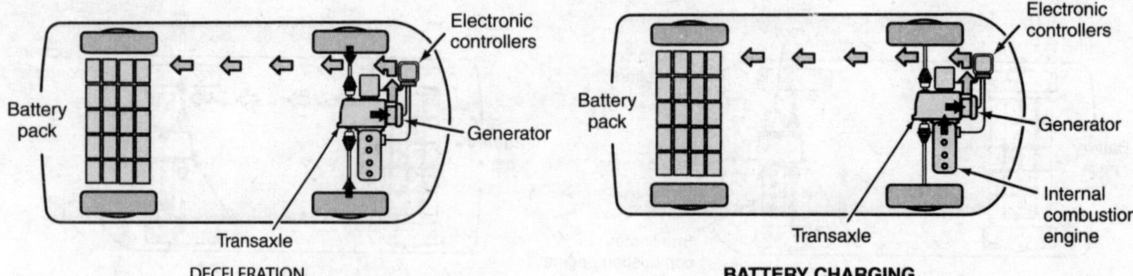

FIGURE 9-11 *During deceleration, the car slowing down is converted to electrical energy to charge the batteries.*

FIGURE 9-12 *The gasoline engine will run with the vehicle stopped to charge the batteries if necessary.*

to the internal combustion engine, the main engine start is quick and quiet compared to the usual gasoline vehicle.

The Honda Insight and the Toyota Prius were among the first widely produced hybrid vehicles. General Motors, Lexus, Ford, and Daimler Chrysler are all scheduled to release many more hybrid vehicles including trucks and SUVs in the immediate future. Expect to see this category change and develop over the next few years. Do not attempt to service these vehicles without specific service information for the vehicle you are working on since hybrid vehicles have high-voltage circuits that may cause severe injuries or property damage.

Fuel Cells

A fuel cell is a device that converts fuel into electricity. Fuel cell technology has been used in several non-automotive applications such as aeronautics, spacecraft, and submarines. Fuel cells are being utilized to drive the entire vehicle or just to power certain accessories or vehicle subsystems. The fuel cells do not store electricity. When necessary, the electricity is converted to drive electric motors that propel the vehicle. A fuel cell system consists of a fuel processor, air supply subsystem, cooling subsystem, and various controls. Combining these subsystems with the fuel cell creates a complete power generating system. A single cell is sometimes referred to as a proton exchange membrane, or PEM. A PEM fuel cell (Figure 9-13) is made of two plates sandwiched together with a plastic membrane coated with a catalyst in the center.

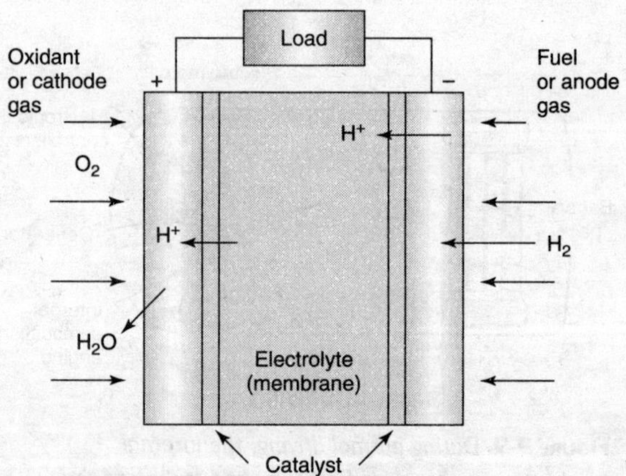

FIGURE 9-13 *Basic operation of a fuel cell.*

Hydrogen from methanol, natural gas, or petroleum along with oxygen from the air is fed through channels in the plates—hydrogen on one side and oxygen on the other. Chemically speaking, the hydrogen and oxygen want to be together. The shortest way to join is through the membrane, but only part of the hydrogen atom, the proton, can pass through the membrane. The other part, the electron, has to take the long way around through an external circuit, or load, creating useful electricity. The oxygen side of the PEM attracts the protons and the electrons that have traveled through the external circuit generating the byproducts of water and heat. As long as hydrogen is supplied, a fuel cell will operate continuously. By combining single cells, a fuel cell stack is formed

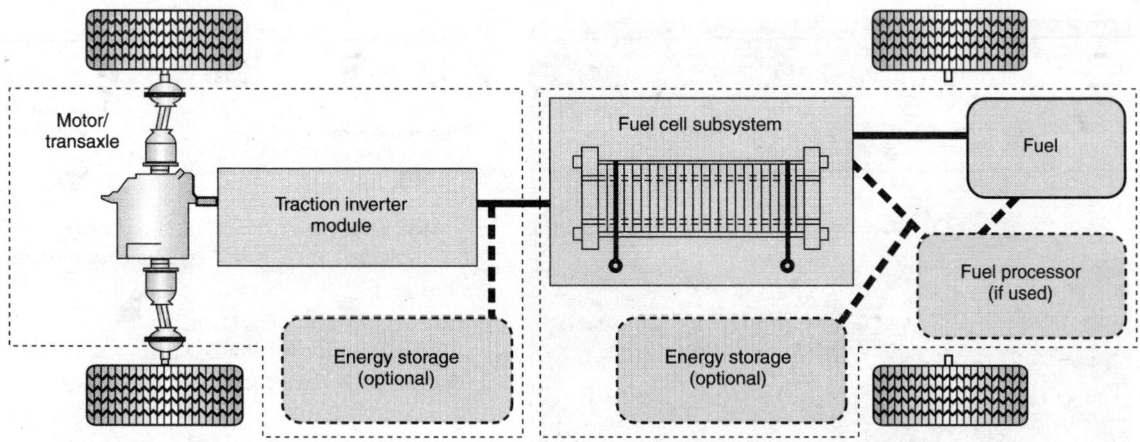

FIGURE 9-14 *Layout of a typical fuel cell vehicle.*

to produce the required amount of power. When the vehicle's power demands exceed the amount the fuel cell can generate, additional current is drawn from storage batteries. One advantage of the fuel cell is that it charges the batteries directly and there is no need for plug-in charging as with other electric vehicles. Fuel cell technology continues to evolve and may be found in production vehicles within the next decade. Figure 9-14 shows the layout of a typical fuel cell vehicle.

FEEDBACK FUEL CONTROL

For the three-way catalyst to work efficiently, the air-fuel mixture must be maintained very close to a 14.7 to 1 ratio. If the air-fuel mixture is too lean, NO_X is not converted efficiently. If the mixture is too rich, HC and carbon monoxide (CO) do not oxidize efficiently. Monitoring the air-fuel ratio is the job of the exhaust gas oxygen sensor (Figure 9-15).

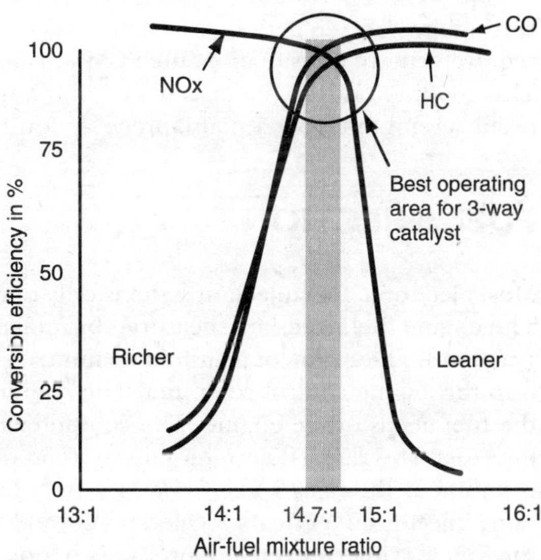

FIGURE 9-15 *The efficiency of a three-way catalytic converter with different air-fuel ratios.*

The feedback system is easy to understand. The prime objective of this system is to maintain an air-fuel ratio as close to 14.7 to 1 as possible so that the catalytic converter will function optimally. Basically, fuel delivery is electronically controlled by the PCM. This is accomplished by increasing or decreasing the amount of fuel to be delivered to the engine based on driving demands and operating conditions. Outputs or commands from the PCM correct the current mixture condition it is sensing. A number of sensors give input to the PCM to indicate the current engine demand and operating environment such as load, air and coolant temperature, barometric pressure, and vehicle and engine speed, to name a few. The oxygen sensor in the exhaust manifold responds to the presence or absence of oxygen in the post combustion exhaust (Figure 9-16). The PCM is programmed to add fuel to the combustion chamber

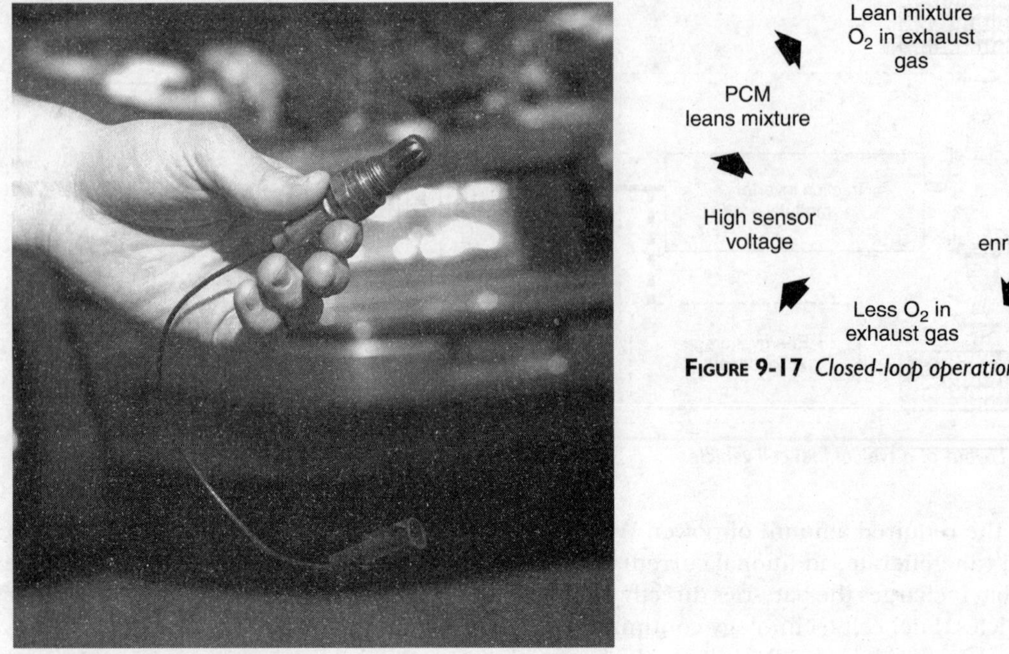

FIGURE 9-16 *An oxygen sensor.*

FIGURE 9-17 *Closed-loop operation.*

(enrich the mixture) when it "sees" a lean condition (low-oxygen sensor voltage input). It will also subtract fuel (lean the mixture) when the exhaust condition is rich (high-oxygen sensor voltage). This process is part of an ongoing cycle of fuel management known as closed loop (Figure 9-17). During the warmup period or under certain driving conditions, the engine may demand a high fuel requirement. In this situation, the PCM will ignore the oxygen sensor and deliver a fixed rate of fuel. This condition is referred to as open loop. Depending on the engine system, the rich-lean cycle can occur several times per second, precisely controlling fuel and emissions.

FUEL INJECTION

Most electronic fuel injection systems only inject fuel during part of the engine's combustion cycle. The engine fuel needs are measured by intake airflow past a sensor or by intake manifold pressure (vacuum). The airflow or manifold vacuum sensor converts its reading to an electrical signal and sends it to the engine control computer. The computer processes this signal (and others) and calculates the fuel needs of the engine. The computer then sends an electrical signal to the fuel injector or injectors. This signal determines the amount of time the injector opens and sprays fuel. This interval is known as the *injector pulse width.* Figure 9-18 shows a typical fuel injector voltage waveform. The same injector under heavy acceleration would show a pattern similar to that in Figure 9-19. Note that the time the injector remains on is much longer, so naturally the mixture would be richer. A similar pattern might be seen if the PCM were trying to compensate for a lean mixture. Figure 9-20 shows an injector waveform that indicates the PCM is trying to reduce the injector on time, such as on deceleration or the PCM is trying to compensate for a very rich mixture.

Electronic fuel injection (EFI) has proven to be the most precise, reliable, and cost effective method of delivering fuel to the combustion chambers of today's vehicles. EFI systems must provide the correct air-fuel ratio for all engine loads, speeds, and temperature conditions. To

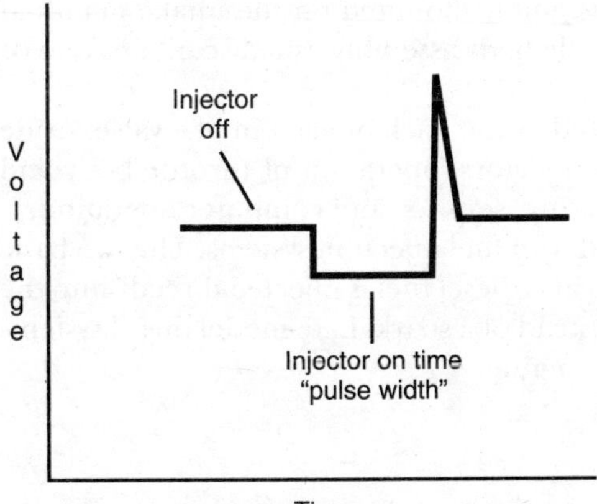

FIGURE 9-18 *Typical injector waveform at normal operation.*

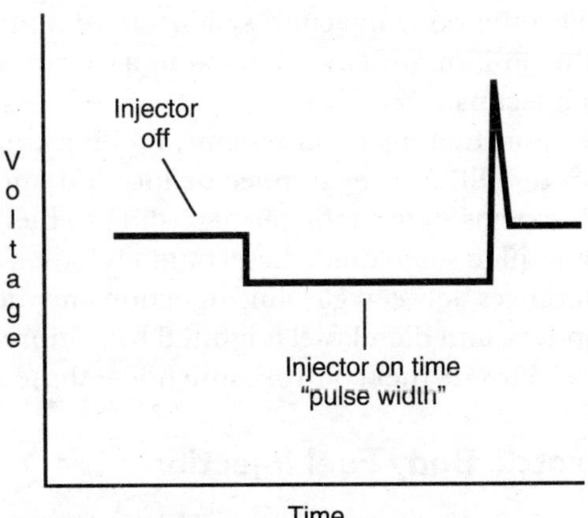

FIGURE 9-19 *On acceleration, the injector pulse width becomes longer to deliver more fuel. The same would be seen if the PCM were correcting for a lean condition.*

accomplish this, an EFI system uses a fuel delivery system, air induction system, input sensors, control computer, fuel injectors, and some sort of idle speed control Throttle Actuator Control (TAC).

Input sensors for fuel injection include:

1. Oxygen (O_2) sensor
2. Engine coolant temperature (ECT) sensor
3. Intake air temperature (IAT) sensor
4. Throttle position sensor (TP Sensor)
5. Manifold absolute pressure (MAP) sensor
6. Mass air flow (MAF) sensor
7. Knock sensor
8. Exhaust gas recirculation valve position (EVP) sensor
9. Vehicle speed sensor (VSS)
10. Neutral drive switch (NDS)
11. Accelerator pedal position sensor (if equipped with TAC)

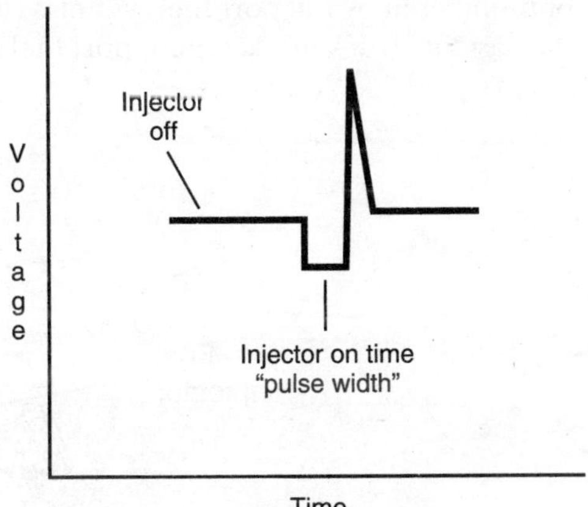

FIGURE 9-20 *During deceleration, or trying to compensate for a rich mixture. Notice how short the pulse width becomes.*

TYPES OF FUEL INJECTION

Although fuel injection technology has been around since the 1920s, it was not until the 1980s that manufacturers began to replace carburetors with **electronic fuel injection (EFI)** systems. Many of the early EFI systems were **throttle body injection (TBI)** systems in which the fuel was injected above the throttle plates. Recently, a similar system, **central port injection (CPI)**, was introduced. In these systems, the injector assembly is located in the lower half of the intake manifold. Engines equipped with TBI have gradually become equipped with **port fuel injection (PFI)** which has injectors located in the intake ports of the cylinders. **Gasoline Direct Injections**, or **GDI**, injects fuel directly into the cylinders. Since the 1995 model year, all new cars are equipped with an EFI system.

Throttle body injection systems have a throttle body assembly mounted on the intake manifold in the position usually occupied by a carburetor. The throttle body assembly usually contains one or two injectors.

In port fuel injection systems, fuel injectors are mounted at the back of each intake valve. Aside from the differences in injector location and number of injectors, operation of throttle body and port systems is quite similar regarding to fuel and air metering, sensors, and computer operation.

For quite some time, diesel engines have been equipped with fuel injection systems. The two basic differences between gasoline injection and diesel injection are: diesel fuel is injected directly into the cylinders, and diesel fuel is ignited by compression heat instead of a spark. Late-model diesel systems use electronic fuel controls, much like those of a gasoline engine.

Throttle Body Fuel Injection

Throttle body fuel injection (TBI) systems were introduced in several configurations in the mid-1980s and was a major improvement over the feedback carbureted systems (Figure 9-21). Many of the carburetor-related systems, including the choke system and manual mixture adjustments, were eliminated. Increased precise fuel control from the TBI system resulted in improved performance and economy as well as a reduction in emissions. The TBI systems were the predecessor to today's port fuel injection systems. Although some applications still use TBI systems, they will soon be outnumbered by the port fuel systems. Today, the production of all new vehicles, including most of the gasoline truck market, have port fuel systems utilizing various designs.

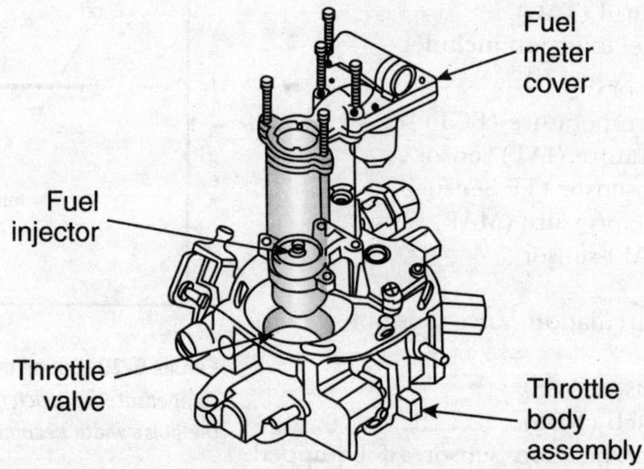

FIGURE 9-21 *Parts of a throttle body injection unit.*

TBI Operation. The basic TBI assembly consists of two major castings: a throttle body with a valve to control airflow and a fuel body to supply the required fuel. A fuel pressure regulator and fuel injector are integral parts of the fuel body (Figure 9-22). Also included as part of the assembly is a device to control idle speed and one to provide throttle valve positioning data.

The throttle body casting has ports that can be located above, below, or at the throttle valve depending on the manufacturer's design. These ports generate vacuum signals for the manifold absolute pressure sensor and for devices in the emission control system such as the exhaust gas recirculation (EGR) valve, the canister purge system, and so on.

The **fuel pressure regulator** used on the throttle body assembly is similar to a diaphragm-operated relief valve (Figure 9-23). Fuel pressure is on one side of the diaphragm and atmospheric pressure

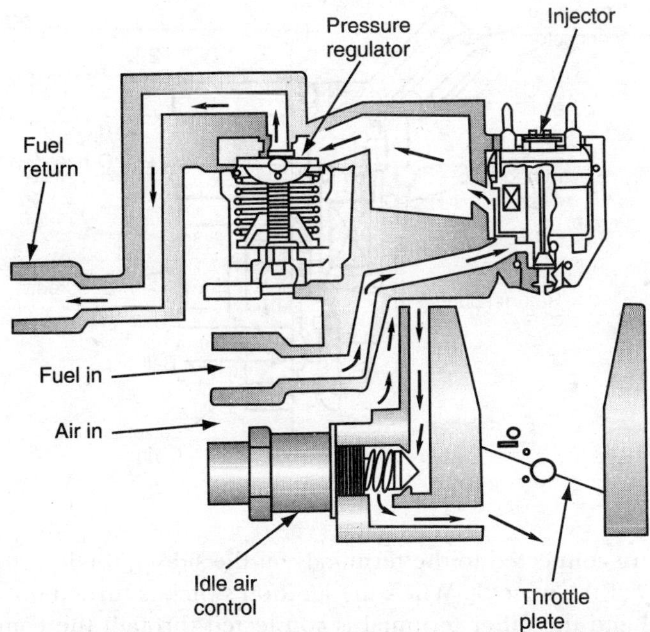

FIGURE 9-22 *Fuel and airflow in a TBI injection system. The injector is a bottom fuel feed design. The idle air control allows air to bypass the throttle plate to regulate engine idle in all operating conditions.*

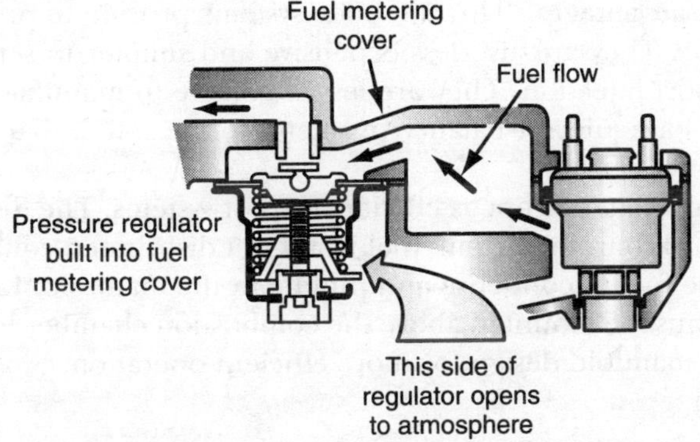

FIGURE 9-23 *A fuel pressure regulator for a TBI system.*

is on the other side. The regulator is designed to provide a constant pressure on the fuel injector throughout the range of engine loads and speeds. If regulator pressure is too high, a strong fuel odor is emitted and the engine runs too rich. On the other hand, regulator pressure that is too low results in poor engine performance or detonation can take place due to the lean mixture.

The fuel injector is solenoid operated and pulsed on and off by the vehicle's engine control computer. Surrounding the injector inlet is a fine screen filter where the incoming fuel is directed. When the injector's solenoid is energized, a normally closed ball valve is lifted (Figure 9-24). Fuel under pressure is then injected at the walls of the throttle body bore just above the throttle plate.

A fuel injector has a moveable armature in the center of the injector, and a pintle with a tapered tip is positioned at the lower end of the armature. A spring pushes the armature and pintle downward so the pintle tip seats in the discharge orifice. The injector coil surrounds the armature, and the two

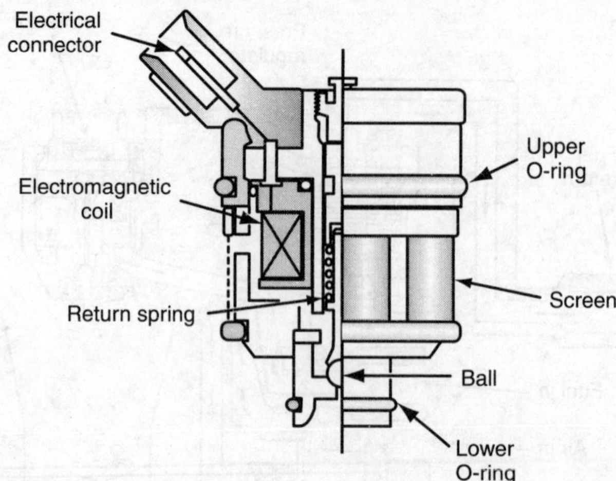

FIGURE 9-24 *Typical TBI injector.*

ends of the winding are connected to the terminals on the side of the injector. An integral filter is located inside the top of the injector. When the ignition switch is turned on, voltage is supplied to one injector terminal and the other terminal is connected through the computer. Each time the control unit completes the circuit from the injector winding to ground, current flows through the injector coil and the coil magnetism moves the plunger and pintle upward. Under this condition, the pintle tip is unseated from the injector orifice and fuel sprays out this orifice.

TBI Advantages and Disadvantages. Throttle body systems provide improved fuel metering when compared to carburetors. They are also less expensive and simpler to service. TBI units also have some advantages over port injection. They are less expensive to manufacture, simpler to diagnose and service, and do not have injector balance problems to the extent that port injection systems do when the injectors begin to clog.

However, throttle body units are not as efficient as port systems. The disadvantages are primarily manifold related. Like a carburetor system, fuel is still not distributed equally to all cylinders, and a cold manifold may cause fuel to condense and puddle in the manifold. Like a carburetor, throttle-body injection systems must be mounted above the combustion chamber level, which eliminates the possibility of tuning the manifold design for more efficient operation.

Port Fuel Injection

PFI systems use one injector at each cylinder. They are mounted in the intake manifold near the cylinder head where they can inject a fine, atomized fuel mist as close as possible to the intake valve (Figure 9-25). Fuel lines that run to each cylinder from a fuel manifold are usually referred to as a **fuel rail**. The fuel rail assembly on a PFI system of V6 and V8 engines usually consists of a left- and right-hand rail assembly. The two rails can be connected either by crossover and return fuel tubes or by a mechanical bracket arrangement. A typical fuel rail arrangement is shown in Figure 9-26. Fuel tubes crisscross between the two rails. Figure 9-27 shows a fuel rail on a transverse four-cylinder engine. Since each cylinder has its own injector, fuel distribution is exactly equal. With little or no fuel to wet the manifold walls, there is no need for manifold heat or any early fuel evaporation system. Fuel does not collect in puddles at the base of the manifold. This means that the intake manifold passages can be tuned or designed for better low-speed power availability (Figure 9-28). The port-type systems provide a more accurate and efficient delivery of fuel. Some engines are now equipped

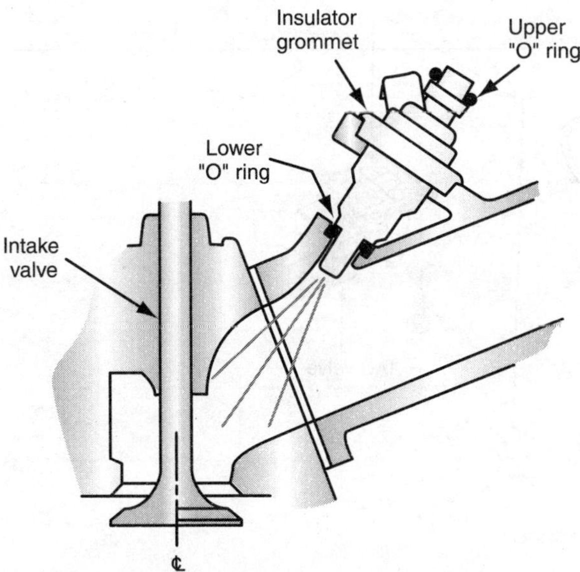

FIGURE 9-25 *Port injection sprays fuel into the intake port and fills the port with fuel vapor before the valve opens.*

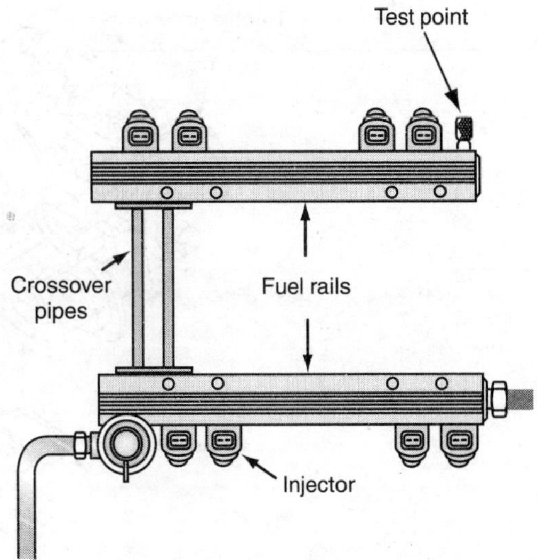

FIGURE 9-26 *Typical fuel rail for a V8 engine.*

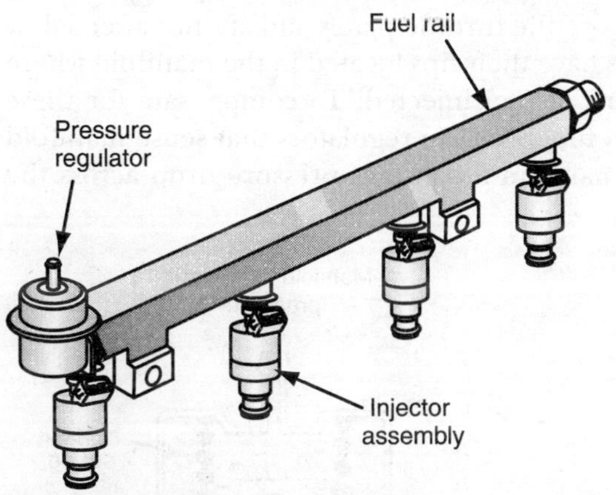

FIGURE 9-27 *Fuel rail and injectors for a four-cylinder engine.*

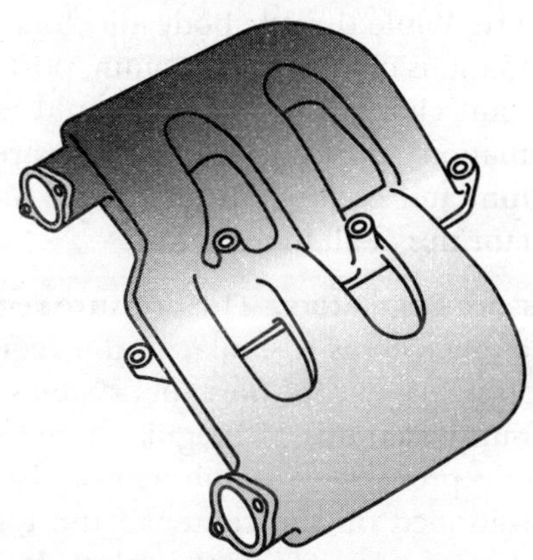

FIGURE 9-28 *Typical tuned intake manifold for a port injection engine.*

with variable induction intake manifolds that have separate runners for low and high speeds. This technology is only possible with port injection.

The throttle body in a port fuel injection system controls the amount of air that enters the engine as well as the amount of vacuum in the manifold. It also houses and controls the idle air control (IAC) motor and the throttle position sensor (TP sensor). The TP sensor enables the PCM to know where the throttle is positioned at all times.

The throttle body (Figure 9-29) is a single cast aluminum housing typically consisting of a single throttle blade attached to the throttle shaft. The TP sensor and the IAC valve/motor are also attached to the housing. The throttle shaft is controlled by the accelerator pedal. The throttle shaft extends the full length of the housing. The throttle bore controls the amount of incoming air that enters the

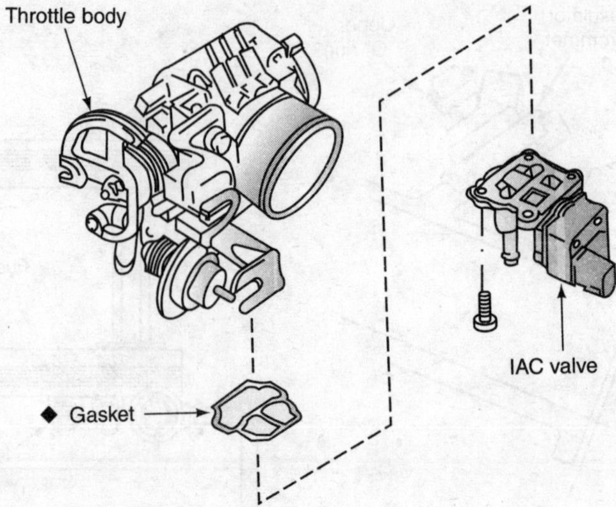

FIGURE 9-29 *A throttle body assembly of a port fuel injection system.*

air induction system. A small amount of coolant is also routed through a passage in the throttle body to prevent icing during cold weather.

Port systems require an additional control system that throttle body injection units do not require. While throttle body injectors are mounted above the throttle plates and are not affected by fluctuations in manifold vacuum, port system injectors have their tips located in the manifold where constant changes in vacuum would affect the amount of fuel injected. To compensate for these fluctuations, port injection systems are equipped with fuel pressure regulators that sense manifold vacuum and continually adjust the fuel pressure to maintain a constant pressure drop across the injector tips at all times.

Pressure Regulators. The pressure regulator in port injection systems is similar to the regulator used in TBI systems, except port fuel systems use manifold pressure (vacuum) TBI regulators are open to atmospheric pressure. A diaphragm and valve assembly is positioned on the center of the regulator and a diaphragm spring seats the valve on the fuel outlet (Figure 9-30).

When fuel pressure reaches the setting of the regulator, the diaphragm moves against the spring tension and the valve opens. This action allows fuel to flow through the return line to the fuel tank. The fuel pressure drops slightly when the pressure regulator valve opens and the spring closes the regulator valve.

A vacuum hose is connected from the intake manifold to the vacuum inlet on the pressure regulator on port fuel vehicles. This hose supplies vacuum to the area where the diaphragm spring is located. This vacuum works with the fuel pressure to move the diaphragm and open the valve. When

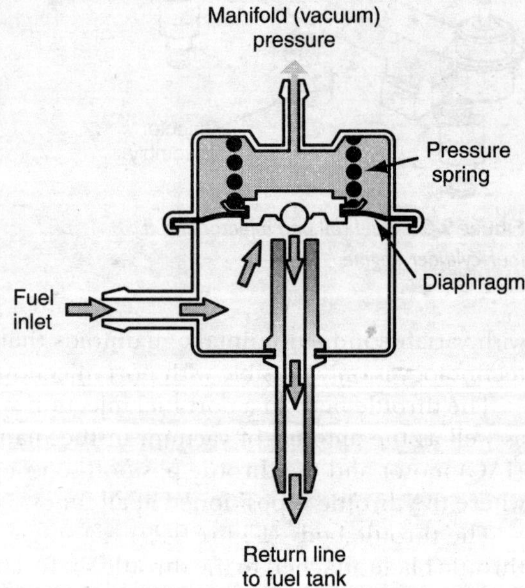

FIGURE 9-30 *A vacuum-controlled fuel pressure regulator.*

the engine is running at idle speed, high manifold vacuum is supplied to the regulator. Under this condition, the specified fuel pressure opens the regulator valve. When the engine is running under heavy load and/or wide-open throttle, a very low vacuum is supplied to the regulator. During these times, the vacuum does not help open the regulator valve and a higher fuel pressure is required to open the valve.

The change in fuel pressure allows the fuel to be sprayed into the manifold with the same effect regardless of the pressure present in the manifold. When there is a high vacuum in the manifold, a very low pressure exists and the pressure difference between the fuel spray and the vacuum is the same as when there is a higher pressure in the manifold (low vacuum) and a higher fuel pressure.

Port Injector Control. While all port injection systems operate using an injector at each cylinder, they do not fire the injectors in the same manner. This one statement best defines the difference between typical multiport injection systems (MPI) and sequential fuel injection systems (SFI).

SFI systems control each injector individually so that it is opened just before the intake valve opens. This means that the mixture is never static in the intake manifold and that adjustments to the mixture can be made almost instantaneously between the firing of one injector and the next. Sequential firing is the most accurate and desirable method of regulating port injection.

In MPI systems, the injectors are grouped together in pairs or groups, and these pairs or groups of injectors are turned on at the same time. When the injectors are split into two equal groups, the groups are fired alternatively with one group firing each engine revolution.

Since only two injectors can be fired relatively close to the time when the intake valve is about to open, the fuel charge for the remaining cylinders must stand in the intake manifold for varying periods of time. These periods of time are very short. Therefore, the standing of fuel in the intake manifold is not that great a disadvantage of MPI systems. At idle speeds, this wait is about 150 milliseconds, and at higher speeds the time is much less. The primary advantage of SFI is the ability to make instantaneous changes to the mixture.

In SFI systems, each injector is connected individually into the computer, and the computer completes the ground for each injector, one at a time. In MPI systems, the injectors are grouped, and all injectors within the group share the same common ground wire.

Some injection systems fire all of the injectors at the same time for every engine revolution. This type of system offers easy programming and relatively fast adjustments to the air-fuel mixture. The injectors are connected in parallel so the ECU sends out just one signal for all injectors. They all open and close at the same time. It simplifies the electronics without compromising injection efficiency. The amount of fuel required for each four-stroke cycle is divided in half and delivered in two injections, one for every 360 degrees of crankshaft rotation. The fact that the intake charge must still wait in the manifold for varying periods of time is the system's major drawback.

Central Port Injection

In a central port injection (CPI) system, a central injector assembly is mounted in the lower half of the intake manifold. Fuel inlet and return lines are connected from the rear of the intake to the CPI assembly. A retaining clip attaches these lines to the CPI assembly. Small poppet nozzles are positioned in each intake port in the lower half of the intake. Nylon fuel lines connect these nozzles to the CPI assembly (Figure 9-31).

The pressure regulator is mounted with the central injector. Since this regulator is mounted inside the intake manifold, vacuum from the intake is supplied through an opening in the regulator cover to the regulator diaphragm. The regulator spring pushes downward on the diaphragm and closes the valve. Fuel pressure from the in-tank fuel pump pushes the diaphragm upward and opens the valve, which allows fuel to flow through this valve and the return line to the fuel tank (Figure 9-32).

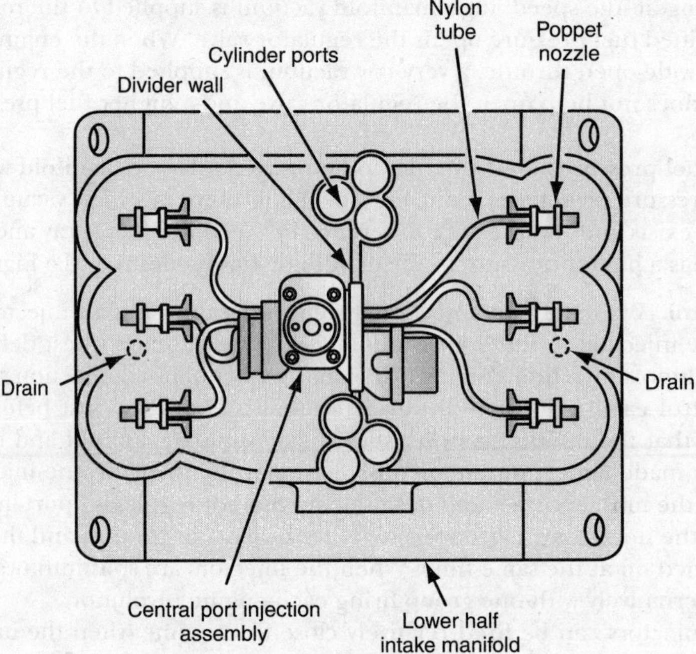

FIGURE 9-31 *CPI components shown in the lower half of the intake manifold.*

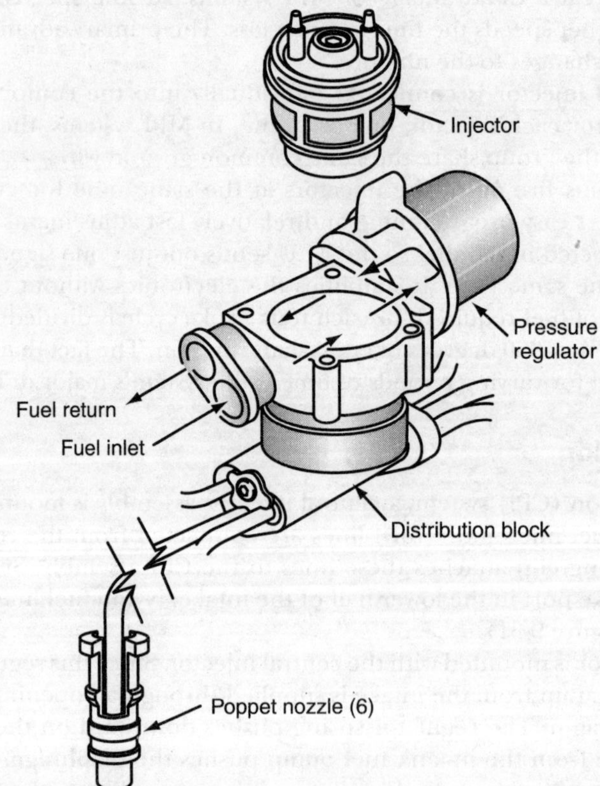

FIGURE 9-32 *The pressure regulator system of a CPI.*

The pressure regulator is designed to regulate fuel pressure from 54 to 64 psi (370 to 440 kPa), which is higher than many port fuel injection systems. Higher pressure is required in the CPI system to prevent fuel vaporization from the extra heat encountered with the CPI assembly, poppet nozzles, and lines mounted inside the intake manifold. The pressure regulator operates the same as the regulators explained previously in this chapter. The newest version of this type of system is a Sequential Central Port Injection (SCPI) system.

Direct Fuel Injection

Direct injection has been around for many years on diesel engines. Until recently, this type of injection had been seldom used on gasoline. With gasoline direct injection (GDI), the gasoline is injected directly into the combustion chamber. GDI engines use special injectors that deliver the fuel into the high pressures and temperatures in the cylinders. To prevent this heat from igniting the fuel in the injector, the injectors are designed to completely seal after the fuel is sprayed. The injectors must also be able to spray the fuel at a much higher pressure than what is in the cylinder. If this did not happen, the fuel would not spray into the cylinder, but the pressure of the cylinder would enter the injector.

GDI allows for very lean operation (as much as 35:1) during cruising. When the engine is operating under heavy loads, the system provides near stoichiometric air-fuel ratios. By being able to run at such lean ratios, the engine's fuel economy is increased by nearly 30 percent, and the emissions levels are substantially decreased.

Spraying the fuel directly into the cylinders also increases volumetric efficiency because the intake manifold and port only delivers air to the cylinders. GDI decreases the tendency to knock, therefore it allows for higher compression ratios without the need for high octane fuel. Both factors provide for increased horsepower and torque outputs from the engine without consuming more fuel.

With GDI, fuel can be injected at any time, not only when the intake valve is open. Also, the injectors can pulse twice during the transition from compression stroke to combustion. The two pulses promote complete combustion when the PCM senses operating conditions may prevent a complete burning of the fuel.

During most driving conditions, a GDI engine operates in a very lean mode called stratified mode (Figure 9-33). This results in decreased fuel consumption. While in this mode, fuel is injected late in the compression stroke right before ignition. When the engine is under a heavy load or operating at high speed, fuel is injected during the intake stroke called homogeneous mode (Figure 9-34). As a result of this action, the cylinder has a homogeneous, cooler air-fuel mixture, which reduces the chances of engine knock.

The fuel is highly pressurized (typically between 400 and 2,100 psi) when it is sprayed into the cylinder. Under this pressure, the fuel arrives as a vapor. The injectors release a relatively small, precisely shaped spray of fuel around the spark plug just before ignition. This means that only the area around the spark plug has air and fuel to begin combustion; the rest of the combustion chamber is filled with air or recirculated exhaust gas. The fuel pump that delivers this high pressure to the fuel injectors is driven by the engine. The engine-driven fuel pump is fed by an in-tank electric pump. A PCM controls the timing of injection and ignition for each cylinder.

GDI offers many advantages over port fuel injection, but there is concern over the NO_x levels produced by the engine. The very lean air-fuel ratios and the high compression ratios, combined with combustion temperatures that are very high during highway cruising, greatly enhance the production of NO_x. Manufacturers have developed new catalytic converters and exhaust gas recirculation systems to reduce the NO_x levels so the use of GDI can become more common. Some engines are equipped with a GDI system with moderate compression ratios and normal air-fuel mixtures (not lean). These engines realize an increase in power without the production of high NO_x levels.

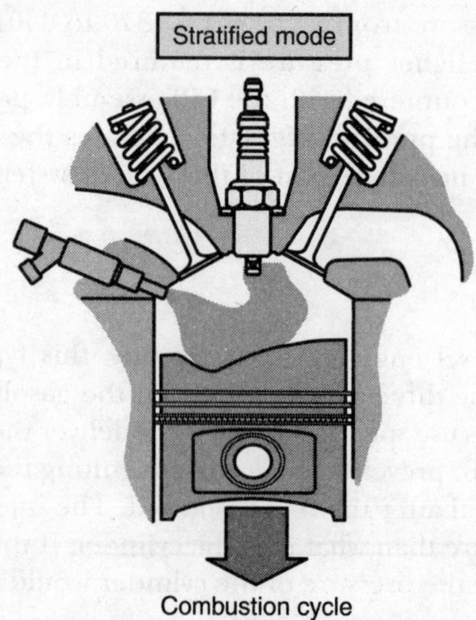

FIGURE 9-33 *In stratified mode, a small amount of fuel is sprayed into the combustion chamber. The special design of the piston makes the area around the spark plug rich enough to start the very lean mixture.*

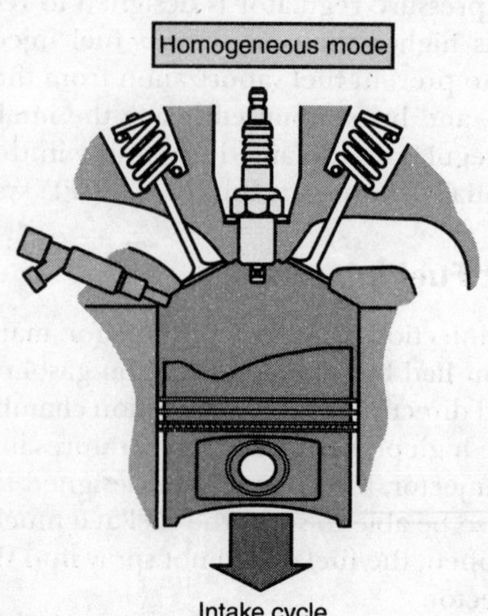

FIGURE 9-34 *In homogenous mode, fuel is injected into the combustion chamber during the intake stroke, and the mixture is at a normal 14.7:1.*

FUEL DELIVERY SYSTEM

The components of a typical gasoline delivery system are fuel tanks, fuel lines, fuel filters, and fuel pumps. Figure 9-35 shows a typical EFI fuel delivery system. Fuel is drawn from the fuel tank by an in-tank or chassis-mounted electric fuel pump. Before it reaches the injectors, the fuel passes through a filter that removes dirt and impurities. A fuel line pressure regulator maintains a constant fuel line pressure that may be as high as 64 psi in some systems. This fuel pressure generates the spraying force needed to inject the fuel. Excess fuel not required by the engine returns to the fuel tank through a fuel return line.

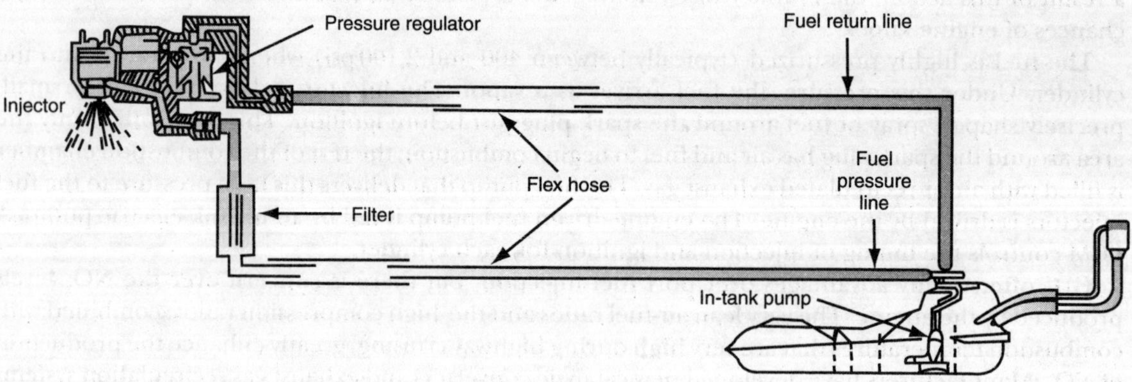

FIGURE 9-35 *Components of a throttle body injection (TBI) fuel system.*

Returnless Fuel Systems

Some fuel systems do not have a return line and are called returnless fuel systems. In these systems, the fuel pressure regulator is located at the fuel pump sender assembly instead of the fuel rail. The advantages of this system include no warm fuel sent to the fuel tank, which raises the volatility of the fuel and makes a larger fuel charcoal canister necessary, and the elimination of a fuel line that extends the length of the vehicle.

Evaporative Emissions and Fuel Tanks

Evaporative emission controls were introduced in the late 1960s after it was discovered that about 20 percent of the vehicle hydrocarbon (HC) emissions were due to gasoline evaporation. Modern fuel systems must be able to prevent unburned fuel release in the form of vapor. A method had to be found to allow the fuel to expand and contract without the release of HC. The fuel tank had to be vented in some fashion because when fuel was consumed, the tank would develop an internal vacuum, making fuel difficult (if not impossible) to pump from the tank. Also, if the tank were full of fuel and the temperature increased, the fuel tank would be placed under pressure by the volatility of the fuel.

The answer was to store the fuel vapors that were being released in a canister filled with activated charcoal, usually called a **charcoal canister** (Figure 9-36). When the vehicle was at operating temperature, the PCM opened a **purge solenoid** that was attached to the charcoal canister that allowed the fuel vapors to be drawn into the throttle body and burned. This action vents the tank and frees the charcoal to store more vapors when needed. Evaporative emission systems are closely monitored for leaks by the OBD II system and will be covered in more detail in a later chapter.

The problem of fuel tank expansion has been addressed by adding an internal expansion tank to the fuel tank, or making the fuel tank impossible to completely fill, leaving space at the top of the tank for expansion (Figure 9-37).

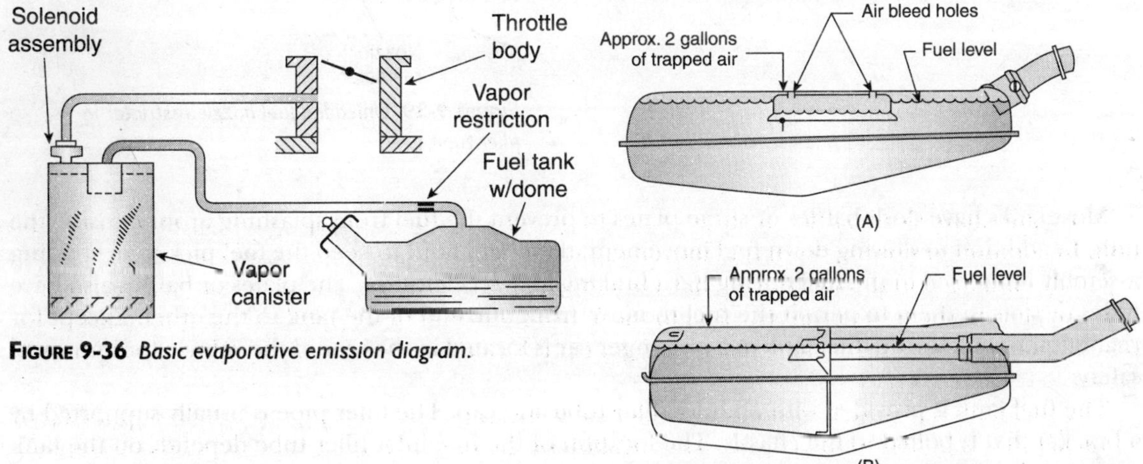

FIGURE 9-36 *Basic evaporative emission diagram.*

FIGURE 9-37 *Two types of gas tank overflow protection.*

The gas cap usually contains an overpressure and vacuum release valve in the case of failure of the evaporative emission system to adequately vent the system.

The most recent development in evaporative emission controls is that of on-board **refueling vapor recovery** (ORUR). It has been discovered that more HC emissions were released when refueling a vehicle than were released by burning a tank of fuel! This has lead to a redesign of some components in the fuel filler neck and tank assembly to help prevent these emissions.

Fuel Tank Construction

Fuel tanks can be constructed of pressed corrosion-resistant steel, aluminum, or molded reinforced polyethylene plastic. Aluminum and molded plastic fuel tanks are becoming more common as manufacturers attempt to reduce the overall weight of the vehicle. Metal tanks are usually ribbed to provide added strength. Seams are welded, and heavier gauge steel is often used on exposed sections for added strength. Fuel tanks are normally mounted with insulators between the top of the tank and the chassis to protect the tank and prevent noise from transferring into the passenger compartment (Figure 9-38).

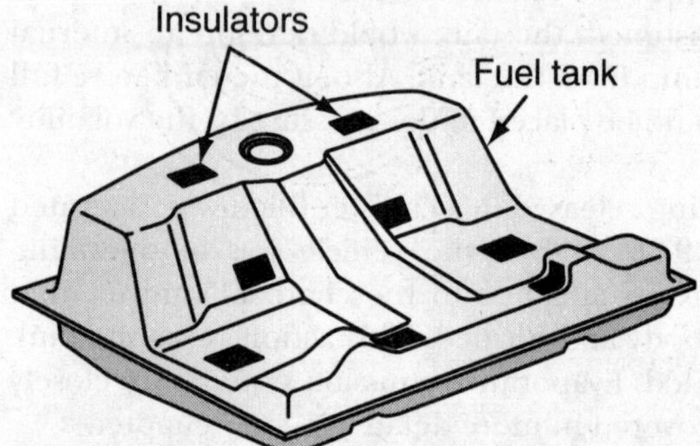

FIGURE 9-38 *Insulators positioned between the top of the fuel tank and the chassis.*

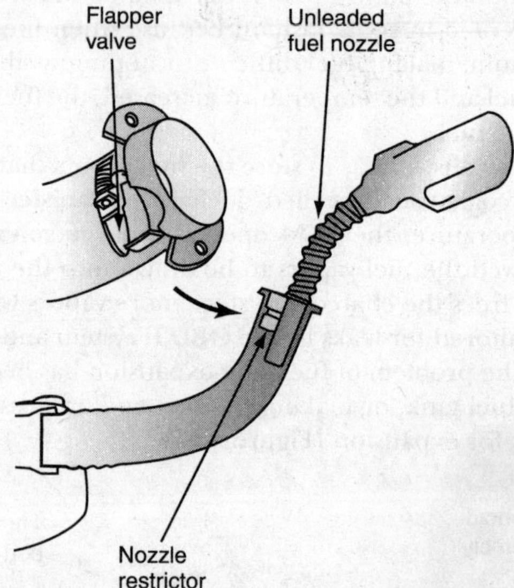

FIGURE 9-39 *Unleaded fuel nozzle restrictor in filler tube.*

Most tanks have slosh baffles or surge plates to prevent the fuel from splashing around inside the unit. In addition to slowing down fuel movement, the plates tend to keep the fuel pickup or sending assembly immersed in the fuel during hard braking and acceleration. The plates or baffles also have holes or slots in them to permit the fuel to move from one end of the tank to the other. Except for rear-engine vehicles, the fuel tank in a passenger car is located in the rear of the vehicle for improved safety.

The fuel tank is provided with an inlet filler tube and cap. The filler pipe is usually supported by a bracket that is bolted to the chassis. The location of the fuel inlet filler tube depends on the tank design and tube placement. It is usually positioned behind the filler cap or a hinged door in the center of the rear panel or in the outer side of either rear fender panel. All vehicles manufactured today are designed for unleaded fuel and have a restrictor in the filler tube that prevents the entry of an incorrect fuel delivery nozzle at the gas pumps (Figure 9-39). The filler pipe can be a rigid one-piece tube soldered to the tank or a three-piece unit. The three-piece unit has a lower neck soldered to the tank and an upper neck fastened to the inside of the body sheet metal panel.

Filler tube caps are non-venting and usually have some type of pressure-vacuum relief valve arrangement (Figure 9-40). Under normal operating conditions, the valve is closed, but whenever pressure or vacuum is more than the calibration of the cap, the valve opens. Once the pressure or vacuum has been relieved, the valve closes.

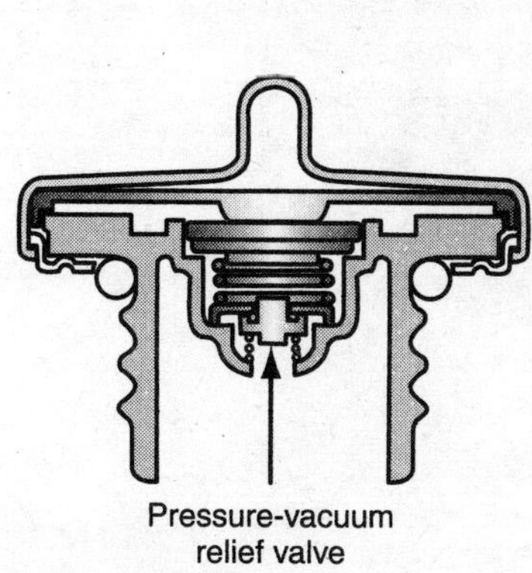

FIGURE 9-40 *Pressure-vacuum gasoline filler cap.*

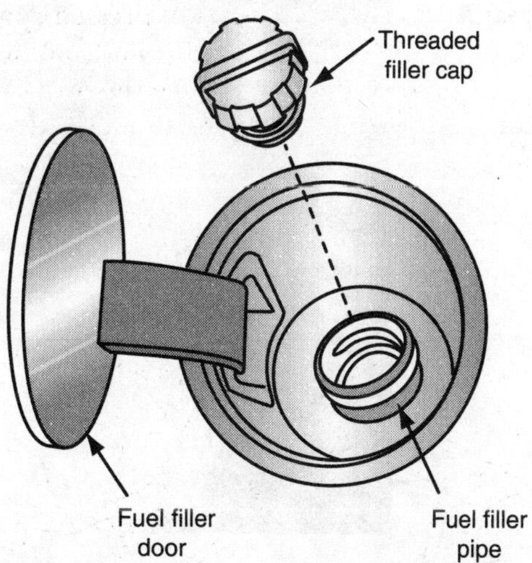

FIGURE 9-41 *Filler door and threaded filler cap.*

A threaded filler cap may be threaded into the upper end of the filler pipe. These caps require several turns counterclockwise to remove (Figure 9-41). The long threaded area on the cap is designed to allow any remaining fuel tank pressure to escape during cap removal. The cap and filler neck have a ratchet-type, torque-limiting design to prevent overtightening. When the cap is installed, tighten the cap until a clicking noise is heard. This noise indicates the cap is properly tightened and fully seated. Some fuel caps have a cap that is pushed down and turned one-quarter. These are called a bayonet mount. These caps were developed to prevent the OBD II system from setting a code for an evaporative emissions control leak. Some owners had difficulty making the cap tight enough to prevent these leaks.

Starting with the 1976 model year, a Federal Motor Vehicle Safety Standard (FMVSS 301) required a control on gasoline leakage from passenger cars, certain light trucks, and buses after they were subjected to barrier impacts and rolled over. A rollover check valve located in the fuel sender is pictured in Figure 9-42.

A check valve might also be fitted in the fuel tank filler cap, and most caps' pressure-vacuum relief valve settings have been increased so that fuel pressure cannot open them in a rollover.

Some fuel line systems contain a fuel return arrangement that aids in keeping the gasoline cool, thus reducing chances of vapor lock. The return system consists of a special fuel pump equipped with an extra outlet fitting and necessary fuel line. The fuel return line generally runs next to the conventional fuel line. The fuel return system allows a metered amount of cool fuel to circulate through the tank and fuel pump, thus reducing vapor bubbles caused by overheated fuel in the tank.

Some form of liquid vapor separator is incorporated into most modern vehicles to stop liquid fuel or bubbles from reaching the vapor storage canister or the engine crankcase. It can be located inside the tank, on the tank (Figure 9-43), in fuel vent lines, or near the fuel pump.

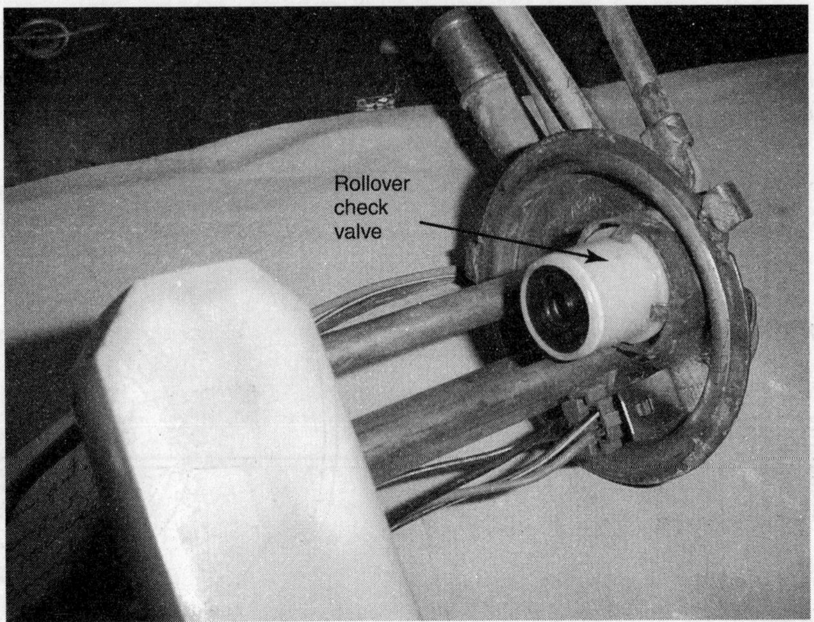

FIGURE 9-42 *Rollover leakage protection on a fuel injected vehicle.*

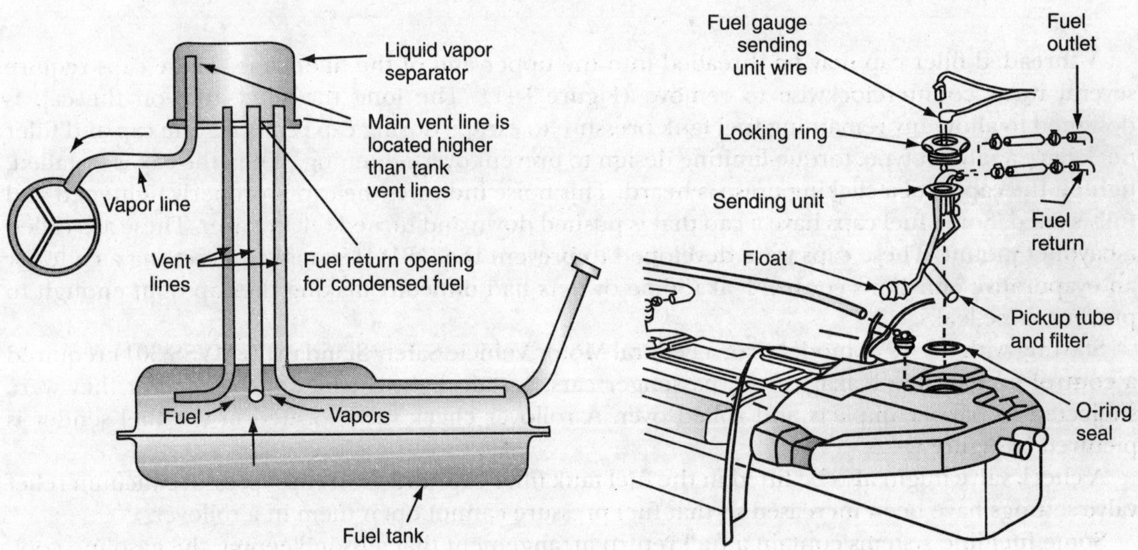

FIGURE 9-43 *A fuel tank vapor separator allows some of the fuel vapors to condense back into liquid and return to the tank.*

FIGURE 9-44 *Fuel tank sending unit assembly.*

Inside the fuel tank there is also a sending unit that includes a pickup tube and float-operated fuel gauge (Figure 9-44). The fuel tank pickup tube is connected to the fuel pump by fuel line. Some electric fuel pumps are combined with the sending unit. The pickup tube extends nearly, but not completely, all the way to the bottom of the tank. This prevents rust, dirt, sediment, and water from being drawn into the fuel tank filter, which can cause it to clog. A ground wire is often attached to the fuel tank unit.

Fuel Lines and Fittings

Fuel lines can be made of either metal tubing or flexible nylon or synthetic rubber hose. The latter must be able to resist gasoline. It must also be nonpermeable, so gas and gas vapors cannot evaporate through the hose. Ordinary rubber hose, such as that used for vacuum lines, deteriorates when exposed to gasoline. Only hoses made for fuel systems should be used for replacement. Similarly, vapor vent lines must be made of material that resist attack by fuel vapors. Replacement vent hoses are usually marked with the designation EVAP to indicate their intended use. The inside diameter of a fuel delivery hose is generally larger (5/16 to 3/8 inch) than that of a fuel return hose (1/4 inch).

The fuel lines carry fuel from the fuel tank to the fuel injection assembly. These lines are usually made of rigid metal, although some sections are constructed of rubber hose to allow for car vibrations. Clips retain the fuel lines to the chassis to prevent line movement and damage (Figure 9-45). This fuel line, unlike filler neck or vent hoses, must work under pressure or vacuum. Because of this, the flexible synthetic hoses must be stronger. This is especially true for the hoses on fuel injection systems where pressures reach 64 psi or more. For this reason, flexible fuel line hose must also have special resistance properties. Many auto manufacturers recommend that flexible hose only be used as a delivery hose to the fuel metering unit in a fuel injection system. It should not be used on the pressure side of the injector systems. This application requires a special high-pressure hose.

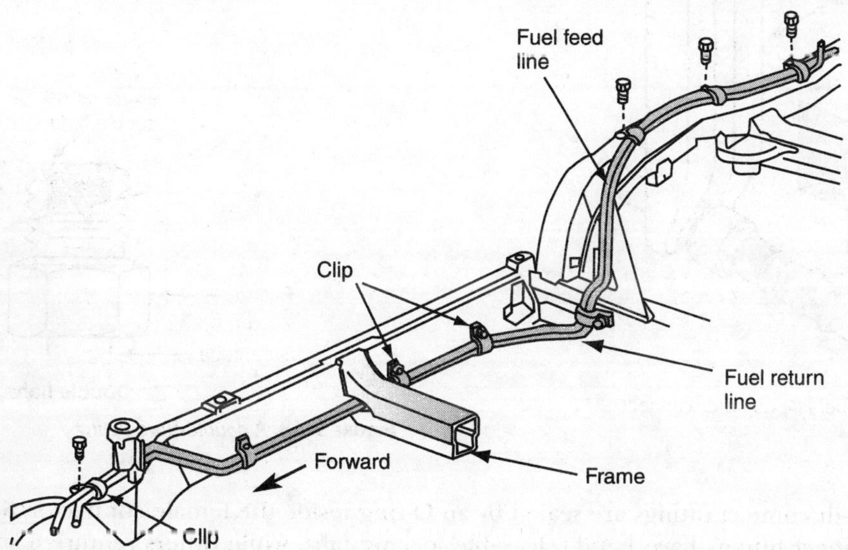

FIGURE 9-45 *Gaps between the frame and tank are joined with flexible hose, and the tubing is held to the chassis by clips.*

Fuel supply lines from the tank to the carburetor or injectors are routed to follow the frame along the underchassis of vehicles. Generally, rigid lines are used extending from near the tank to a point near the fuel pump. To absorb engine vibrations, the gaps between the frame and tank or fuel pump are joined by short lengths of flexible hose.

Sections of fuel line are assembled together by fittings. Some of these fittings are a threaded-type fitting, while others are a quick-release design. Quick-disconnect fuel line fittings may be hand releasable or a special tool may be required to release these fittings. Many fuel lines have quick-disconnect fittings with a unique female socket and a compatible male connector (Figure 9-46).

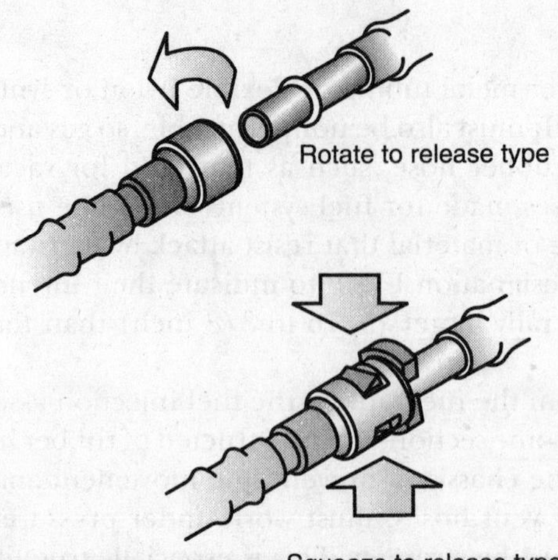

FIGURE 9-46 *Quick-disconnect hand releasable fuel line fittings.*

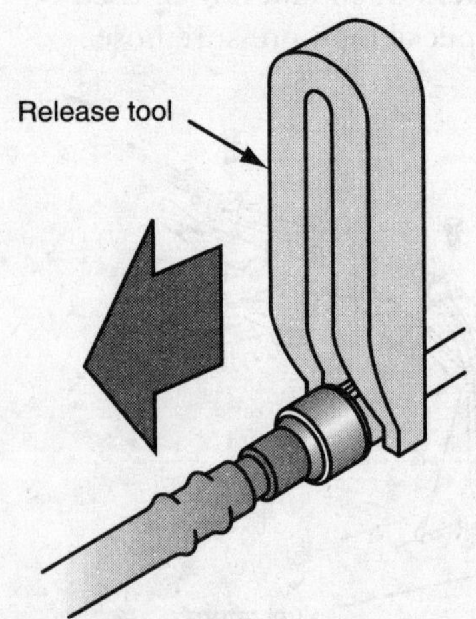

FIGURE 9-47 *Fuel line quick-disconnect separator tool.*

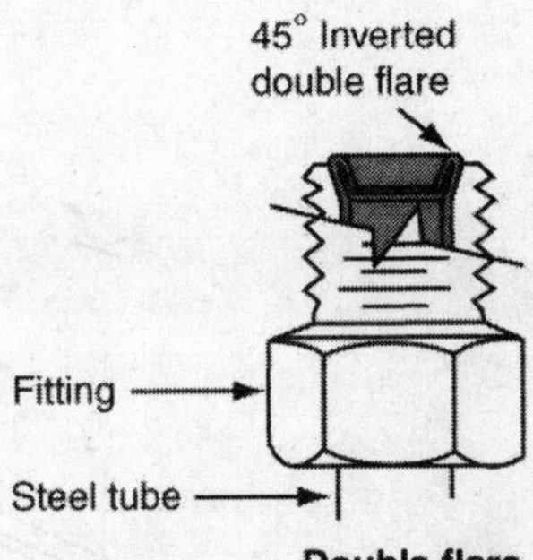

FIGURE 9-48 *A double-flare fitting.*

These quick-disconnect fittings are sealed by an O-ring inside the female connector. Some of these quick-disconnect fittings have hand-releasable locking tabs, while others require a special tool to release the fitting (Figure 9-47).

One of the most common threaded-type tube fittings is the *double-flare* (Figure 9-48). The double-flare is made with a special tool that has an anvil and a cone. Another common fuel line connection on many Japanese vehicles is the "banjo" bolt style of attachment. It uses a special bolt with a drilled passage and a set of sealing washers (Figure 9-49).

Some fuel lines have threaded fittings with an O-ring seal to prevent fuel leaks (Figure 9-50). These O-ring seals are usually made from Viton, which resists deterioration from gasoline. On some other fuel lines, the fuel hose is clamped to the steel line and the hose and clamp must be properly positioned on the steel line (Figure 9-51).

To control the rate of vapor flow from the fuel tank to the vapor storage tank, a plastic or metal restrictor may be placed in either the end of the vent pipe or in the vapor-vent hose itself.

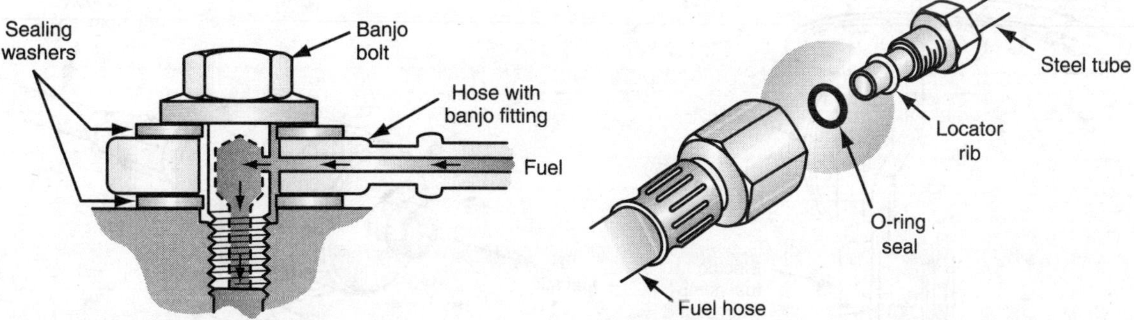

FIGURE 9-49 *A banjo-style fuel line fitting.*

FIGURE 9-50 *Threaded fuel line fitting with an O-ring seal.*

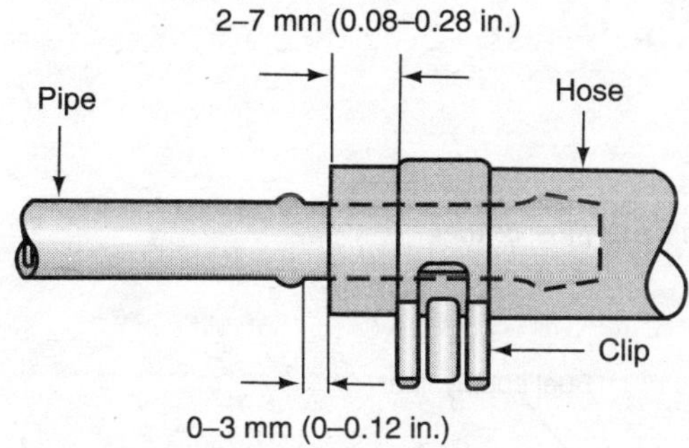

FIGURE 9-51 *Fuel hose clamped to the steel tubing.*

Fuel Filters

Automobiles and light trucks usually have an in-tank strainer and a gasoline filter (Figure 9-52). The strainer, located in the gasoline tank, is made of a finely woven fabric. The purpose of this strainer is to prevent large contaminant particles from entering the fuel system where they could cause excessive fuel pump wear or plug fuel metering devices. It also helps to prevent passage of any water that might be present in the tank. Service of the fuel tank strainer is seldom required.

On fuel injected vehicles, the fuel filter is connected in the fuel line between the fuel tank and the engine. Many of these filters are mounted under the vehicle (Figure 9-53) and others are mounted in the engine compartment. Most fuel filters contain a pleated paper element mounted in the filter housing, which may be made from metal or plastic. Fuel filters on fuel injected vehicles usually have a metal case. On many fuel filters, the inlet and outlet fittings are identified and the filter must be installed properly. An arrow on some filter housings indicates the direction of fuel flow through the filter.

Electric Fuel Pumps

Electric fuel pumps offer important advantages over mechanical fuel pumps. Because electric fuel pumps maintain constant fuel pressure, they aid in starting and reduce vapor lock problems.

An electric fuel pump can be located inside (Figure 9-54) or outside the fuel tank. The electric fuel pump may also be combined with the fuel gauge's sending unit (Figure 9-55). There are four basic types of electric fuel pumps: the diaphragm, plunger, bellows, and impeller or rotary pump. The in-

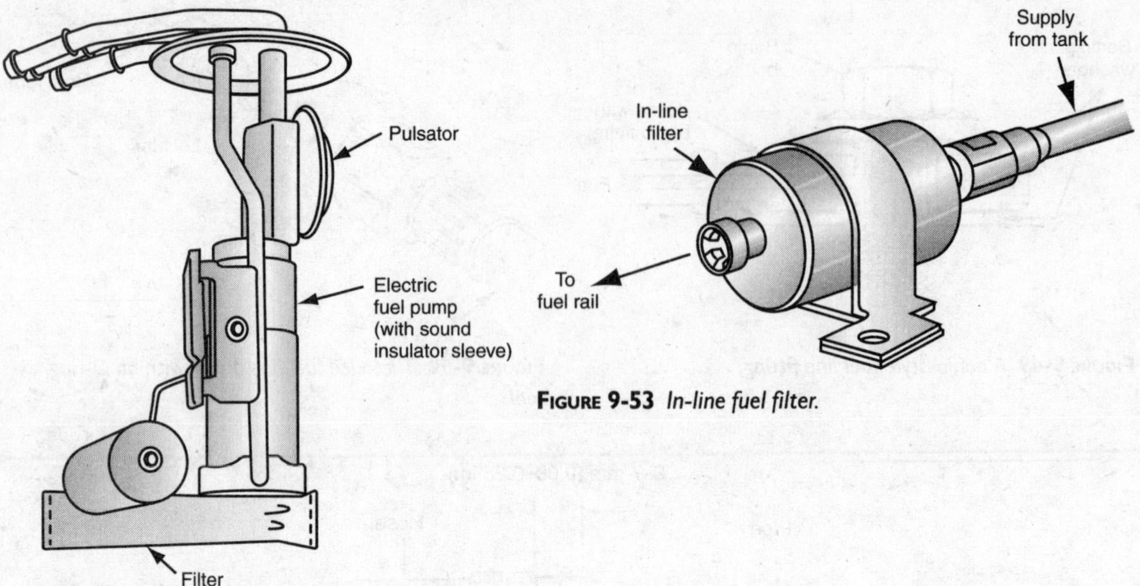

FIGURE 9-52 *An in-tank pump with a fuel filter at the pump inlet.*

FIGURE 9-53 *In-line fuel filter.*

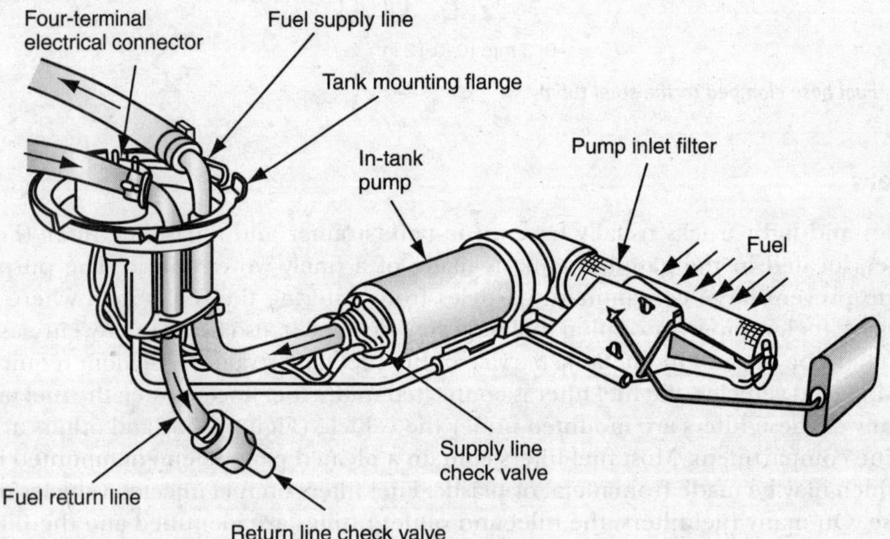

FIGURE 9-54 *An in-tank electric fuel pump.*

tank electric pump is usually a rotary type. The diaphragm, plunger, and bellows type (Figure 9-56) are usually the demand style. That is, when the ignition is turned on, the pump begins operation. They shut off automatically when the fuel line is pressurized. When there is a demand for more fuel, the pump provides more. When demand is lower, it pumps less so proper fuel flow and pressure are constantly maintained. A typical wiring diagram for an electric fuel pump is shown in Figure 9-57.

Vehicles equipped with EFI usually have electric fuel pumps mounted in the fuel tank. A few carbureted engines also have this type of fuel pump. Some carbureted engines have an electric fuel

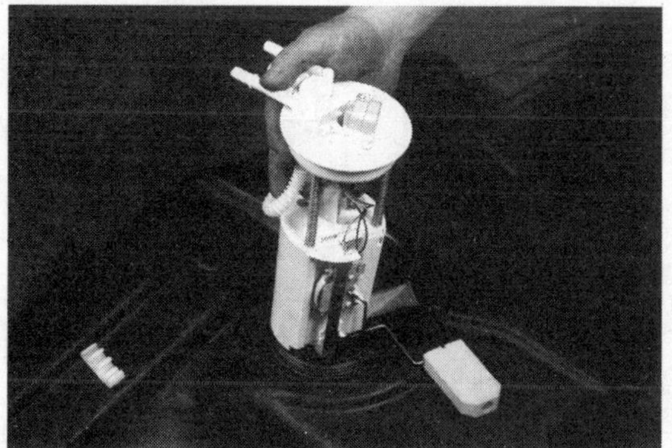

FIGURE 9-55 *Combination of fuel pump and fuel gauge sending unit. This is sometimes referred to as a Modular Reservoir Assembly (MRA).*

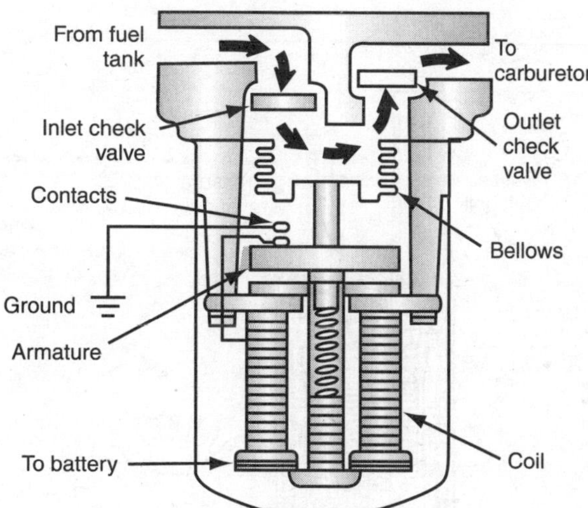

FIGURE 9-56 *Bellows fuel pump.*

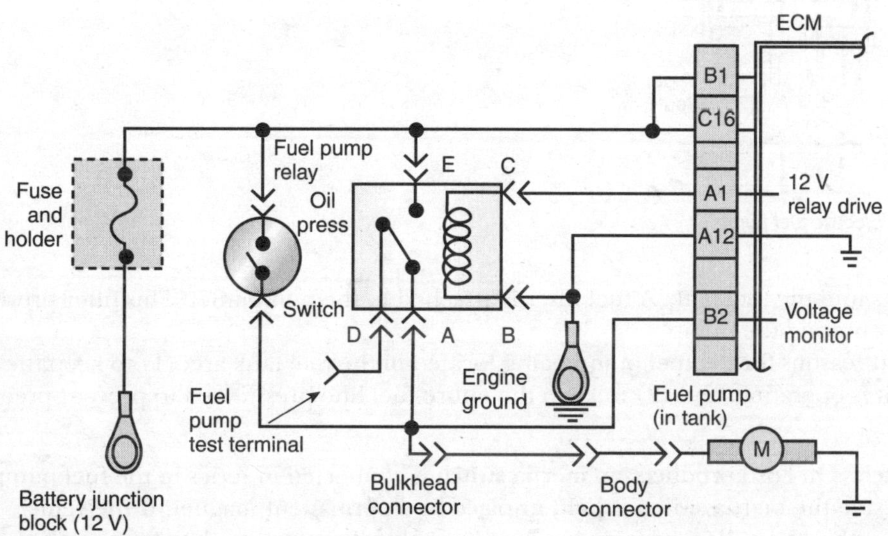

FIGURE 9-57 *Typical wiring diagram for an electric fuel pump.*

pump mounted under the vehicle. Some EFI-equipped vehicles have an in-tank electric pump and a second electric fuel pump mounted under the vehicle. The electric fuel pump in the fuel tank contains a small direct current (DC) electric motor with an impeller mounted on the end of the motor shaft. A pump cover is mounted over the impeller, and this cover contains inlet and discharge ports. When the armature and impeller rotate, fuel is moved from the tank to the inlet port, and the impeller grooves pick up the fuel and force it around the impeller cover and out the discharge port (Figure 9-58).

Fuel moves from the discharge port through the inside of the motor and out the check valve and outlet connection, which is connected via the fuel line to the fuel filter and underhood fuel system components. A pressure relief valve near the check valve opens if the fuel supply line is restricted and pump pressure becomes very high. When the relief valve opens, fuel is returned through this valve to the pump inlet. This action protects fuel system components from high fuel pressure. Each time the engine is shut off, the check valve prevents fuel from draining out of the underhood fuel system

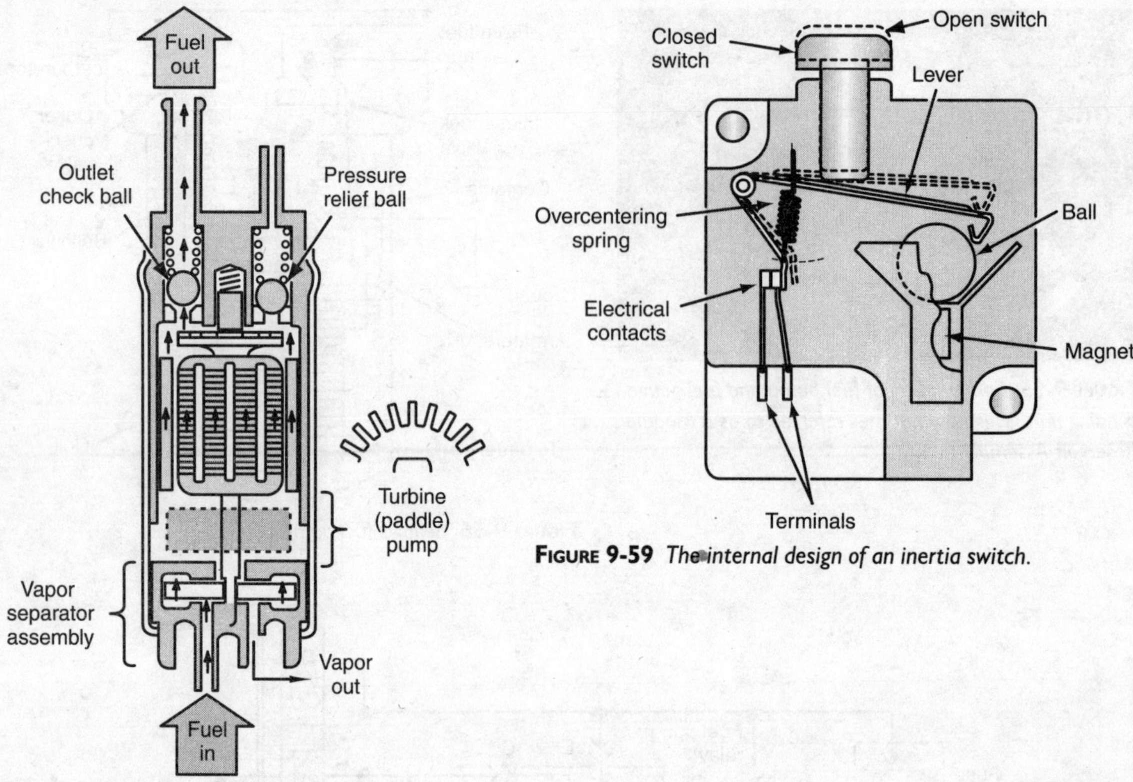

Figure 9-58 *Electric fuel pump.*

Figure 9-59 *The internal design of an inertia switch.*

components into the fuel tank. A fuel filter is attached to the pump inlet. This filter prevents dirt or water from entering the pump.

The main reasons for the fuel pump being located in the fuel tank are: (1) to keep the fuel pump cool while it is operating, and (2) to keep the entire fuel line pressurized to prevent premature fuel evaporation.

Inertia Switch. On Ford products, an **inertia switch** is connected in series in the fuel pump circuit. A steel ball inside the inertia switch is held in place by a permanent magnet. If the vehicle is involved in a collision, this ball pulls away from the magnet and strikes a target plate to open the points in the switch (Figure 9-59). This inertia switch action opens the fuel pump circuit and stops the fuel pump.

A reset button on top of the inertia switch must be pressed to close the switch and restore fuel pump operation. The inertia switch is located in the trunk area on most Ford cars. A decal in the trunk of later-model cars indicates the inertia switch location. On EFI-equipped trucks, the inertia switch is located under the dash.

Oil Pressure Switch. In a late-model General Motors fuel pump circuit, the powertrain control module (PCM) supplies voltage to the winding of the fuel pump relay when the ignition switch is turned on. This action closes the relay points, and voltage is supplied through the points to the in-tank fuel pump (Figure 9-60). The fuel pump remains on while the engine is cranking or running. If the ignition switch is on for 2 seconds and the engine is not cranked, the PCM shuts the voltage to the fuel pump relay off and the relay points open to stop the pump.

If the ignition switch is on and the fuel line is broken during an accident, PCM and fuel pump relay action is a safety feature that prevents the fuel pump from pumping gasoline from the ruptured

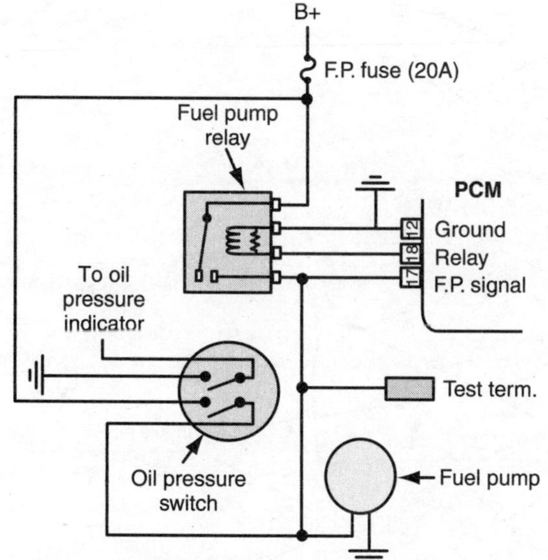

FIGURE 9-60 *Typical GM fuel pump circuit.*

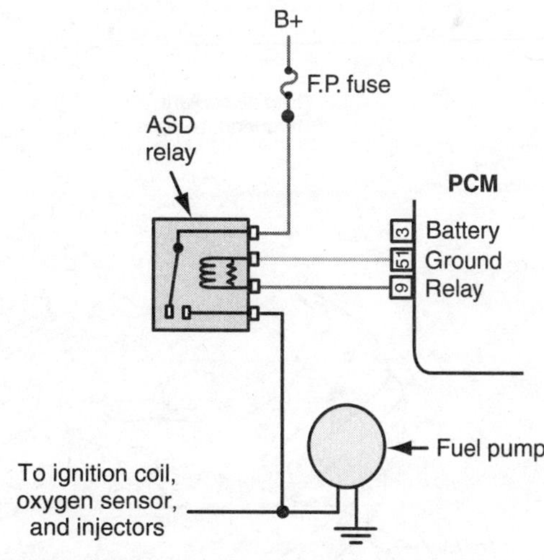

FIGURE 9-61 *Chrysler fuel pump circuit with an ASD relay.*

fuel line. An oil pressure switch is connected parallel to the fuel pump relay points. If the relay becomes defective, voltage is supplied through the oil pressure switch points to the fuel pump. This action keeps the fuel pump operating and the engine running even though the fuel pump relay is defective. When the engine is cold, oil pressure is not immediately available and the engine may be slow to start if the fuel pump relay is defective.

ASD Relay. The fuel pump relay in Chrysler EFI systems is referred to as an automatic shutdown (ASD) relay. If the ignition switch is turned on, the PCM grounds the windings of the fuel pump relay and the relay points close. The ASD relay points supply voltage to the fuel pump, positive primary coil terminal, oxygen sensor heater, and the fuel injectors in some systems (Figure 9-61).

On Chrysler products with a power module and logic module, the engine must be cranked before the power module grounds the ASD relay winding. The later-model PCM grounds the ASD relay winding when the ignition switch is turned on, and the relay remains closed while the engine is cranking or running. If the ignition switch is on for 1/2 second and the engine is not cranked, the PCM opens the circuit from the ASD relay winding to ground. Under this condition, the ASD relay points open and voltage is no longer supplied to the fuel pump, positive primary coil terminal, injectors, and oxygen sensor heater.

Later-model Chrysler fuel pump circuits have a separate ASD relay and a fuel pump relay. In these circuits, the fuel pump relay supplies voltage to the fuel pump, and the ASD relay powers the positive primary coil terminal, injectors, and oxygen sensor heater. The ASD relay and the fuel pump relay operate the same as the previous ASD relay. The PCM grounds both relay windings through the same wire.

Circuit Opening Relay. On many Toyota vehicles, the fuel pump relay is called a circuit opening relay. This relay has dual windings and it is mounted on the firewall (Figure 9-62). One of the windings of the circuit opening relay is connected between the starter relay points and ground, and the second relay winding is connected from the battery positive terminal to the PCM. When the engine is cranking and the starter relay points are closed, current flows through the starter relay points and the circuit opening relay winding to ground. This current flow creates a magnetic field around the circuit opening relay winding that closes the relay points. When these points close, current flows through the points to the fuel pump (Figure 9-63).

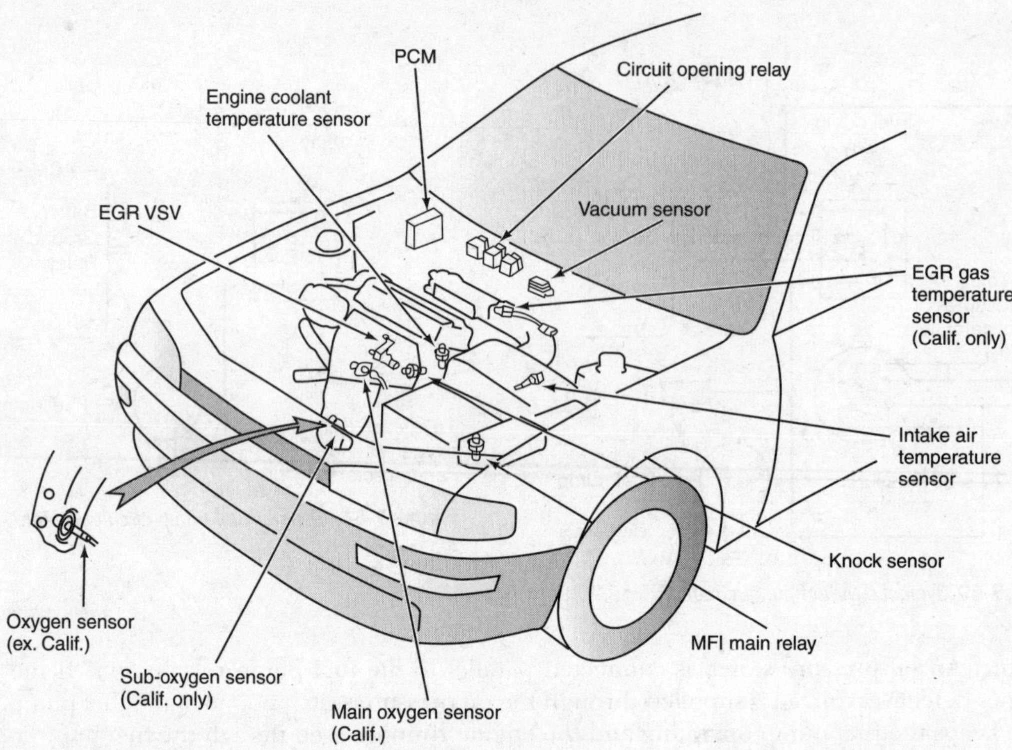

FIGURE 9-62 *Location of circuit opening relay and other EFI components.*

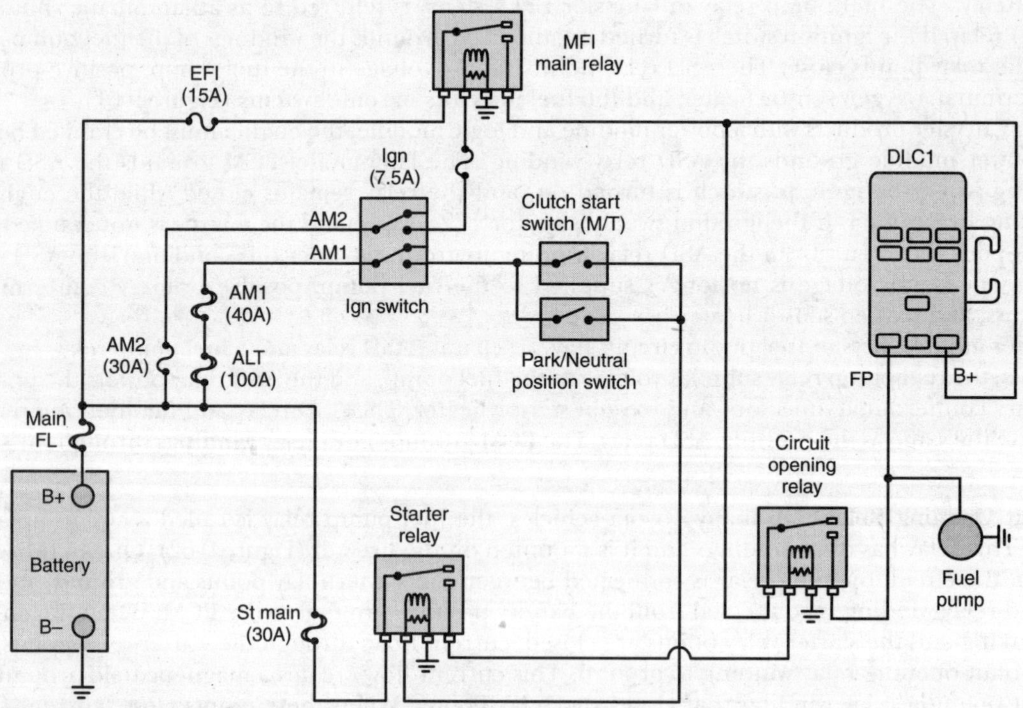

FIGURE 9-63 *Wiring diagram for the circuit opening relay.*

Once the engine starts, the starter relay is no longer energized and current stops flowing through these relay points and the winding of the circuit opening relay. However, the PCM grounds the other winding of the circuit opening relay when the engine starts. This action keeps the relay points closed while the engine is running.

REVIEW QUESTIONS

Short Answer Essays

1. Explain the major differences between throttle body fuel injection and port fuel injection systems.
2. What is meant by sequential firing of fuel injectors?
3. Name the two forms of natural gas commonly used as an automotive fuel.
4. Name the components of a typical fuel delivery system.
5. Name an advantage of a returnless fuel system.
6. Briefly describe the operation of a hybrid electric vehicle.
7. Name the differences in the multiport and central fuel injection systems.
8. Explain how the fuel pressure regulator operates.
9. Explain the purpose of the relief valve and one-way check valve in an electric fuel pump.
10. Explain the purpose of the inertia switch in a fuel pump circuit, including the switch reset procedure.

Fill-in-the-Blanks

1. Some fuel tank filler caps contain a pressure relief valve and a ______________ ______________ valve.
2. In a TBI system, the injector(s) spray into the ______________ ______________. On port fuel injection systems, the injectors spray as close as possible to the ______________ ______________.
3. If the fuel is ignited in the cylinder before the spark, ______________ has occurred.
4. In an electric fuel pump, the relief valve opens if the fuel-supply line becomes ______________.
5. Compared to TBI systems, MFI and SFI systems require ______________ fuel pressure.
6. In central port systems, the fuel pressure must be high enough to prevent ______________ ______________.
7. On an SFI system, each injector has an individual ______________ connected to the computer.
8. If the injector pulse width is increased on TBI, MFI, or SFI systems, the air-fuel ratio becomes ______________.
9. A lean mixture burns ______________ than a rich mixture.
10. In a gasoline engine, ______________ occurs when the flame front fails to reach a pocket of air-fuel mixture before the temperature in that area reaches the point of self-ignition.

Multiple Choice

1. *Technician A* says a high compression engine has greater efficiency than a low-compression engine of the same displacement.
   Technician B says a high compression engine has to have greater structural integrity.
   Who is correct?
   A. Technician A C. Both technicians
   B. Technician B D. Neither technician

2. *Technician A* says that the octane number of gasoline refers to the power it contains.
   Technician B says there are two ways to determine the octane of fuel, the MON method and the RON method.
   Who is correct?
   A. Technician A C. Both technicians
   B. Technician B D. Neither technician

3. *Technician A* says that the ability of fuel to go from a vapor to a liquid is called volatility.
   Technician B says that summer fuel is more volatile than winter fuel.
   Who is correct?
   A. Technician A C. Both technicians
   B. Technician B D. Neither technician

4. *Technician A* says that ethanol raises the octane of gasoline by 2.5 to 3 points.
   Technician B says that ethanol increases CO emissions when burned with gasoline.
   Who is correct?
   A. Technician A C. Both technicians
   B. Technician B D. Neither technician

5. *Technician A* says diesel fuel is more volatile than gasoline.
   Technician B says that the viscosity of diesel fuel changes with temperature.
   Who is correct?
   A. Technician A C. Both technicians
   B. Technician B D. Neither technician

6. *Technician A* says the air-fuel ratio must be held close to 14.7:1 for the catalytic converter to work effectively.
   Technician B says that if the mixture is too rich the converter cannot oxidize HC and CO correctly.
   Who is correct?
   A. Technician A C. Both technicians
   B. Technician B D. Neither technician

7. *Technician A* says the fuel injection pulse width can vary depending on the needs of the engine.
   Technician B says the injector pulse width is longer on a deceleration.
   Who is correct?
   A. Technician A C. Both technicians
   B. Technician B D. Neither technician

8. *Technician A* says the TBI fuel pressure regulator operates much like a diaphragm operated relief valve.
   Technician B says that port fuel was the predecessor to TBI.
   Who is correct?
   A. Technician A C. Both technicians
   B. Technician B D. Neither technician

9. *Technician A* says a fuel rail is the fuel lines that run to each cylinder from a fuel manifold on a port fuel injected vehicle.
   Technician B says port fuel injected vehicles do not need manifold heat to keep the fuel vaporized in the manifold.
   Who is correct?
   A. Technician A C. Both technicians
   B. Technician B D. Neither technician

10. *Technician A* says that direct fuel injection started with diesel engines.
    Technician B says that gasoline direct injection systems inject fuel directly into the combustion chamber, not the intake manifold.
    Who is correct?
    A. Technician A C. Both technicians
    B. Technician B D. Neither technician

ELECTRONIC FUEL INJECTION 10

Upon completion and review of this chapter, you should be able to:

- Explain the principles of operation of a fuel injection system.
- Explain the design and function of major electronic fuel injection (EFI) components.
- Describe how the computer supplies the correct air-fuel ratio on a throttle body injection (TBI) system.
- Explain how the clear flood mode operates on a TBI system.
- Describe the effect of high fuel pressure in a TBI system.
- Explain the purpose of the throttle body temperature sensor.
- Explain how the computer provides air-fuel ratio enrichment while starting a cold engine equipped with a TBI system.
- Describe the difference between a sequential fuel injection (SFI) system and a multiport fuel injection (MFI) system.
- Explain why manifold vacuum is connected to the pressure regulator in an MFI system.
- Describe the operation of the pressure regulator in a returnless EFI system.

- Describe the operation of the central injector and poppet nozzles in a central port injection (CMFI) system.
- Explain the purpose of the intake manifold tuning valve (IMTV).
- List the components located in a constant control relay module.
- Explain the purpose of a dropping resistor assembly connected in series with the fuel injectors.
- Describe the inputs used by the computer to control the idle air control and idle air control bypass air motors.
- Explain how an idle air control bypass air motor controls idle speed.
- Explain the operation of the fast idle thermo valve.
- Explain the operation of Direct Fuel Injection.
- Explain the operation of the Throttle Actuator Control (TAC) system.

INTRODUCTION

Fuel injection involves spraying or injecting fuel directly into the engine's intake manifold or combustion chamber (Figure 10-1). Fuel injection, especially when it is electronically controlled, has several major advantages over carbureted systems. These include improved driveability under all conditions, improved fuel control and economy, decreased exhaust emissions, and an increase in engine efficiency and power. Gasoline direct fuel injection (DFI) does not utilize the intake manifold at all. It sprays fuel directly into the combustion chamber (Figure 10-2).

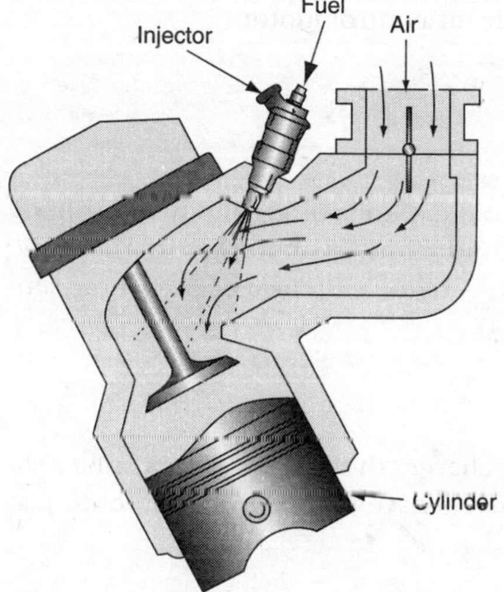

FIGURE 10-1 *In a port fuel injection system, air and fuel are mixed right outside the combustion chamber.*

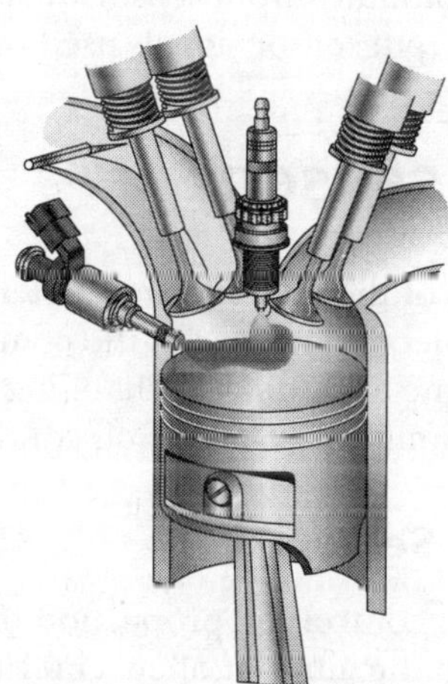

FIGURE 10-2 *A gasoline direct injection system.*

During the 1980s, automotive engineers changed many engines from carburetors or computer-controlled carburetors to electronic fuel injection systems. This action was taken to improve fuel economy, performance, and emissions levels. Automotive manufacturers had to meet increasingly stringent corporate average fueled economy (CAFE) regulations and comply with emission standards at the same time.

Many of the early electronic fuel injection (EFI) systems were throttle body injection systems in which the fuel is injected above the throttles. The throttle body injection (TBI) systems have gradually been changed to port fuel injection systems with the injectors located in the intake ports. On carbureted and throttle body injected engines, some intake manifold heating was required to prevent fuel condensation on the intake manifold passages. When the injectors are positioned in the intake ports, intake manifold heating is not required. This provided engineers with increased intake manifold design flexibility. Intake manifolds could now be designed with longer, curved air passages that increased airflow and improved torque and horsepower.

Since intake manifolds no longer require heating, they can now be made from plastic materials such as glass-fiber reinforced nylon resin. This material is considerably lighter than cast iron or even aluminum. Saving weight means an improvement in fuel economy. The plastic-type intake manifold does not transfer heat to the air and fuel vapor in the intake passages, which improves economy and hot start performance.

The objective of this chapter is to present the common components found in most EFI systems and the principles of various types of EFI. Some typical EFI systems are included, but not all the EFI systems used on domestic and imported vehicles are covered. If you are familiar with EFI components and principles, you will be able to understand the many different EFI systems when you encounter them.

Electronic fuel injection has proven to be the most precise, reliable, and cost-effective method of delivering fuel to the combustion chambers of today's vehicles. EFI systems must provide the correct air-fuel ratio for all engine loads, speeds, and temperature conditions. To accomplish this, an EFI system uses a fuel delivery system, air induction system, input sensors, control computer, fuel injectors, and some sort of idle speed control.

Idle speed control is a computer output function on electronic fuel injection systems. It is very important that technicians understand how these systems operate. Since improper idle rpm is often the result of faulty input sensor or switch signals, it is even more important that technicians understand the input sensor signals used by the computer control idle air control motor.

INPUT SENSORS

The ability of the fuel injection system to control the air-fuel ratio depends on its ability to properly time the injector pulses with the compression stroke of each cylinder and its ability to vary the injector "on" time according to changing engine demands. Both tasks require the use of electronic sensors that monitor the operating conditions of the engine.

Air Flow Sensors

In order to control the proportion of fuel to air in the air-fuel charge, the fuel system must be able to measure the amount of air entering the engine. Several sensors have been developed to do just that.

Volume Air flow Sensor. The airflow sensor shown in Figure 10-3 measures airflow, or air volume. The sensor consists of a spring-loaded flap, potentiometer, damping chamber, backfire protection valve, and idle bypass channel. As air is drawn into the engine, the flap is deflected against the spring.

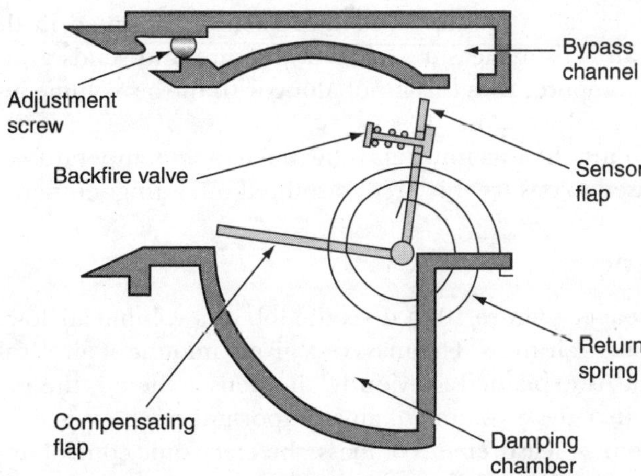

FIGURE 10-3 *A vane-type sensor.*

A potentiometer attached to the flap shaft monitors the flap movement and produces a corresponding voltage signal. The strength of the signal increases as the flap opens. The signal voltage is relayed to the electronic control module.

Damping Chamber. The curved shape of the airflow sensor is the damping chamber. The damping flap in this chamber is on the same shaft as the airflow sensing flap and is also about the same area. As a result, the damping flap smoothens out any possible pulsations caused by opening and closing of the intake valves. Airflow measurement can be a steady signal, closely related to airflow as controlled by the movement of the flap.

Backfire Protection. The airflow sensor flap provides for backfire protection with a spring-loaded valve. If the intake manifold pressure suddenly rises because of a backfire, this valve releases the pressure and prevents damage to the system.

Idle Bypass. The airflow sensor assembly includes an extra air passage for idle, bypassing the airflow sensor plate. When the throttle is closed at idle, the opening and closing of intake valves can cause pulsations in the intake manifold. Without the idle bypass, such pulsations could cause the flap to shudder resulting in an uneven air-fuel mixture. The idle bypass smoothes the flow of the idle intake air, ensuring regular signals to the electronic control.

Another design of airflow sensor, called a Karman Vortex sensor, works on a different operating principle. Air entering the airflow sensor assembly passes through vanes arranged around the inside of a tube. As the air flows through the vanes, it begins to swirl. The outer part of the swirling air exerts high pressure against the outside of the housing. There is a low-pressure area in the center.

The low-pressure area moves in a circular motion as the air swirls through the intake tube. Two pressure-sensing tubes near the end of the tube sense the low-pressure area as it moves around. An electronic sensor counts how many times the low-pressure area is sensed.

As airflow speed increases, the number of times the low-pressure area is sensed increases. This is translated into a signal that indicates to the combustion control computer how much air is flowing into the intake manifold.

Air Temperature Sensor

Cold air is denser than warm air. Cold, dense air can burn more fuel than the same volume of warm air because it contains more oxygen. This is why airflow sensors that only measure air volume must have their readings adjusted to account for differences in air temperature.

Most systems do this by using an air temperature sensor mounted in the throttle body of the induction system. The air sensor measures air temperature and sends an electronic signal to the control computer. The computer uses this input along with the air volume input in determining the amount of oxygen entering the engine.

In some early EFI systems, the incoming air is heated to a set temperature. In these systems, an air temperature sensor is used to ensure this predetermined operating temperature is maintained.

Mass Air Flow Sensor

A **mass airflow (MAF) sensor** (Figure 10-4) does the job of a volume airflow sensor and an air temperature sensor; it measures air mass. The mass of a given amount of air is calculated by multiplying its volume by its density. As explained previously, the denser the air, the more oxygen it contains. Monitoring the oxygen in a given volume of air is important since oxygen is a prime catalyst in the combustion process. From a measurement of mass, the electronic control unit adjusts the fuel delivery for the oxygen content in a given volume of air. The accuracy of air-fuel ratios is greatly enhanced when matching fuel to air mass instead of fuel to air volume.

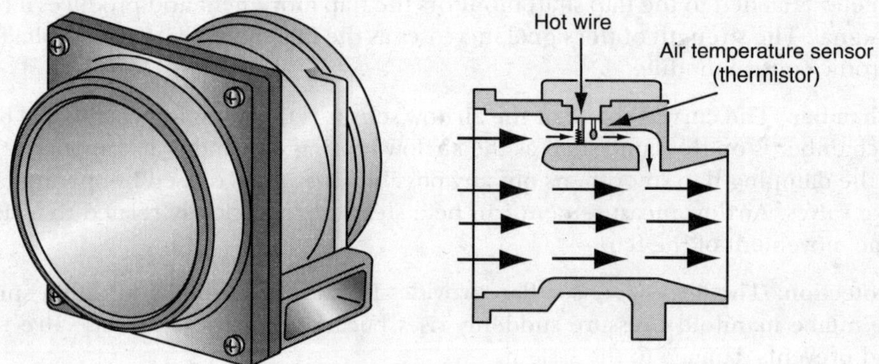

FIGURE 10-4 *A MAF sensor.*

The mass airflow sensor converts air flowing past a heated sensing element into an electronic signal. The strength of this signal is determined by the energy needed to keep the element at a constant temperature above the incoming ambient air temperature. As the volume and density (mass) of airflow across the heated element changes, the temperature of the element is affected and the current flow to the element is adjusted to maintain the desired temperature of the heating element. The varying current flow parallels the particular characteristics of the incoming air (hot, dry, cold, humid, high/low pressure). The electronic control unit monitors the changes in current to determine air mass and to calculate precise fuel requirements.

There are two basic types of mass airflow sensors: hot wire and hot film. In the first type, a very thin wire (about 0.2 mm thick) is used as the heated element. The element temperature is set at 100 to 200°C above the incoming air temperature. Each time the ignition switch is turned to the off position, the wire is heated to approximately 1,000°C for 1 second to burn off any accumulated dust and contaminants.

The second type uses a nickel foil sensor which is kept 75°C above ambient air temperatures. It does not require a burnoff period, thus it is potentially longer lasting than the hot wire type.

Manifold Absolute Pressure Sensor

Some EFI systems do not use airflow or air mass to determine the base pulse of the injector(s). Instead, the base pulse is calculated on manifold absolute pressure (MAP).

The MAP sensor (Figure 10-5) measures changes in the intake manifold pressure that result from changes in engine load and speed. The pressure measured by the MAP sensor is the difference between an absolute vacuum and manifold pressure. At closed throttle, the engine produces a low MAP value. A wide-open throttle produces a high value. This high value is produced when the pressure inside the manifold is the same as pressure outside the manifold and 100 percent of the outside air is being measured. This MAP output is the opposite of what is measured on a vacuum gauge. The use of this sensor also allows the control computer to adjust automatically for different altitudes.

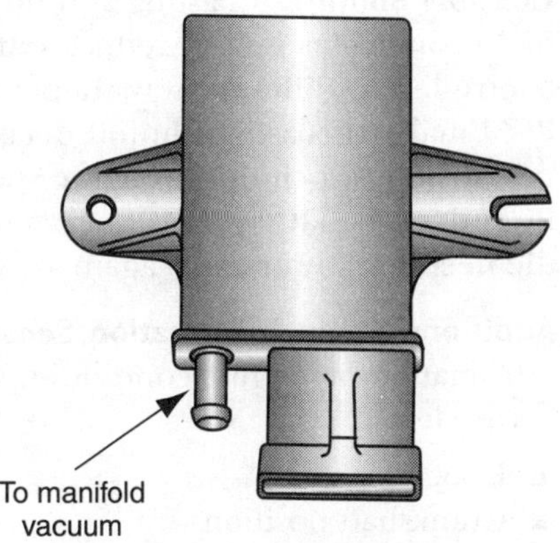

FIGURE 10-5 *A typical Ford MAP sensor.*

The PCM sends a voltage reference signal to the MAP sensor. As the MAP changes, the electrical resistance of the sensor also changes. The PCM can determine the manifold pressure by monitoring the sensor output voltage. A high-pressure, low-vacuum condition, such as wideopen throttle, requires more fuel. A low pressure, high vacuum requires less fuel. Like an airflow sensor, a MAP sensor relies on an air temperature sensor to adjust its base pulse signal to match incoming air density.

Many EFI systems with MAF sensors do not have MAP sensors. However, there are a few engines with both of these sensors. In those applications, the engine design characteristics require a fuel delivery strategy known as idle mode fueling to enhance idle quality and maintain low rpm performance. Such designs will use the MAP input for idle range and the MAF for off-idle operations. In addition, the MAP can be used as a backup in the event of a MAF-related malfunction. When the EFI system has a MAF, the computer calculates the intake airflow from the MAF and rpm inputs.

Other EFI Systems Sensors

In addition to airflow, air mass, or manifold absolute pressure readings, the control computer relies on input from a number of other system sensors. This input further adjusts the injector pulse width to match engine operating conditions. Operating conditions are communicated to the control computer by the following types of sensors.

Coolant Temperature. The coolant temperature sensor signals the PCM when the engine needs cold enrichment, as it does during warmup. This adds to the base pulse but decreases to zero as the engine warms up.

Throttle Position. The sensor on the throttle shaft signals the PCM of how far the throttle is opened and how fast it was opened.

Engine Speed. The ignition system sends a tachometer signal reference pulse corresponding to engine speed to the electronic control unit. This also times the start of the injection according to the intake stroke cycle.

Cranking Enrichment. The starter circuit sends a signal for fuel enrichment during cranking operations even when the engine is warm.

Altitude Compensation. As the car operates at higher altitudes, the thinner air needs less fuel. Altitude compensation in a fuel injection system is accomplished by monitoring the MAP sensor when the key is turned on and before the engine is started. There are also strategies to measure barometric pressure during deceleration, closed throttle.

Coasting Shutoff. Coasting shutoff can be found on a number of control systems. It can improve fuel economy as well as reduce emissions of hydrocarbons and carbon monoxide. Fuel shutoff is controlled in different ways depending on the type of transmission (manual or automatic). The PCM makes a coasting shutoff decision based on a closed throttle as indicated by the throttle position or idle switch or on engine speed as indicated by the signal from the ignition coil. When the PCM detects that power is not needed to maintain vehicle speed, the injectors are turned off until the need for power exists again.

Additional Input Information Sensors. Additional sensors are also used to provide the following information on engine conditions. Only the most common sensors that are used by all manufacturers are listed.

- Knock sensor
- Crankshaft position
- Camshaft position
- Intake Air Temperature
- Air conditioner operation
- Gearshift lever position
- Battery voltage
- Vehicle speed
- Oxygen in exhaust gases
- EGR valve position

Figure 10-6 shows the typical inputs and outputs of the powertrain control module responsible for controlling the EFI system.

BASIC EFI

In an electronic fuel injection (EFI) system, the computer must know the amount of air entering the engine so it can supply the stoichiometric air-fuel ratio. In EFI systems with a MAP sensor, the computer program is designed to calculate the amount of air entering the engine from the MAP and rpm input signals. The distributor pickup supplies an rpm signal to the computer. This type of EFI system is referred to as a **speed density** system because the computer calculates the air intake flow from the engine rpm, or speed, input, altitude, intake air temperature, and volumetric efficiency. Therefore, the computer must have accurate signals from these inputs to maintain the stoichiometric air-fuel ratio. EGR flow must also be calculated and subtracted since it does not burn. Other inputs are used by the computer to "fine tune" the air-fuel ratio. For example, if the TP sensor input indicates sudden acceleration, the computer momentarily supplies a richer air-fuel ratio.

Powertrain Control Module

The heart of the fuel injection system is the computer or powertrain control module (PCM). The PCM is a small computer that is usually mounted within the passenger compartment to keep it away from the heat and vibration of the engine. The PCM includes solid state devices, such as integrated circuits and a microprocessor.

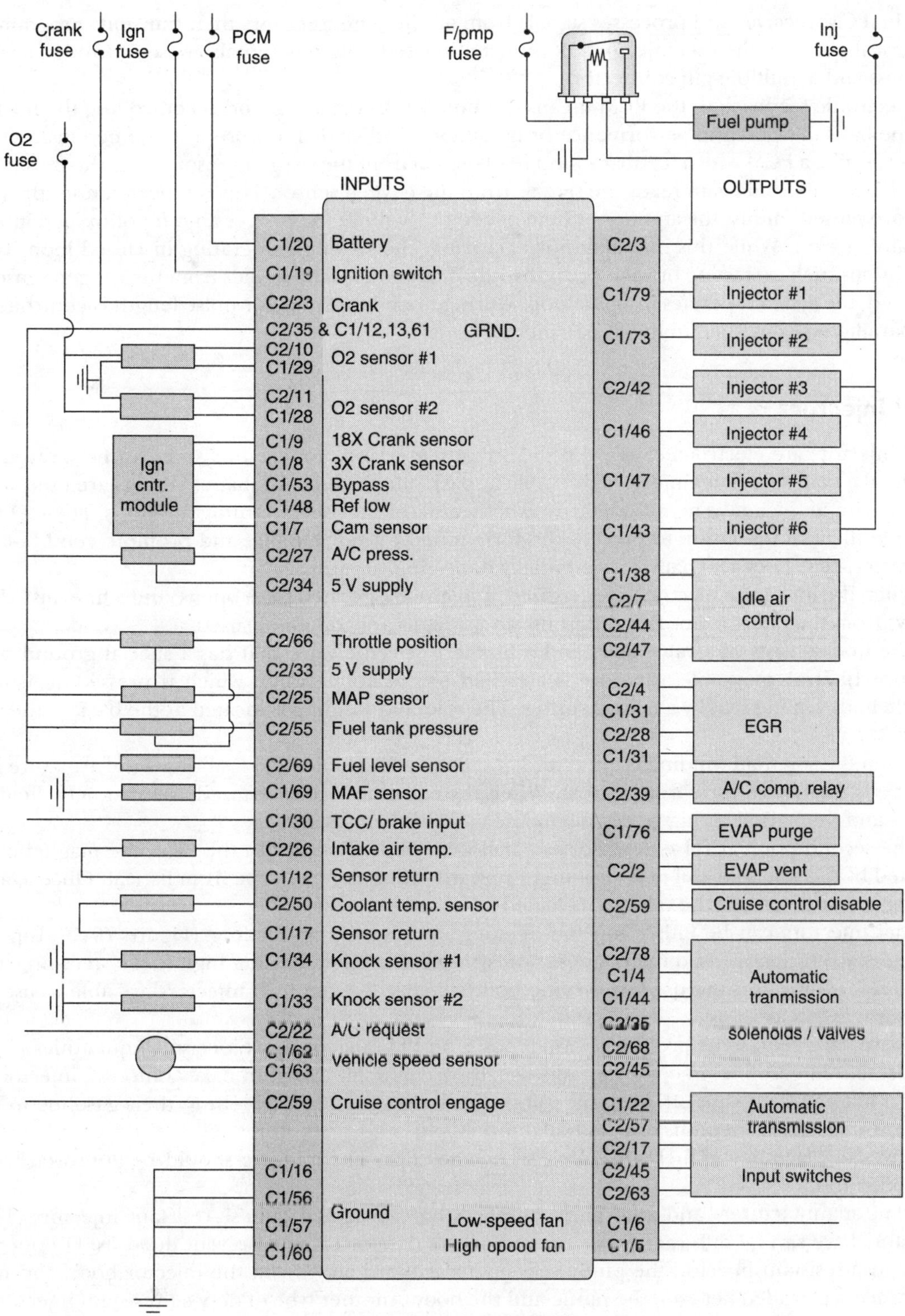

FIGURE 10-6 *Input sensors from all engine systems supply the control computer (PCM) with the data needed to calculate the correct injector pulse for driving conditions and driver demands.*

The PCM receives and processes signals from all the system sensors then transmits programmed electrical pulses to the fuel injectors. Both incoming and outgoing signals are sent through a wiring harness and a multiple-pin connector.

Electronic feedback in the PCM means the unit is self-regulating and is controlling the injectors on the basis of operating performance or parameters rather than on preprogrammed instructions. For example, a PCM with a feedback loop reads signal from the oxygen sensor, varies the pulse width of the injectors, and again reads the signals from the oxygen sensor. This is repeated until the injectors are pulsed for just the amount of time needed to achieve the proper amount of oxygen into the exhaust stream. While this interaction is occurring, the system is operating in closed loop. When conditions such as starting or wide-open throttle demand that the signals from the oxygen sensor be ignored, the system operates in open loop. During open loop, injector pulse length is controlled by set parameters contained in the PCM's memory.

Fuel Injectors

Fuel injectors are electromechanical devices that meter and atomize fuel so it can be sprayed into the intake manifold. Fuel injectors resemble a spark plug in size and shape. O-rings are used to seal the injector at the intake manifold, throttle body, and/or fuel rail mounting positions. These O-rings provide thermal insulation to prevent the formation of vapor bubbles and promote good hot start characteristics. They also dampen potentially damaging vibration.

When the injector is electrically energized, a solenoid-operated valve opens, and a fine mist of fuel sprays from the injector tip. Two different valve designs are commonly used.

The first consists of a valve body and a nozzle or needle valve that has a special ground **pintle** (Figure 10-7). A moveable armature is attached to the nozzle valve, which is pressed against the nozzle body sealing seat by a helical spring. The solenoid winding is located at the back of the valve body.

When the solenoid winding is energized, it creates a magnetic field that draws the armature back and pulls the nozzle valve from its seat. When the solenoid is de-energized, the magnetic field collapses and the helical spring forces the nozzle valve back on its seat.

The second popular valve design uses a ball valve and valve seat. In this case, the magnetic field created by the solenoid coil pulls a plunger upward lifting the ball valve from its seat. Once again, a spring is used to return the valve to its seated or closed position.

Fuel injectors can be either top fuel feeding or bottom fuel feeding (Figure 10-8). Top feed injectors are primarily used in port injection systems that operate using high fuel system pressures. Bottom feed injectors are used in throttle body systems. Bottom feed injectors are able to use fuel pressures as low as 10 psi.

There have been some problems with deposits on PFI injector tips. Since small quantities of gum are present in gasoline, injector deposits usually occur when this gum bakes onto the injector tips after a hot engine is shut off. Most oil companies have added a detergent to their gasoline to help prevent injector tip deposits. Car manufacturers and auto parts stores sell fuel injector detergent additives to place in the fuel tank to clean injector tips. The additive should be approved by the manufacturer.

Some manufacturers and auto parts suppliers have designed deposit-resistant injectors. These injectors have several different pintle tip and orifice designs to help prevent deposits. On one type of deposit-resistant injector, the pintle seat opens outward away from the injector body, and more clearance is provided between the pintle and the body. Another type of deposit-resistant injector has four orifices in a metering plate rather than a single orifice. Some deposit-resistant injectors may be recognized by the color of the injector body. For example, regular injectors supplied by Ford Motor Company are painted black, whereas their deposit-resistant injectors have tan or yellow bodies.

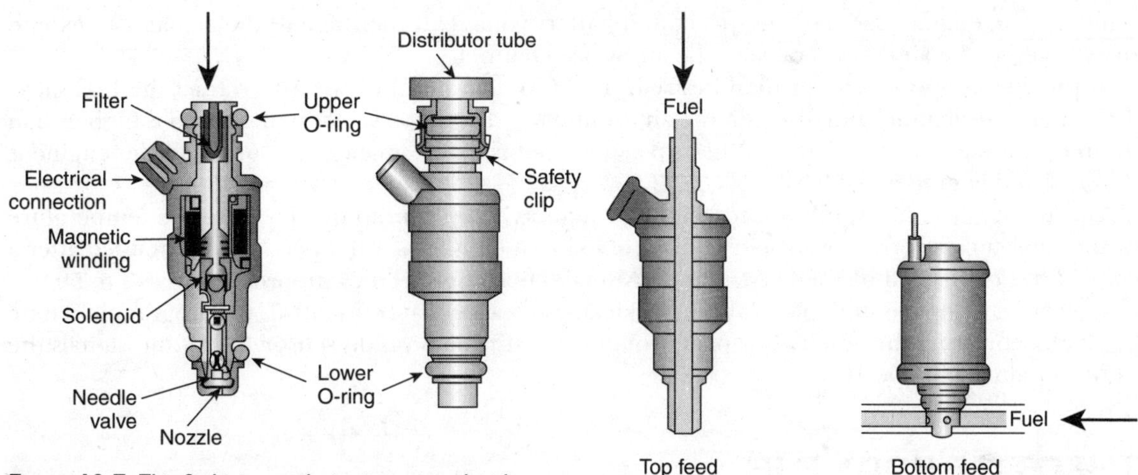

FIGURE 10-7 *This fuel injector design is equipped with a specially ground pintle for precise fuel control.*

FIGURE 10-8 *Examples of bottom and top feed injectors.*

Each fuel injector is equipped with a two-wire connector. The connector is often retained by a wire clip that must be unlocked before the connector can be removed from the injector.

One wire of the connector supplies voltage to the injector. This voltage supply wire may connect directly to the fuse panel or the PCM, which in turn connects to the fuse panel. In some systems, a resistor at the fuse panel or PCM is used to reduce the 12-volt battery supply voltage to 3 volts or less (Figure 10-9). Most systems supply the injectors full battery voltage.

The second wire of the connector is a ground wire. This ground wire is routed to the PCM. The PCM energizes the injector by grounding its electrical circuit. The pulse width of the injector equals the length of time the injector circuit is grounded. Typical pulse widths at full load range from 1 millisecond to 10 milliseconds. Port fuel injection systems having four, six, or eight injectors use a special wiring harness to simplify and organize injector wiring.

FIGURE 10-9 *Injector diagram.*

Idle Speed Control

In throttle body and port EFI systems, engine idle speed is controlled by bypassing a certain amount of airflow past the throttle valve in the throttle body housing. Two types of air bypass systems are used: auxiliary air valves and **idle air control (IAC)** valves. IAC valve systems are more common.

The IAC system consists of an electrically controlled stepper motor or actuator that positions the IAC valve in the air bypass channel around the throttle valve. The air bypass channel is part of the throttle body casting (Figure 10-10). The PCM calculates the amount of air needed for smooth idling based on input data such as coolant

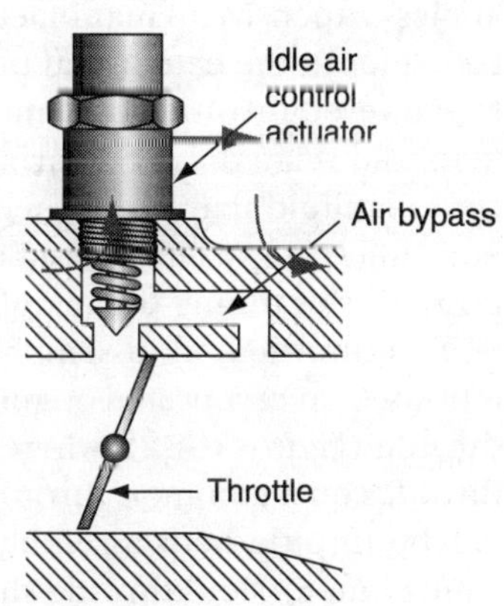

FIGURE 10-10 *An IAC fitted in the casting of a TBI assembly.*

temperature, engine load, engine speed, and battery voltage. It then signals the actuator to extend or retract the idle air control valve in the air bypass channel.

If the engine speed is lower than desired, the PCM activates the motor to retract the IAC valve. This opens the channel and diverts more air around the throttle valve. If engine speed is higher than desired, the valve is extended and the bypass channel is made smaller. Air supply to the engine is reduced and engine speed falls.

During the cold starts, idle speed can be as high as 2,100 rpm to quickly raise the temperature of the catalytic converter for proper control of exhaust emissions. Idle speed that is attained after a cold start is controlled by the PCM. The PCM maintains idle speed for approximately 40 to 50 seconds even if the driver attempts to alter it by kicking the accelerator. After this preprogrammed time interval, depressing the accelerator pedal rotates the throttle position sensor (TPS) and signals the PCM to reduce idle speed.

THROTTLE BODY FUEL INJECTION

For some auto manufacturers, throttle body injection (TBI) served as a stepping stone from carburetors to more advanced port fuel injection systems. TBI units were used on many engines during the 1980s and are still used on some engines. The throttle body unit is similar in size and shape to a carburetor and, like a carburetor, mounted on the intake manifold (Figure 10-11). The injector(s) spray fuel down into a throttle body chamber leading to the intake manifold. The intake manifold feeds the air-fuel mixture to all cylinders.

FIGURE 10-11 *A dual-injector throttle body injection systyem.*

TBI Advantages

Throttle body systems provide improved fuel metering when compared to carburetors. They are also less expensive and simpler to service. TBI units also have some advantages over port injection. They are less expensive to manufacture, simpler to diagnose and service, and do not have injector balance problems to the extent that port injection systems do when the injectors begin to clog.

However, throttle body units are not as efficient as port systems. The disadvantages are primarily manifold related. Like a carburetor system, fuel is still not distributed equally to all cylinders and a cold manifold may cause fuel to condense and puddle in the manifold. Like a carburetor, throttle body injection systems must be mounted above the combustion chamber level, which eliminates the possibility of tuning the manifold design for more efficient operation.

The throttle body assembly is mounted on top of the intake manifold where the carburetor was mounted on carbureted engines. Four-cylinder engines have a single throttle body assembly with one throttle (Figure 10-12), whereas V6 and V8 engines are equipped with dual throttle bodies with two throttles on a common throttle shaft (Figure 10-13).

The throttle body assembly contains a pressure regulator, injector or injectors, TPS, idle speed control motor, and throttle shaft and linkage assembly. A fuel filter is located in the fuel line under the vehicle or in the engine compartment. When the engine is cranking or running, fuel is sup-

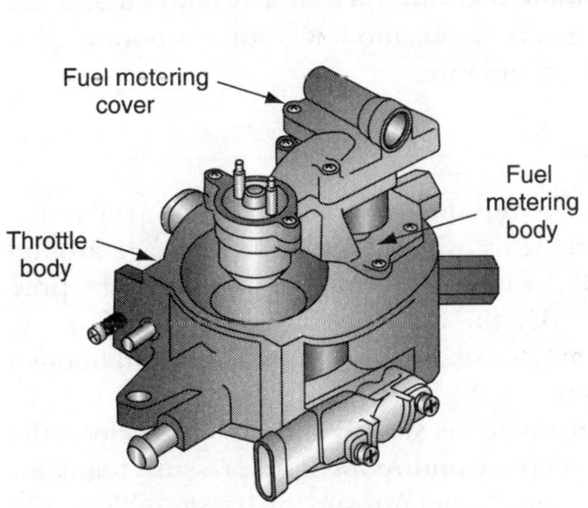

FIGURE 10-12 *Single injector throttle body.*

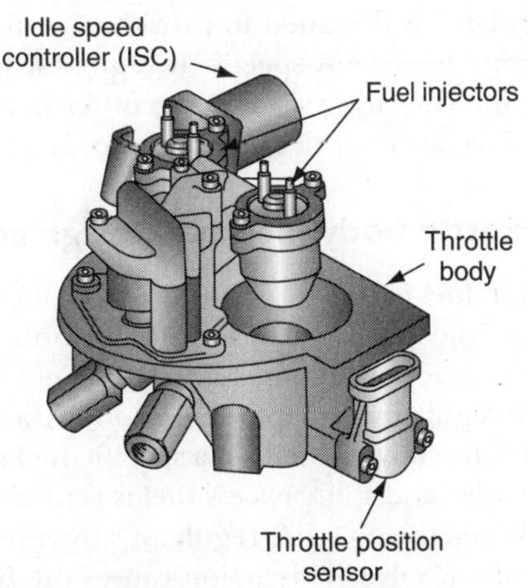

FIGURE 10-13 *Throttle body assembly used on some eight-cylinder and V6s.*

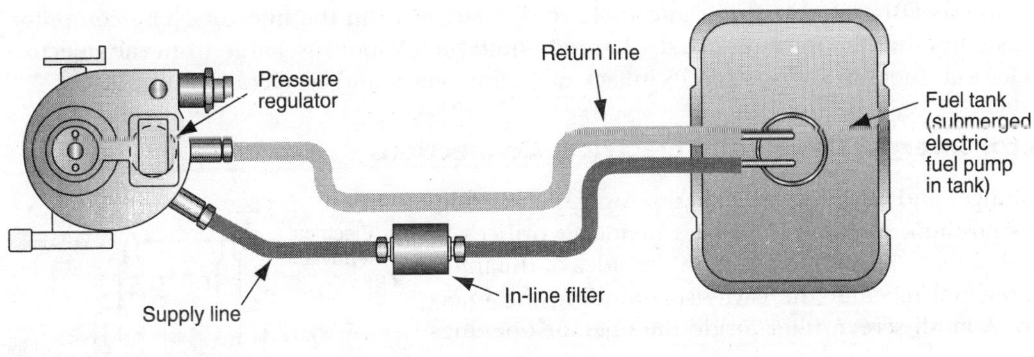

FIGURE 10-14 *Fuel lines and filter location on TBI system.*

plied from the fuel pump through the lines and filter to the throttle body assembly. A fuel return line connected from the throttle body to the fuel tank returns excess fuel to the fuel tank (Figure 10-14).

The throttle body casting has ports that can be located above, below, or at the throttle valve depending on the manufacturer's design. These ports generate vacuum signals for the manifold absolute pressure sensor and for devices in the emission control system, such as the EGR valve and the canister purge system.

The fuel pressure regulator used on the throttle body assembly is similar to a diaphragm-operated relief valve (Figure 10-15). Fuel pressure is on one side of the diaphragm and atmospheric pressure is on the other side. The

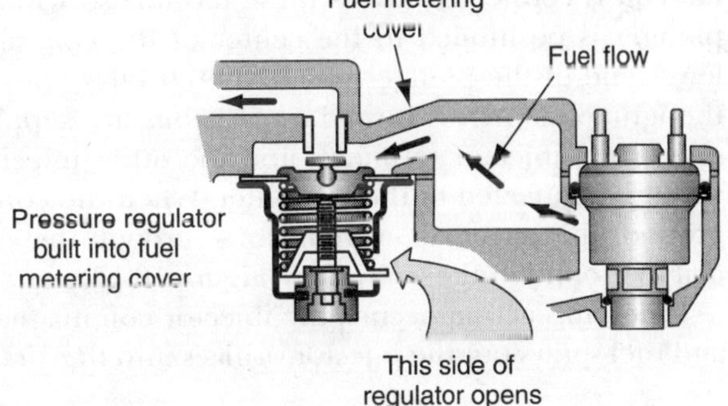

FIGURE 10-15 *Operation of a diaphragm-operated fuel pressure regulator.*

regulator is designed to provide a constant pressure on the fuel injector throughout the range of engine loads and speeds. If regulator pressure is too high, a strong fuel odor is emitted and the engine runs too rich. On the other hand, regulator pressure that is too low results in poor engine performance, or detonation can take place due to the lean mixture.

Throttle Body Internal Design and Operation

When fuel enters the throttle body fuel inlet, the fuel surrounds the injector or injectors at all times. Each injector is sealed into the throttle body with O-ring seals, which prevent fuel leakage around the injector at the top or bottom. Fuel is supplied from the injector through a passage to the pressure regulator. A diaphragm and valve assembly is mounted in this regulator, and a diaphragm spring holds the valve closed. At a specific fuel pressure, the regulator diaphragm is forced upward to open the valve and some excess fuel is returned to the fuel tank.

When the pressure regulator valve opens, fuel pressure decreases slightly and the spring closes the regulator valve. This action causes the fuel pressure to increase and reopen the pressure regulator valve. In most TBI systems, the fuel pressure regulator controls fuel pressure at 10 psi to 25 psi (70 kPa to 172 kPa). The fuel pressure must be high enough to prevent fuel boiling in the TBI assembly. When the pressure on a liquid is increased, the boiling point is raised proportionally. If fuel boiling occurs in the TBI assembly, vapor and fuel are discharged from the injectors. The computer program assumes that the injectors are discharged liquid fuel. Vapor discharge from the injectors creates a lean air-fuel ratio, which results in lack of engine power and acceleration stumbles.

Injector Internal Design and Electrical Connections

The plunger and valve seat are held downward by a spring. In this position, the seat closes the metering orifices in the end of the injector. Openings in the sides of the injector allow fuel to enter the cavity surrounding the injector tip. A mesh screen filter inside the injector openings removes dirt particles from the fuel. In some injectors, a diaphragm is located between the valve seat and the housing (Figure 10-16). The tip of the injector may contain up to six metering orifices, but some injectors have a single metering orifice. Injector design varies depending on the manufacturer.

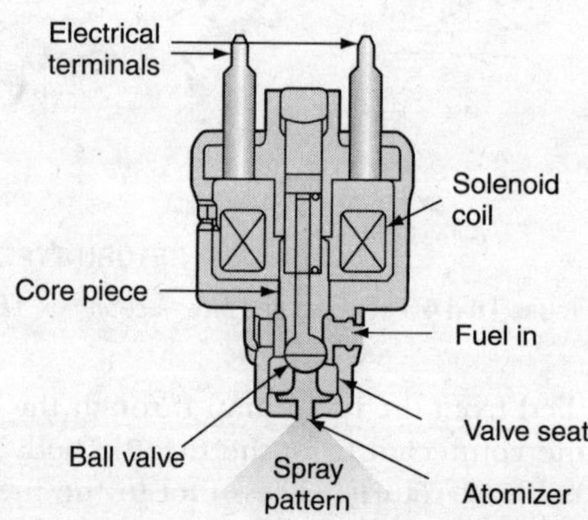

FIGURE 10-16 *Solenoid-operated ball-type fuel injector used in a TBI system. When electronically energized, the ball valve lifts off the valve seat, allowing fuel to spray into the throttle body opening.*

Each injector contains two terminals, and an internal coil is connected across these terminals. A moveable plunger is positioned in the center of the coil, and the lower end of the plunger has a tapered valve seat. When the ignition switch is turned on, 12 volts are supplied to one of the injector terminals and the other injector terminal is connected to the computer. When the computer grounds this terminal, current flows through the injector coil to ground in the computer (Figure 10-17).

When this action occurs, the injector coil magnetism moves the plunger and valve seat upward, and fuel sprays out the injector orifices into the airstream above the throttle.

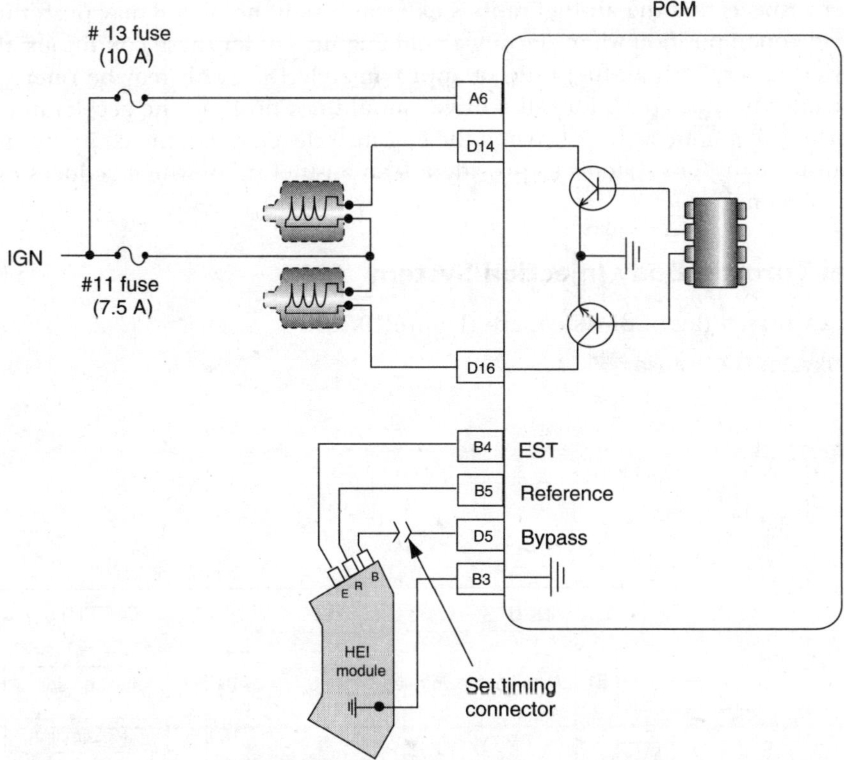

FIGURE 10-17 *With the ignition on, 12 volts are applied to one terminal of each injector. The other injector terminal is connected to and completed by the computer.*

Pulse Width

The length of time that the computer grounds the injector is referred to as pulse width. Under most operating conditions, the computer provides the correct injector pulse width to maintain the stoichiometric air-fuel ratio. For example, the computer might ground the injector for 2 milliseconds at idle speed and 7 milliseconds at wide-open throttle to provide the stoichiometric air-fuel ratio. In many TBI systems, the computer grounds an injector each time a signal is received from the distributor pickup. This type of TBI system may be referred to as a synchronized system because the injector pulses are synchronized with the pickup signals. In a dual injector throttle body assembly, the computer grounds the injectors alternately under most operating conditions.

Air-Fuel Ratio Enrichment

When the coolant temperature sensor signal to the computer indicates that the engine coolant is cold, the computer increases the injector pulse width to provide a richer air-fuel ratio. This action eliminates the need for a conventional choke on a TBI assembly. The PCM supplies the proper air-fuel ratio and engine rpm when starting a cold engine. This eliminates the need for the driver to depress the accelerator pedal while starting the engine.

When a TBI-equipped engine is cold, the computer provides a very rich air-fuel ratio for faster starting. However, if the engine does not start because of an ignition defect, the engine becomes flooded quickly. Under this condition, excessive fuel may run past the piston rings into the crankcase. Therefore, when a cold TBI engine does not start, periods of long cranking should be avoided.

If the driver suspects that the air-fuel ratio is extremely rich, he or she may push the accelerator pedal to the wide-open position when starting a cold engine. Under these conditions, the computer program provides a very lean air-fuel ratio of approximately 18:1. This may be referred to as **clear flood mode**. Under normal conditions, the driver should not push on the accelerator pedal at any time when starting an engine with TBI. When the engine is decelerated, the computer reduces injector pulse width in many TBI systems to provide a lean air-fuel ratio, which reduces emissions and improves fuel economy.

Typical Dual Throttle Body Injection System

The inputs in a Chrysler dual TBI system are (Figure 10-18):

1. Heated oxygen (O_2) sensor

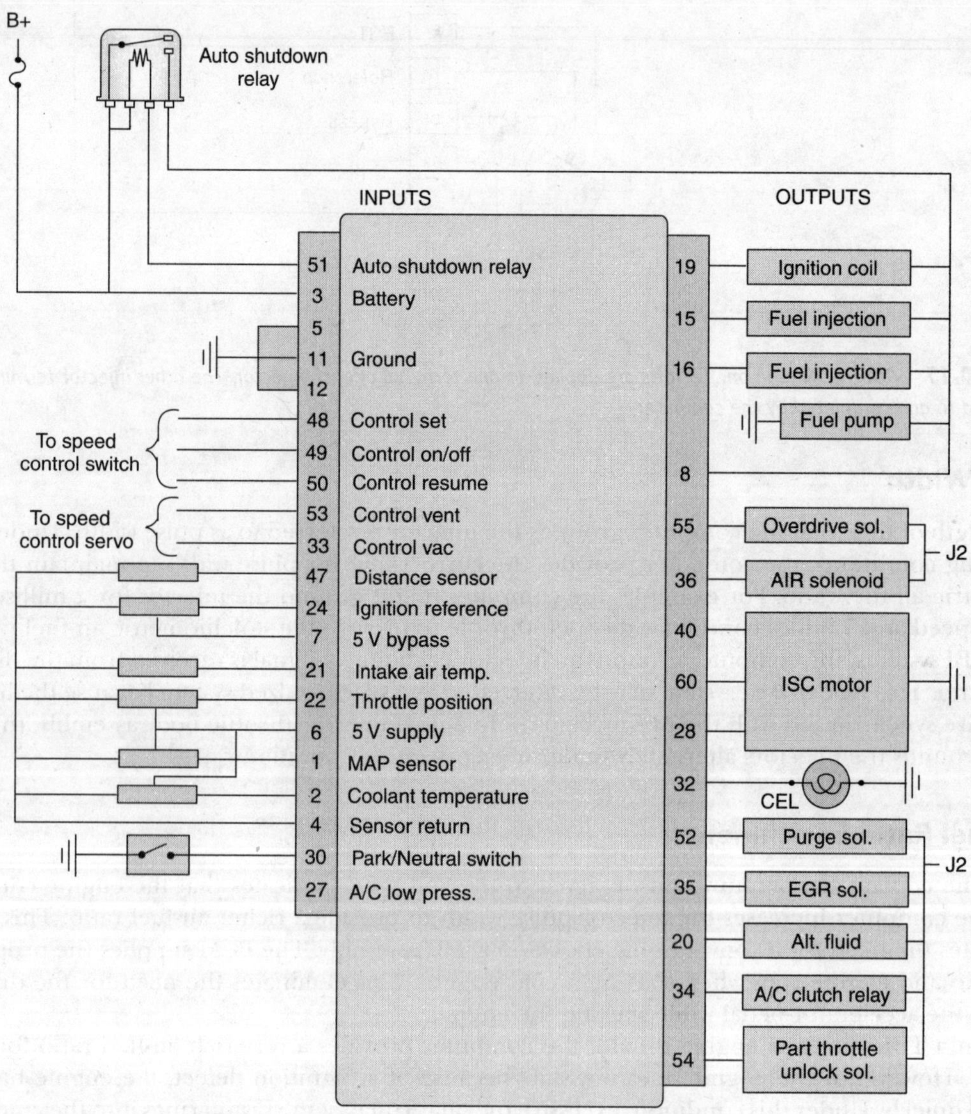

FIGURE 10-18 *Chrysler's dual TBI system that is used on 3.9L, 5.2L, and 5.9L engines.*

2. Distance/speed sensor
3. Distributor pickup
4. Manifold absolute pressure (MAP) sensor
5. Coolant temperature sensor
6. Park/neutral switch
7. Cruise control switches
8. Brake switch
9. Ignition switch
10. A/C switch

The outputs on the Chrysler TBI system are

1. Injectors
2. Spark advance
3. Automatic shutdown (ASD) relay
4. Alternator field
5. Cruise control vent and vacuum solenoids
6. Throttle kicker motor
7. Purge solenoid
8. EGR solenoid
9. Check engine lamp
10. Part throttle unlock solenoid
11. Up overdrive solenoid
12. Air switching solenoid
13. A/C clutch relay
14. Tachometer

As shown in the figure, the alternator field and the cruise control switches are connected to the PCM terminals. These connections indicate that the voltage regulator and the cruise control module are part of the PCM board.

If the A/C mode is selected on the instrument panel controls, an input signal is sent from the A/C control panel switch and the A/C low pressure switch to the PCM. When this signal is received, the PCM grounds the A/C relay winding, which closes the relay points and supplies voltage to the compressor clutch. If the engine is operating at wide-open throttle, the PCM will not ground the A/C relay winding.

The throttle kicker, or idle speed, motor is a reversible electric motor. The stem of this motor pushes against the throttle linkage. The PCM operates this motor to control the idle speed under all engine operating conditions (Figure 10-19).

Typical Single Throttle Body Injection System

The inputs on a General Motors 2.5L, four-cylinder, single TBI system are (Figure 10-20 and Figure 10-21):

1. Coolant temperature sensor
2. Oxygen (O_2) sensor
3. Distributor reference
4. Power steering switch
5. Ignition on
6. Manifold absolute pressure (MAP) sensor
7. Throttle position sensor (TPS)
8. Vehicle speed sensor (VSS)

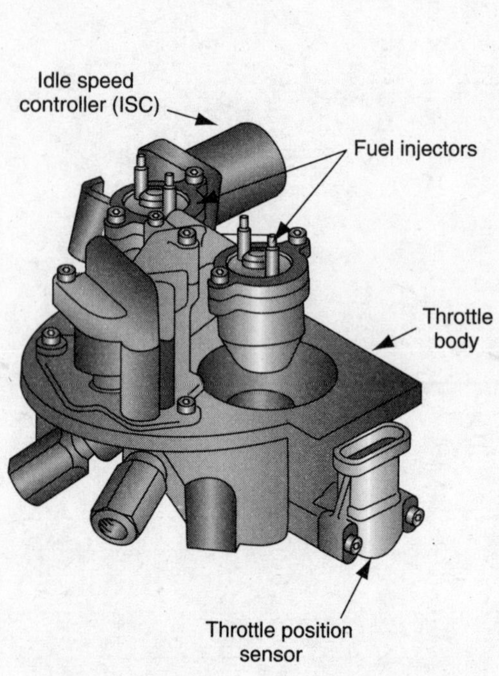

FIGURE 10-19 *Idle speed control motor.*

9. Park/neutral switch
10. Crank signal
11. A/C switch

The outputs on a 2.5L TBI system are:

1. Injector
2. Spark advance
3. Idle air control (IAC) valve
4. A/C relay
5. A/C fan relay
6. Fuel pump relay
7. Torque converter clutch (TCC)
8. Malfunction indicator light (MIL)
9. Shift lamp, manual transaxles only

PORT FUEL INJECTION

Port fuel injection (PFI) systems use one injector at each cylinder. They are mounted in the intake manifold near the cylinder head where they can inject a fine, atomized fuel mist as close as possible to the intake valve (Figure 10-22). Fuel lines run to each cylinder from a fuel manifold, usually referred to as a fuel rail. The fuel rail assembly on a PFI system of V6 and V8 engines usually consists

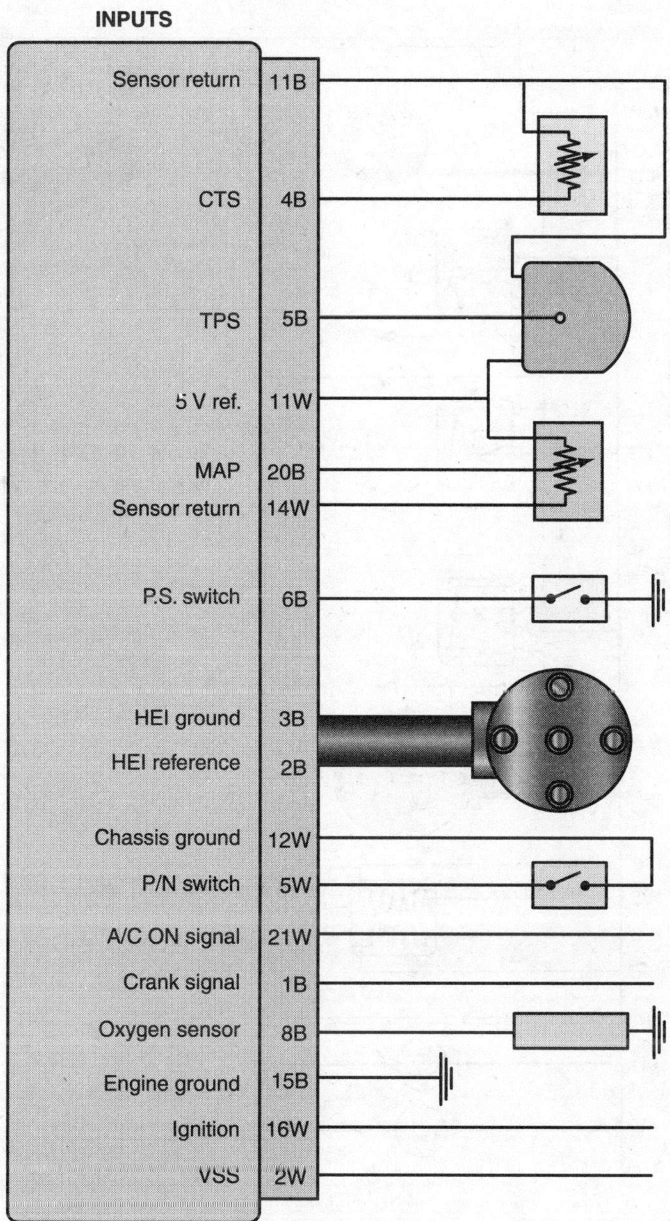

FIGURE 10-20 *Inputs, single TBI system used on GM's 2.5L engine.*

of a leftand right-hand rail assembly. The two rails can be connected either by crossover and return fuel tubes or by a mechanical bracket arrangement. Since each cylinder has its own injector, fuel distribution is exactly equal. With little or no fuel to wet the manifold walls, there is no need for manifold heat or any early fuel evaporation system. Fuel does not collect in puddles at the base of the manifold.

The throttle body in a port fuel injection system controls the amount of air that enters the engine, as well as the amount of vacuum in the manifold. It also houses and controls the idle air control motor and the throttle position sensor. The (TP sensor) enables the PCM to know where the throttle is positioned at all times.

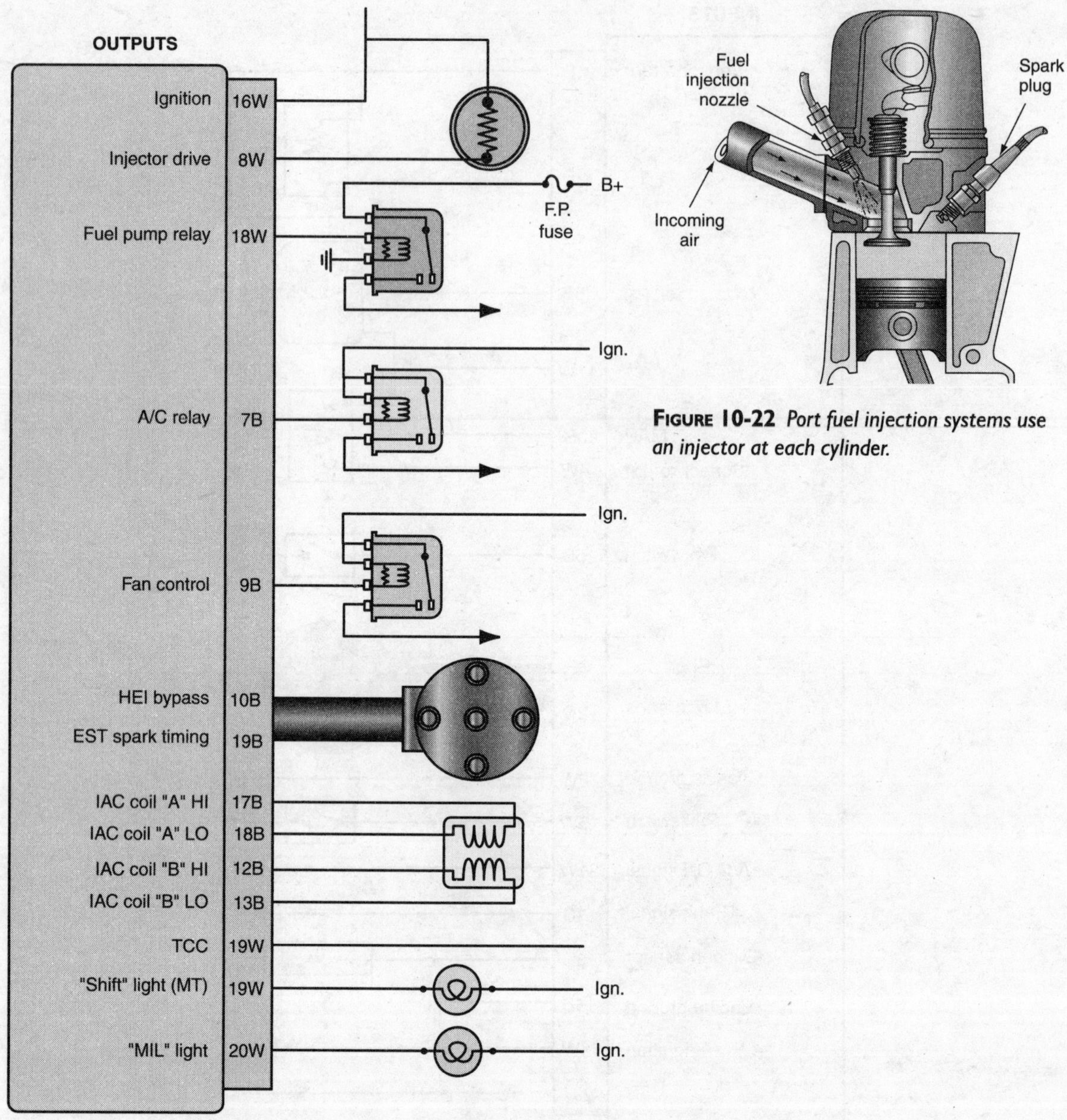

FIGURE 10-22 *Port fuel injection systems use an injector at each cylinder.*

FIGURE 10-21 *Outputs, single TBI system used on GM's 2.5L engine.*

The throttle body is a single cast aluminum housing with a single throttle blade attached to the throttle shaft. The TP sensor and the IAC valve/motor are also attached to the housing. The throttle shaft is controlled by the accelerator pedal. The throttle shaft extends the full length of the housing. The throttle bore controls the amount of incoming air that enters the air induction system. A small amount of coolant is also routed through a passage in the throttle body to prevent icing during cold weather.

Port systems require an additional control system that throttle body injection units do not require. While throttle body injectors are mounted above the throttle plates and are not affected by fluctuations in manifold vacuum, port system injectors have their tips located in the manifold where constant changes in vacuum would affect the amount of fuel injected (at a given pulse width). To compensate for these fluctuations, port injection systems are equipped with fuel pressure regulators (Figure 10-23) that sense manifold vacuum and continually adjust the fuel pressure to maintain a constant pressure drop across the injector tips at all times.

There are basically two different types of port fuel injection in use. The first type was multiport fuel injection, called **MPFI, or MFI**. Simply, more than one injector (port) was activated at one time, hence the name **multiport**. Multiport can fire all of the injectors at the same time, or a bank of injectors, like the four cylinders shown in Figure 10-24. When all the cylinder injectors can be fired at the same time, the first impression most technicians have is that it cannot be efficient to fire the injectors regardless of valve position, but the fact is that the wait is very short, and is shorter as rpm is increased above idle. One advantage of multiport is the fact that a cam sensor is not needed, especially if used in conjunction with waste spark ignition discussed later in the text. The other and more popular version of port fuel is **sequential port fuel injection,** or **SFI.** In SFI, the injectors are opened just as the intake valve opens for a particular cylinder. This results in a smoother idle and a slight increase in fuel mileage. The PCM controls each injector individually by switching the ground side of the injector. The wiring for the injectors is different depending on whether the vehicle is MFI or SFI. It is important to note that many engines that are SFI can operate in MFI as a backup fuel delivery method if needed.

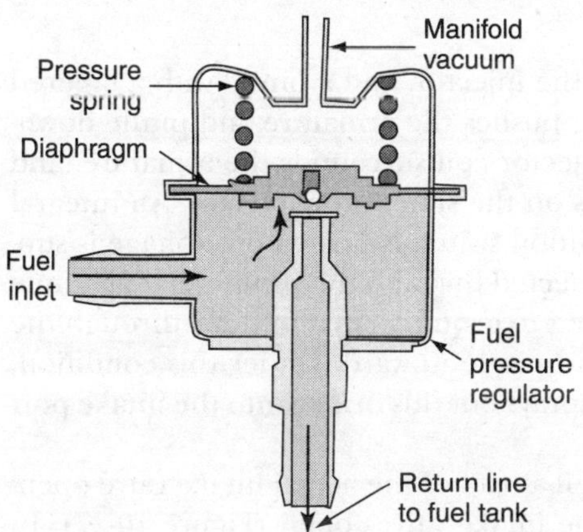

FIGURE 10-23 *Operation of a vacuum-operated fuel pressure regulator. Low pressure increases fuel pressure.*

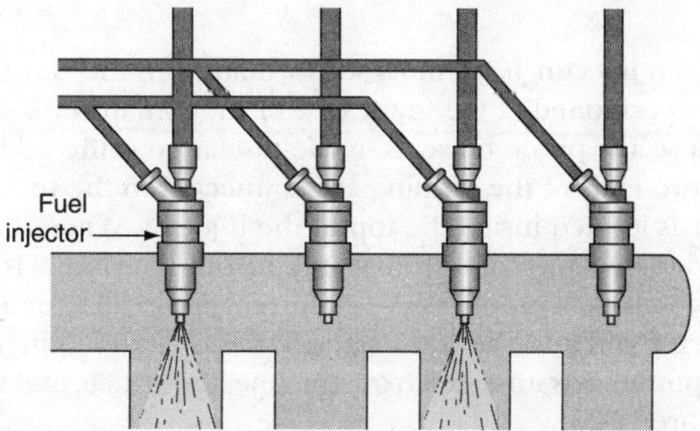

FIGURE 10-24 *A grouped fire port injection system.*

Port Fuel Injection System Design

Basically the same electric in-tank fuel pumps and fuel pump circuits are found on TBI, MFI, and SFI systems. Some MFI and SFI systems, such as those on Ford trucks, have a booster fuel pump on the frame rail in addition to the in-tank pump. A fuel filter is connected in the fuel line from the tank to the injectors. This filter may be under the vehicle or in the engine compartment. The fuel line from the filter is connected to a hollow fuel rail that is bolted to the intake manifold. The lower end of each port injector is sealed in the intake manifold with an O-ring seal and a similar seal near the top of the injector seals the injector to the fuel rail. Most fuel rails have a Schrader valve. A pressure gauge may be connected to this valve when testing fuel pressure (Figure 10-25). A dust cap on the Schrader valve must be removed prior to gauge installation.

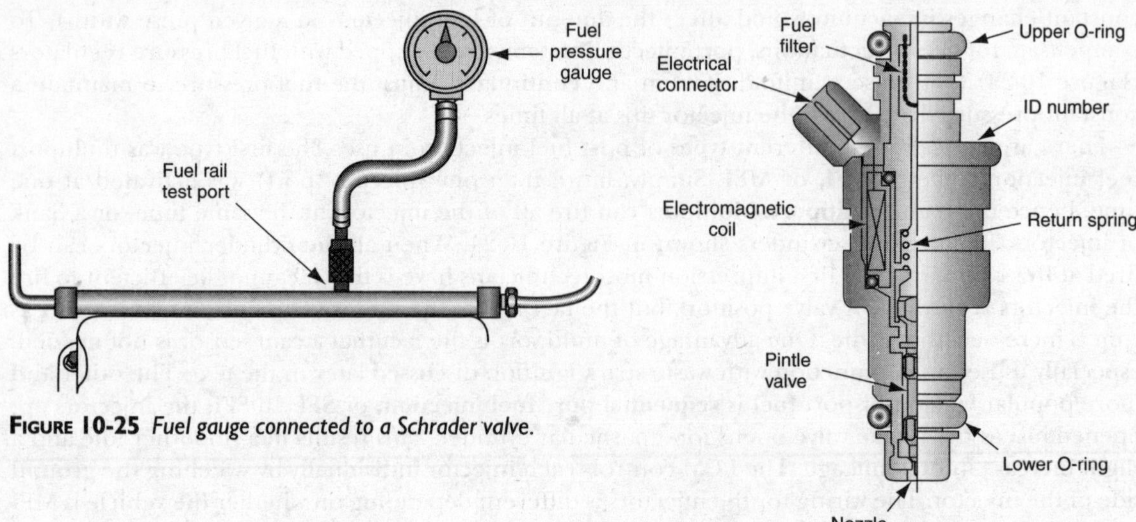

FIGURE 10-25 *Fuel gauge connected to a Schrader valve.*

FIGURE 10-26 *A typical fuel injector used in port fuel injection systems.*

Each injector has a moveable armature in the center of the injector, and a pintle with a tapered tip is positioned at the lower end of the armature. A spring pushes the armature and pintle downward so the pintle tip seats in the discharge orifice. The injector coil surrounds the armature, and the two ends of the winding are connected to the terminals on the side of the injector. An integral filter is located inside the top of the injector. When the ignition switch is turned on, voltage is supplied to one injector terminal and the other terminal is connected through the computer. Each time the computer completes the circuit from the injector winding to ground, current flows through the injector coil and the coil magnetism moves the plunger and pintle upward. Under this condition, the pintle tip is unseated from the injector orifice, and fuel sprays out this orifice into the intake port (Figure 10-26).

The computer is programmed to ground the injectors well ahead of the actual intake valve openings so the intake ports are filled with fuel vapor before the intake valves open (Figure 10-27). In both SFI and MFI systems, the computer supplies the correct injector pulse width to provide the stoichiometric air-fuel ratio. The computer increases the injector pulse width to provide air-fuel ratio enrichment while starting a cold engine. A clear flood mode is also available in the computer in MFI and SFI systems. On some TBI, MFI, and SFI systems, if the ignition system is not firing, the computer stops operating the injectors. This action prevents severe flooding from long cranking periods while starting a cold engine. On many MFI and SFI systems, the computer decreases injector pulse width while the engine is decelerating to provide improved emission levels and fuel economy. On some of these systems, the computer stops operating the injectors while the engine is decelerating in a certain rpm range.

On many V6 and V8 engines, there is a fuel rail on each side of the intake manifold. On these engines, the fuel is supplied to one rail and a connecting hose carries fuel to the second rail. A pressure regulator is connected to the end of the fuel rail and excess fuel is returned from the regulator through a return line to the fuel tank. On some V6 engines, the fuel rail is U-shaped and each injector is mounted in this one-piece rail (Figure 10-28). Many fuel rails are made from steel or aluminum alloy. Plastic-type fuel rails have been installed recently on some cars. These fuel rails transfer less heat to the fuel and reduce the possibility of fuel boiling in the rail. On some V6 engines, such as the

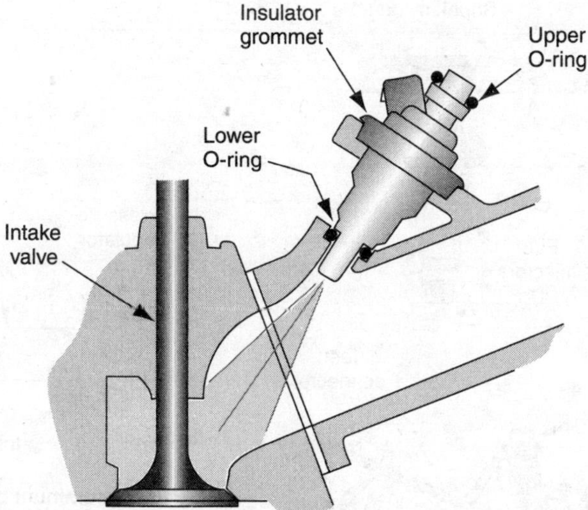

FIGURE 10-27 *A port fuel injector sprays fuel into the intake port and fills the port with fuel vapors before the intake valve opens.*

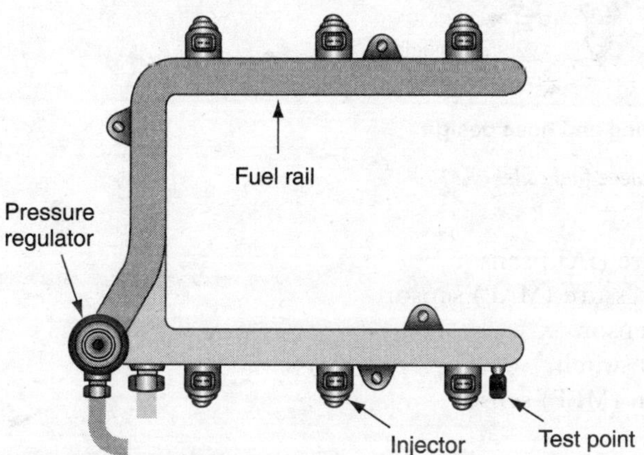

FIGURE 10-28 *A one-piece, U-shaped fuel rail for a V6 engine.*

General Motors 3.1L/3.4L V6, a one-piece fuel rail is mounted under the top of the intake manifold. In these MFI systems, the top of the intake must be removed to gain access to the fuel rail and injectors (Figure 10-29).

Typical Multiport Fuel Injection System

In many Ford MFI systems on V8 engines, the injectors are connected in groups of four on the ground side. Each group shares a common ground wire to the powertrain control module (Figure 10-30). When the injectors are connected in groups of four on the ground side, a group of injectors is grounded by the computer every crankshaft revolution. The inputs are:

1. Heated exhaust gas oxygen (HEGO) sensor
2. Engine coolant temperature (ECT) sensor
3. Throttle position sensor (TP sensor)

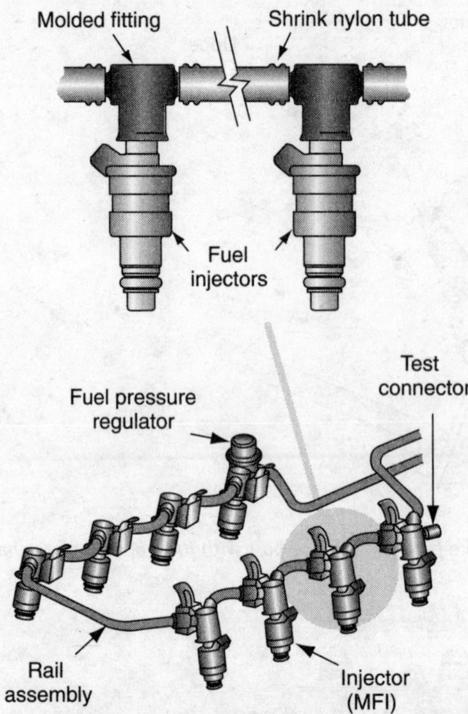

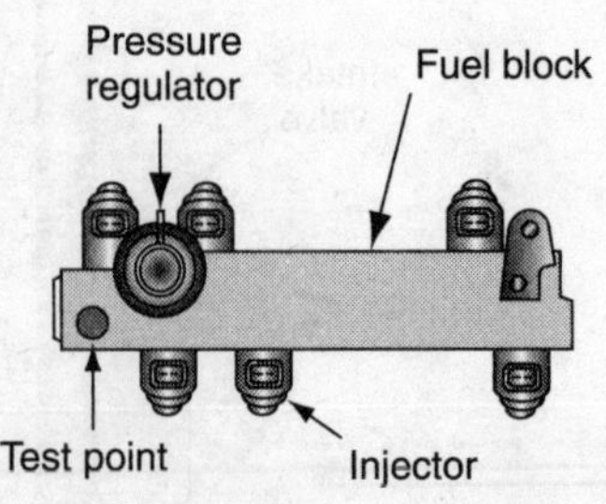

FIGURE 10-29 *Plastic and one-piece fuel rails.*

4. Intake air temperature (IAT) sensor
5. Manifold absolute pressure (MAP) sensor
6. EGR valve position sensor
7. Brake on/off (BOO) switch
8. Manual lever position (MLP) sensor
9. Neutral/park switch
10. Self-test connector
11. Self-test input

The outputs on the 5.8L V8 MFI system are:

1. Injectors
2. Spark advance
3. Idle speed control (IAC) solenoid
4. EGR vacuum regulator (EVR) solenoid
5. Canister purge solenoid
6. Secondary air injection bypass (AIRB) solenoid
7. Secondary air injection diverter (AIRD) solenoid

Typical Import Multiport Fuel Injection System

Some Toyota Camry models are equipped with a multiport fuel injection system. In these systems, injectors one and three and injectors two and four share common ground wire connections to the PCM (Figure 10-31). The PCM grounds a pair of injectors once every crankshaft revolution.

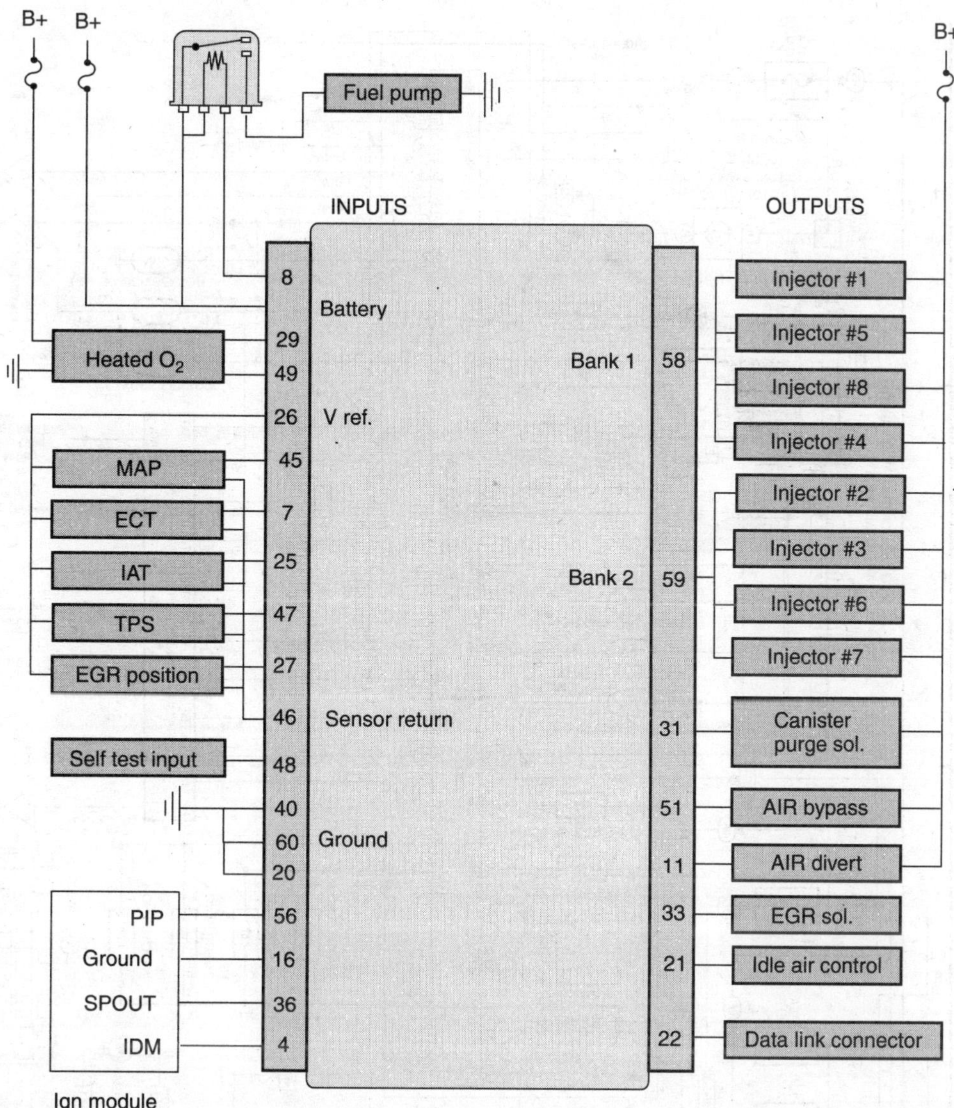

FIGURE 10-30 *Inputs and outputs for a Ford multiport fuel injection system.*

The inputs in this MFI system are:

1. Dual oxygen sensors (O_2S)
2. Knock sensor (KS)
3. Throttle position sensor (TP sensor)
4. Exhaust gas recirculation (EGR) gas temperature sensor
5. Intake air temperature (IAT) sensor
6. Engine coolant temperature sensor (ECT)
7. MAP sensor
8. Distributor pickup

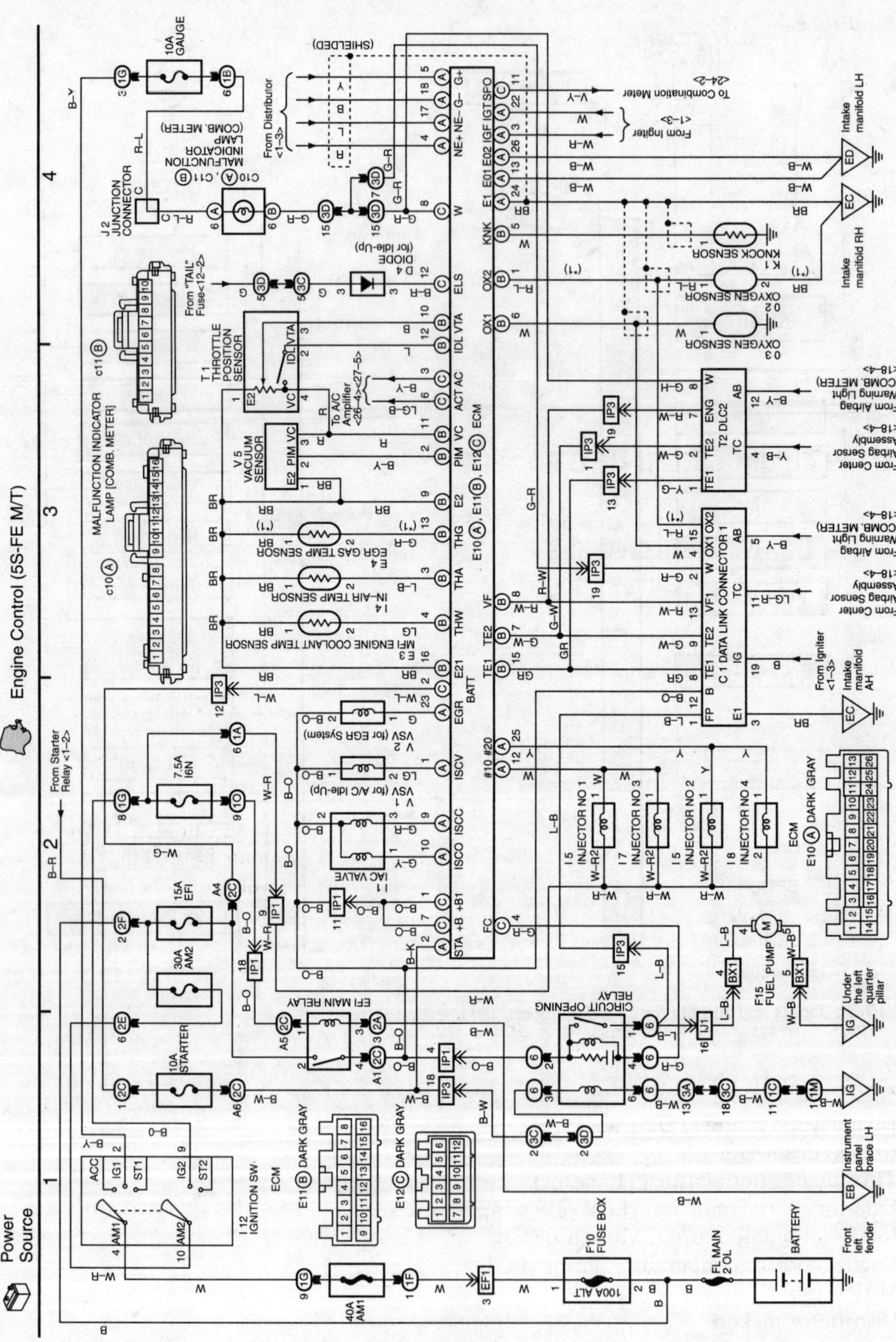

FIGURE 10-31 *The multiport fuel injection system for a Toyota Camry.*

The outputs on this MFI system are:

1. Injectors
2. Spark advance
3. Vacuum switching valve (VSV) for EGR
4. VSV for idle up
5. Idle air control (IAC) valve
6. Malfunction indicator light (MIL)
7. Data link connector (DLC)

The VSV solenoid for idle up is energized by the PCM under certain conditions, such as when the A/C is turned on. When the VSV solenoid is energized, it allows more airflow through the solenoid into the intake manifold to increase the idle speed. The malfunction indicator lamp (MIL) light is illuminated by the PCM if the PCM senses a defect in the system. During the diagnostic procedure, the MIL light flashes the fault codes.

SEQUENTIAL FUEL INJECTION SYSTEMS

Sequential fuel injection (SFI) systems control each injector individually so that it is opened just before the intake valve opens. This means that the mixture is never static in the intake manifold and that adjustments to the mixture can be made almost instantaneously between the firing of one injector and the next. Sequential firing is the most accurate and desirable method of regulating port injection.

In SFI systems, each injector is connected individually into the computer, and the computer completes the ground for each injector one at a time. In MPI systems, the injectors are grouped and all injectors within the group share the same common ground wire.

Typical Sequential Fuel Injection System

In a Chrysler SFI system on a 3.5L engine, each injector has a separate ground wire connected into the PCM (Figure 10-32). Voltage is supplied through the ASD relay points to the injectors when the ignition switch is turned on, and a separate fuel pump relay supplies voltage to the fuel pump. This engine is equipped with an electronic ignition system, and the crank and cam sensors are inputs for this system. Since these inputs are connected to the PCM, the ignition module is contained in the PCM.

Returnless Fuel System Pressure Regulators

Some manufacturers use a returnless fuel delivery system. In these systems, the fuel pressure regulator and filter are mounted in the top of the assembly containing the fuel pump and fuel gauge sending unit in the fuel tank (Figure 10-33). The fuel line from the fuel rail under the hood is connected to the filter with a quick-disconnect fitting.

Fuel enters the filter through the fuel supply tube in the center of the regulator and filter assembly. Fuel pressure is applied against the regulator seat washer, which is seated by the seat control spring (Figure 10-34). At the specified regulator pressure, the seat is forced downward against the spring and fuel flows past the seat into the cavity around the seat control spring. Fuel returns from this cavity to the fuel tank. When the pressure drops slightly, the seat closes again. With the returnless fuel system, only the fuel needed by the engine is filtered, thus allowing the use of a smaller fuel filter.

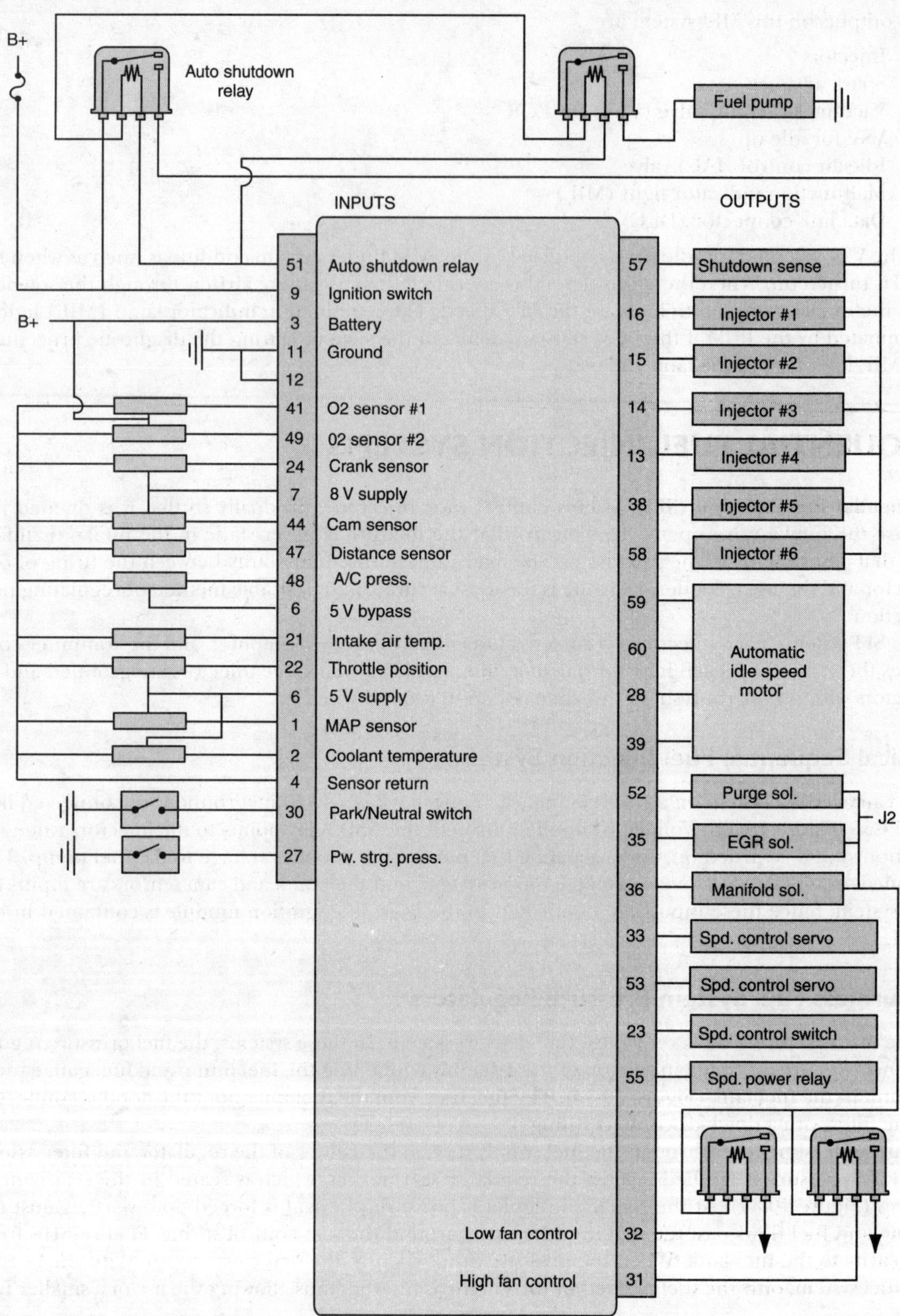

FIGURE 10-32 *PCM inputs and outputs for Chrysler's SFI system used on 3.5L engine.*

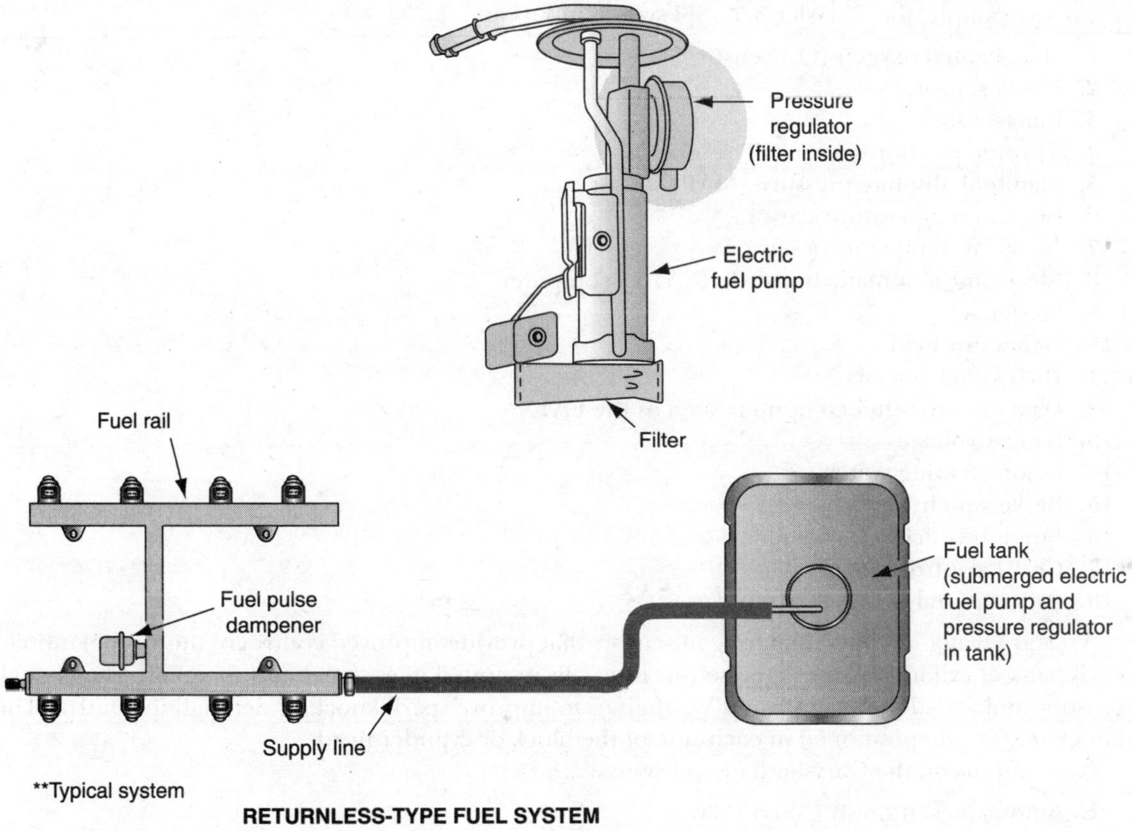

Pressure regulator (filter inside)

Electric fuel pump

Filter

Fuel rail

Fuel tank (submerged electric fuel pump and pressure regulator in tank)

Fuel pulse dampener

Supply line

**Typical system

RETURNLESS-TYPE FUEL SYSTEM

FIGURE 10-33 *Returnless fuel system with the pressure regulator mounted in the fuel tank with the fuel pump and fuel gauge sending unit.*

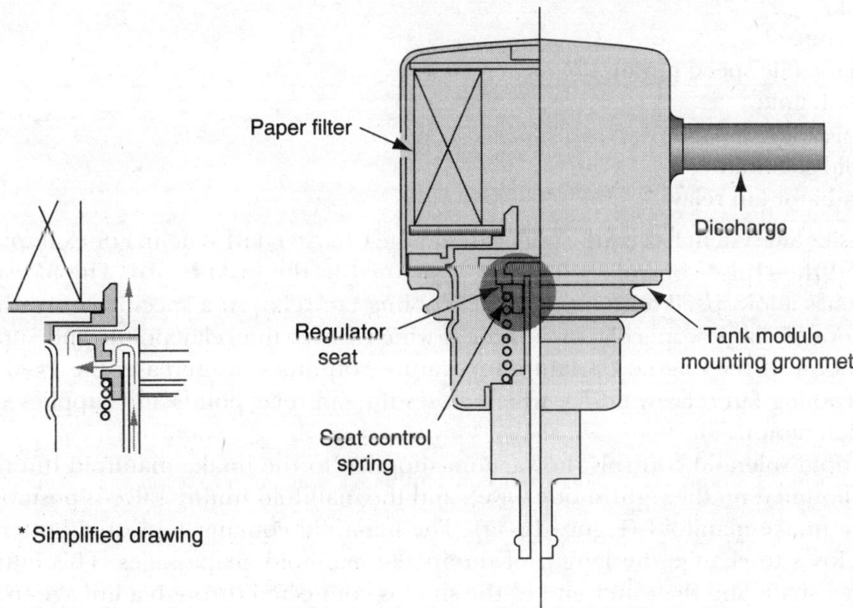

FIGURE 10-34 *Pressure regulator and fuel filter from a returnless fuel system.*

As an example, the Chrysler 3.5L SFI system inputs are:

1. Dual heated oxygen (O_2) sensor
2. Crank sensor
3. Cam sensor
4. Throttle position sensor (TP sensor)
5. Manifold absolute pressure (MAP) sensor
6. Coolant temperature sensor
7. Intake air temperature sensor
8. Electronic automatic transaxle (EATX) computer
9. Starter relay
10. Generator field
11. Dual knock sensors
12. Data links to other computers such as the EATX
13. Battery voltage
14. Power steering switch
15. Brake switch
16. Ignition switch
17. Cruise control switches
18. Park/neutral switch, starter relay

V6 and V8 engines have dual oxygen sensors that provide improved control of the air-fuel ratio in each bank of cylinders. An oxygen sensor is usually mounted in each exhaust manifold. Dual knock sensors are located in many V6 and V8 engines to improve spark knock or detonation control. The knock sensors are positioned in each side of the block or cylinder heads.

The outputs on the Chrysler 3.5L SFI system are

1. Automatic shutdown (ASD) relay
2. Fuel pump relay
3. Ignition coil
4. Spark advance
5. Injectors
6. Cruise control
7. Automatic idle speed motor
8. Purge solenoid
9. EGR solenoid
10. Manifold solenoid
11. Dual radiator fan relays

The Chrysler SFI system has many similarities to the Chrysler TBI system. For example, the voltage regulator and the cruise control module are contained in the PCM board. The SFI system on the 3.5L engine has a low-speed and a high-speed cooling fan relay. At a specific coolant temperature, the PCM grounds the low-speed relay winding, which closes the relay points and supplies voltage to the fan motor. If the engine coolant temperature continues to increase, the PCM grounds the high-speed cooling fan relay winding, which closes the fan relay points and supplies voltage to the high-speed fan motor.

The manifold solenoid controls the vacuum supplied to the intake manifold tuning valve. This solenoid is mounted on the right shock tower, and the manifold tuning valve is positioned near the center of the intake manifold (Figure 10-35). The manifold contains a pivoted butterfly valve that opens and closes to change the length of the intake manifold air passages. This butterfly valve is mounted on a shaft, and the outer end of the shaft is connected through a linkage to a diaphragm in a sealed vacuum chamber. A vacuum hose is connected from the outlet fitting on the manifold

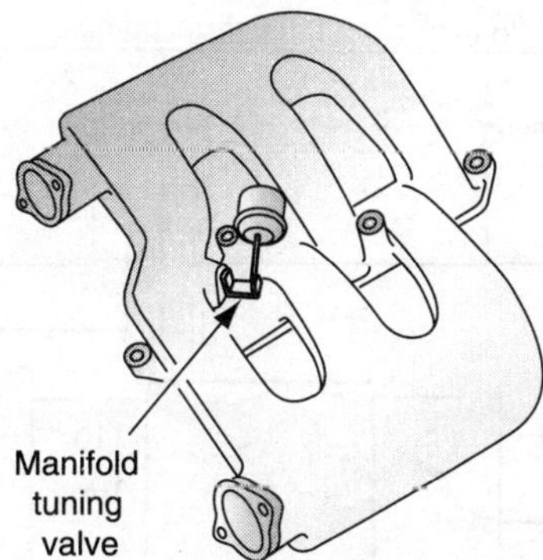

FIGURE 10-35 *Intake manifold tuning valve for a Chrysler 3.5L engine.*

solenoid to the vacuum chamber in the manifold tuning valve. Another vacuum hose is connected from the inlet fitting on the manifold solenoid to the intake manifold.

One terminal on the manifold solenoid winding is connected to the ignition switch, and the other terminal on this winding is connected to the PCM. While the engine is running at lower rpm, the PCM opens the manifold solenoid circuit. Under this condition, the solenoid shuts off the manifold vacuum to the intake manifold tuning valve, and the butterfly valve closes some of the air passages inside the intake manifold.

At higher engine rpm, the PCM ground the manifold solenoid winding and energizes the solenoid. This action opens the vacuum passage through the solenoid and supplies vacuum to the intake manifold tuning valve. Under this condition, the butterfly valve is moved so it opens additional air passages inside the intake manifold to improve airflow and increase engine horsepower and torque.

Typical Import Sequential Fuel Injection System

The Nissan electronic concentrated engine control system (ECCS) is an SFI system that has many of the same inputs and outputs as the other systems. The inputs shown in the wiring diagram for the ECCS are (Figure 10-36):

1. Crank (CKP) sensor
2. Engine coolant temperature (ECT)
3. Vehicle speed sensor (VSS)
4. Knock sensor (KS)
5. EGR sensor
6. Throttle position sensor (TP sensor)
7. Volume airflow meter

A barometric pressure sensor is located in the PCM. This sensor is not serviced separately. This sensor sends a signal to the PCM in relation to barometric pressure as it varies with altitude and climatic conditions. The crank angle sensor is located in the distributor. It sends engine rpm and crankshaft position signals to the PCM (Figure 10-37).

System outputs as shown in the wiring diagram for the ECCS are

1. Injectors
2. Spark advance
3. Air regulator
4. Idle control valve (ICV)

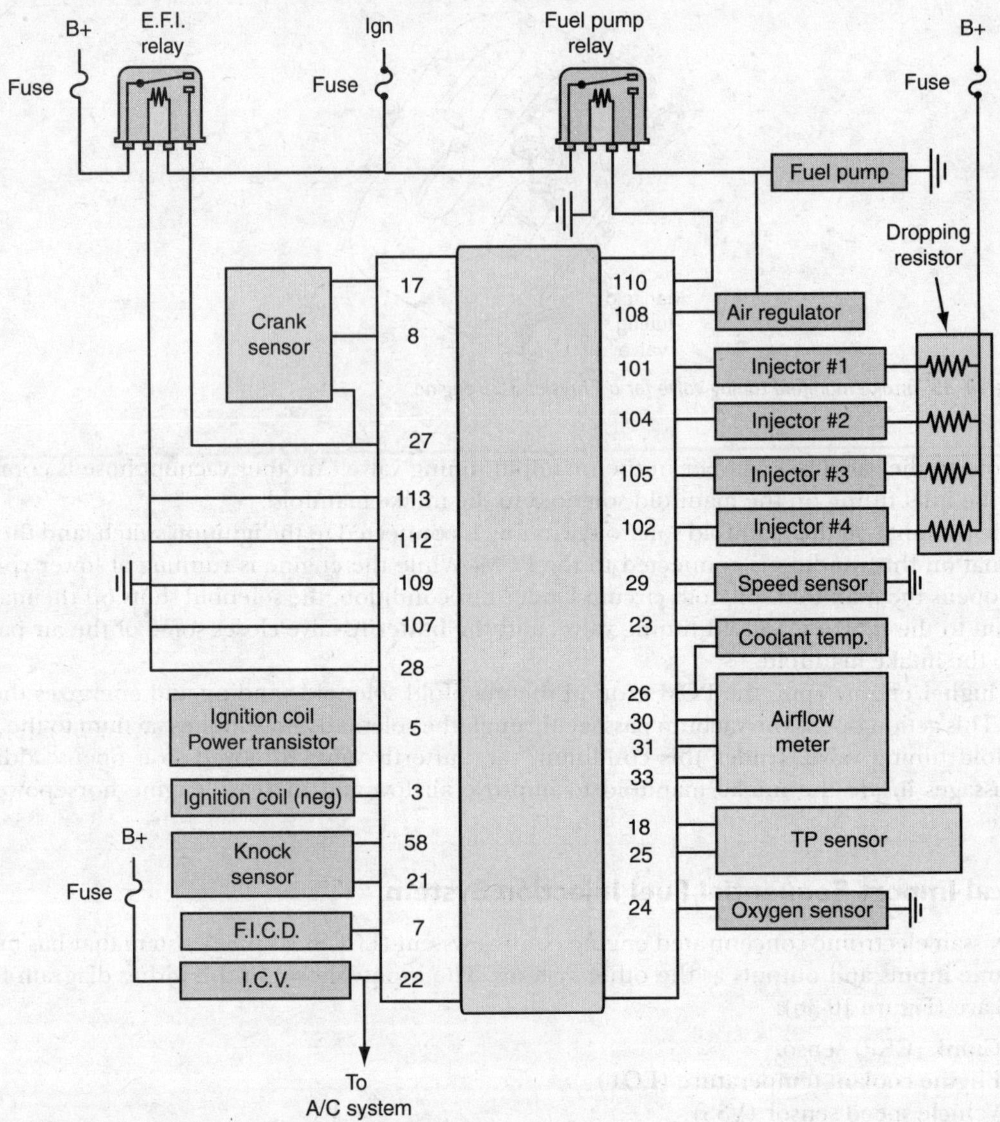

FIGURE 10-36 *Inputs and outputs in Nissan's ECCS system.*

5. Fast idle control device (FICD)
6. Fuel pump relay
7. Electronic fuel injection (EFI) relay

The system also uses some components that are not commonly found on other systems such as the dropping resistor assembly that contains a resistor connected in series with each injector. These resistors protect the injectors from sudden voltage changes and provide constant injector operation. The system uses a vane-type airflow sensor. The throttle valve switch is mounted in the throttle chamber and the switch contacts are closed when the throttle is in the idle position (Figure 10-38). When the throttle is opened from the idle position, the switch contacts open. The throttle valve switch signal informs the PCM when the throttle is in the idle position.

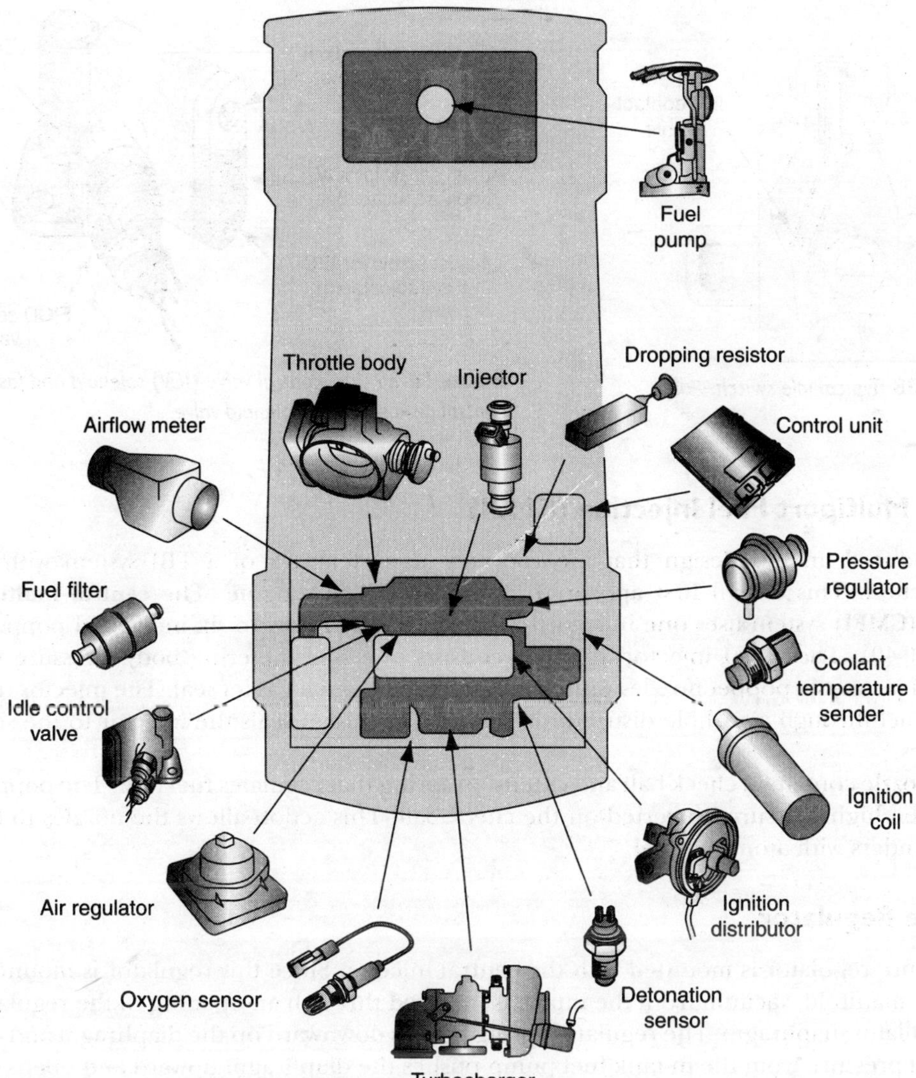

FIGURE 10-37 *Component location in the ECCS system.*

The idle control valve (ICV) solenoid and the fast idle control device (FICD) solenoid are mounted on the intake manifold. When the idle speed drops below a specific rpm, the PCM energized the ICV solenoid and additional air is bypassed through this solenoid into the intake manifold to increase the idle speed. The FICD solenoid is energized when the A/C is on and air flows past this solenoid into the intake manifold to maintain idle speed and compensate for the compressor load on the engine. The ICV and FICD assemblies contain an idle adjust screw to set the specified idle rpm (Figure 10-39).

The operation of the fuel pump relay and in-tank fuel pump is similar to other fuel pump circuits. When the ignition switch is turned on, voltage is supplied to the EFI relay winding and current flows through this winding and the PCM to ground. This action closes the EFI relay points and voltage is supplied through these points to the PCM and the crank angle sensor.

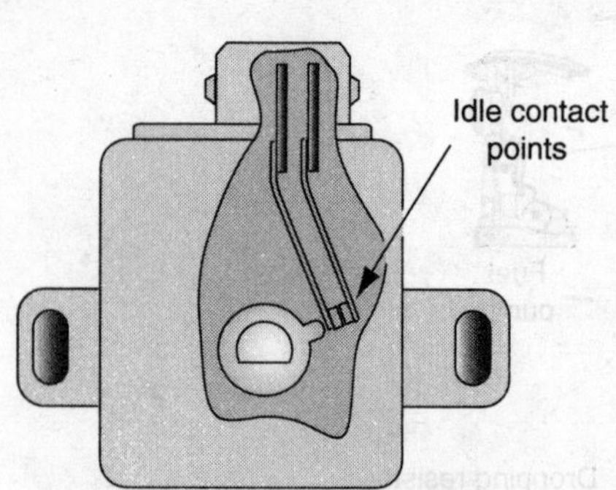

FIGURE 10-38 *Typical idle switch.*

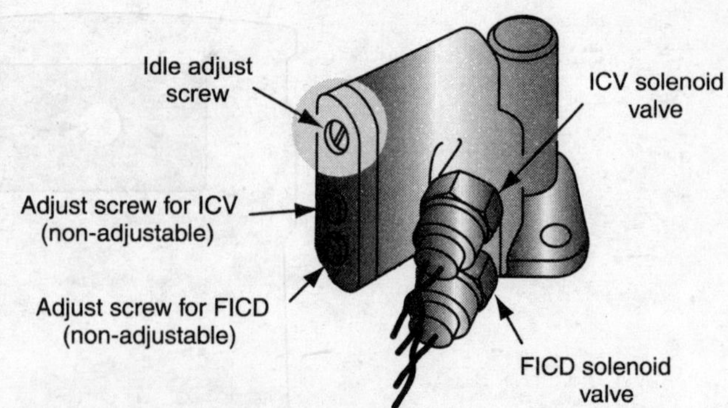

FIGURE 10-39 *Idle control valve (ICV) solenoid and fast idle control device (FICD) solenoid valve.*

Central Multiport Fuel Injection (CMFI)

GM introduced an EFI design that incorporates many features of a TBI system with those of port injection. This design first appeared on GM's 4.3L V6 engine. The **central multiport fuel injection (CMFI)** system uses one injector to control the fuel flow to six individual poppet nozzles (Figure 10-40). The CMFI injector assembly consists of a fuel metering body, pressure regulator, one fuel injector, six poppet nozzles with nylon fuel tubes, and a gasket seal. The injector distributes metered fuel through a six-hole distribution gasket. The gasket seals the injector to the six lines to the nozzles.

Each nozzle contains a check ball and extension spring that regulates fuel flow. The poppet nozzle opens when high pressure is exerted on the check ball. This action allows the nozzles to feed individual cylinders with atomized fuel.

Pressure Regulator

The pressure regulator is mounted with the central injector. Since this regulator is mounted inside the intake manifold, vacuum from the intake is supplied through an opening in the regulator cover to the regulator diaphragm. The regulator spring pushes downward on the diaphragm and closes the valve. Fuel pressure from the in-tank fuel pump pushes the diaphragm upward and opens the valve, which allows fuel to flow through this valve and the return line to the fuel tank (Figure 10-41).

The pressure regulator is designed to regulate fuel pressure at 54 to 64 psi (370 to 440 kPa), which is higher than many port fuel injection systems. Higher pressure is required in the CMFI system to prevent fuel vaporization from the extra heat encountered with the CMFI assembly, poppet nozzles, and lines mounted inside the intake manifold. The pressure regulator operates the same as the regulators explained previously in this chapter.

Injector Design and Operation

A pivoted armature is mounted under the injector winding in the central injector. The lower side of this armature acts as a valve that covers the six outlet ports to the nylon tubes and poppet nozzles. A supply of fuel at a constant pressure surrounds the injector armature while the ignition switch is on. Each time the PCM grounds the injector winding, the armature is lifted upward, which operates the injector ports. Under this condition, fuel is forced from the nylon tubes to the poppet nozzles (Figure 10-42).

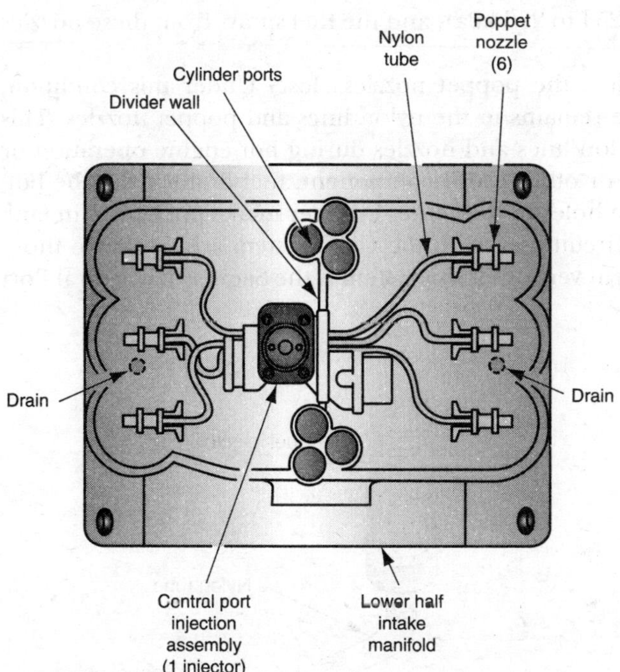

FIGURE 10-40 *Central multiport injection (CMFI) components in the lower half of the intake manifold.*

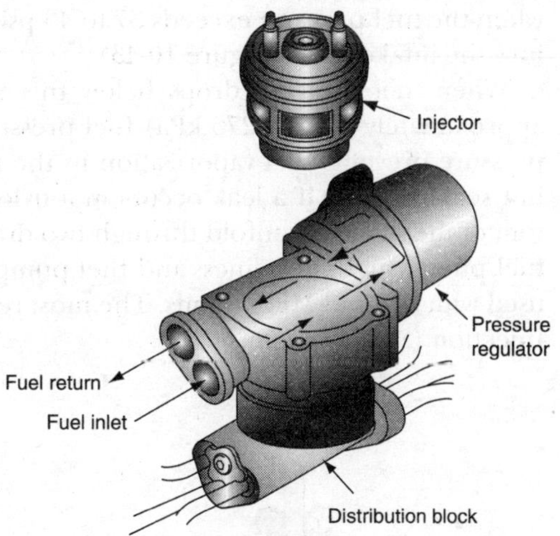

FIGURE 10-41 *Pressure regulator for a CMFI system.*

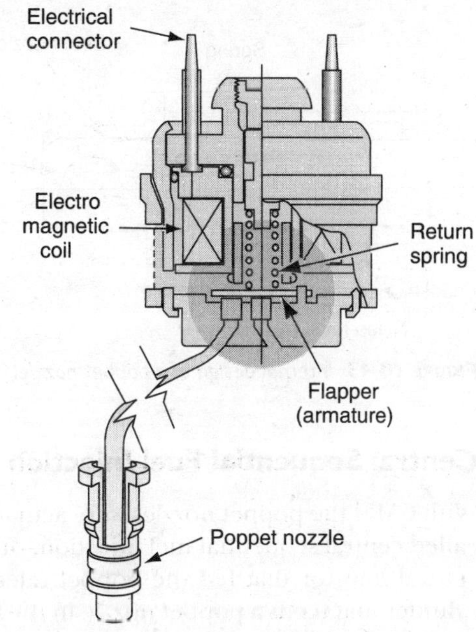

FIGURE 10-42 *CMFI system injector.*

The amount of fuel delivered by the central injector is determined by the length of time that the PCM keeps the injector winding grounded. This time is referred to as pulse width. When the PCM opens the injector ground circuit, the injector spring pushes the armature downward and closes the injector ports. The injector winding has low resistance, and the PCM operates the injector with a peak-and-hold current. When the PCM grounds the injector winding, the current flow in this circuit increases rapidly to 4 amperes. When the current flow reaches this value, a current-limiting circuit in the PCM limits the current flow to 1 ampere for the remainder of the injector pulse width. The peak-and-hold function provides faster injector armature opening and closing.

Poppet Nozzles

The **poppet nozzles** are snapped into openings in the lower half of the intake manifold, and the tip of each nozzle directs fuel into an intake port. Each port nozzle contains a valve with a check ball seat in the tip of the nozzle. A spring holds the valve and check ball seat in the closed position. When fuel pressure is applied from the central injector through the nylon lines to the poppet nozzles, this pressure forces the valve and check ball seat open against spring pressure. The poppet nozzles open when the fuel pressure exceeds 37 to 43 psi (254 to 296 kPa), and the fuel sprays from these nozzles into the intake ports (Figure 10-43).

When fuel pressure drops below this value, the poppet nozzles close. Under this condition, approximately 40 psi (276 kPa) fuel pressure remains in the nylon lines and poppet nozzles. This pressure prevents fuel vaporization in the nylon lines and nozzles during hot engine operation or hot soak periods. If a leak occurs in a nylon or other CMFI component, fuel drains from the bottom of the intake manifold through two drain holes to the center cylinder intake ports. The in-tank fuel pump, fuel filter, lines, and fuel pump circuit used with the CMFI system are similar to those used with SFI and MFI systems. The most recent version of this system is the Sequential Central Port Injection (SCPI) system.

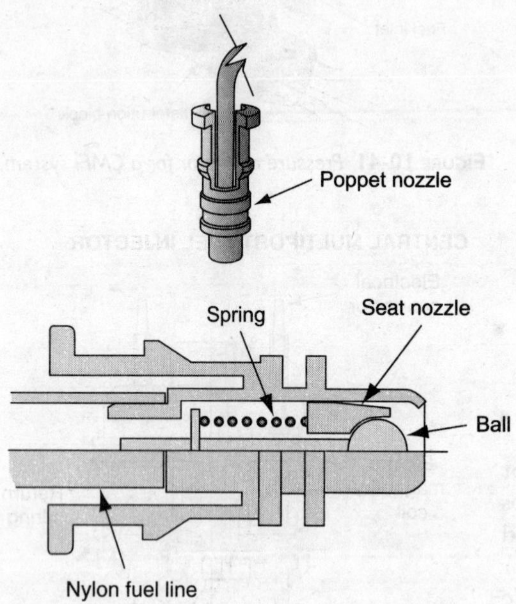

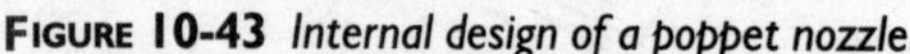

FIGURE 10-43 *Internal design of a poppet nozzle.*

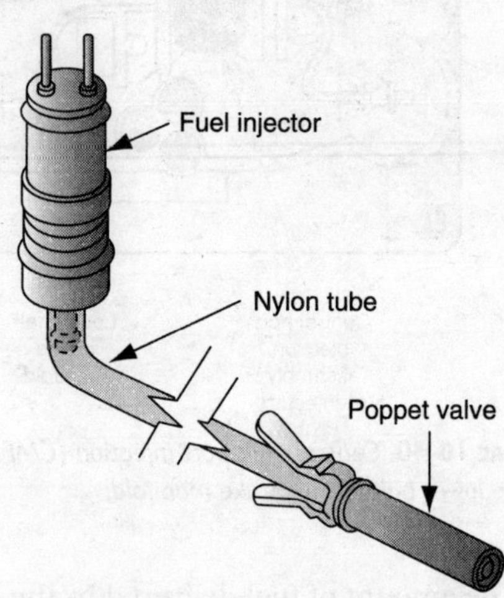

FIGURE 10-44 *A CSFI injector with poppet nozzle.*

Central Sequential Fuel Injection

With CMFI the poppet nozzles were actuated from a central injector (Figure 10-44). A similar design, called central sequential fuel injection, or CSFI, was implemented on trucks beginning in 1996. The central injector that fed the poppet injectors has been replaced by an electrical injector for each cylinder that feeds a poppet nozzle in the fuel meter assembly. The fuel meter assembly also includes the fuel pressure regulator (Figure 10-45). The electrical injector is fired from the fuel meter assembly which then forces the poppet nozzle check ball off its seat, spraying fuel into the cylinder. The separate electrical injectors allow the injection to be sequential instead of multiport. Figure 10-46 shows the CSFI assembly located inside the lower intake manifold.

Intake Manifold Tuning Valve

The two-piece aluminum intake manifold has an integral throttle body. An **intake manifold tuning valve (IMTV)** assembly is mounted in the top of the intake manifold. The IMTV assembly contains an electric solenoid that operates a rectangular-shaped valve inside the manifold. Two zip tubes

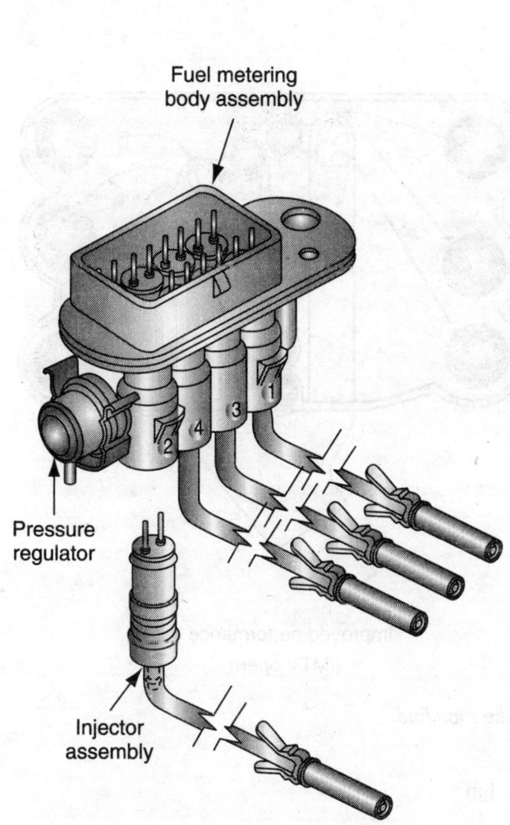

FIGURE 10-45 *Central sequential fuel injection.*

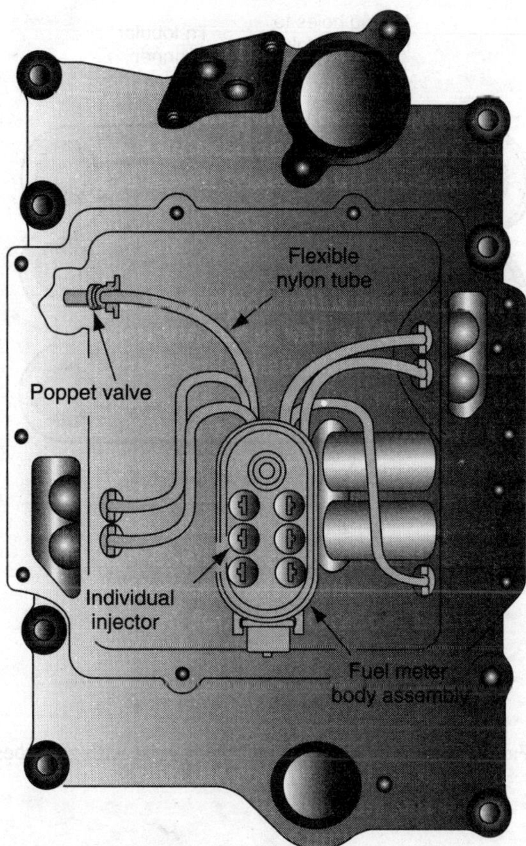

FIGURE 10-46 *A CFSI fuel meter and poppet nozzles from the lower half of the intake manifold.*

are connected from the throttle body to dual plenums in the upper half of the intake manifold (Figure 10-47). Each plenum feeds three tuned intake runners.

The IMTV rectangular valve is mounted in an opening between the two halves of the upper intake manifold. While the engine is operating at lower rpm, the IMTV remains closed, and airflow in the two halves of the upper intake is separated.

When the engine rpm reaches 3,025 to 4,650 and the throttle opening exceeds 36 percent, the PCM energizes the IMTV solenoid. This action opens the rectangular valve and the two halves of the intake are now joined through this valve opening. Airflow in the intake increases to improve horsepower and torque.

One end of the IMTV relay winding is connected to the ignition switch and the other end to the PCM. When the engine operating conditions require IMTV operation, the PCM grounds the IMTV relay winding. This action closes the relay points. Current flows through the IMTV relay points to the IMTV solenoid winding in the intake manifold to open the rectangular valve (Figure 10-48).

Gasoline Direct Fuel Injection

With the development of fuel injection systems, technological advancements continue to evolve. The most recent fuel delivery system to be released is the gasoline direct injection (GDI) system. The typical port fuel injection system delivers a fuel spray before the intake valve. Similar to the die-

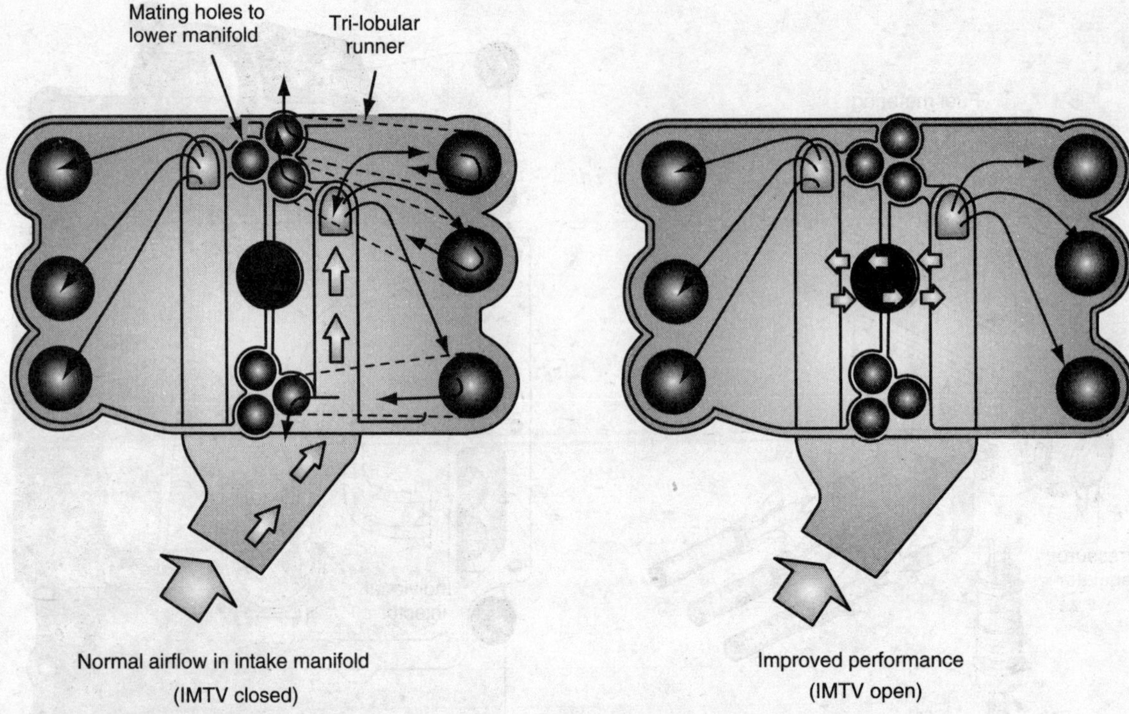

FIGURE 10-47 *Intake manifold tuning valve with zip tubes in the intake manifold.*

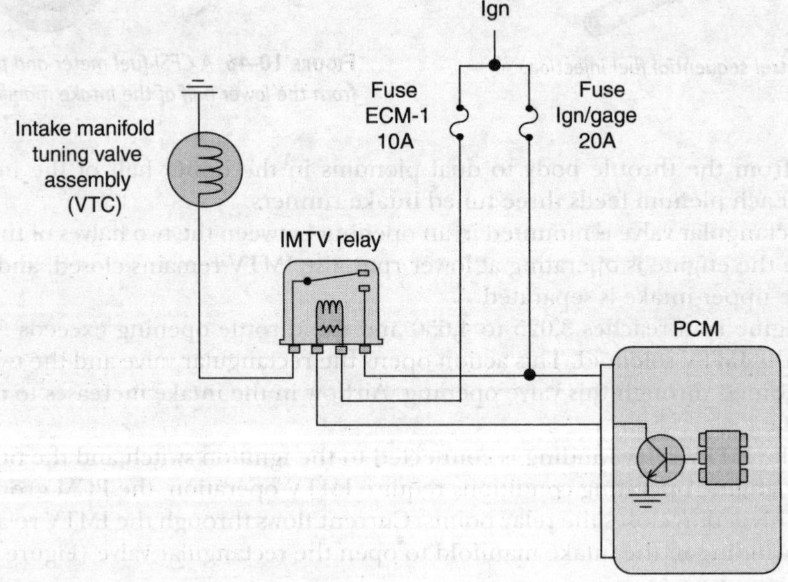

FIGURE 10-48 *IMTV relay and solenoid wiring diagram.*

sel injection system, the GDI system delivers the fuel charge directly into the combustion chamber (Figure 10-49). The fuel pressure is much higher than the typical fuel injections systems and can reach 1,700 psi. Under this amount of pressure, the fuel is vaporized as it is injected into the cylin-

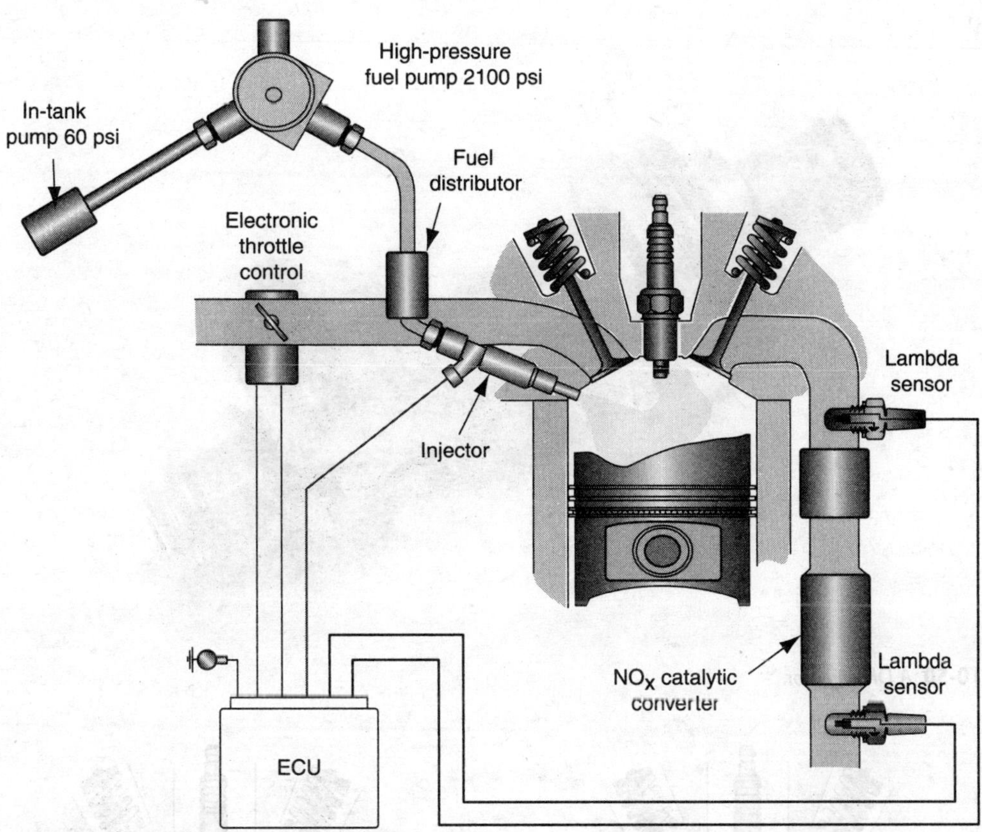

FIGURE 10-49 *A GDI system diagram.*

der. With GDI, mixtures can be substantially leaner (up to 35:1). This can improve fuel economy by as much as 30 percent and helps to virtually eliminate fuel deposit or carbon buildup that can occur on the intake side of the intake valve. The introduction of the GDI systems will likely phase out traditional port fuel systems and become commonplace as system application expands to more engine systems.

The DFI engine uses a special piston design, high-pressure swirl injectors, 12:1 compression, and intake manifold design to help burn a leaner fuel mixture than possible with conventional fuel injection. Since the injection of fuel is not dependent on the opening of the intake valve, the fuel can be injected during the compression stroke or the intake stroke depending on the mode of operation. Since the intake carries only air, the intake can be designed for optimal performance. The fuel pump on the DFI engine is increased by an engine-driven pump producing fuel pressures of around 1,500 psi. See Figure (11-50).

DFI Modes

The DFI has two different modes of operation called stratified and homogeneous (Figure 10-51). During cruising, the DFI engine is operating in the stratified or direct injection lean mode and fuel is injected late in the combustion cycle. Piston design and injector spray pattern produce this stratified air-fuel charge in the cylinder and make the fuel burn at a very lean 35:1 compared to 14.7:1 in a conventional engine. DFI is capable of saving 35 to 40 percent of the fuel consumed by a conventional gasoline engine at idle and cruising.

FIGURE 10-50 *A DFI injector.*

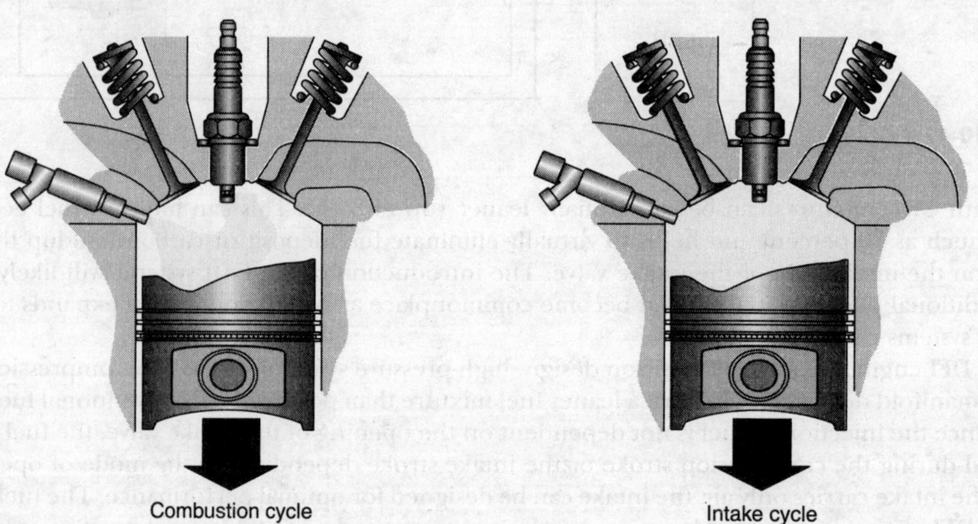

FIGURE 10-51 *Two modes of DFI injection. Note piston design.*

During acceleration, high speed, or heavy load, the fuel spray occurs in the intake stroke, like that of a conventional fuel injected engine. This mode is called homogeneous, and since the fuel in this mode is injected during the intake stroke, it is much like regular port fuel injection.

The fuel injector is also able to be pulsed twice; once during a stratified charge mode and also during the homogenous mode as required for a smooth transition.

Emissions

One early concern with DFI was NO_x emissions developed under high compression and high temperatures produced by the lean burning fuel. The development of a new high-flow EGR system along with the development of a new lean NO_x catalyst seems to have solved this problem.

IDLE SPEED CONTROL SYSTEMS

Idle speed control is a function of the PCM. Based on operating conditions and inputs from various sensors, the PCM regulates the idle speed to control emissions.

Idle Air Control Bypass Air (IAC BPA) Motors

Most multiport fuel injection (MFI) and sequential fuel injection (SFI) systems have an idle air control bypass (IAC BPA) motor in the throttle body to control idle speed. This type of IAC BPA motor is also used on some TBI assemblies. In any of these systems, the IAC BPA motor is threaded or bolted into the throttle body assembly (Figures 10-52 and 10-53).

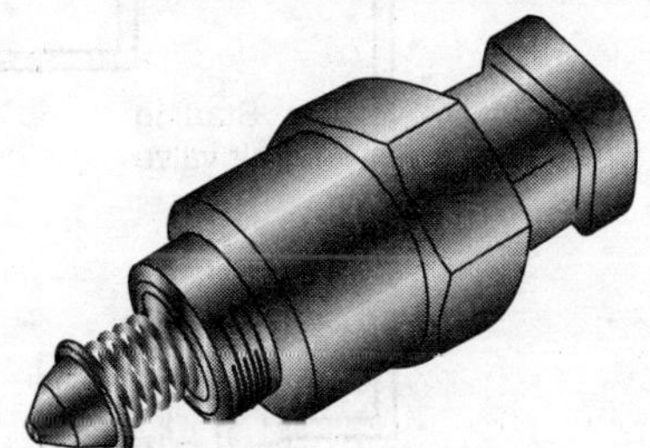

Figure 10-52 *IAC BPA motor that threads into the TBI assembly.*

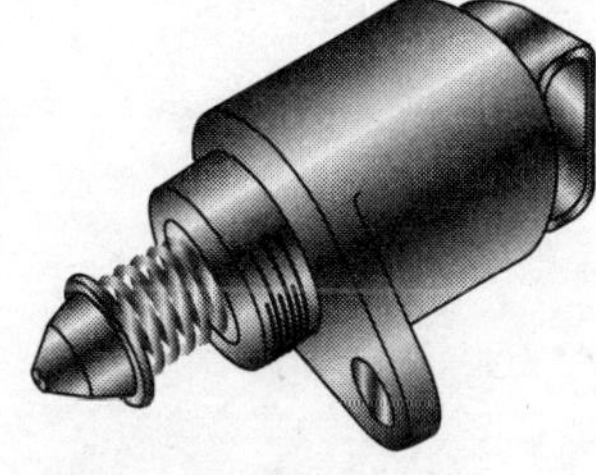

Figure 10-53 *IAC BPA motor that bolts onto the TBI assembly.*

The IAC BPA motor contains a reversible DC motor that is operated by the PCM. A tapered valve is located on the end of the IAC motor stem with air passages above and below the throttle connected to this tapered valve.

The position of this valve controls idle speed by regulating the amount of air bypassing the throttle. If the motor opens the tapered valve and allows more air to bypass the throttle, engine speed is increased. Decreasing the amount of air bypassing the throttle reduces idle speed. Four wires from the motor are connected to the PCM. On many systems, the PCM operates the motor to move the plunger and tapered valve inward and outward in steps or counts.

IAC BPA Valves

Some MFI or SFI systems have a flap-type IAC BPA valve that regulates the amount of air bypassing the throttle to control idle speed. The PCM opens and closes this valve to regulate the airflow past the throttle. Three wires are connected from the valve to the PCM.

Other MFI and SFI systems have an IAC BPA valve used with a starting air valve and a fast idle thermo switch (Figure 10-54). Two wires are connected from the IAC BPA valve winding to the PCM (Figure 10-55). When the PCM energizes the valves winding, the valve shaft is moved by the coil magnetism. This action opens the valve airflow from the air cleaner through the valve into the intake manifold. If the PCM de-energizes the valve's winding, the shaft spring pushes the valve closed (Figure 10-56). The PCM pulses the valve open and closed to regulate airflow past the valve intake manifold and control idle speed.

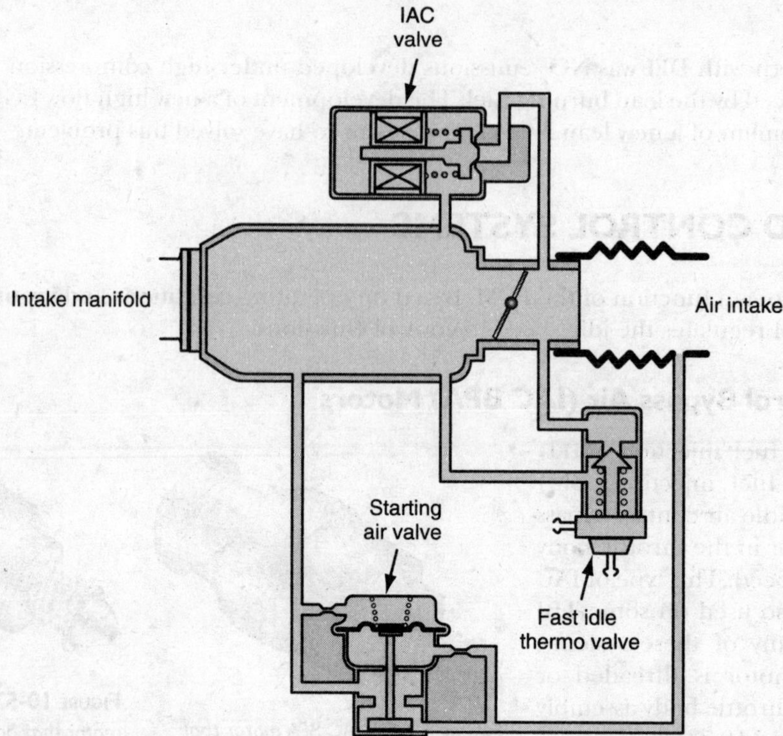

FIGURE 10-54 *IAC BPA valve used with a starting air valve and fast idle thermo valve.*

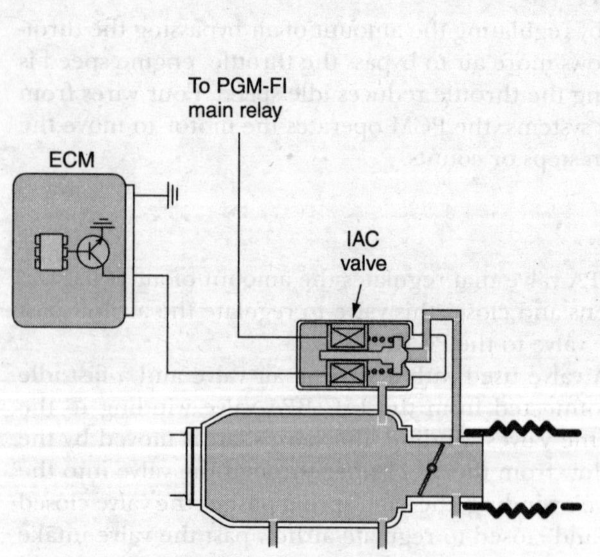

FIGURE 10-55 *IAC BPA valve wiring schematic.*

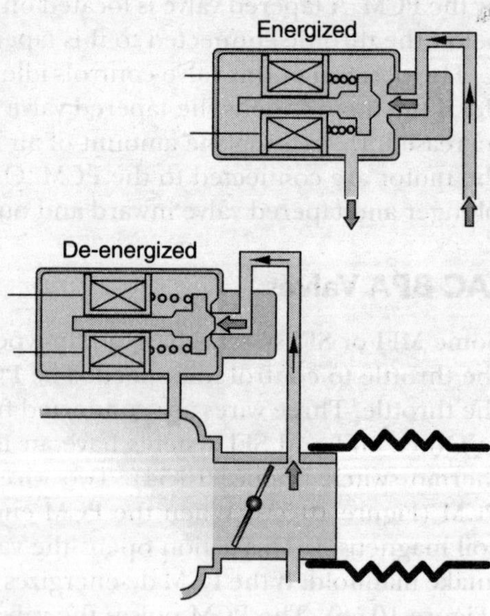

FIGURE 10-56 *Internal design of an IAC BPA valve.*

Fast Idle Thermo Valve

The fast idle thermo valve is positioned under the throttle body (Figure 10-57). A thermowax element is located in the bottom of this valve. When the engine is cold, the thermowax contracts, moving the valve plunger to open the air bypass valve (Figure 10-58). This valve opening allows air to flow past the valve into the intake manifold, which increases engine speed. As the engine warms up, the thermowax expands and gradually closes the valve, which slowly reduces engine speed. When the engine reaches normal operating temperature, the thermowax expands enough to close the valve and stop the airflow past the valve. The PCM is programmed to operate the IAC BPA valve with the fast idle thermo valve to provide the proper engine idle speed at all engine temperatures.

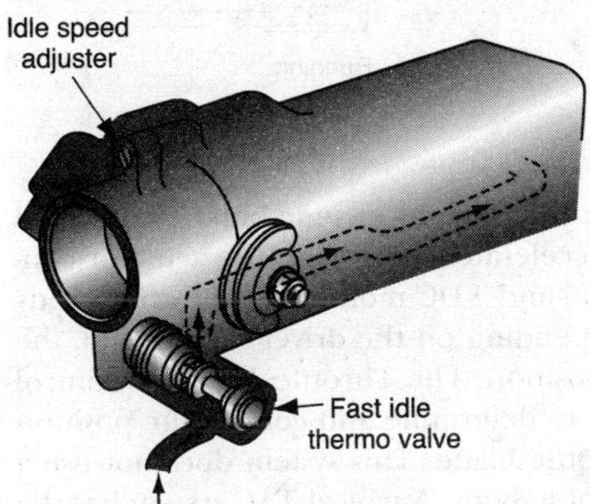

FIGURE 10-57 *Fast idle thermo valve location.*

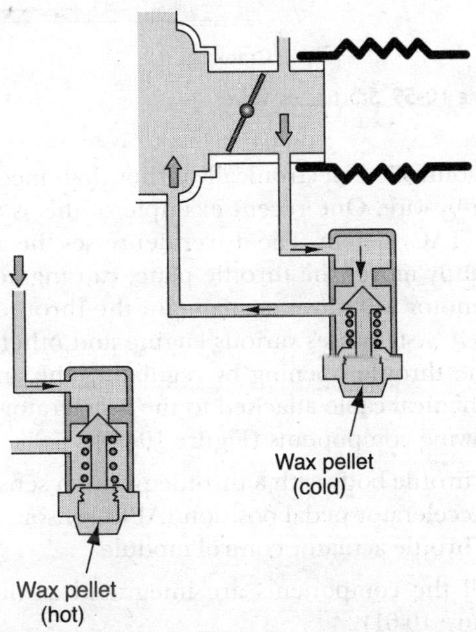

FIGURE 10-58 *Internal design of a fast idle thermo valve.*

Starting Air Valve

The starting air valve contains a diaphragm in the upper part of the valve. A stem is connected from this diaphragm to a valve in the lower part of the valve (Figure 10-59). A spring above the diaphragm forces the diaphragm downward and opens the valve. Intake manifold vacuum is supplied to the area above the diaphragm.

When the engine is cranking, the intake manifold vacuum will not move the diaphragm in the starting air valve. Under this condition, air flows past the valve into the intake manifold to provide the proper air-fuel ratio for starting. Once the engine starts, the manifold vacuum moves the diaphragm upward and closes the valve, which stops the airflow past the valve. This valve remains closed under all engine operating conditions. The PCM is programmed to operate the injectors and supply the proper air-fuel ratio while starting with air flowing through the starting air valve.

Throttle Actuator Control (TAC) System

As technology advances, vehicle systems will begin to use electronics rather than mechanical devices to control outputs. This is commonly referred to as drive by wire. In other words, various systems

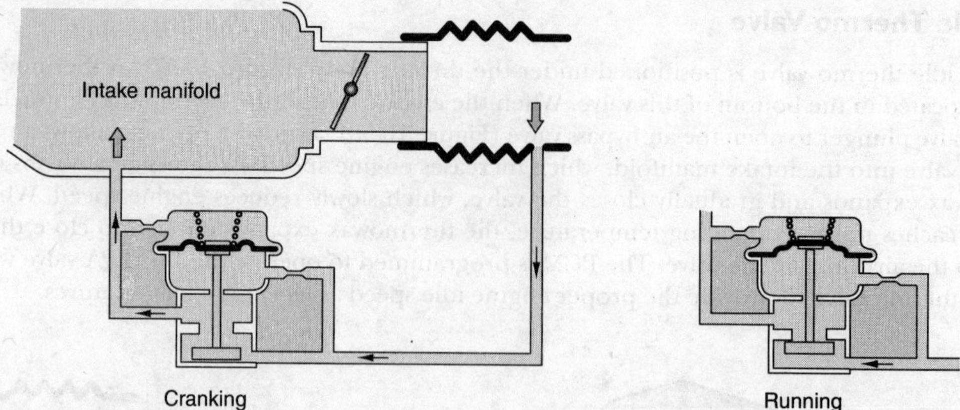

FIGURE 10-59 *Starting air valve.*

are controlled electronically rather than mechanically. Emerging systems include brake-by-wire and steer-by-wire. One recent example of this is the cable-less accelerator or the throttle actuator control (TAC) system. The driver depresses the accelerator pedal and a DC motor on the throttle body instantly moves the throttle plate, causing acceleration. Depending on the driver's command, the DC motor will move or maintain the throttle plate in any position. The Throttle Actuator Control (TAC) System uses various engine and other vehicle inputs to determine and control the position of the throttle opening by regulating the angle of the throttle blade. This system does not use a mechanical cable attached to the accelerator pedal and throttle body. A typical TAC system has the following components (Figure 10-60):

- Throttle body with a throttle position sensor and DC motor unit
- Accelerator pedal position (APP) sensor
- Throttle actuator control module

All the components are integrated as one system to accurately control the throttle position (Figure 10-61).

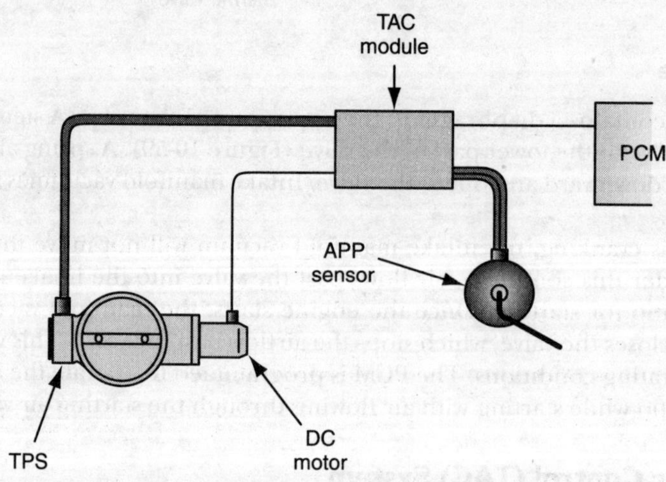

FIGURE 10-60 *Typical Throttle Actuator Control (TAC) system arrangement.*

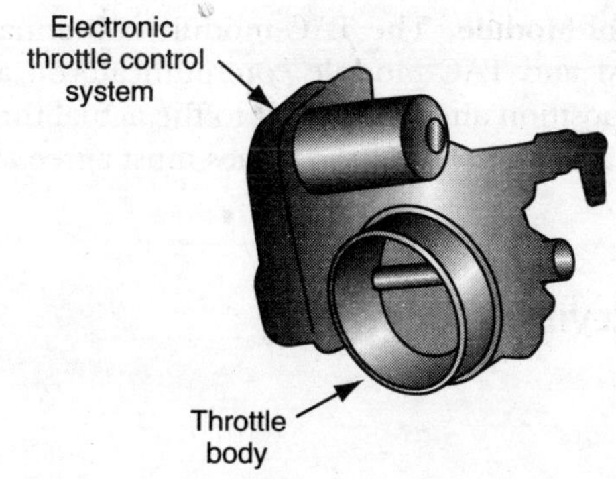

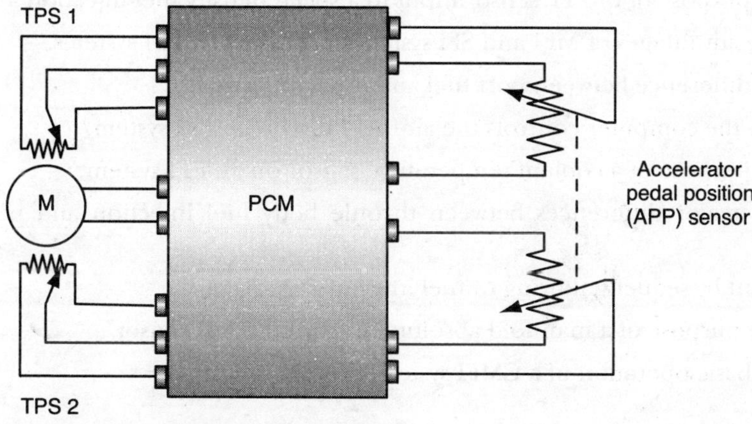

FIGURE 10-61 *The PCM monitors several signals simultaneously.*

Accelerator Pedal Position (APP) Sensor. The APP is mounted on the accelerator pedal assembly. Multiple signals generated from the single sensor must coordinate to determine exact pedal movement. Three signals are produced from a single sensor. The APP sensor number one voltage signal should increase at the same time the accelerator is depressed from under 1 volt at closed throttle (0 percent pedal travel) to over 2 volts at wide-open throttle (100 percent pedal travel). The APP sensor number two signal voltage should decrease from over 4 volts at 0 percent pedal travel to under 2.9 volts at 100 percent pedal travel. APP sensor number three signal should decrease from over 3.8 volts at 0 percent pedal travel to under 3.1 volts at 100 percent pedal travel.

Throttle Body Assembly. The throttle body unit used in the TAC system is similar to other types of throttle bodies. However, a DC motor is mounted on the throttle body because there is no mechanical throttle cable to the accelerator pedal to move the throttle plate. Another difference is the throttle position sensor. Instead of a traditional TPS, the TAC system uses a unique dual signal sensor. The TPS actually consists of two sensors in one housing. Separate 5-volt and low-reference circuits are used and are connected to the TAC control module. Like the APP sensor multiple signals, they must agree. The TPS number one signal voltage increases at the same time the throttle opens. The voltage increases from about 1 volt at 0 percent throttle to over 3.5 volts at 100 percent throttle. TPS number two signal voltage decreases from about 3.8 volts at 0 percent to under 1 volt at 100 percent throttle at the same time the throttle opens.

Throttle Actuator Control (TAC) Control Module. The TAC module is the main control unit for the electronic throttle system. The PCM and TAC module communicate on a dedicated circuit. They monitor the commanded throttle position and compare it to the actual throttle position. This is accomplished by monitoring the APP and TPS. These two values must agree and be within a calibrated value of each other.

REVIEW QUESTIONS

Short Answer Essays

1. Describe how an IAC BPA motor controls idle speed.
2. Explain the purpose of the TP sensor input in a speed density fuel injection system.
3. Describe the advantages of MFI and SFI systems compared to TBI systems.
4. Explain the difference between port fuel and direct injection.
5. Explain how the computer controls the air-fuel ratio on an EFI system.
6. Explain the purpose of a coolant temperature sensor on an EFI system.
7. Explain the major differences between throttle body fuel injection and port fuel injection systems.
8. What is meant by sequential firing of fuel injectors?
9. Describe the purpose of a manifold absolute pressure (MAP) sensor.
10. Explain the basic operation of a CMFI system.

Fill-in-the-Blanks

1. The length of time that an injector is energized is called ______________ ______________.
2. When the IAC BPA motor increases the amount of air bypassing the throttle, engine rpm is ______________.
3. The computer determines the air entering the engine from the ______________ and ______________ input signals in a speed density EFI system.
4. Port fuel injection systems use one injector for each ______________.
5. In EFI systems, the fuel pressure must be high enough to prevent ______________.
6. The ______________ ______________ can measure the intake air speed, volume weight, and temperature.
7. On an SFI system, each injector has an individual ______________ ______________ connected to the computer.
8. If the injector pulse width is increased on EFI systems, the air-fuel ratio becomes ______________.
9. When an engine is idling, the pressure regulator provides ______________ fuel pressure compared to the fuel pressure at wide-open throttle.
10. On a Gasoline Direct Injection vehicle, fuel is injected into the ______________ ______________.

Multiple Choice

1. *Technician A* says that the intake manifold of TBI style fuel injection must use a heated intake manifold.

   Technician B says that TBI systems have been gradually replaced by port fuel systems.

   Who is correct?

   A. Technician A C. Both technicians
   B. Technician B D. Neither technician

2. *Technician A* says that idle speed is a computer output.

   Technician B says proper idle speed is seldom the fault of faulty input signals.

   Who is correct?

   A. Technician A C. Both technicians
   B. Technician B D. Neither technician

3. *Technician A* says that the volume air flow sensor uses a flap to determine the amount of air flow into the engine.

   Technician B says that air flow sensors that only measure volume do not need an air temperature sensor to account for differences in air temperature.

   Who is correct?

   A. Technician A C. Both technicians
   B. Technician B D. Neither technician

4. *Technician A* says a MAF sensor calculates the mass of air flow into the engine by multiplying its mass times the temperature.

   Technician B says the accuracy of air-fuel ratios is greatly enhanced by matching fuel to air volume.

   Who is correct?

   A. Technician A C. Both technicians
   B. Technician B D. Neither technician

5. All of the following are true of MAP sensors ***except***:

   A. Measures changes in manifold pressure that result from changes in engine speed
   B. At closed throttle, the MAP value is low
   C. The MAP value is opposite of a vacuum gauge reading.
   D. The MAP sensor is used to adjust for different altitudes

6. *Technician A* says the injection module is the heart of the fuel injection system.

   Technician B says when the PCM is using feedback from the oxygen sensor to control fuel injection, it is in closed loop.

   Who is correct?

   A. Technician A C. Both technicians
   B. Technician B D. Neither technician

7. *Technician A* says most fuel injection systems supply the injectors a full 12 volts.

   Technician B says the injector ground wire is routed to the PCM.

Who is correct?

A. Technician A C. Both technicians

B. Technician B D. Neither technician

8. While discussing TBI,

Technician A says four cylinder TBI units usually have a single injector.

Technician B says V6 and V8 systems generally have two injectors and two throttle bores mounted on a common shaft.

Who is correct?

A. Technician A C. Both technicians

B. Technician B D. Neither technician

9. *Technician A* says on SFI systems, each injector is connected individually into the computer, and the computer completes the ground for each injector one at a time.

Technician B says MFI systems injectors are grouped, and all the injectors in the group share the same common ground wire.

Who is correct?

A. Technician A C. Both technicians

B. Technician B D. Neither technician

10. *Technician A* says that central sequential fuel injection (CSFI) was introduced in 1993.

Technician B says this design uses separate electrical fuel injectors.

Who is correct?

A. Technician A C. Both technicians

B. Technician B D. Neither technician

11

Distributor Ignition

Upon completion and review of this chapter, you should be able to:

- Describe the three major functions of the ignition system.
- Name the operating conditions that affect ignition timing.
- Describe the basic operation of distributor-based ignition systems.
- Describe the operation of distributorless ignition systems.
- Explain the operation of the ignition primary circuit.
- Explain the operation of the ignition secondary circuit.
- Define ignition dwell and explain its importance to ignition system operation.
- Explain how high voltage is induced in the secondary coil windings.
- Explain the operation of the magnetic pickup coil.
- Explain the operation of the Hall effect switch.
- Describe the various types of spark timing systems.
- Describe the difference between base and computerized timing.
- Explain the operation of engine position sensors.
- Describe spark plug internal design.
- Explain the difference between a hot and cold range spark plug.

INTRODUCTION

One of the requirements for an efficient running engine is the correct amount of heat delivered into the cylinders at the right time. This requirement is the responsibility of the ignition system. The ignition system supplies properly timed, high-voltage surges to the spark plugs. These voltage surges cause combustion inside the cylinder.

The ignition system must create a spark or current flow across each pair of spark plug electrodes at the proper instant under all engine operating conditions. This may sound relatively simple, but when one considers the number of spark plug firings required and the extreme variation in engine operating conditions, it is easy to understand why ignition systems are so complex.

If a six-cylinder engine is running at 4,000 revolutions per minute (rpm), the ignition system must supply 12,000 sparks per minute. Since the ignition system must fire three spark plugs per revolution, these plug firings must also occur at the correct time and generate the correct amount of heat. If the ignition system fails to accomplish this, fuel economy, engine performance, and emission levels will be adversely affected.

Most distributor ignition (DI) systems function the same. They will all use components of a similar type, but specific to the manufacturer or application. The term *distributor* defines itself. It distributes spark produced by the ignition system to the appropriate cylinder at the precise time. There are two electrical sides to the ignition system that are referred to as the primary and the secondary. High voltage spark production begins as a function of the primary or low side of the ignition circuit and spark distribution as a function of the secondary or high voltage side of the ignition. Although it begins with 12 volts, the primary voltage in the ignition coil can surge as high as 400 volts when the secondary ignition fires. This is sometimes referred to as flyback or feedback voltage. The ignition coil is part of both the primary and secondary ignition systems. Most coil secondaries have a voltage potential ranging from 25,000 to 50,000 volts. The typical system operating voltage required to fire the sparkplugs at idle will usually range from 8,000 to 12,000 volts. The remaining coil capacity is used as a reserve for when certain operating conditions occur, such as climbing a hill, pulling a trailer, passing another vehicle and cold engine starts. Some of these conditions may demand the coil's entire potential.

PURPOSE OF THE IGNITION SYSTEM

Although today's ignition systems look different compared to the breaker point-controlled systems used for over sixty years, their purpose is the same. The ignition system has three main jobs:

1. Spark production—The ignition system must be able to quickly build enough high voltage sufficient to satisfy the requirements to ignite the air-fuel mixture and maintain adequate burn time for complete combustion.
2. Spark timing control—The ignition system must be able to alter the delivery time of the spark to account for rpm, varying load, and demand conditions.
3. Spark distribution—The ignition system must be able to deliver a spark to the correct cylinder at the right time during the compression stroke in order to begin the combustion process.

When the combustion process is completed, a very high pressure is exerted against the top of the piston. This pressure pushes the piston down on its power stroke. This pressure is the force that gives the engine power. In order for an engine to produce the maximum amount of power that it can, the maximum pressure from combustion should be present when the piston is at 10 degrees to 20 degrees **after top dead center (ATDC)**. Because combustion of the air-fuel mixture within a cylinder takes a short period of time, usually measured in thousandths of a second (milliseconds), the combustion process must begin before the piston is on its power stroke. Therefore, the delivery of the spark must be timed to arrive at some point before the piston reaches top dead center.

Determining how much before **top dead center (TDC)** the spark should begin is complicated by the fact that the speed of the piston, as it moves from its compression stroke to its power stroke, increases, and the time needed for combustion stays about the same. This means that the spark should be delivered earlier as the engine's speed increases (Figure 11-1). However, as the engine has to provide more power to do more work, the load on the crankshaft tends to slow down the acceleration of the piston and the spark needs to be somewhat delayed.

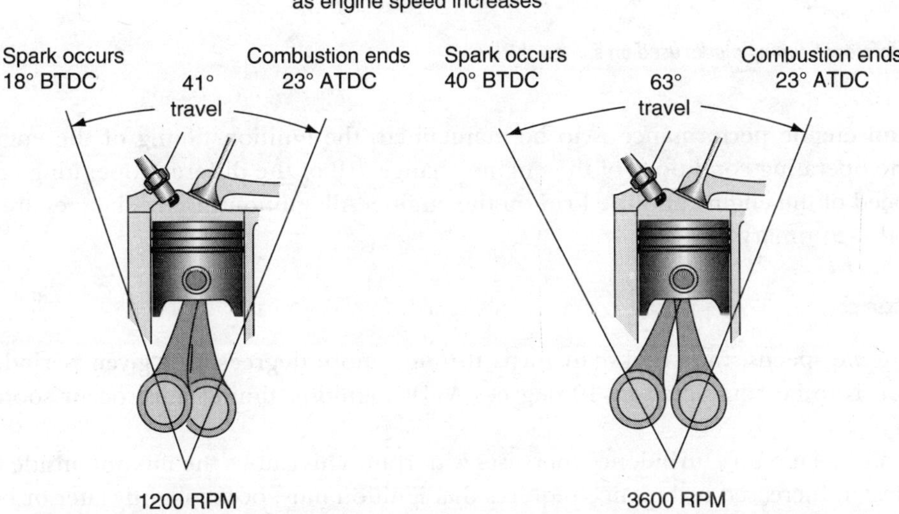

FIGURE 11-1 *With an increase in speed, ignition must begin earlier to end by 23 degrees ATDC.*

Figuring out when the spark should begin becomes more complicated with the fact that the rate of combustion varies according to certain factors. Higher compression pressures tend to speed up combustion. Higher octane gasolines ignite less easily and require more burning time. Increased vaporization and turbulence tend to decrease combustion times. Other factors, including intake air temperature, humidity, and barometric pressure, also affect combustion. Because of all of these complications, delivering the spark at the right time is a difficult task.

IGNITION TIMING

Ignition timing refers to the precise time that spark occurs. Ignition timing is specified by referring to the position of the number one piston in relationship to crankshaft position in degrees relative to top dead center. Ignition timing reference timing marks can be located on engine parts and on a pulley or flywheel to indicate the position of the first piston (Figure 11-2). Vehicle manufacturers specify initial or **basic** ignition **timing**.

When the marks are aligned at TDC, or 0, the piston in cylinder one is at TDC of its compression stroke. Additional numbers on a scale indicate the number of degrees of crankshaft rotation **before top dead center (BTDC)** or after top dead center (ATDC). In a majority of engines, the initial timing is specified at a point between TDC and 20 degrees BTDC.

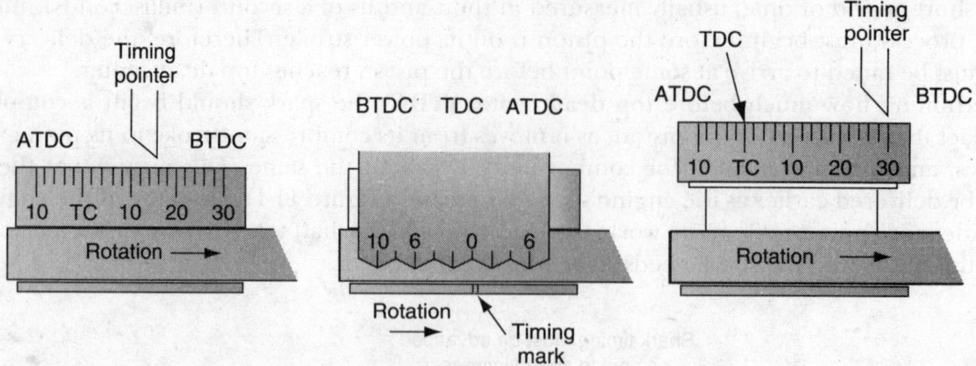

FIGURE 11-2 *Reference timing marks used on some vehicles.*

If optimum engine performance is to be maintained, the ignition timing of the engine must change as the operating conditions of the engine change. All of the different operating conditions affect the speed of the engine and the load on the engine. All ignition timing changes are made in response to these primary factors.

Engine Speed

At higher engine speeds, the crankshaft turns through more degrees in a given period of time. If combustion is to be completed by 10 degrees ATDC, ignition timing must occur sooner or be advanced.

However, air-fuel mixture turbulence increases with rpm. This causes the mixture inside the cylinder to turn faster. Increased turbulence requires that ignition must occur slightly later or be slightly retarded.

These two factors must be balanced for best engine performance. Therefore, while the ignition timing must be advanced as engine speed increases, the amount of advance must be decreased some to compensate for the increased turbulence.

Engine Load

The load on an engine is related to the work it must do. Driving up hills or pulling extra weight increases engine load. Under load, the pistons accelerate slower and the engine runs less efficiently. A good indication of engine load is the amount of vacuum formed during the intake stroke.

Under light loads and with the throttle plate(s) partially opened, such as during steady driving, a high vacuum exists in the intake manifold. The amount of air-fuel mixture drawn into the manifold and cylinders is small. On compression, this thin mixture produces less combustion pressure and combustion time is slow. To complete combustion by 10 degrees ATDC, ignition timing must be advanced. This advance also improves fuel economy.

Under heavy loads, when the throttle is opened fully, a larger mass of air-fuel mixture can be drawn in and the vacuum in the manifold is low. High combustion pressure and rapid burning results. In such a case, the ignition timing must be retarded to prevent complete burning from occurring before 10 degrees ATDC.

Firing Order

Up to this point, the primary focus of discussion has been ignition timing as it relates to any one cylinder. However, the function of the ignition system extends beyond timing the arrival of a spark to a single cylinder. It must perform this task for each cylinder of the engine in a specific sequence.

Each cylinder of an engine produces power once every 720 degrees of crankshaft rotation. Each cylinder must have a power stroke at its own appropriate time during the rotation. To make this possible, the pistons and rods are arranged in a precise fashion. The firing order is arranged to reduce rocking and imbalance problems. Because the potential for this rocking is determined by the design and construction of the engine, the firing order varies from engine to engine. Vehicle manufacturers simplify identifying each cylinder identification by numbering them (Figure 11-3). Regardless of the particular firing order used, the number one cylinder always starts the firing order with the rest of the cylinders following in a fixed sequence.

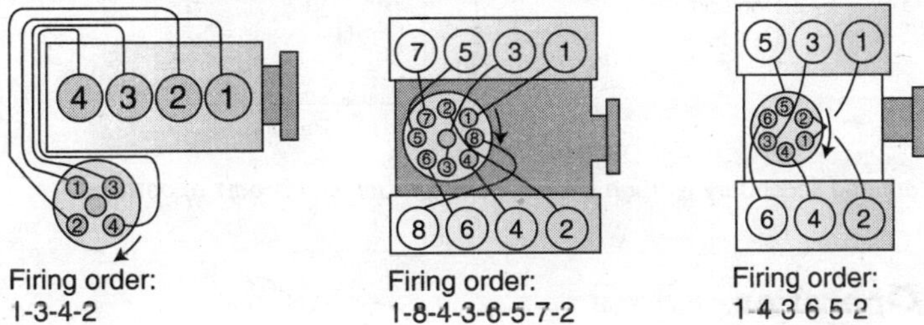

FIGURE 11-3 *Cylinder numbering and firing orders.*

The ignition system must be able to monitor the rotation of the crankshaft and the relative position of each piston in order to determine which piston is on its compression stroke. It must also be able to deliver a high-voltage surge to each cylinder at the proper time during its compression stroke. How the ignition system accomplishes this depends on the design of the system.

BASIC IGNITION SYSTEM

Manufacturers use the electrical principles of induction to accomplish spark production. An inductive ignition system requires two main electrical circuits: a primary and a secondary circuit. All ignition systems consist of two interconnected electrical circuits: a **primary** (low voltage) **circuit** and a **secondary** (high voltage) **circuit** (Figure 11-4).

Depending on the exact type of ignition system, components in the primary circuit include the following:

- battery
- ignition switch
- ignition coil primary winding
- triggering device
- control module

The secondary circuit includes these components:

- ignition coil secondary winding
- distributor cap and rotor (some systems)
- ignition (spark plug) cables (some systems)
- spark plugs

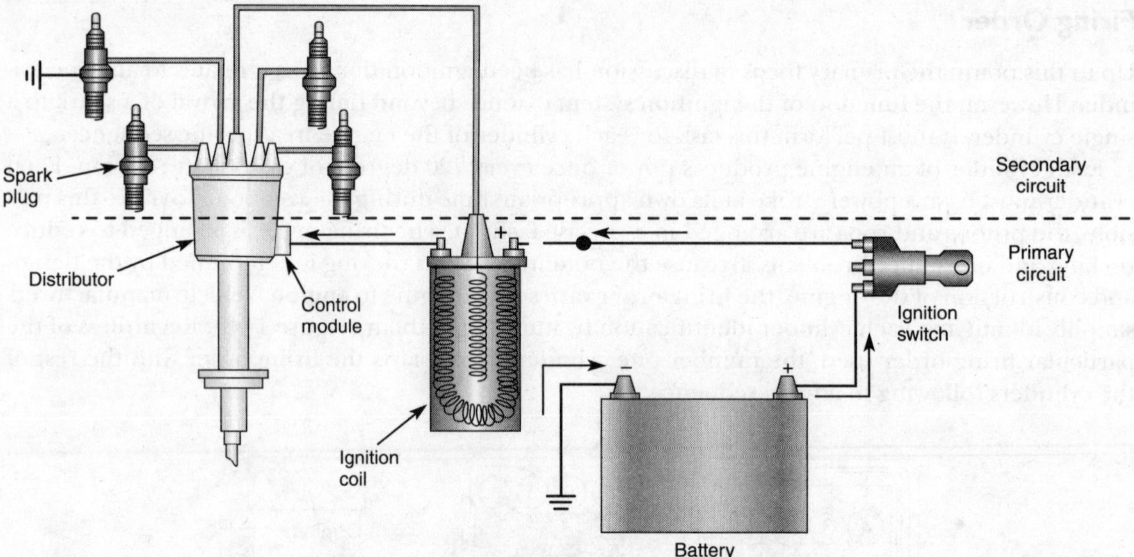

FIGURE 11-4 *Basic primary and secondary ignition circuits. The ignition coil is part of both.*

Primary Circuit Operation

The ignition coil works on the principle of magnetic induction to change 12 volts in the primary to 40,000 volts or more in the secondary. The primary windings in the coil are relatively large and few in number compared to the secondary windings. The secondary windings are smaller and there are many more of them. When the primary circuit is switched on, the primary windings build a magnetic field. When the primary circuit is opened, the magnetic field that has been surrounding both sets of windings collapses. This collapse of the magnetic field creates a high voltage surge in the secondary which provides the spark. Controlling the precise time the coil switches on or off is the function of the ignition module, because it electronically controls the coil ground connection. The positive lead is connected from the ignition switch. The module is informed when to switch by a triggering device signal or the PCM depending on operating conditions. The amount of time the coil is turned on is called **dwell time**, and the time that the coil is switched off is determined by the ignition timing.

When the ignition switch is in the on position, current from the battery flows through the ignition switch and primary circuit resistor to the primary winding of the ignition coil. From here it passes through some type of switching device and back to ground.

Secondary Circuit Operation

The secondary circuit carries high voltage to the spark plugs. The exact manner in which the secondary circuit delivers these high-voltage surges depends on the system design.

In a **distributor ignition (DI)** system, high voltage from the secondary winding passes through an ignition cable running from the coil to the distributor. The distributor then distributes the high voltage to the individual spark plugs through a set of ignition cables. The cables are arranged in the distributor cap according to the firing order of the engine. A rotor driven by the distributor shaft rotates and completes the electrical path from the secondary winding of the coil to the individual spark plugs. The distributor delivers the spark to match the compression stroke of the piston. The distributor assembly may also have the capability of advancing or retarding ignition timing.

The distributor cap is mounted on top of the distributor assembly and an alignment notch in the cap fits over a matching lug on the housing (Figure 11-5). Therefore, the cap can only be installed in one position, thereby assuring the correct firing sequence.

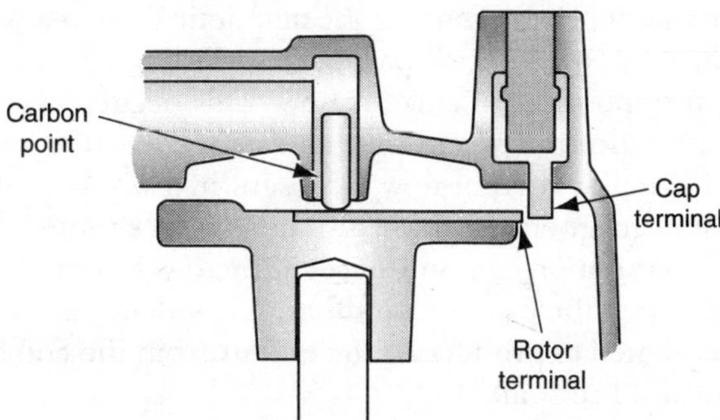

FIGURE 11-5 *Relationship of a rotor and distributor cap.*

The rotor is positioned on top of the distributor shaft, and a projection or other key-way inside the rotor fits into a slot in the shaft. This allows the rotor to only be installed in one position. A metal strip on the top of the rotor makes contact with the center distributor cap terminal, and the outer end of the strip passes by the cap terminals as it rotates. This action completes the circuit between the ignition coil and the individual spark plugs according to the firing order.

IGNITION COIL ACTION

All ignition systems share a number of common components. Some, such as the battery and ignition switch, perform simple functions. The battery supplies battery voltage to the ignition primary circuit. Current flows when the ignition switch is in the "start" or the "run" position.

To generate a spark to begin combustion, the ignition system must deliver high voltage to the spark plugs. Because the amount of voltage required to bridge the gap of the spark plug varies with the operating conditions, most late-model vehicles can easily supply 30,000 to 60,000 volts to force a spark across the air gap. Since the battery delivers 12 volts, a method of stepping up the voltage must be used. Multiplying battery voltage is the job of a coil.

The ignition coil is a **pulse transformer**. It transforms battery voltage into short bursts of high voltage. As explained previously, when a wire is moved through a magnetic field, voltage is induced in the wire. The inverse of this principle is also true—when a magnetic field moves across a wire, voltage is induced in the wire.

If a wire is bent into loops forming a coil and a magnetic field is passed through the coil, an equal amount of voltage is generated in each loop of wire. The more loops of wire in the coil, the greater the total voltage induced.

Also, the faster the magnetic field moves through the coil, even higher voltage is induced in the coil. If the speed of the magnetic field is doubled, the voltage output doubles.

An ignition coil uses these principles and has two coils of wire wrapped around an iron core. An iron or steel core is used because it has low **inductive reluctance**. The primary coil winding is normally composed of 100 to 200 turns of 20-gauge wire. This coil of wire conducts battery current. When a current is passing through the primary coil, it magnetizes the iron core. The strength of the magnet depends directly on the number of wire loops and the amount of current flowing through those loops. The secondary coil of wires may consist of 15,000 to 25,000 or more turns of very fine copper wire.

Because of the effects of counter EMF (electromotive force) on the current flowing through the primary winding, it takes some time for the coil to become fully magnetized or saturated. Therefore, current flows in the primary winding for some time between firings of the spark plugs. The period of time that there is primary current flow is called **dwell**. The length of the dwell period is important.

When current flows through a conductor, it will immediately reach its maximum value as allowed by the resistance in the circuit. If a conductor is wound into a coil, maximum current will not be immediately present. As the magnetic field begins to form as the current begins to flow, the magnetic lines of force of one part of the winding pass over another part of the winding. This tends to cause an opposition to current flow. This occurrence is called reactance. Reactance causes a temporary resistance to current flow and delays the flow of current from reaching its maximum value. When maximum current flow is present in a winding, the winding is said to be saturated and the strength of its magnetic field will also be at a maximum.

Saturation can only occur if the dwell period is long enough to allow for maximum current flow through the primary windings. A less-than-saturated coil will not be able to produce the voltage it was designed to produce. If the energy from the coil is too low, the spark plugs may not fire long enough or not fire at all.

When the primary coil circuit is suddenly opened, the magnetic field instantly collapses. The sudden collapsing of the magnetic field produces a very high voltage in the secondary windings. This high voltage is used to push current across the gap of the spark plug. Figure 11-6 simplistically shows the coil's primary and secondary circuits.

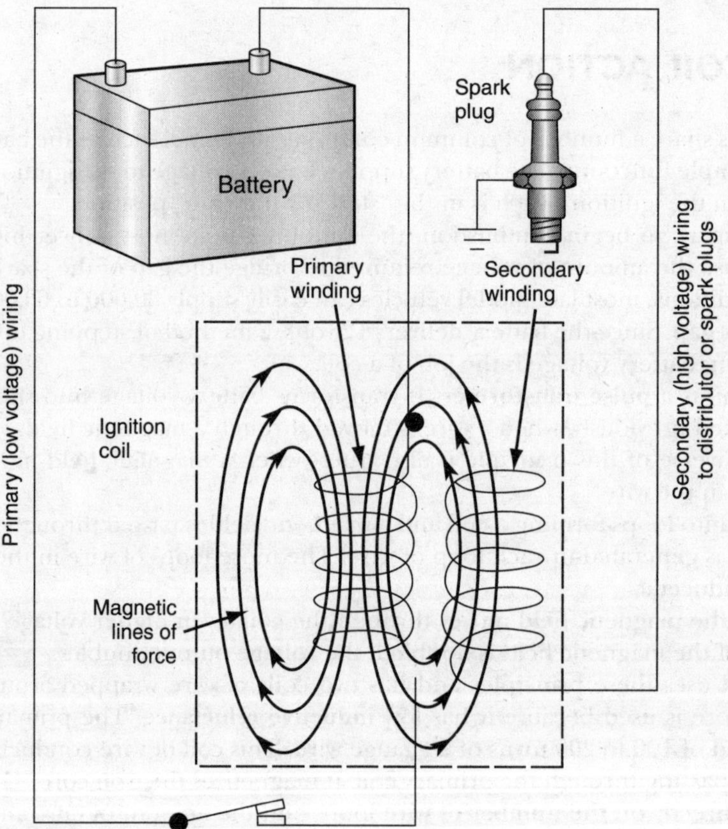

FIGURE 11-6 *Primary and secondary ignition coil action.*

Ignition Coil Construction

A laminated soft iron core is positioned at the center of the ignition coil, and an insulated primary winding is wound around this core. The primary winding has approximately 200 turns of heavy wire, and the two ends of this winding are connected to the primary terminals on top of the coil

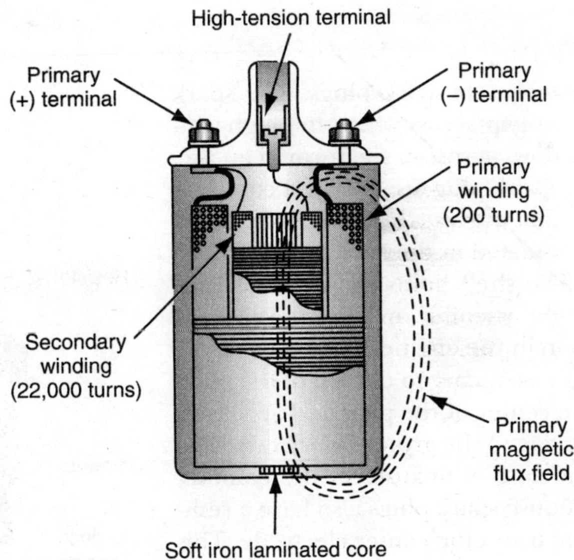

Figure 11-7 *Cutaway of a typical ignition coil.*

(Figure 11-7). These terminals are usually identified with positive and negative symbols. An enamel-type insulation prevents the primary windings from touching each other. Paper insulation is also placed between the layers of windings.

Secondary coil windings are made of very fine wire. These windings are on the inside of the primary winding. A similar insulation method is used on the secondary and primary windings. The ends of the secondary winding are usually connected to one of the primary terminals and to the high-tension terminal in the coil tower. When the windings and core assembly is mounted in the coil container, the core rests on a ceramic insulating cup in the bottom of the container. Metal sheathing is placed around the outside of the coil windings in the container. This sheathing concentrates the magnetic field on the outside of the windings. A sealing washer is positioned between the tower and the container to seal the unit.

Most modern coils are called E-core because the laminated sheets of steel the primary and secondary windings are wound around are shaped like the letter E. In the past, coils were tall cylinders with the windings cooled by oil. It was found that the E-core air coils cool more rapidly and are more compact than the old oil cooled variety.

Secondary Voltage

The typical amount of secondary coil voltage required to jump the spark plug gap is 10,000 volts. Most coils have a secondary voltage potential of at least 25,000 volts. The difference between the required voltage and the maximum available voltage is referred to as secondary reserve voltage. This reserve voltage is necessary to compensate for high cylinder pressures and increased secondary resistances as the spark plug gap increases through use. The maximum available voltage must always exceed the required firing voltage or ignition misfire will occur. If there is an insufficient amount of voltage available to push current across the gap, the spark plug will not fire. It is important to note that a decrease in primary voltage will decrease the output of the secondary. Normally a decrease of 1 volt in the primary will cause a decrease of 5 kV in the secondary.

SPARK PLUGS

Every type of ignition system uses spark plugs. The spark plugs provide the crucial air **gap** across which the high-voltage current from the coil flows across in the form of an arc. The three main parts of a spark plug are the steel core, the ceramic core or insulator that acts as a heat conductor, and a pair of electrodes, one insulated in the core and the other grounded on the shell. The shell holds the ceramic core and electrodes in a gas-tight assembly and has the threads needed for plug installation in the engine (Figure 11-8). An ignition cable connects the secondary to the top of the plug. Current flows through the center of the plug and arcs from the tip of the center electrode to the ground electrode. The resulting spark ignites the air-fuel mixture in the combustion chamber. Most automotive spark plugs also have a resistor between the top terminal and the center electrode. This resistor reduces radio frequency interference (RFI) which prevents noise on stereo equipment. Voltage peaks from RFI could also interfere with or damage on-board computers. Therefore, when resistor-type spark plugs are used as original equipment, replacement spark plugs must also be resistor-type. The resistor, like all other resistances in the secondary, increases the voltage needed to jump the gap of the spark plug. However, it also reduces amperage, extending plug life.

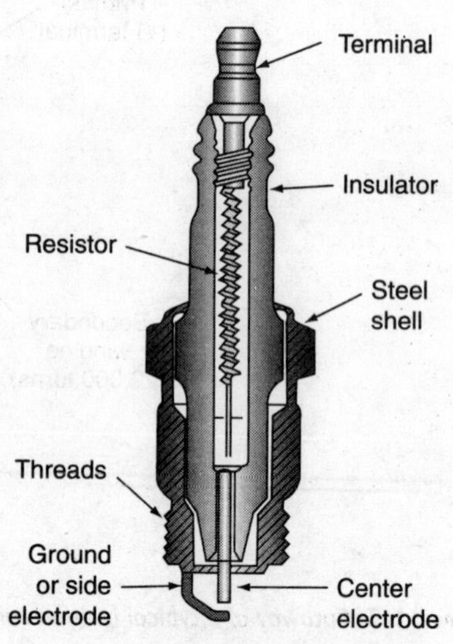

FIGURE 11-8 *Components of a typical spark plug.*

Spark plugs come in many different sizes and designs to accommodate different engines. To fit properly, spark plugs must be of the proper size and reach. Another design factor that determines the usefulness of a spark plug for a specific application is its **heat range**. The desired heat range depends on the design of the engine and on the type of driving conditions the vehicle is subject to.

A terminal post on top of the center electrode is the point of contact for the spark plug cable. The center electrode, commonly made of a copper alloy, is surrounded by a ceramic insulator, and a copper and glass seal is located between the electrode and the insulator. These seals prevent combustion gases from leaking out of the cylinder. Ribs on the insulator increase the distance between the terminal and the shell to help prevent electric arcing on the outside of the insulator. The steel spark plug shell is crimped over the insulation and a ground electrode, on the lower end of the shell, is positioned directly below the center electrode. There is an air gap between these two electrodes and the width of this air gap is specified by the auto manufacturer.

A spark plug socket may be placed over a hex-shaped area near the top of the shell for plug removal and installation. Threads on the lower end of the shell allow the plug to be threaded into the engine's cylinder head. The thread length is referred to as reach (Figure 11-9). Various thread lengths are designed to match the cylinder head and combustion chamber design.

Some spark plugs have a metal gasket positioned between the seat on the steel shell and the cylinder head, whereas other shells have a tapered seat with a matching seat in the cylinder head that do not use a gasket. Platinum tipped spark plug electrodes extended the life of a spark plug greatly (Figure 11-10), and more recently iridium tipped spark plugs have appeared in several vehicles. Iridium is harder, has a higher melting point than platinum, and has less electrical resistance (Figure 11-11).

Spark plugs are designed with different heat ranges to compensate for various operating conditions. When the engine is running, most of the plug's heat is concentrated on the center electrode. Heat is quickly dissipated from the ground electrode because it is threaded into the cylinder head.

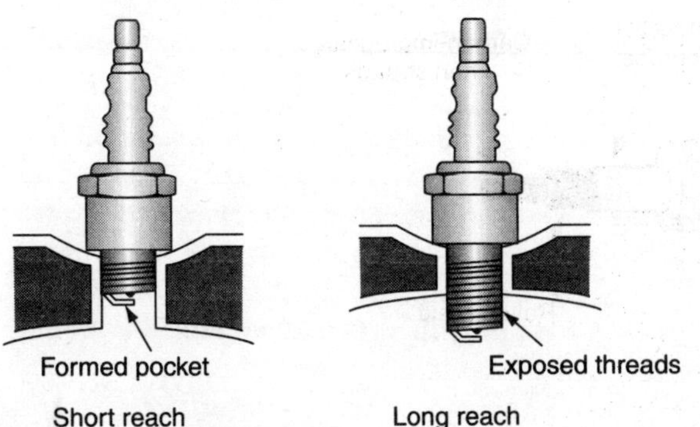

Figure 11-9 *Spark plug reach: short versus long.*

Figure 11-10 *A platinum-tipped spark plug.*

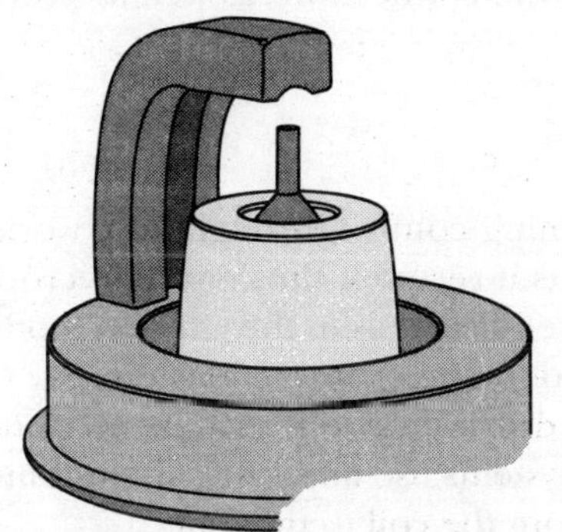
Figure 11-11 *Iridium spark plug tips have a higher melting point than platinum.*

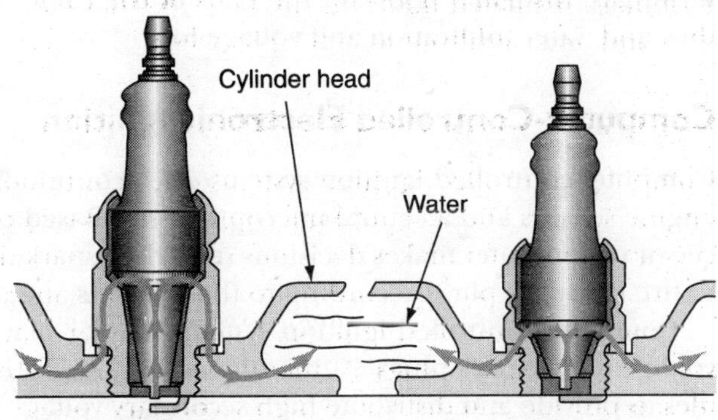

Figure 11-12 *Spark plug heat range: hot versus cold.*

The spark plug heat path is from the center electrode through the insulator into the shell and to the cylinder head where the heat is absorbed by engine coolant circulating through the cylinder head. Spark plug heat range is determined by the depth of the insulator before it contacts the shell. For example, in a cold-range spark plug, the depth of the insulator is short before it contacts the shell. This cold-type spark plug has a short heat path, which provides cooler electrode operation (Figure 11-12).

In a hot spark plug, the insulator depth is increased before it makes contact with the shell. This provides a longer heat path and increases electrode temperature. A spark plug needs to retain enough heat to clean itself between firings but not so hot that it damages itself or causes premature ignition of the air-fuel mixture in the cylinder. If an engine is driven continually at low speeds, the spark plugs may become carbon fouled. Under this condition, a hotter range spark plug may be required. Severe high-speed driving over an extended time period may require a colder range spark plug to prevent electrode burning from excessive combustion chamber heat.

Ignition Cables

Spark plug or ignition cables make up the secondary wiring. These cables carry the high-voltage current from the distributor to the spark plugs. The cables are not solid wire; rather, they contain fiber cores that act as a resistor in the secondary circuit (Figure 11-13). They cut down on radio and television interference, increase firing voltages, and reduce spark plug wear by decreasing current. Metal terminals on each end of the spark plug wires contact the spark plug and the distributor cap

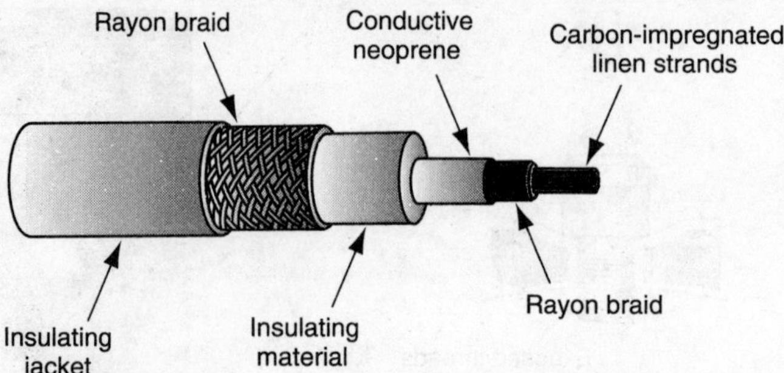

FIGURE 11-13 *Static suppression ignition cable.*

terminals. Insulated boots on the ends of the cables strengthen the connections as well as prevent dust and water infiltration and voltage loss.

Computer-Controlled Electronic Ignition

Computer-controlled ignition systems offer continuous spark timing control through a network of engine sensors and a central microprocessor. Based on the inputs it receives, the central microprocessor or computer makes decisions regarding spark timing and sends signals to the ignition module to fire the spark plugs according to those inputs and according to the programs in its memory.

Computer-controlled ignition systems may or may not use a distributor to distribute secondary voltage to the spark plugs. As mentioned earlier, distributorless systems use multiple coils and modules to provide and distribute high secondary voltages directly from the coil to the plug.

IGNITION MODULES

Ignition modules control the ground connection to the primary coil winding. When the ground is completed by the module, current flows in the primary circuit and the coil saturates. When the module opens the ground connection, spark is produced. Of course, the module needs to know the correct time to turn the coil on and off according to piston position. This is the job of the **triggering device**, also sometimes referred to as a **crankshaft position sensor**. To explain the operation of the triggering device, refer to Figure 11-14. Although this is an oversimplified representation of an

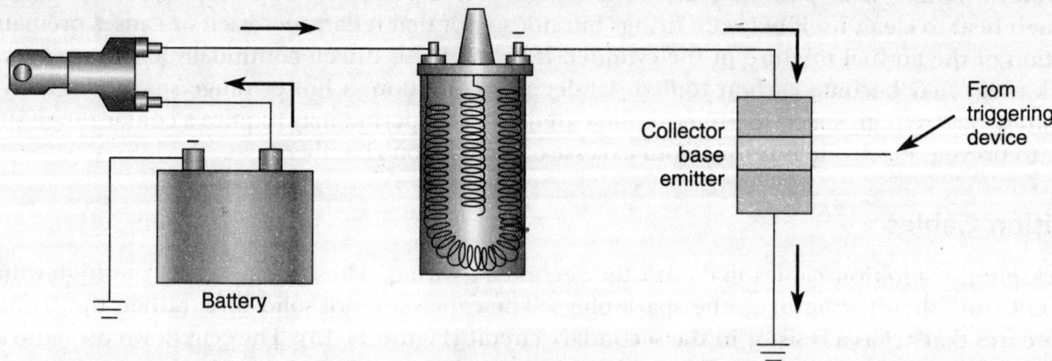

FIGURE 11-14 *When the triggering device supplies a small amount of current to the transistor's base, the primary coil circuit is closed and current flows.*

ignition module, this will help explain its operation. Think of the module as an NPN transistor with the emitter connected to ground, the collector to the negative terminal of the coil, and the base connected to the triggering device output. When a signal is received from the triggering device, the base of the transistor turns on, allowing current flow into the coil. When the triggering device signal stops, the transistor turns off, current flow stops, and secondary voltage is induced and sent to a spark plug. Later in this chapter we will look at computer timing control and how it relates to the module.

Electronic Dwell

As discussed earlier, dwell is the time that the primary current to the ignition coil is turned on. The ignition coil must be able to supply sufficient energy at wide-open throttle as well as idle speeds. At idle, the coil has more than enough time to saturate; at wide-open throttle there is just enough time. The problem is that if the coil is allowed to stay saturated at idle, the current flow will cause the coil to overheat. Early electronic ignition systems used a ballast resistor to control current flow. The ballast resistor would heat up with increased current and the resulting increase in resistance would limit current flow. At high speeds when the coil had a little time to saturate, the resistor would cool off and allow more to current flow in the coil primary. Improvements in the accuracy and speed of electronics allowed the introduction of electronically controlled dwell. When at idle and low rpm and plenty of time to saturate the coil, the dwell was started later in crankshaft rotation. At increased rpm and less time between coil firings, dwell begins earlier to allow for coil saturation. Electronic dwell change can be seen on an ignition scope or dwell meter.

Triggering Devices/Engine Position Sensors

Primary ignition on/off time (or ignition timing) must coincide with the correct position of the pistons and crankshaft. There are several types of crankshaft and camshaft position sensors and a variety of systems that are used to trigger the ignition module and provide a signal for timing. Some of the commonly used sensors we will examine include:

- Magnetic pulse generators
- Metal detection sensors
- Hall effect sensors
- Photoelectric sensors

The mounting location of these sensors depends on the design of the ignition system. All four types of sensors can be located in the distributor, which is turned by the camshaft.

Magnetic Pulse Generator

Basically, a magnetic pulse generator consists of two parts: a timing disc and a pickup coil. The pickup coil consists of a length of wire wound around a weak permanent magnet. Depending on the type of ignition system used, the timing disc may be mounted on the distributor shaft (Figure 11-15), at the rear of the crankshaft (Figure 11-16), or on the crankshaft vibration damper (Figure 11-17).

The magnetic pulse or PM generator operates on basic electromagnetic principles. Remember that a voltage can only be induced when a conductor moves through a magnetic field. The magnetic field is provided by the pickup unit, and the rotating timing disc provides the movement through the magnetic field needed to induce voltage.

As the disc teeth approach the pickup coil, they repel the magnetic field, forcing it to concentrate around the pickup coil (Figure 11-18). Once the tooth passes by the pickup coil, the magnetic field is free to expand or unconcentrate until the next tooth on the disc approaches. Approaching teeth concentrate the magnetic lines of force while passing teeth allow them to expand. This pulsation of

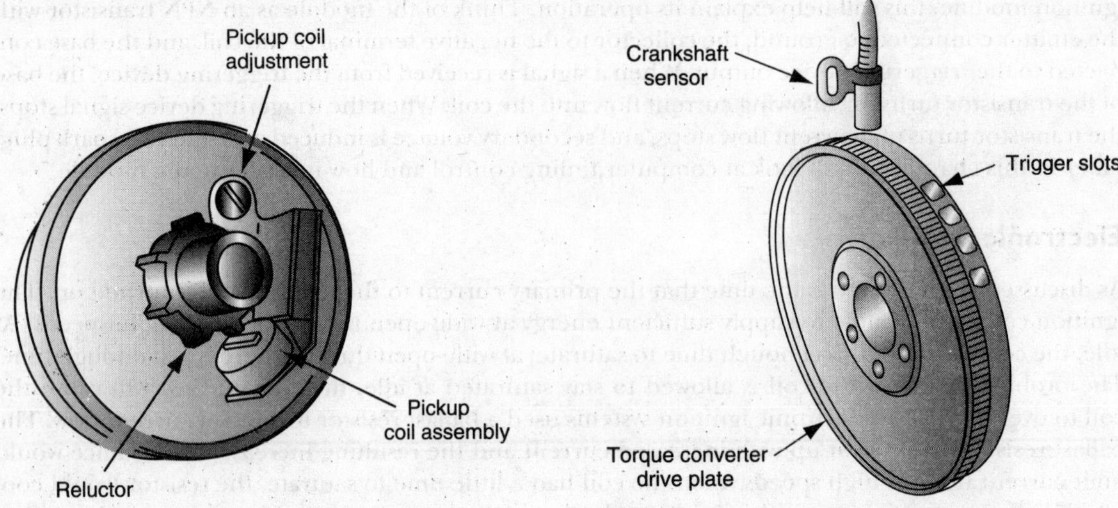

FIGURE 11-15 *A pickup coil mounted in a distributor.*

FIGURE 11-16 *A flywheel crank timing sensor.*

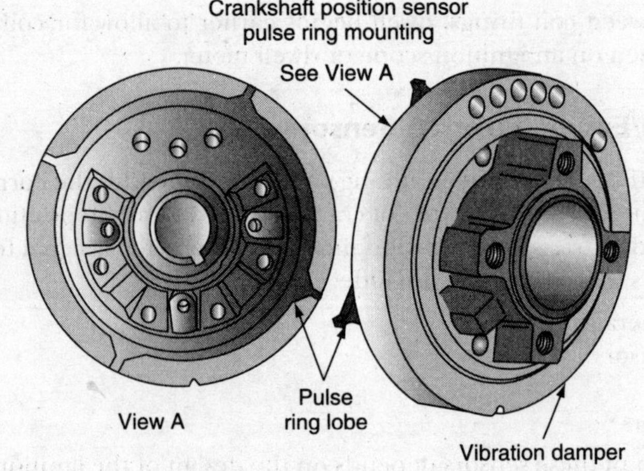

FIGURE 11-17 *The pulse ring on a crankshaft pulley.*

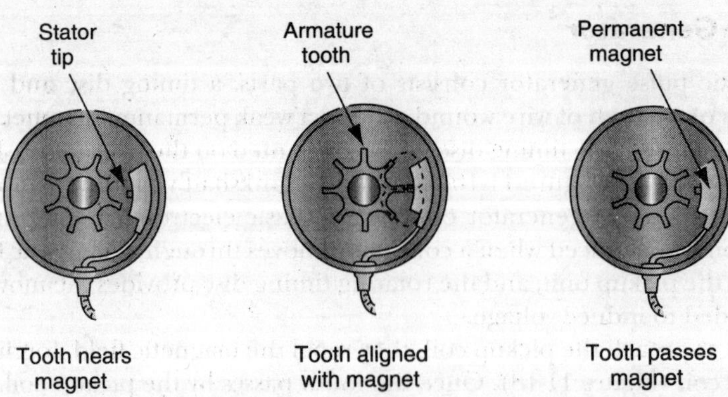

FIGURE 11-18 *When the reluctor high point is aligned with the pickup coil, the gap is narrower and the magnetic field is stronger.*

the magnetic field causes the lines of magnetic force to cut across the winding in the pickup coil, inducing a small amount of AC voltage that is sent to the switching device in the primary circuit.

When a disc tooth is directly in line with the pickup coil, the magnetic field is neither expanding nor contracting. Since there is no movement or change in the field, voltage at this precise movement drops to zero. At this point, the switching device inside the ignition module reacts to the zero voltage signal by turning the ignition's primary circuit current off. As explained earlier, this forces the magnetic field in the primary coil to collapse, discharging a secondary voltage to the distributor or directly to the spark plug.

As soon as the tooth rotates past the pickup coil, the magnetic field expands again and another voltage signal is induced. The only difference is that the polarity of the charge is reversed. Negative becomes positive or positive becomes negative. Upon sensing this change in voltage, the switching device turns the primary circuit back on and the process begins all over.

The timing disc is mounted in a very precise manner. When the disc teeth align with the pickup coil, this corresponds to the exact time certain pistons are nearing TDC. This means the zero voltage signal needed to trigger the secondary circuit occurs at precisely the correct time.

The pickup coil might have only one pole as shown in Figure 11-19. Other magnetic pulse generators have pickup coils with two or more poles. The one shown in Figure 11-20 has as many poles as it has trigger teeth.

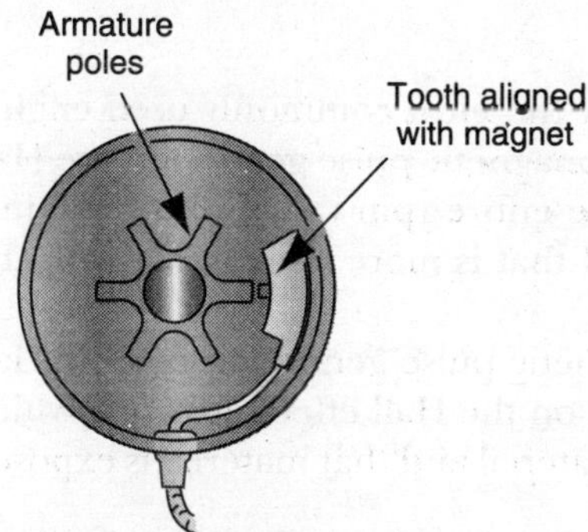

FIGURE 11-19 *A single pole pickup coil.*

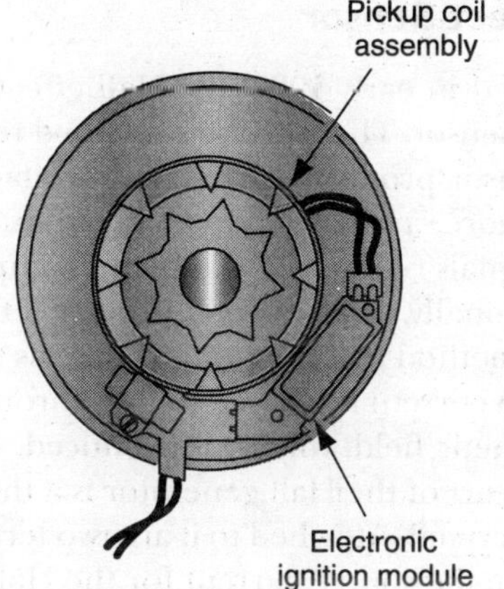

FIGURE 11-20 *A pick-up with as many poles as there are cylinders.*

Metal Detection Sensors

Metal detection sensors are found on many early electronic ignition systems. They work much like a magnetic pulse generator with one major difference.

A trigger wheel is pressed over the distributor shaft and a pickup coil detects the passing of the trigger teeth as the distributor shaft rotates. However, unlike a magnetic pulse generator, the pickup coil of a metal detection sensor does not have a permanent magnet. Instead, the pickup coil is an electromagnet. A low level of current is supplied to the coil by an **electronic control unit (ECU)**, inducing a weak magnetic field around the coil. As the reluctor on the distributor shaft rotates, the trigger teeth pass very close to the coil (Figure 11-21). As the teeth pass in and out of the coil's magnetic field, the magnetic field builds and collapses, producing a corresponding change in the coil's voltage. The voltage changes are monitored by the control unit to determine crankshaft position.

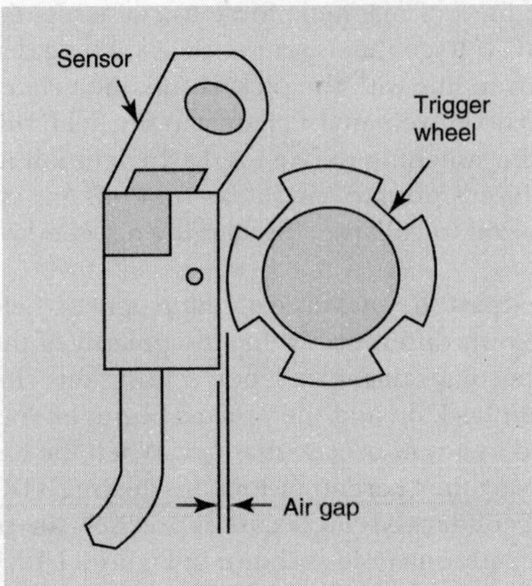

FIGURE 11-21 *A metal detection sensor.*

Hall Effect Sensor

Introduced in early 1982, the Hall effect sensor or switch is now the most commonly used engine position sensor. There are several good reasons for this. Unlike a magnetic pulse generator, the Hall effect sensor produces an accurate voltage signal throughout the entire rpm range of the engine. Furthermore, a Hall effect switch produces a square wave signal that is more compatible with the digital signals required by on-board computers.

Functionally, a Hall switch performs the same tasks as a magnetic pulse generator, but the Hall switch's method of generating voltage is quite unique. It is based on the Hall effect principle which states: If a current is allowed to flow through a thin conducting material and that material is exposed to a magnetic field, voltage is produced.

The heart of the Hall generator is a thin semiconductor layer (Hall layer) derived from a gallium arsenate crystal. Attached to it are two terminals—one positive and the other negative—that are used to provide the source current for the Hall transformation.

Directly across from this semiconductor element is a permanent magnet. It is positioned so that its lines of flux bisect the Hall layer at right angles to the direction of current flow. Two additional terminals located on either side of the Hall layer form the signal output circuit.

When a moving metallic shutter blocks the magnetic field from reaching the Hall layer or element, the Hall effect switch produces a voltage signal. When the shutter blade moves and allows the magnetic field to expand and reach the Hall element, the Hall effect switch does not generate voltage signal (Figure 11-22).

The Hall switch is described as being on any time the Hall layer is exposed to a magnetic field and a Hall voltage is being produced. However, before this signal voltage can be of any use, it must be modified. After leaving the Hall layer, the signal is routed to an amplifier where it is strengthened and inverted so that the signal reads high when it is actually coming in low and vice versa. Once it has been inverted, the signal goes through a **Schmitt trigger**, where it is turned into a clean square wave signal. After conditioning, the signal is sent to the base of a switching transistor that is designed to turn on and off in response to the signals generated by the Hall effect switch assembly.

The shutter wheel is the last major component of the Hall switch. The shutter wheel consists of a series of alternating windows and vanes that pass between the Hall layer and magnet. The shutter wheel may be part of the distributor rotor (Figure 11-23) or separate from the rotor.

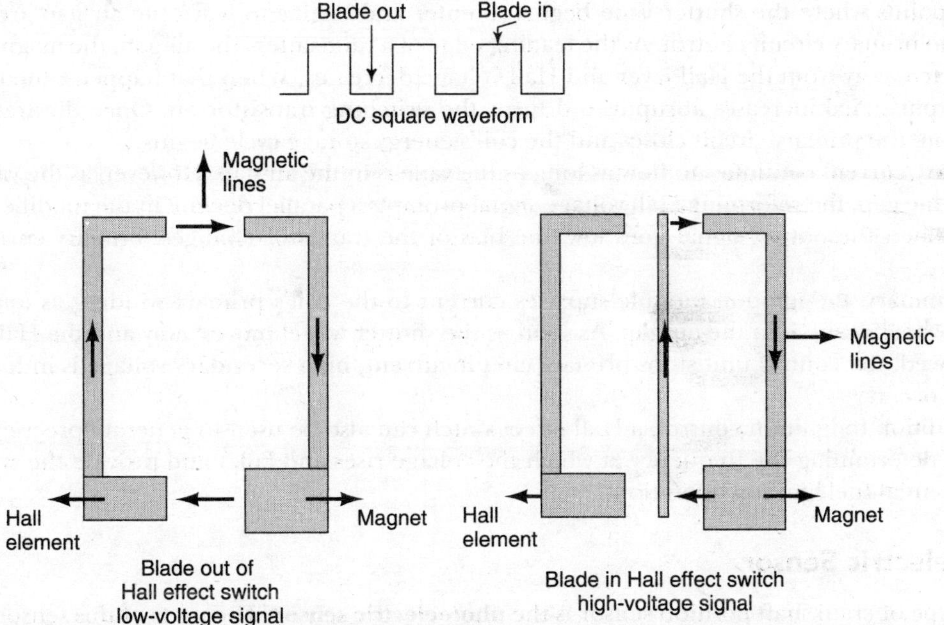

FIGURE 11-22 *As the blade moves through the Hall effect switch, a voltage signal is produced.*

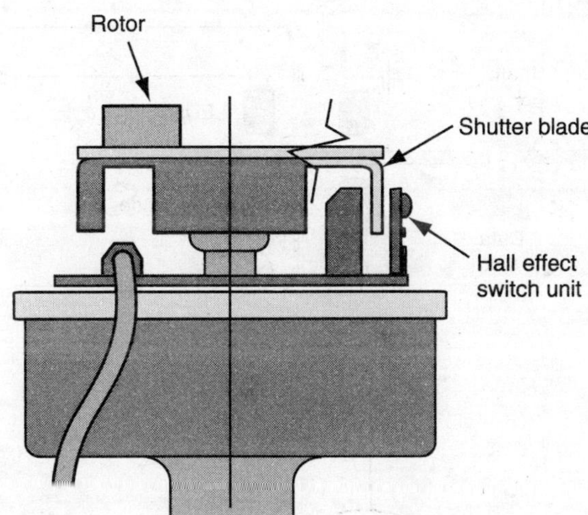

FIGURE 11-23 *A distributor rotor with a shutter blade for the Hall effect switch.*

The shutter wheel performs the same function as the timing disc on magnetic pulse generators. The only difference is with a Hall effect switch there is no electromagnetic induction. Instead, the shutter wheel creates a magnetic shunt that changes the field strength through the Hall element. When a vane of the shutter wheel is positioned between the magnet and Hall element, the metallic vane blocks the magnetic field and keeps it from permeating the Hall layer. As a result, only a few residual electrons are deflected in the layer, and Hall output voltage is low. Conversely, when a window rotates into the air gap, the magnetic field is able to penetrate the Hall layer, which in turn pushes the Hall voltage to its maximum range.

The points where the shutter vane begins to enter and begins to leave the air gap are directly related to primary circuit control. As the leading edge of a vane enters the air gap, the magnetic field is deflected away from the Hall layer and Hall voltage decreases. When that happens, the modified Hall output signal increases abruptly and turns the switching transistor on. Once the transistor is turned on, the primary circuit closes and the coil's energy storage cycle begins.

Primary current continues to flow as long as the vane is in the air gap. However, as the vane starts to leave the gap, the reforming Hall voltage signal prompts a parallel decline in the modified output signal. When the output signal goes low, the bias of the transistor changes. Primary current flow stops.

In summary, the ignition module supplies current to the coil's primary winding as long as the shutter wheel's vane is in the air gap. As soon as the shutter wheel moves away and the Hall voltage is produced, the control unit stops primary circuit current, high secondary voltage is induced, and ignition occurs.

In addition to ignition control, a Hall effect switch can also be used to generate precise rpm signals (by determining the frequency at which the voltage rises and falls) and provide the sync pulse for sequential fuel ignition operation.

Photoelectric Sensor

A fifth type of crankshaft position sensor is the **photoelectric sensor**. The parts of this sensor include a light-emitting diode (LED), a light-sensitive phototransistor, and a slotted disc called a light beam interrupter (Figure 11-24).

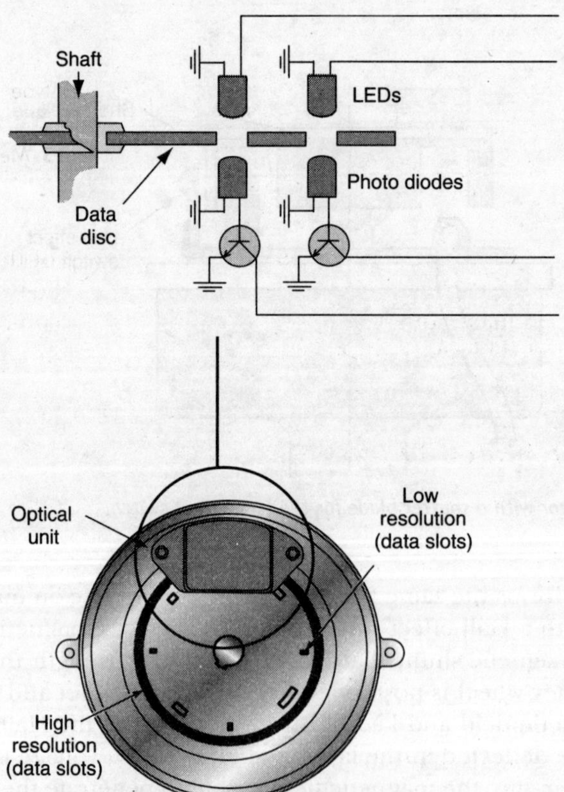

FIGURE 11-24 *Distributor with an optical-type pickup.*

The slotted disc is attached to the distributor shaft. The LED and the photocell are situated over and under the disc opposite of each other. As the slotted disc rotates between the LED and photocell, light from the LED shines through the slots. The intermittent flashes of light are translated into voltage pulses by the photocell. When the voltage signal occurs, the control unit turns the primary system on. When the disc interrupts the light and the voltage signal ceases, the control unit turns the primary system off, causing the magnetic field in the coil to collapse and sending a surge of voltage to a spark plug.

The photoelectric sensor sends a very reliable signal to the control unit, especially at low engine speeds. These units have been primarily used on Chrysler and Mitsubishi engines. Some Nissan and General Motors products have used them as well.

SPARK DISTRIBUTION

The distributor cap and rotor receive the high voltage from the secondary winding via a high-tension wire. The voltage enters the distributor cap through the coil tower or center terminal. The rotor then sends the voltage from the coil tower to the spark plug electrodes inside the distributor cap. The rotor mounts on the upper portion of the distributor shaft and rotates with it.

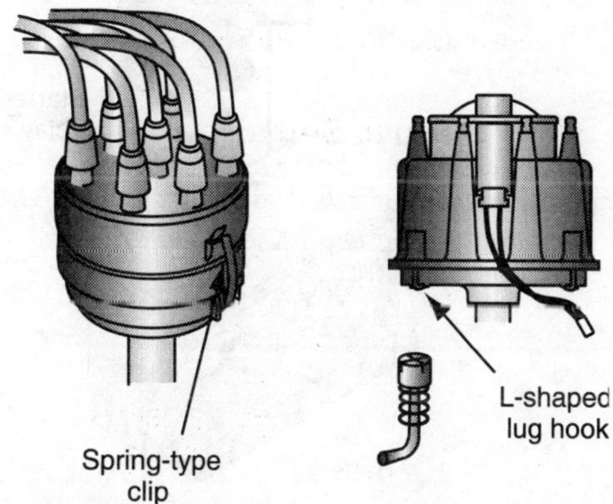

FIGURE 11-25 *Methods of retaining the distributor cap.*

The distributor cap (Figure 11-25) is made from silicone plastic or similar material that offers protection from chemical attack. It is attached to the distributor housing with screws or spring-loaded clips. The coil tower contains a carbon insert that carries the voltage from the high-tension coil lead to the raised portion of the electrode on the rotor. Spaced evenly around the coil tower are the spark plug electrodes and towers for each spark plug.

An air gap of a few thousandths of an inch exists between the tip of the rotor electrode and the spark plug electrode inside the cap. This gap is necessary to prevent the two electrodes from making contact. If they did make contact, both would wear out rapidly. This gap cannot be measured when the distributor is assembled. Therefore, the gap is usually described in terms of the voltage needed to create an arc between the electrodes.

Ford's Thick Film Integrated-IV Ignition

A distributor module can be mounted either directly on the distributor or remotely. Ford's **thick film integrated (TFI) IV** ignition system is an example that used both types. This popular system also had two different versions that differed in the way the computer and module work together to control ignition timing. The system was utilized for several years on EEC-IV systems. The TFI IV ignition system (Figure 11-26) consisted of the distributor, a Hall effect camshaft sensor (CMP) located inside the distributor, an E-core coil, spark plug wires and plugs, and the PCM. As mentioned, there were two versions; one had a module mounted on the distributor, and one had the module mounted remotely from the distributor.

The TFI IV distributor contains the Hall effect switch, which serves as the camshaft position sensor. The signal produced by the Hall effect (CMP) sensor is called the PIP, or **profile ignition pickup** signal, sent to the distributor module and the PCM to indicate piston position and rpm (Figure 11-27).

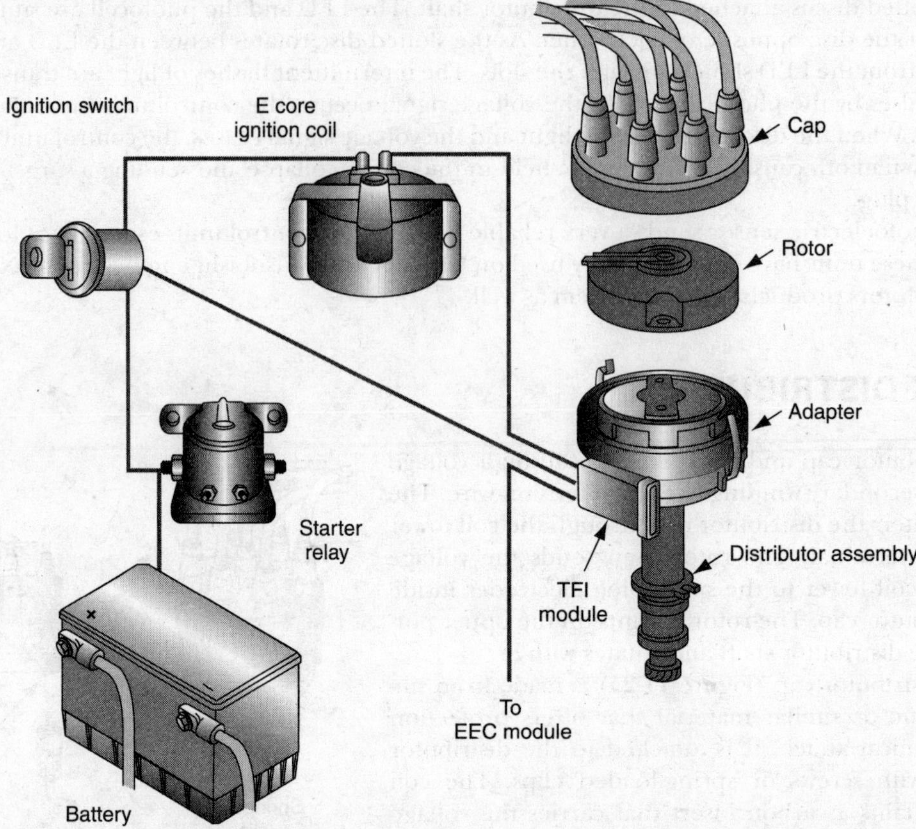

FIGURE 11-26 *TFI-IV ignition system.*

The spark timing signal sent to the module for timing control is called **SPOUT**, for **spark out**. SPOUT is the signal that the computer uses to control timing advance.

There were two different types of control modules used in the TFI systems. Ford refers to the systems as **push start** and CCD. Of course, push start has nothing to do with push starting a vehicle, but instead refers to ignition timing. The push start system allows for a longer dwell period during engine start. After the engine starts, the module determines dwell time based on engine rpm, previous spark position, and coil charge time. The PCM controls the coil turn-off time through the SPOUT signal. Basically, the control module calculates dwell for coil saturation, and the PCM calculates timing of the spark. Modules that are of the push start variety are gray in color.

In the **CCD**, or **computer-controlled dwell** system, the PCM determines the correct dwell based on measuring the time it takes the coil to charge. The timing is also controlled by the PCM. Using the PCM to determine the dwell time cuts down on excess coil on time that tends to cause the module to overheat. The CCD modules are black in color.

The distribution of spark to the cylinders is accomplished in the same way as in other distributors by using a distributor cap, rotor, and spark plug wires. The octane rod inside the distributor allows for fixed octane adjustments. The adjustment is made by replacing the standard (normal octane fuel) 0-degree retard rod with a 3- or 6-degree (lower octane) retard rod.

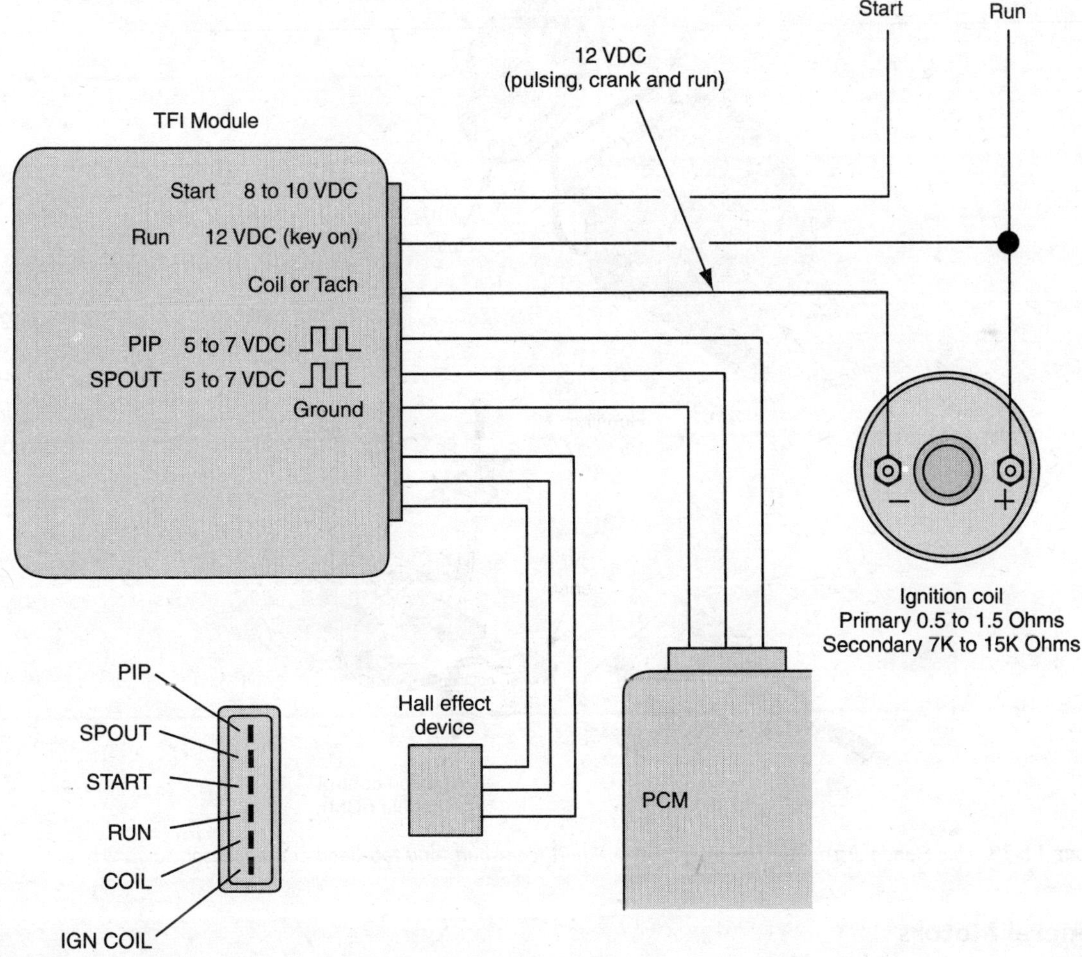

FIGURE 11-27 *PIP and SPOUT signals.*

Other Systems

Several import vehicles used primarily the same system designs as domestic manufacturers. Typically, the ignition coil is controlled by the ignition control module, which is triggered by a magnetic pickup coil or Hall effect switch. The electronic ignition module was sometimes referred to as an ignitor. An example of this is a typical Nippondenso distributor system or the Honda distributor system as shown in Figure 11-28.

The Honda distributor shown has an integral crankshaft and TDC sensor. The crankshaft position sensor determines timing for ignition, fuel injection, and rpm. The top-dead center sensor determines ignition timing at cranking and as a backup if the crankshaft sensor signal is abnormal. The camshaft sensor determines the position of cylinder number 1.

Toyota also uses distributor-mounted sensors that are referred to as rpm and camshaft angle sensors. The rpm sensor is the equivalent of the sensor most often called the crankshaft sensor in that there is a rotor with four teeth corresponding to top-dead center of each piston. A pickup coil sends this signal to the ECM. The camshaft angle sensor signals the ECM of number one cylinder TDC by utilizing a rotor with one tooth.

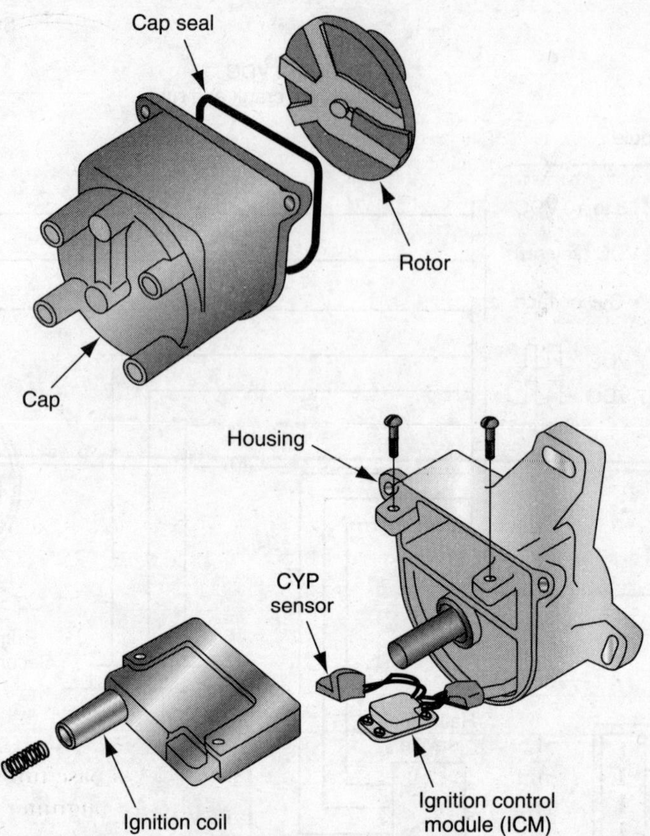

FIGURE 11-28 *This Honda distributor has integral crankshaft, camshaft, and top-dead-center sensor.*

General Motors

Perhaps the best example of a DI system with the ignition control module *inside* the distributor is the General Motor's **High Energy Ignition (HEI)** system. The HEI magnetic pickup coil surrounds the distributor shaft that has one mating tooth for each cylinder. The pickup coil leads are connected to the ignition control module mounted in the distributor housing (Figure 11-29).

Although reverse installation of pickup coil leads to the module is virtually impossible due to the difference in connector size, it is possible for an *incorrect* pickup coil to be installed. GM uses several types of pickup coils. Though similar in appearance, they are different and are specific to each engine application. It is imperative to confirm the correct part number for a particular engine application. Be sure to identify the engine code by using the vehicle identification number and verify the part number of any component being replaced or installed. Specific pickup coils are manufactured to be compatible with magnetic fields produced by other electrical components under the hood of the vehicle, such as the starter motor and ignition coil. The magnetic polarity of the pickup coil must be matched or properly phased to the magnetic field created by the starter motor during cranking. If this is not accomplished, the stronger magnetic field created by the starter can alter or cancel the weaker field created by the pickup coil. In addition, the integral-type ignition coils are matched to the engine. The ignition coils can be identified by the tach wire color (yellow or white). For the same reason, the magnetic field produced by the coil needs to be matched or properly phased to the pickup coil. The pickup coil wires are always green and white in color. Depending on the application, the reverse colors coming out of the pickup coil are an identifiable difference.

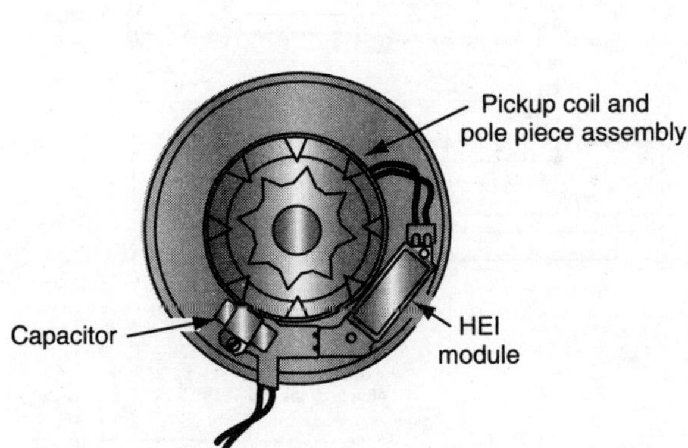

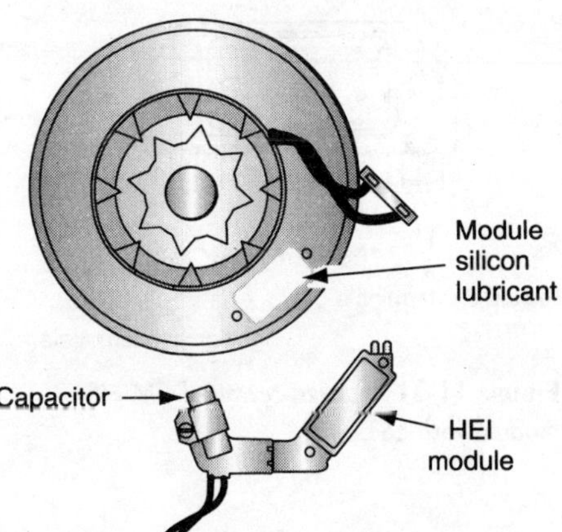

FIGURE 11-29 *HEI component location.*

FIGURE 11-30 *HEI control module mounting.*

The HEI ignition control module is mounted inside, directly to the distributor housing. The distributor housing acts as a heat sink for the module to dissipate the incredible amount of heat produced while the engine is running. Heat transfer lubricant must be applied to the module's mating surface to the distributor in order to prevent damage to the module (Figure 11-30).

HEI System Operation

When the engine is being cranked or is running below about 400 rpm, the ignition module controls dwell and timing based on signal from the pickup coil. This is called base timing, or module mode. As the engine is cranked and the timer core high points approach alignment with the pole piece teeth, a positive voltage is induced in the pickup coil. This voltage signal causes the module to close the primary circuit and current begins to flow through the primary circuit. Under this condition, the magnetic field expands around the coil windings.

At the instant of alignment between the timer core high points and pole piece teeth, the pickup coil voltage drops to zero. As these high points move out of alignment, a negative voltage is induced in the pickup coil. This voltage signal to the module causes the module to open the primary circuit. When this action occurs, the magnetic field collapses across the ignition coil windings, and the high induced secondary voltage forces current through the secondary circuit and across the spark plug gap.

After the engine starts and is running, the PCM sends a 5-volt signal to the module called bypass to tell the module to switch to the computer-controlled timing signal referred to as **electronic spark timing**, or **EST**. After switching to EST, the PCM tells the module where to set dwell and timing, and the module conditions the pickup coil signal and sends it to the PCM as the **reference** or rpm signal. There is a ground wire that runs between the PCM and the distributor module referred to as the **reference low.** The reference low is used to ensure that the electrical ground is the same at both the PCM and distributor. Figure 11-31 identifies the terminals of a seven-pin HEI module, and Figure 11-32 shows a simplified schematic of the HEI module, pickup coil, and PCM wiring.

CHRYSLER DI SYSTEMS

On some Chrysler systems, the Hall effect switch and distributor plate are a one-piece assembly (Figure 11-33), and the shutter blades are attached to the rotor. In other Chrysler systems

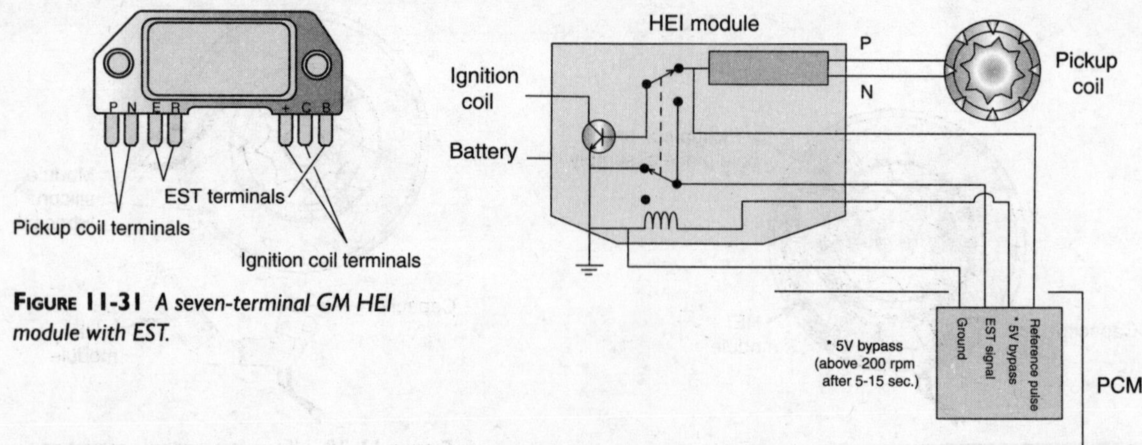

FIGURE 11-31 *A seven-terminal GM HEI module with EST.*

FIGURE 11-32 *Schematic of an HEI system with EST.*

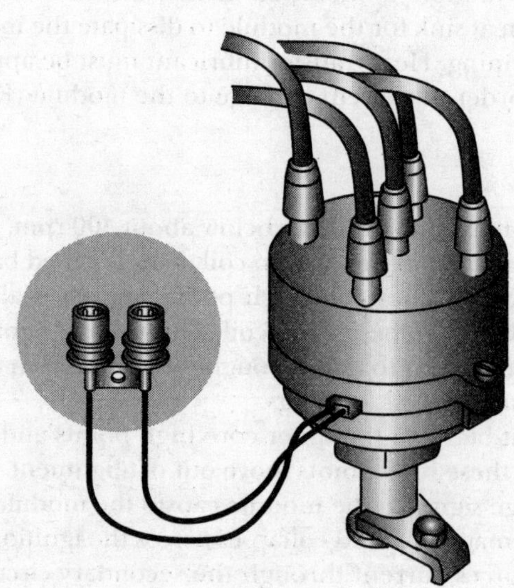

FIGURE 11-33 *Distributor assembly with a reference and sync pickup.*

(Figure 11-34), the shutter blades are part of the shaft. The shutter blades are insulated from the secondary electrode of the rotor. When the ignition switch is on, 9.2 volts are supplied by the PCM to the distributor pickup. A ground wire extends from the Hall effect pickup to the PCM. The Hall effect pickup signal is sent through a wire to the PCM.

Each time a shutter blade moves into the Hall effect pickup, the pickup signal changes from 0 volt to 8 volts. This signal always occurs at the same crankshaft position such as 10 degrees BTDC on the compression stroke. The 0-to-8-volt Hall effect pickup signal informs the PCM of crankshaft speed and piston position. When the 0-to-8-volt signal is received, the PCM scans the sensor inputs and calculates the exact spark advance required for the next cylinder firing.

This calculation is completed in a few milliseconds. Next, the PCM opens the primary ignition circuit and fires the next spark plug in the firing order at the correct instant to provide the precise spark advance required by the engine.

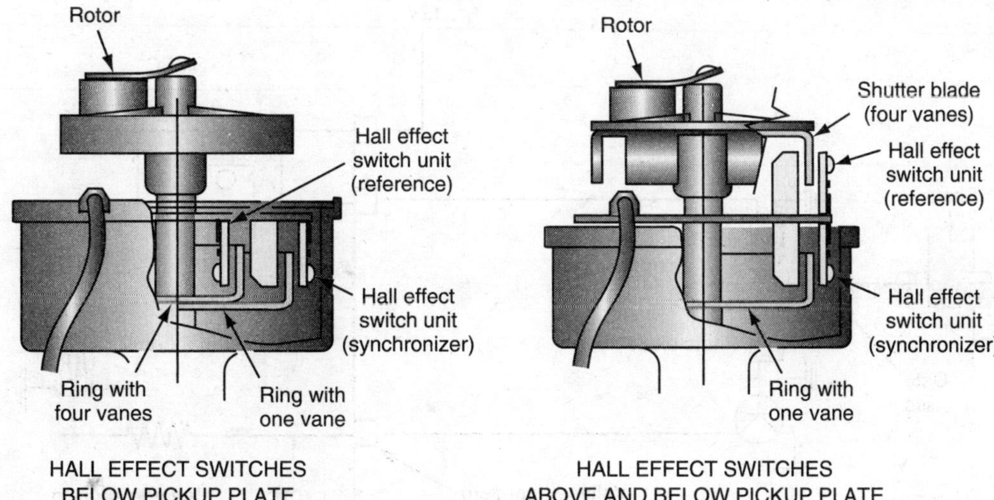

FIGURE 11-34 *Distributor assembly with two Hall effect switches.*

There are two Hall effect pickups in distributors used with Chrysler port fuel injection, whereas the distributors used with throttle body injection have a single pickup. When the SYNC pickup signal is received by the PCM every one half distributor shaft revolution or once every crankshaft revolution, the PCM grounds two injectors to inject fuel into two cylinders.

DISTRIBUTORS WITH OPTICAL-TYPE PICKUPS

The 3.0L V6 engine available in some Chrysler products has a distributor fitted with an optical pick-up assembly with two light-emitting diodes and two photo diodes. A thin plate attached to the distributor shaft rotates between the LEDs above the plate and the photo diodes below the plate (Figure 11-35). This plate contains six equally spaced slots that rotate directly below the inner LED and photo diode.

The inner LED and photo diode act as the reference pickup. As in Hall effect pickup systems, the reference pickup in the optical distributor provides a crankshaft position and speed signal to the PCM. When the ignition switch is on, the PCM supplies voltage to the optical pickup that causes the LEDs to emit light. If a solid part of the plate is under the reference LED, this light does not shine on the photo diode. Under this condition, the photo diode does not conduct current and the reference voltage signal to the PCM is 5 volts. As a reference slot moves under the LED, the light shines on the photo diode, and this diode conducts current. When this action occurs, the reference voltage signal to the PCM is 0 volt.

The outer LED, photo diode, and row of slots perform a similar function to the SYNC pickup in a distributor with Hall effect pickups. The outer row of slots is closely spaced and the width between each slot represents 2 degrees of crankshaft rotation. On the outer row there is one area where the slots are missing. When this blank area rotates under the LED, a different SYNC voltage signal is pro duced that informs the PCM regarding the number one piston position. The PCM uses this signal for injector control. As the outer row of slots rotates under the outer LED, the SYNC voltage signal to the PCM cycles from 0 volt to 5 volts. The reference pickup signal informs the PCM when each piston is a specific number of degrees before TDC on the compression stroke.

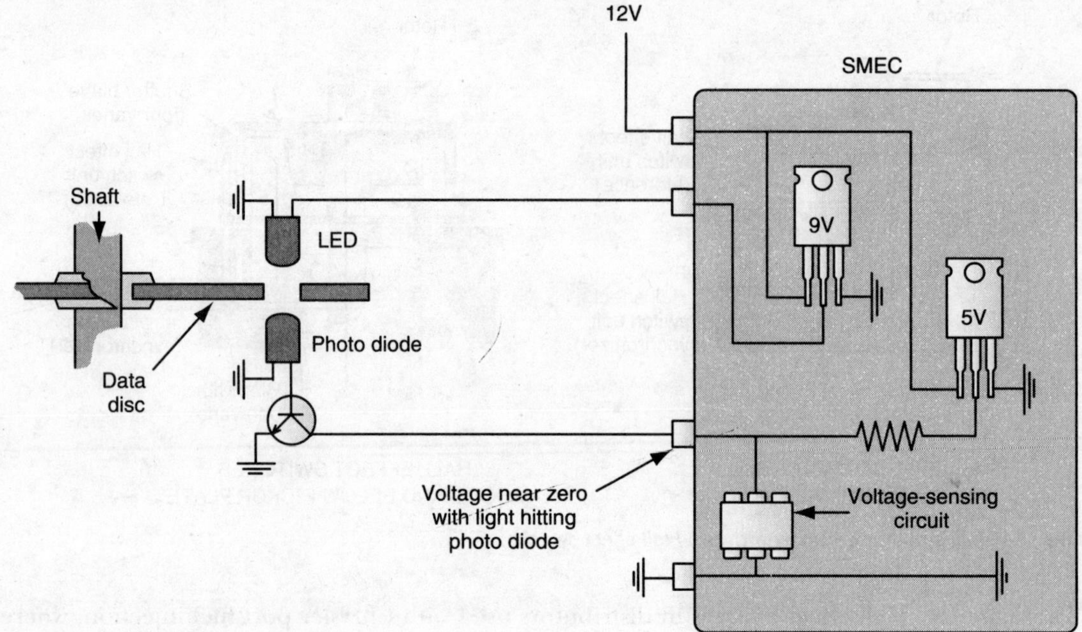

FIGURE 11-35 *Location of LEDs and photo diodes.*

When this signal is received, the PCM scans the inputs and calculates the spark advance required by the engine. The SYNC sensor signals always keep the PCM informed regarding the exact crankshaft position. The PCM opens the primary ignition circuit and fires the next spark plug in the firing order to provide the calculated spark advance.

COMPUTER-CONTROLLED IGNITION SYSTEM OPERATION

Today's vehicles have a PCM with a large array of sensors that make extremely accurate ignition timing possible. Accurate timing is essential for maximum fuel efficiency, performance, and reduced emissions under all driving conditions. Spark timing is based on engine load and temperature, air-fuel ratio, rpm, intake air temperature and volume, crankshaft position, and more depending on application.

Spark timing during engine cranking is controlled by the ignition module based on signals received from the triggering device (crankshaft position sensor). This type of timing control, when the computer is not in control, has been called base, **initial timing**, or module mode. The triggering device output is also used to form the rpm signal for the computer. Some manufacturers call this the reference signal. Once the rpm reaches approximately 200 to 400, the computer assumes the engine has started and sends a **bypass** signal to the module switching over control of ignition timing, directly informing the module when to fire the coil. The signal from the computer to the module is called electronic spark timing (EST) or SPOUT (spark output). On many vehicles, if the timing signal from the PCM is lost due to a wiring or computer problem, the module still has the capability of providing some timing control on its own. This would not be as accurate as the timing the PCM provides, but good enough for the owner to get the vehicle to a shop.

The computer continuously monitors existing conditions, adjusting timing to match what its memory tells it is the ideal setting for those conditions (Figure 11-36). It can do this very quickly,

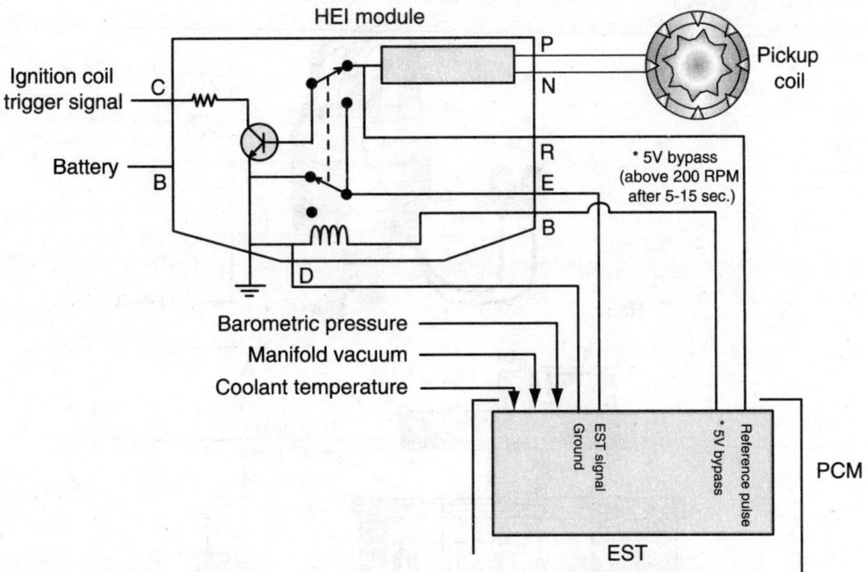

FIGURE 11-36 *A computer-controlled ignition system acts on signals received from sensors.*

making thousands of decisions in a single second. The control computer typically has the following types of information permanently programmed into it.

- *Speed-related spark advance.* As engine speed increases to a particular point, there is a need for more advanced timing. As the engine slows, the timing should be retarded or have less advance. The computer bases speed-related spark advance decisions on engine speed and signals from the TP sensor.
- *Load-related spark advance.* This is used to improve power and fuel economy during acceleration and heavy load conditions. The computer defines the load and the ideal spark advance by processing information from the TPS, MAP, and engine speed sensors. Typically, the more load on an engine, the less spark advance is needed.
- *Warmup spark advance.* This is used when the engine is cold since a greater amount of advance is required while the engine warms up.
- *Special spark advance.* This is used to improve fuel economy during steady driving conditions. During constant speed and load conditions, the engine will be more efficient with much advance timing.
- *Spark advance due to barometric pressure.* This is used when barometric pressure exceeds a preset calibrated value.

All of this information is looked at by the computer to determine the ideal spark timing for all conditions. The calibrated or programmed information in the computer is contained in what is called software **lookup tables**.

Ignition timing can also work in conjunction with the electronic fuel control system to provide emission control, optimum fuel economy, and improved driveability. They are all dependent on spark advance. An example of this type of system is used by Chrysler.

Chrysler's system has two Hall effect switches in the distributor when the engine is equipped with port fuel injection (Figure 11-37). In some units, the pickup unit used for ignition triggering is located above the pickup plate in the distributor and is referred to as the reference pickup. The second pickup unit is positioned below the plate. A ring with two notches is attached to the distribu-

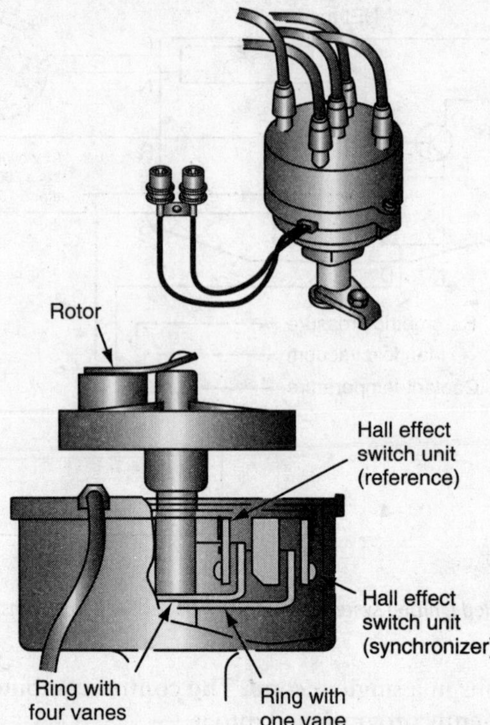

FIGURE 11-37 *A Chrysler distributor with dual Hall effect switches, both located below the breaker plate.*

tor shaft and rotates through the lower pickup unit. This lower pickup is called the synchronizer (SYNC) pickup.

In other designs, the two pickup units are mounted below the pickup plate and one set of blades rotates through both Hall effect units. The shutter blade representing number one cylinder has a large opening in the center of the blade. When this blade rotates through the SYNC pickup, a different signal is produced compared to the other blades. This number one blade signal informs the PCM when to activate the injectors.

REVIEW QUESTIONS

Short Answer Essays

1. Describe the design of the primary and secondary coil windings.
2. Explain how the voltage is induced in the distributor pickup coil as the reluctor high point approaches alignment with the pickup coil.
3. Define spark plug reach.
4. Describe the type of driving conditions when a colder range spark plug may be required.
5. Explain how the high voltage is induced in the secondary coil winding in an electronic ignition system.
6. Explain why dwell time is important to ignition system operation.

7. Name the three major functions of an ignition system.
8. What is the basic difference between the primary and secondary ignition circuits?
9. Name the engine operating conditions that affect ignition timing requirements.
10. What primary role does a rotor have in the ignition system?

Fill-in-the-Blanks

1. Modern ignition cables contain fiber cores that act as a ______________ in the secondary circuit to cut down on radio and television interference and reduce spark plug wear.
2. The ends of the secondary coil winding are usually connected to the terminal in the coil tower and one of the ______________ terminals.
3. The arrival of the spark is timed to coincide with the ______________ stroke of the piston.
4. Basic ignition timing is typically ______________ with increases in engine speed and ______________ with heavy engine load.
5. The ignition system has two interconnected electrical circuits: a ______________ circuit and a ______________ circuit.
6. The ______________ interrupts primary current flow, collapsing the magnetic field and creating a high-voltage surge in the ignition coil secondary winding.
7. The switching device used in electronic systems is a(n) ______________.
8. ______________ ______________ ______________ and ______________ ______________ sensors are the most widely used engine position sensors.
9. A cold-range spark plug has a ______________ heat path compared to a hot-range spark plug.
10. Computer-controlled ignition systems rely on the inputs from various ______________ to control ignition timing.

Multiple Choice

1. *Technician A* says that the primary voltage can surge as high as 4,000 volts when the secondary ignition fires.

   Technician B says most distributor ignitions have a secondary voltage potential as high as 25,000 to 50,000 volts.

   Who is correct?

   A. Technician A C. Both technicians
   B. Technician B D. Neither technician

2. All of the listed are jobs of the ignition system ***except:***

   A. Spark production C. Valve timing
   B. Spark timing D. Duration

3. *Technician A* says the crankshaft turns through more degrees in a given amount of time at a higher rpm.

   Technician B says that the timing must be retarded at higher engine speeds.

Who is correct?

A. Technician A C. Both technicians
B. Technician B D. Neither technician

4. While discussing engine loads and ignition timing,

Technician A says that under a heavy load, the throttle plates are closed and the air-fuel mixture is restricted, creating a slow burning mixture, which means the ignition timing, must be advanced.

Technician B says that under a light load, the throttle plates are open and the air-fuel mixture is large, creating a fast burning mixture, which means the ignition timing must be retarded.

Who is correct?

A. Technician A C. Both technicians
B. Technician B D. Neither technician

5. *Technician A* says the ignition coil is actually where the primary and secondary circuits meet.

Technician B says the ignition system must take 12 volts and produce 40,000 volts or more in the secondary.

Who is correct?

A. Technician A C. Both technicians
B. Technician B D. Neither technician

6. *Technician A* says the amount of time the coil is switched on is called dwell time.

Technician B says the amount of time the coil is switched off depends on the ignition timing.

Who is correct?

A. Technician A C. Both technicians
B. Technician B D. Neither technician

7. While discussing ignition coils,

Technician A says enough saturation time is important to be able to properly fire the spark plugs.

Technician B says that saturation is the point of minimum current flow through the coil.

Who is correct?

A. Technician A C. Both technicians
B. Technician B D. Neither technician

8. *Technician A* says the ignition module controls the power connection to the ignition coil.

Technician B says the correct time to turn the coil on and off is determined from the triggering device.

Who is correct?

A. Technician A C. Both technicians
B. Technician B D. Neither technician

9. The ignition module triggering devices can be all of the below ***except:***

A. Photoelectric sensor
B. Metal detection sensor
C. Hall effect sensor
D. Piezoelectric sensor

10. *Technician A* says the Hall effect sensor is not commonly used today.

    Technician B says these sensors were first used in early 1982.

    Who is correct?

    A. Technician A
    B. Technician B
    C. Both technicians
    D. Neither technician

ELECTRONIC IGNITION (EI) SYSTEMS

12

Upon completion and review of this chapter, you should be able to:

- Explain the purpose of the electronic control unit.
- Describe the various types of spark timing systems, including electronic switching systems and their related engine position sensors.
- Explain how the fuel injection system may rely on components of the ignition system.
- Describe the advantages and operation of distributorless electronic ignition (EI) systems.
- Describe the secondary ignition wiring connections on an EI system, including an explanation of how the spark plugs fire.
- Explain the coil and injector sequencing on a Chrysler system while cranking the engine.
- Explain why some EI systems may be called "fast-start" systems.
- Explain the purpose of the SYNC sensor signal in an EI system with a combined crankshaft and SYNC sensor.
- Describe the operating principles of a coil-on-plug (COP) system.
- Explain the basic operation of ion sensing ignition
- Explain the basic operation of compression sense ignition

INTRODUCTION

The purpose of the ignition system is to supply the spark needed to initiate the combustion of the air-fuel charge in the correct cylinder at the correct time for the proper duration. The ignition system functions similarly in all engines because a spark will arc across the gap of the spark plug at the right moment, igniting the mixture in the combustion chamber. The delivery of the spark is the function of the secondary ignition system, while the production and timing of the spark is the function of the primary ignition circuit. These principles have not changed in decades. What *has* changed are the components that make these events occur and how they operate. Ignition systems have progressed from fully mechanical breaker point systems with vacuum- and mechanically-controlled timing advance units to systems that have no moving parts and are purely electronically operated. In this chapter, we will build on the concepts previously introduced and explore the operation and design of distributorless electronic ignition (EI) systems.

EI and DI systems do of course share many elements. The primary circuit, secondary circuit, and the ignition coil work basically the same way they do in a distributor ignition with some variations. The module still needs a trigger to tell it when to fire, the module still controls the primary circuit, and the secondary circuit still provides the voltage to fire the spark plug. If you have a good understanding of distributor ignition (DI), electronic ignition (EI) should not be difficult.

The PCM still controls timing advance using its array of sensors such as TP sensor, MAF, or MAP, CTS, IAT, and others that result in a system that is efficient and provides the most power possible.

Distributorless ignition systems manufactured today, now simply referred to as electronic ignition (EI) systems, can be categorized similarly. The ignition control modules can be mounted directly with the coil pack(s), remotely mounted from the coil pack(s), or as an internal function of the vehicle's PCM. All EI systems manufactured today have computer-controlled timing. Variations of the EI systems include one coil for two spark plugs or one coil per plug either mounted directly over the spark plug or connected with a spark plug wire. The single coil mounted directly to the spark plug is commonly referred to as a coil-on-plug (COP) system, while the single coil connected to a spark plug with a spark plug wire is referred to as a coil-near-plug (CNP).

Ignition Coils and Primary Circuit Controls

As we discussed in the chapter on distributor ignitions, ignition current control depends on engine speed. At idle, there is more than enough time to saturate the ignition coil between cylinder firings. One of the advantages of EI ignition is the fact that there is more than one coil and, consequently, more time for saturation. The control of timing is the responsibility of the ignition module until the engine starts, at which time the PCM takes over timing based on inputs from the engine sensors such as TP sensor, MAP, MAF, IAT, CTS, KS, and others, much as in the DI systems from the previous chapters.

Triggering Devices

Just as in the DI system, the triggering device shows the crankshaft position. Waste spark systems only need to know which pair of cylinders is coming to TDC, not which cylinder is under compression. Some EI systems, such as coil near plug and coil over plug, need to know the position of the camshaft also in which case the cam sensor is also a triggering device. The Hall effect, permanent magnet, and magneto resistive sensors have seen heavy use as EI triggering sensors on EI systems. The triggering device signal has to be amplified to be used by both the ignition control module (ICM) and the PCM. The ICM sends a signal to the PCM to inform it of engine speed. Based on its inputs, the PCM then adds in the proper amount of ignition timing and sends this information back to the ICM.

Hall Effect Switches

As was described in detail in Chapter 11, the Hall effect switch is a highly accurate triggering device that has found popularity in EI systems (Figure 12-1). When a metal vane passes between a magnet and a semiconductor, the magnetic field is temporarily interrupted and the module voltage supply is pulled high by the sensor. After going through the Schmidt trigger, the waveform is inverted, so a high signal is low and vice versa.

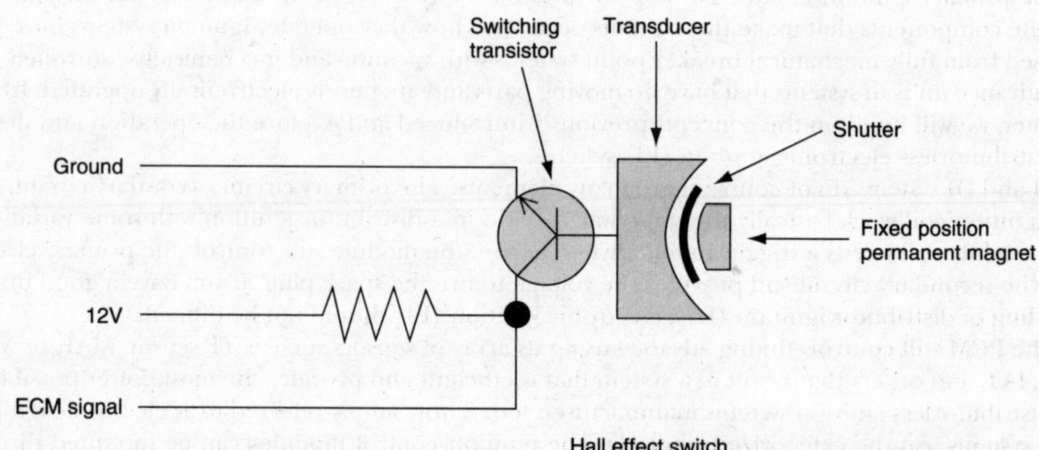

FIGURE 12-1 *The position of the shutter blade in or out of the Hall effect sensor will produce either an on or off signal.*

Hall effect sensors are also used as crankshaft sensors. The shutter or interrupter blades are usually part of the engine's lower crankshaft pulley. The Hall effect sensor is mounted in a fashion that allows the interrupter blades of the crankshaft pulley to pass through the sensor opening. Some sensors are configured to read two sets of interrupter blades—an inner ring and an outer ring. In a slightly different arrangement, Hall effect sensors are also used as camshaft position sensors and are often mounted where the distributor used to be. Multiple camshaft sensors can be found on engines with multiple camshafts. Additional information on these types and other sensors used on EI systems is discussed later in this chapter.

Pull-up and Pull-down Hall Effect Circuits

The Hall effect switch can be used to ground or open a circuit with the interrupter blade located within the switch. This is referred to as either a pull-up or a pull-down-type circuit. The Hall effect switch may switch a source voltage provided internally by the module to ground or switch an externally sourced supply voltage going to the module. It will be necessary to understand the function of the switch in order to interpret the expected results when testing.

Permanent Magnet Sensors

The permanent magnet sensor is similar in construction to the pickup coil used in distributor ignitions although they appear to be much different (Figure 12-2). The sensor is basically a magnet and a coil of wires that produces an A/C output voltage as a gear, reluctor ring, or toothed wheel passes nearby in order to send an analog signal to the PCM and/or the ignition module which is then converted to a useable digital signal.

Magneto Resistive Sensor

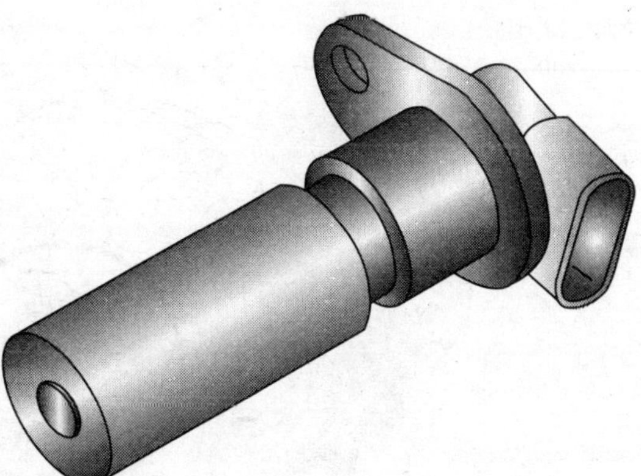

FIGURE 12-2 *A permanent magnet type crankshaft sensor.*

The magneto resistive sensor is nothing more than an enhanced Hall effect crankshaft sensor and is able to produce two signals from a single source. The MR sensor is triggered by a crankshaft reluctor wheel. Similar to the Hall effect switch, the MR sensor has three wires and outputs a digital signal. A permanent magnet is located within the sensor and is positioned between two magnetic reluctance pickups. The magnetic fields within the sensor react to the passing reluctor wheel. The two pickups read the approaching reluctor tooth. After the tooth passes the first pickup, it immediately passes the second pickup. Both pickups produce identical signals. However, the signal from the second pickup is slightly delayed because of its position in relation to the approaching reluctor tooth. The data received by any of the triggering systems discussed is essential to ignition and fuel injection control. Advances in the triggering systems, electronics, and processors used in many late-model designs make it possible to control ignition timing on a per-cylinder basis and store misfire information in the PCM's memory. In addition, most systems employ some failsafe strategies in the event of a compound failure. If necessary, the PCM is programmed to default to other incoming signals as a substitute, thereby keeping the engine running until it can be serviced.

ELECTRONIC IGNITION (EI) SYSTEMS (DISTRIBUTORLESS)

Electronic ignition (EI) systems (Figure 12-3), have no distributor. Spark distribution is controlled by an electronic control unit and/or the vehicle's computer. Instead of a single ignition coil for all cylinders, each cylinder may have its own ignition coil, or two cylinders may share one coil. The coils are wired directly to the spark plug they control. An ignition control module, tied into the vehicle's computer control system, controls the firing order and the spark timing and advance. This module is typically located under the coil assembly.

In many EI systems, a crank sensor located at the front of the crankshaft is used to trigger the ignition system. When a distributor is used in the ignition system, the distributor drive gear, shaft, and bushings are subject to wear. Worn distributor components cause erratic ignition timing and spark advance, which result in reduced economy and performance plus increased exhaust emissions. Since the distributor is eliminated in EI systems, ignition timing remains more stable over the life of the engine, which means improved economy and performance with reduced emissions.

There are many advantages of a **distributorless ignition system** over one that uses a distributor. Here are some of the more important ones:

- Fewer moving parts, therefore less friction and wear.
- Flexibility in mounting location. This is important with today's smaller engine compartments.
- Less required maintenance—there is no rotor or distributor cap to service.
- Reduced radio frequency interference because there is no rotor to cap gap.
- Elimination of a common cause of ignition misfire—the buildup of water and ozone/nitric acid in the distributor cap.
- Elimination of mechanical timing adjustments.
- Has no mechanical load on the engine to operate.

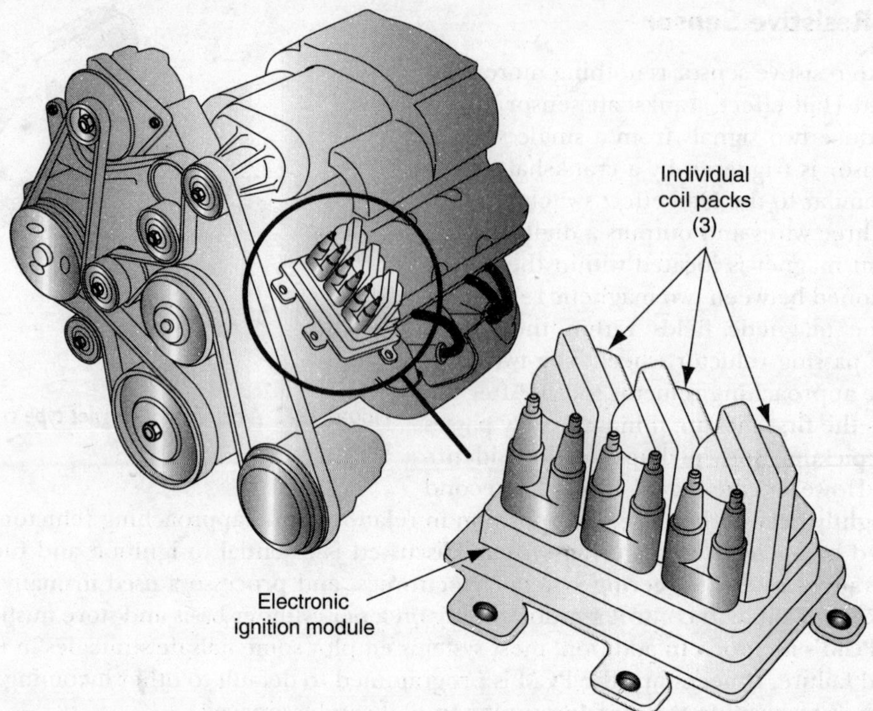

FIGURE 12-3 *A supercharged Buick 3800 V6 engine with an electronic ignition (EI) system.*

- Increased available time for coil saturation.
- Increased time between firings, which allows the coil to cool more.

In a distributorless ignition system, each end of the secondary winding of a coil is connected to a spark plug. These two spark plugs are on companion cylinders and are at TDC at the same time. One of them is on the compression stroke, and the other is on its exhaust stroke. When a coil fires its two spark plugs, the plug that fires into the exhaust stroke is the waste plug.

Since the polarity of the primary and secondary windings are fixed, one plug always fires in a forward direction and the other in a reverse direction. The voltage dropped across each plug is determined by its polarity and cylinder pressure. Therefore, the spark plug firing into the exhaust requires much less voltage than the one firing into the compressed gases. The voltage demand to fire both plugs in series is greater than the required voltage to fire one plug. This is not a problem in these systems. There is plenty of voltage available because of the longer coil saturation times due to the longer intervals between firings.

It is no mystery how an individual coil pack simultaneously fires two spark plugs. It is nothing more than a standard ignition coil reconfigured to connect to two spark plugs rather than a single ignition coil tower to a coil wire. When a distributor ignition system coil fires, the voltage leaves the coil terminal through a coil wire connected to the center terminal of the distributor cap. The center terminal inside the cap is in contact with the rotor terminal that passes by the appropriate terminal of the distributor cap in order to deliver spark to the correct spark plug wire. The wire delivers the voltage to the spark plug in the cylinder at the end of its compression stroke. Once the voltage jumps the gap of the spark plug, a spark is formed. However, this is not the end of the voltage journey. Once the spark has crossed the gap of the spark plug, it must return to its source in order to complete the circuit. In other words, it must return to the ignition coil. Various manufacturers have utilized several designs that accomplish this. The best example of this concept is the GM HEI system, which uses an integral ignition coil. Once the spark plug fires, the residual voltage is returned to the ignition coil. It travels through the cylinder head, engine, module housing, and, finally, to a single wire that returns to the core of the ignition coil. This black wire is the other end of the secondary winding in the epoxy of the ignition coil. Instead of a direct connection, if another spark plug were placed in series with the wire, the voltage would have to pass through the second spark plug to complete the circuit. Of course, this would cause a spark to jump the gap of the second spark plug in the series circuit. The single coil pack units designed for EI systems use the same principle. The coils are designed to have enough substantial voltage potential to satisfy all types of operating conditions as well as fire two spark plugs in the same circuit.

BASIC COMPONENTS

Electronic ignition systems electronically perform the functions of a distributor. They control spark timing and advance in the same manner as the computer-controlled ignition systems. Yet EI is a step beyond the computer-controlled system because it also distributes spark electronically instead of mechanically. The distributor is completely eliminated from these systems. Distributorless systems use multiple coils and modules to provide and distribute high secondary voltages directly from the coil to the plug.

The computer, ignition module, and position sensors combine to control spark timing and advance. The computer collects and processes information to determine the ideal amount of spark advance for the operating conditions. The ignition module uses crank/cam sensor data to control the timing of the primary circuit in the coils. The ignition module synchronizes the coils' firing sequence in relation to crankshaft position and firing order of the engine. Therefore, the ignition module takes the place of the distributor.

Depending on the exact EI system, the ignition coils can be serviced separately or as a complete unit. The coil assembly (Figure 12-4) is typically called a **coil pack** and is comprised of two or more individual coils.

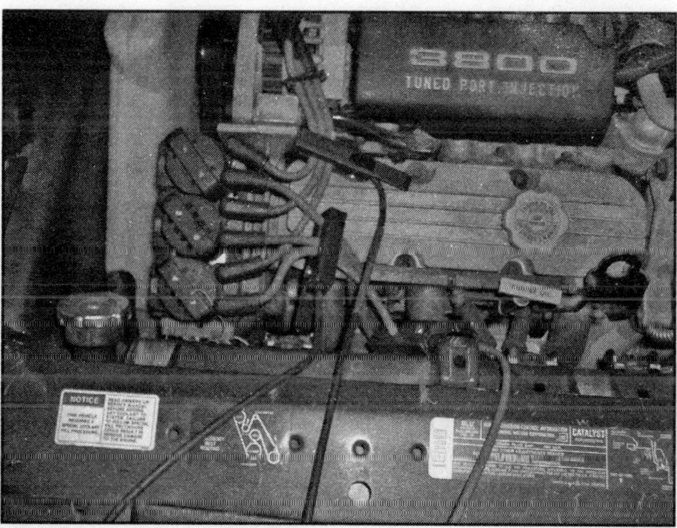

FIGURE 12-4 *A coil pack for a six-cylinder EI system.*

On those EI systems that use one coil per spark plug, the electronic ignition module determines when each spark plug should fire and controls the on/off time of each plug's coil.

The systems with a coil for every two spark plugs also use an electronic ignition module but utilize the **waste spark** method of spark distribution. Each end of the coil's secondary winding is attached to a spark plug. Each coil is connected to a pair of spark plugs. When the field collapses in the coil, voltage is sent to both spark plugs that are attached to the coil. In most V6s, the paired cylinders are 1 and 4, 2 and 5, and 3 and 6 (or 4 and 1 and 3 and 2 on four-cylinder engines). With this arrangement, one cylinder of each pair is on its compression stroke while the other is on the exhaust stroke. Both cylinders receive spark simultaneously, but only one spark generates power while the other is wasted out in the exhaust. During the next revolution, the roles are reversed.

Due to the way the secondary coils are wired, when the induced voltage cuts across the primary and secondary windings of the coil, one plug fires in the normal direction—center electrode to side electrode—and the other plug fires just the reverse-side to center electrode (Figure 12-5). Both plugs fire simultaneously, completing the series circuit. Each plug in the set always fires the same way regardless of the stroke the piston is on.

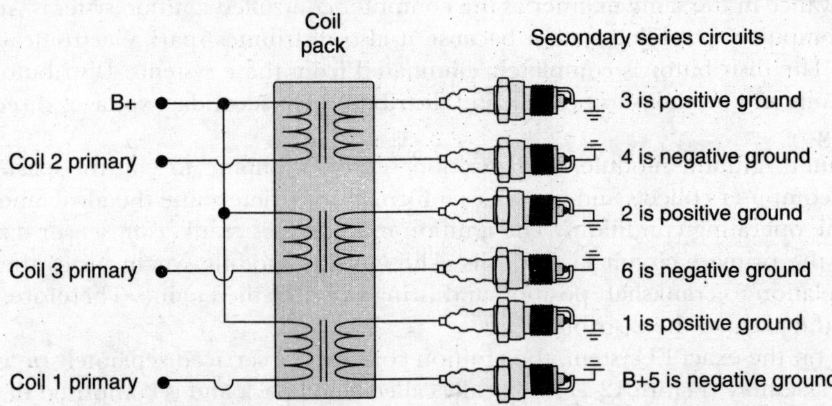

FIGURE 12-5 *Polarity of the spark plugs in an EI system.*

The coil is able to overcome the increased voltage requirements caused by reversed polarity and still fire two plugs simultaneously because each coil is capable of producing very high voltages. There is very little resistance across the plug gap on exhaust so that plug requires very little voltage to fire thereby providing its mate (the plug that is on compression) with plenty of available voltage.

Primary current is controlled by transistors in the control module. There is one switching transistor for each ignition coil in the system. The transistors complete the ground circuit for the primary, thereby allowing for a dwell period. When primary current flow is interrupted, secondary voltage is induced in the coil and the coil's spark plug(s) fire. The timing and sequencing of ignition coil action is determined by the control module and input from a triggering device.

The control module is also responsible for limiting the dwell time. In EI systems, there is time between plug firings to saturate the coil. Achieving maximum current flow through the coil is great if the system needs the high voltage that may be available. If the high voltage is not needed, the high current is not needed and the heat it produces is not desired. Therefore, the control module is programmed to only allow total coil saturation when the very high voltage is needed or the need for it is anticipated.

A few engines have an EI system in which the coils are mounted directly over the spark plugs so that no wiring between the coils and plugs is necessary (Figure 12-6). On other systems, the coil packs are mounted remote from the spark plugs (Figure 12-7). High-tension secondary wires carry high-voltage current from the coils to the plugs.

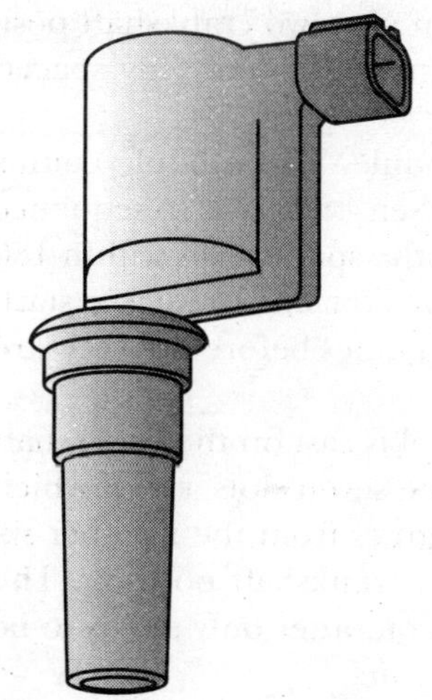

FIGURE 12-6 *A coil-on-plug assembly.*

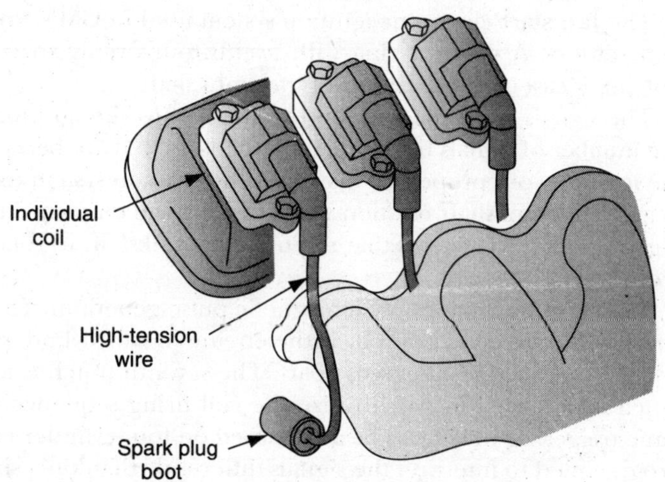

FIGURE 12-7 *Coil-near-plug systems typically have one coil per cylinder.*

EI SYSTEM OPERATION

From a general operating standpoint, most distributorless ignition systems are similar. However, there are variations in the way different distributorless systems obtain a timing reference in regard to crankshaft and camshaft position.

Some engines use separate Hall effect sensors to monitor crankshaft and camshaft position for the control of ignition and fuel injection firing orders. The crankshaft pulley has interrupter rings that equal in number to half of the cylinders of the engine. The resultant signal informs the powertrain control module (PCM) as to when to fire the plugs. The camshaft sensor helps the computer determine when the number one piston is at TDC on the compression stroke.

Defining the different types of EI systems used by manufacturers focuses on the location and type of sensors used. There are other differences, such as the construction of the coil pack, wherein some are a sealed assembly and others have individually mounted ignition coils. Some EI systems have a camshaft sensor mounted in the opening where the distributor was mounted. The camshaft sensor ring has one notch and produces a leading edge and trailing edge signal once per camshaft revolution. These systems also use a crankshaft sensor. Both the camshaft and crankshaft sensors are Hall effect sensors.

Some systems have the camshaft sensor mounted in the front of the timing chain cover. A magnet on the camshaft gear rotates past the inner end of the camshaft sensor and produces a signal for each camshaft revolution.

Other systems use a dual crankshaft sensor located behind the crankshaft pulley. When this type of sensor is used, there are two interrupter rings on the back of the pulley that rotate through the Hall effect switches at the dual crankshaft sensor. The inner ring with three equally spaced blades rotate through the inner Hall effect switch, whereas the outer ring with one opening rotates through the outer Hall effect.

In this dual sensor, the inner sensor provides three leading edge signals, and the outer sensor produces one leading edge during one complete revolution of the crankshaft. The outer sensor is the SYNC sensor.

The examples given so far depend on two revolutions of the crankshaft to inform the PCM as to when the number one cylinder is ready. The engine must crank through up to two crankshaft revolutions before ignition begins.

The **fast start** electronic ignition system used in GM's Northstar system uses two crankshaft position sensors. A reluctor ring with twenty-four evenly spaced notches and eight unevenly spaced notches is cast onto the center of the crankshaft.

The signals from the two sensors are sent to the ignition control module. This module counts the number of signals from one of the sensors that are between the other sensor signals to sequence the ignition coils properly. This allows the ignition system to begin firing the spark plugs within 180 degrees of crankshaft rotation while starting the engine. This system allows for much quicker starting than other EI systems that require the crankshaft to rotate one or two times before the coils are sequenced.

Finally, some engines use a magnetic pulse generator. The timing wheel is cast on the crankshaft and has machined slots on it. If the engine has six cylinders, there will be seven slots, six of which are spaced exactly 60 degrees apart. The seventh notch is located 10 degrees from the number six notch and is used to synchronize the coil firing sequence in relation to crankshaft position. The same triggering wheel can be and is used on four-cylinder engines. The computer only needs to be programmed to interpret the signals differently than on a six-cylinder engine.

The magnetic sensor, which protrudes into the side of the block, generates a small AC voltage each time one of the machined slots passes by. By counting the time between pulses, the ignition module picks out the unevenly spaced seventh slot, which starts the calculation of the ignition coil sequencing. Once its counting is synchronized with the crankshaft, the module is programmed to accept the AC voltage signals of the select notches for firing purposes.

The development and spreading popularity of EI is the result of reduced emissions, improved fuel economy, and increased component reliability brought about by these systems.

EI offers advantages in production costs and maintenance considerations. By removing the distributor, the manufacturers realize a substantial savings in ignition parts and related machining costs. By eliminating the distributor, they also do away with cracked caps, eroded carbon buttons, burned-through rotors, moisture misfiring, base timing adjustments, and other problems.

EI SYSTEMS WITH THE CAM SENSOR IN THE DISTRIBUTOR OPENING

Locating the cam sensor in the opening previously occupied by the distributor merely takes advantage of the bore and gear that was already present. Seeing that the distributor was driven by the camshaft at camshaft speed, driving a camshaft position sensor by the same mechanism just made sense. This modification really made sense when older engine designs were modified for distributorless ignition. A few new engine designs place the cam sensor where the distributor would have been (Figure 12-8).

Ford uses this type of cam sensor on some of their engines. This system is similar to the TFI-IV system except it does not use a distributor. A profile ignition pickup (PIP) sensor is used to monitor crankshaft position and engine speed. A cylinder identification (CID) sensor is used to identify a specific point in piston number one's travel. The EEC-IV module determines spark advance by using the PIP signal to establish base timing. A SPOUT signal is sent to the ignition (DIS) module to fire the coil and to control dwell time. Dwell time is controlled by the EEC module. CID is important to the module; it needs to know which coil to fire.

The CID (Figure 12-9) is a Hall effect switch assembly placed in the distributor bore and driven by the camshaft. The CID is a camshaft position sensor. The PIP is a Hall effect crankshaft position sensor that produces a digital signal. The PIP sends a high signal when the Hall effect switch vane shunts the magnetic lines of flux. It sends a low signal when a window allows the flux lines to cut

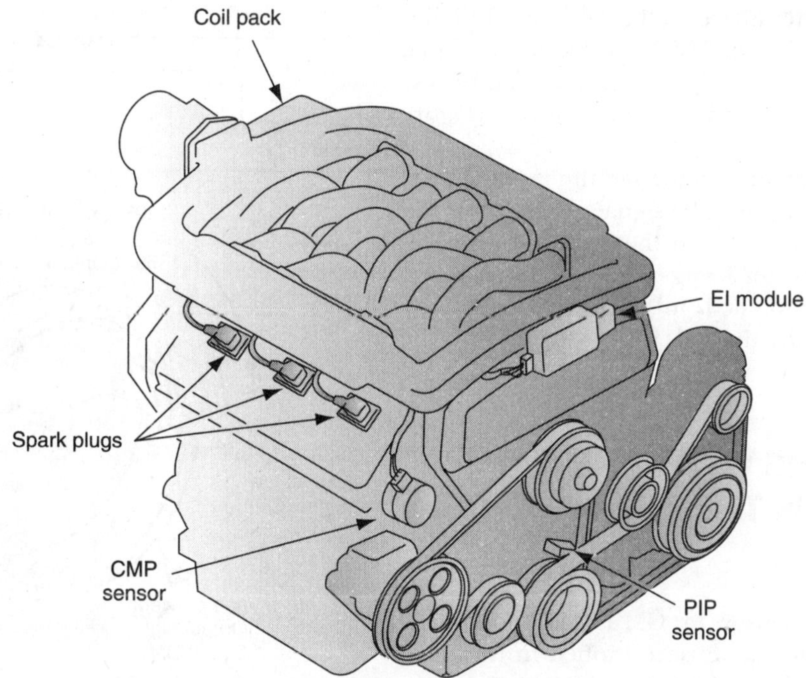

FIGURE 12-8 *Location of EI components. The (CMP) camshaft position sensor is where the distributor was previously located.*

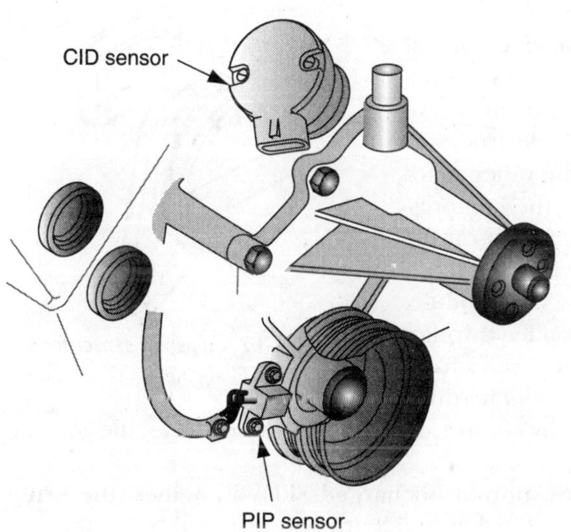

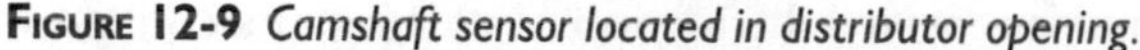

FIGURE 12-9 *Camshaft sensor located in distributor opening.*

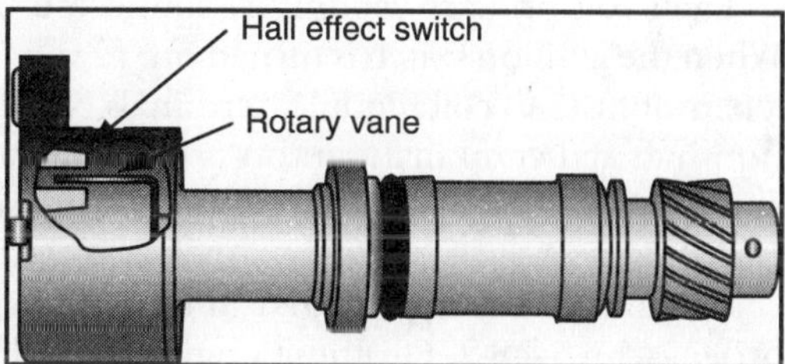

FIGURE 12-10 *Camshaft sensor construction.*

through the Hall unit. On six-cylinder engines, the PIP produces three high signals for every crankshaft revolution. The leading edge of PIP always occurs at 10 degrees BTDC. Therefore, base timing is set at 10 degrees BTDC.

The leading edge of the CID (Figure 12-10) signal to the module occurs when piston number one is at 26 degrees ATDC on its power stroke. The trailing edge always occurs at 26 degrees ATDC on the intake stroke of piston number one. Input from the CID is also used to synchronize fuel injection timing. The difference between the PIP and CID signals is that the CID produces one signal for every two revolutions of the crankshaft or one signal for every revolution of the camshaft (Figure 12-11).

When the engine is cranking, the module waits for a transition in the CID signal, either from low to high or high to low. At that point, it prepares coil number two for firing. Once the transition is complete, the module is in synch with the engine and is ready to fire the coils in accordance with the engine's firing order.

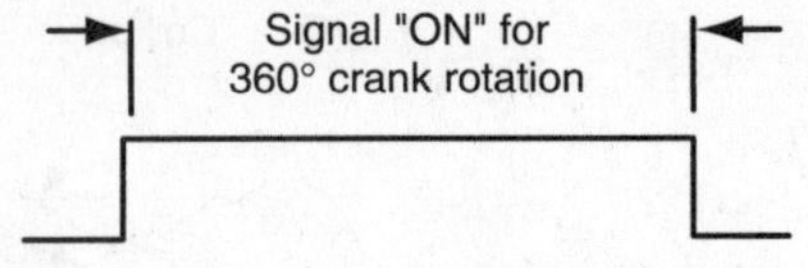

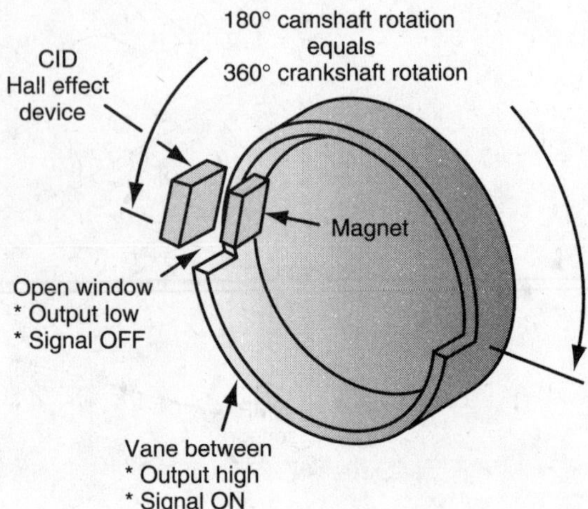

FIGURE 12-11 *Camshaft sensor operation and resulting signal.*

EI SYSTEMS WITH THE CAM SENSOR IN THE TIMING CHAIN COVER

The camshaft sensor in GM's 3.8L non-turbocharged SFI V6 engine is positioned in the front of the timing gear cover (Figure 12-12). A magnet on the camshaft gear rotates past the inner end of the camshaft sensor and produces a signal for each camshaft revolution, or every two crankshaft revolutions.

The secondary coil windings are connected to the external coil terminals, and two spark plug wires are connected to these terminals. In these systems, the secondary voltage and current move from the coil secondary winding down through the electrodes in one spark plug and up through the electrodes in the other spark plug. One spark plug fires while the cylinder is on the compression stroke, and the other spark plug fires with the cylinder on the exhaust stroke.

FIGURE 12-12 *Camshaft sensor for a Buick 3800 SFI engine.*

Each coil primary winding is connected into the coil module. When the ignition switch is turned on, 12 volts are supplied through a pair of fuses to coil module, terminals N and P. Three wires from camshaft and crankshaft sensors are connected to the coil module, and five wires are connected between the powertrain control module and the coil module (Figure 12-13).

On the 3.8L turbocharged SFI engines and 3.8L non-turbocharged SFI V6 engines, the firing order is 1-6-5-4-3-2. On these engines, spark plugs 1-4, 6-3, and 5-2 are paired together on the coil assembly. When a trailing edge camshaft sensor signal is received during initial starting, the coil module prepares to fire the coil connected to spark plugs 5-2. After the camshaft sensor signal is received, the next trailing edge crankshaft sensor signal turns on the primary circuit of the 5-2 coil, and the next leading edge crankshaft sensor signal informs the coil module to open the primary circuit of the 5-2 coil (Figure 12-14). When this coil fires, one of these cylinders is always on the compression stroke and the other cylinder is on the exhaust stroke. After the 5-2 coil firing, the coil module fires the 1-4 coil and the 6-3 coil in sequence. This firing sequence provides the correct firing order.

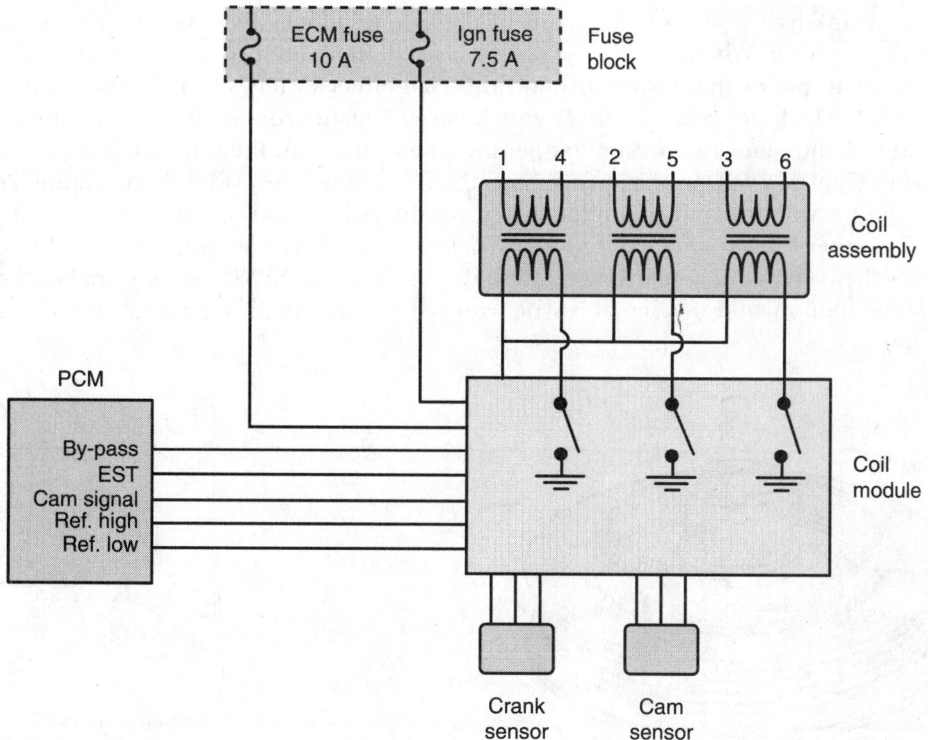

FIGURE 12-13 *Schematic for the EI system on a Buick 3.8L SFI engine.*

Crankshaft sensor signal

Camshaft sensor signal

FIGURE 12-14 *Relationship between camshaft and crankshaft sensor signals on a Buick 3.8L SFI engine.*

On an SFI engine, the PCM grounds each injector individually. The cam sensor signal is also used for injector sequencing on the 3.8L/3800 turbocharged and non-turbocharged SFI engines. This cam sensor signal is sent from the cam sensor through the coil module to the PCM. The PCM grounds each injector in the intake port when the piston for that cylinder is at 70 degrees before TDC on the intake stroke.

When a crankshaft sensor failure occurs, the engine does not start. If the camshaft sensor signal becomes defective with the engine running, the engine continues to run but the PCM reverts to multiport fuel injection without the camshaft signal information. Under this condition, engine performance and economy decrease and emission levels may increase. When the engine is shut off with a defective cam sensor, it will not restart.

EI SYSTEMS WITH A DUAL CRANKSHAFT SENSOR

GM's 3.0L V6 and the 3300 V6 multiport fuel injection engines have a dual crankshaft sensor located behind the crankshaft pulley on the front of the engine block. This system does not use a dedicated camshaft sensor. When this type of sensor is used, there are two interrupter rings on the back of the crankshaft pulley that rotate through the Hall effect switches in the dual crankshaft sensor (Figure 12-15). The inner ring with three equally spaced blades rotates through the inner Hall effect switch, whereas the outer ring with one opening rotates through the outer Hall effect switch in the dual sensor (Figure 12-16). In this dual sensor, the inner sensor provides three leading edge signals per crankshaft revolution and the outer sensor produces one leading edge signal during this time period. This outer sensor is referred to as a synchronizer (SYNC) sensor. The signal from this sensor informs the coil module regarding crankshaft position. The SYNC sensor signal occurs once per crankshaft revolution, and this signal is synchronized with the inner crankshaft sensor signal to fire the 6-3 coil.

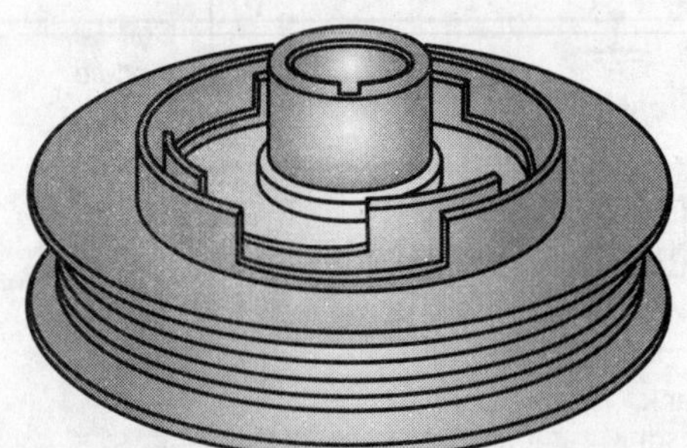

FIGURE 12-15 *Crankshaft pulley vanes for GM's 3.3L and 3300 engines.*

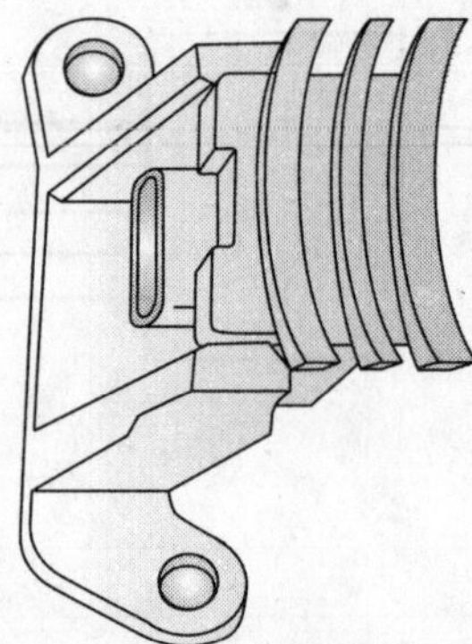

FIGURE 12-16 *Dual crankshaft sensor for GM's 3.3L and 3300 engines.*

The primary and secondary coil winding connections and the coil module-to-PCM wiring on the 3.3L or 3300 V6 engine are much the same as the wiring connections on the 3.8L turbocharged engine. The main difference in the EI systems on these engines is in the sensor wiring. Four wires extend from the dual crankshaft sensor to the coil module (Figure 12-17).

System Operation

During the start of the 3.3L or 3300 MFI engine, the leading edge SYNC sensor signal informs the coil module to sequence the primary of the 5-2 coil. The module grounds the 5-2 coil primary winding when the next trailing edge crankshaft sensor signal is received. The next leading edge inner crankshaft sensor signal informs the coil module to open the primary circuit of coil 5-2 (Figure 12-18). The coil module closes and opens the primary circuits on coils 1-4 and 6-3 in response to the next inner crankshaft sensor signals. Therefore, the firing order of 1-6-5-4-3-2 is obtained from this coil sequencing. Once the engine is running, the coil module sequences the coils properly without using the SYNC sensor signal.

Signals from the SYNC sensor are only required for coil sequencing during engine starting. Since the inner crankshaft sensor blades are spaced 60 degrees apart and the length of each blade is 60 degrees of crankshaft rotation, a leading edge inner crankshaft sensor signal is received every 120 degrees of crankshaft rotation. Each time one of these leading edge signals occurs during initial starting, the coil module opens a coil primary circuit and fires a pair of spark plugs. While the engine is starting, the bypass signal from the PCM to the coil module remains at 0 volt, and leading edge crankshaft sensor signals occur at 10 degrees BTDC on the compression stroke. The basic timing is 10 degrees BTDC and the PCM does not provide spark advance while the engine is starting. The

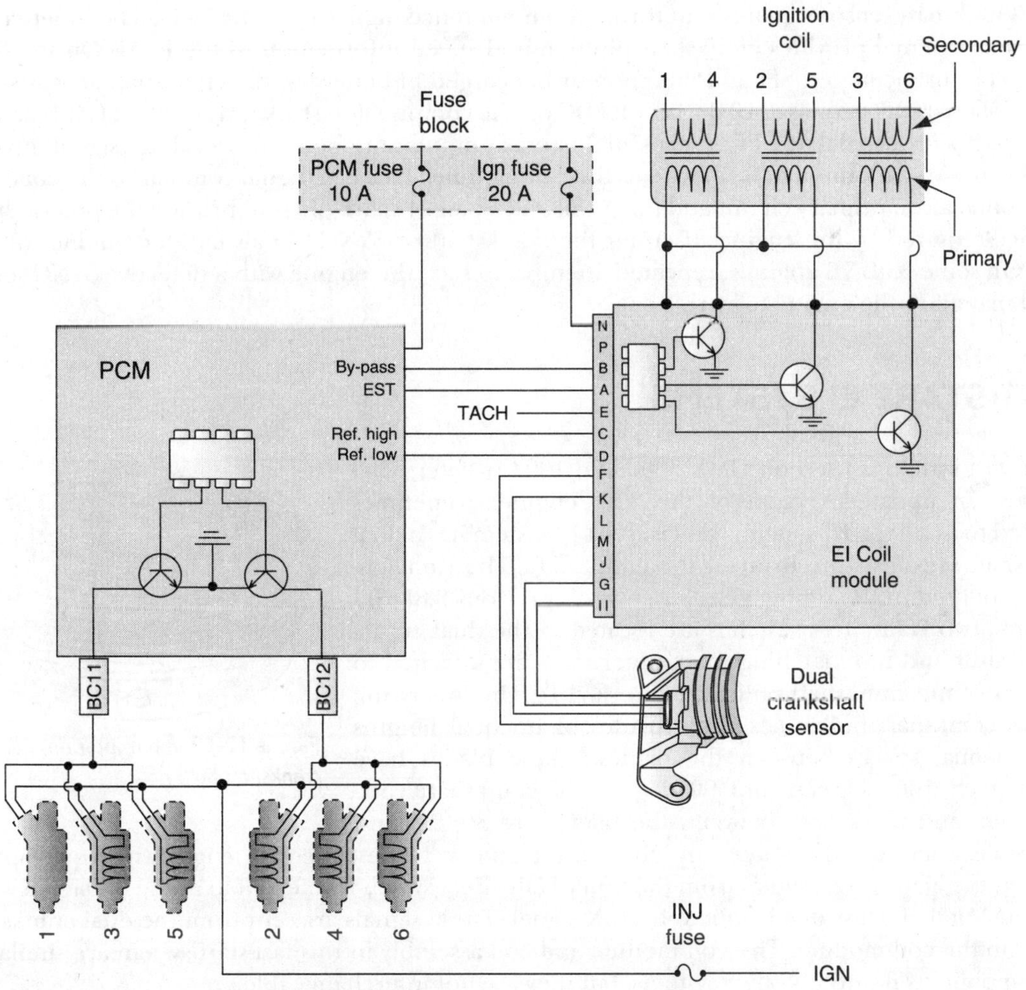

FIGURE 12-17 *Schematic for the EI system used on GM's 3.3L and 3300 engines.*

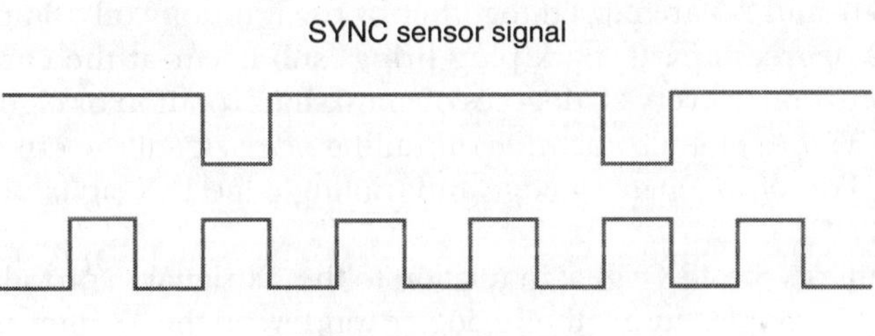

FIGURE 12-18 *Relationship between the inner crankshaft sensor and the outer SYNC signal.*

operation of these EI systems during engine starting may be referred to as a **bypass mode**. Since the SYNC signal is used for coil sequencing, it is sent to the coil module, and this signal is not sent to the PCM.

Once the engine starts, the PCM sends a 5-volt signal through the bypass wire to the coil module and the system enters the electronic spark timing (EST) mode. When this signal is received, the inner crankshaft sensor signal is sent through the reference high wire to the PCM. The inner crankshaft sensor signal provides crankshaft position and speed information to the PCM. On the 3.3L, 3300, 3.8L turbocharged SFI and 3.8L non-turbocharged SFI engines, the crankshaft sensor signal occurs when each piston is at 10 degrees BTDC on the compression stroke. When the PCM receives a crankshaft sensor signal, the PCM scans all the sensor inputs and then sends a voltage signal through the electronic spark timing (EST) wire to the coil module. This EST signal commands the coil module to open a coil primary circuit and fire a coil and a pair of spark plugs to provide the precise spark advance required by the engine. If either the crankshaft or SYNC signals fail, the engine will not start. On some 3.0L V6 engines, repeated attempts to start the engine with a defective SYNC sensor signal may allow the engine to start.

FAST-START EI SYSTEMS

A fast-start system is used on GM's 3800 and 1993 or later 3300 engines, an updated version of the 3.8L engine. Sometimes referred to as a Type-III system, this fast-start EI system has a dual crankshaft sensor at the front of the crankshaft. The cam sensor is mounted in the timing gear cover as on previous 3.8L SFI engines. Two Hall effect switches are located in the dual crankshaft sensor and two matching interrupter rings are attached to the back of the crankshaft pulley (Figure 12-19). The inner ring on the crankshaft pulley has three blades of unequal lengths with unequal spaces between the blades. These blades have 110 degrees, 100 degrees, and 90 degrees of crankshaft rotation each, and the spaces between the blades are 30, 20, and 10 degrees each. On the outer ring, there are eighteen blades of equal length with equal spaces between the blades. The signal from the inner Hall effect switch is referred to as the 3X signal while the outer Hall effect switch is called the 18X signal. These signals are sent from the dual crankshaft sensor to the coil module. The coil module and coil assembly in this fast-start system are similar to the components found on other systems, but they are not interchangeable.

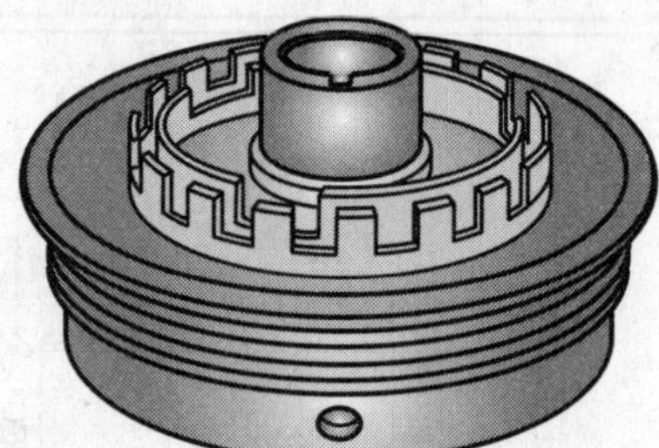

FIGURE 12-19 *Interrupter rings on a crankshaft pulley.*

The leading edge 3X signals are spaced 120 degrees apart, and each pair of cylinders that is connected to the same coil reaches TDC on the compression stroke 75 degrees after the 3X leading edge signal. Cylinders 1-4, 3-6, and 2-5 are paired together by the ignition coils. Since the leading edge 3X signals are spaced 120 degrees apart, spark plug firings still occur at the correct intervals. An 18X leading edge signal occurs once every 20 degrees of crankshaft rotation or eighteen times during one crankshaft revolution. This sensor also provides a trailing edge signal the same number of times per crankshaft revolution. Therefore, leading edge and trailing edge 18X signals occur every 10 degrees of crankshaft rotation.

The coil module monitors the 18X signal in relation to the 3X signal to provide coil sequencing while the engine is starting. For example, during the 10-degree window on the 3X interrupter blade, one trailing edge 18X signal is received. While the 20-degree window in the 18X interrupter blade rotates through the Hall effect switch, one leading edge and one trailing edge 18X signal are produced. During the 30-degree window rotation on the 3X interrupter blade, two trailing edge and one leading edge 18X signals are sent to the coil module (Figure 12-20).

The coil module knows which coil to sequence from the number of 18X signals received during each 3X window rotation. For example, when two 18X signals are received, the coil module is programmed to sequence coil 3-6 next in the firing sequence. Within 120 degrees of crankshaft rotation, the coil module can identify which coil to sequence, and thus start firing the spark

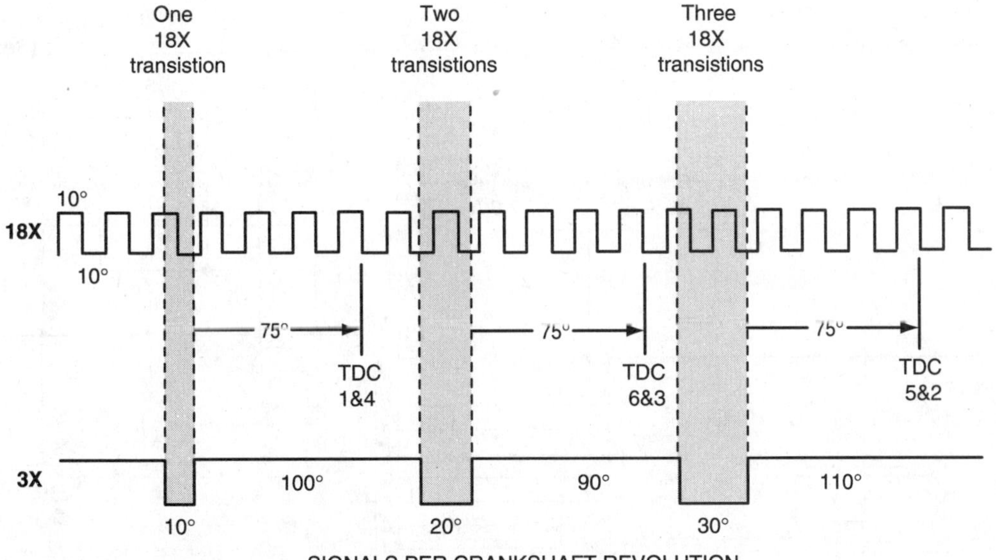

FIGURE 12-20 *3X and 18X crankshaft sensor signals.*

plugs. Therefore, the system fires the spark plugs with less crankshaft rotation during initial starting than the previous slow-start systems.

Once the engine is running, a 5-volt signal is sent from the PCM through the bypass wire to the coil module. When this signal is received, the system switches to the EST mode, and the PCM uses the 18X signal for crankshaft position and speed information. The 18X signal may be referred to as a high resolution signal (Figure 12-21).

If the 18X signal is not present, the engine will not start. When the 3X signal fails with the engine running, the engine continues to run but will refuse to restart.

In this system, the cam sensor signal is used for injector sequencing but it is not required for coil sequencing. If the cam sensor signal fails, the PCM logic begins sequencing the injectors after two cranking revolutions. There is a one in six chance that the PCM logic will ground the injectors in the normal sequence. When the PCM logic does not ground the injectors in the normal sequence, the engine hesitates on acceleration.

FAST-START EI SYSTEMS WITH TWO CRANKSHAFT SENSORS

The fast-start electronic ignition system used in GM's Northstar system uses two crankshaft position sensors. A reluctor ring with twenty-four evenly spaced notches and eight unevenly spaced notches is cast onto the center of the crankshaft (Figure 12-22).

When the reluctor ring rotates past the magnetic-type sensors, each sensor produces 32 high- and low-voltage signals per crankshaft revolution. The "A" sensor is positioned in the upper crankcase, and the "B" sensor is positioned in the lower crankcase. Since the A sensor is above the B sensor, the signal from the A sensor occurs 27 degrees before the B sensor signal (Figure 12-23).

The signals from the two sensors are sent to the ignition control module (ICM). This module counts the number of B sensor signals between the A sensor signals to sequence the ignition coils properly. There can be zero, one, or two B sensor signals between the A signals. When starting the engine, the module begins counting B sensor signals between the A signals as soon as the module

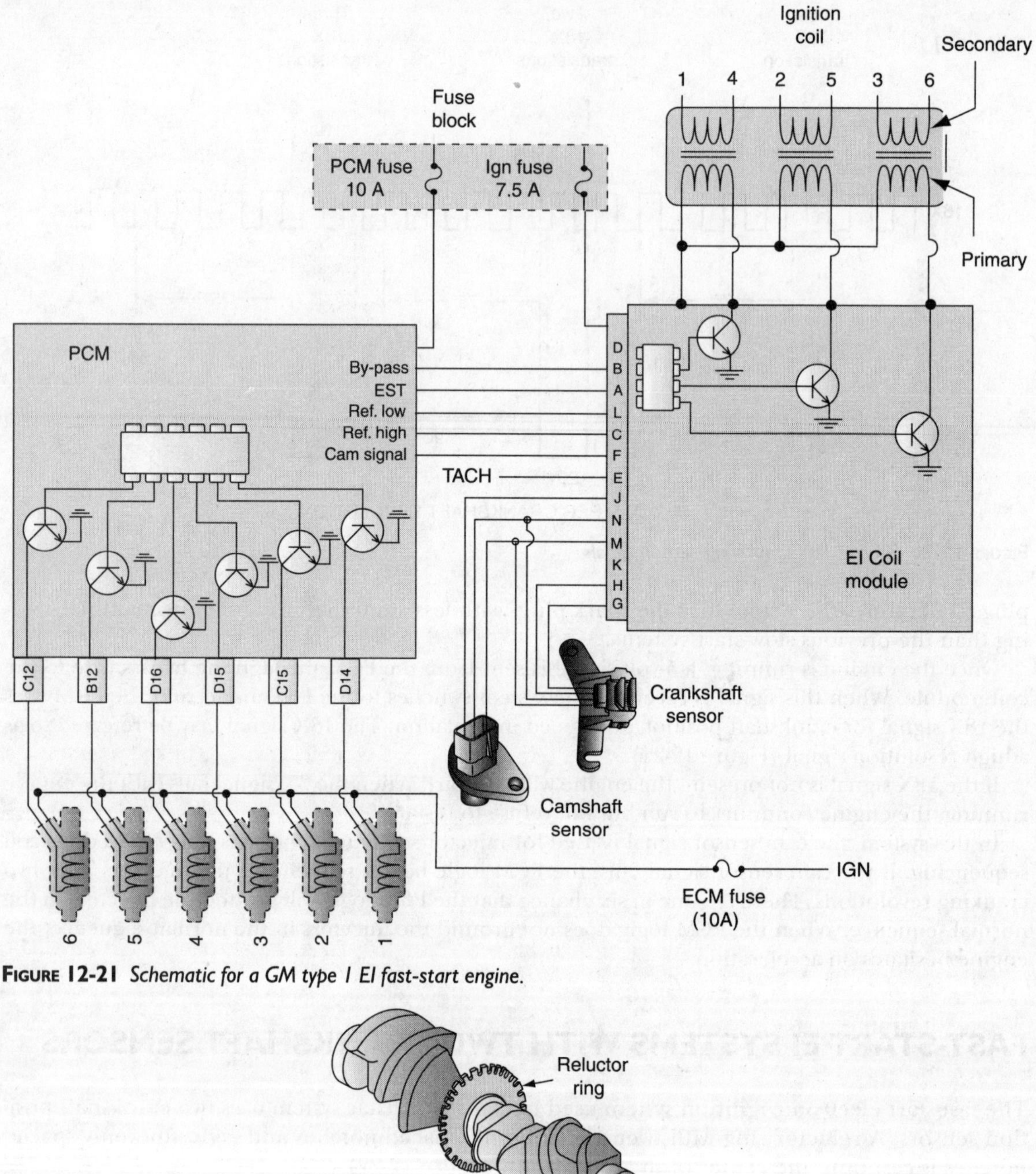

FIGURE 12-21 *Schematic for a GM type 1 EI fast-start engine.*

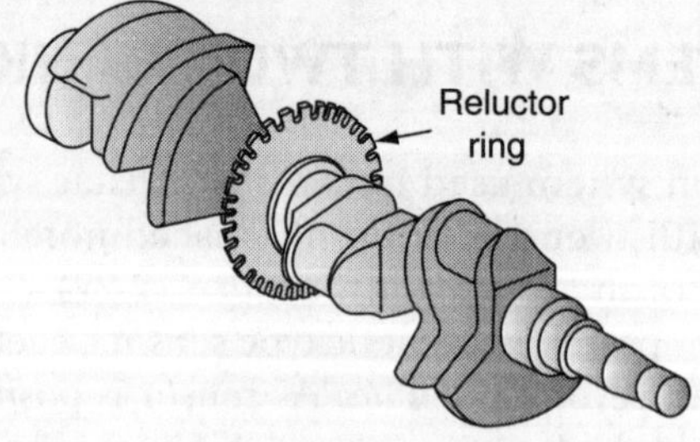

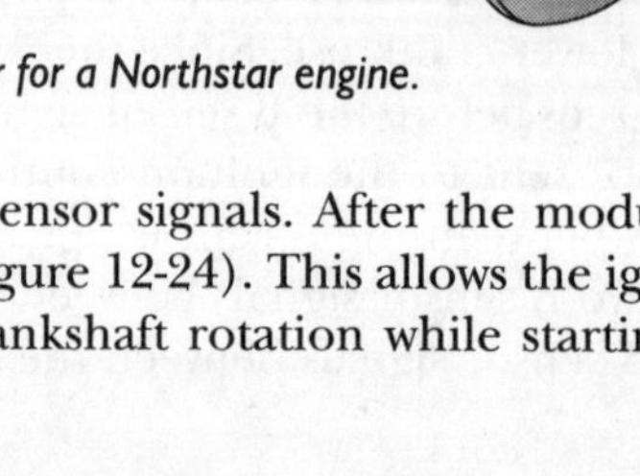

FIGURE 12-22 *Crankshaft with reluctor for a Northstar engine.*

senses zero B signals between sensor signals. After the module senses four B signals, the module sequences the coils properly (Figure 12-24). This allows the ignition system to begin firing the spark plugs within 180 degrees of crankshaft rotation while starting the engine. This system allows for

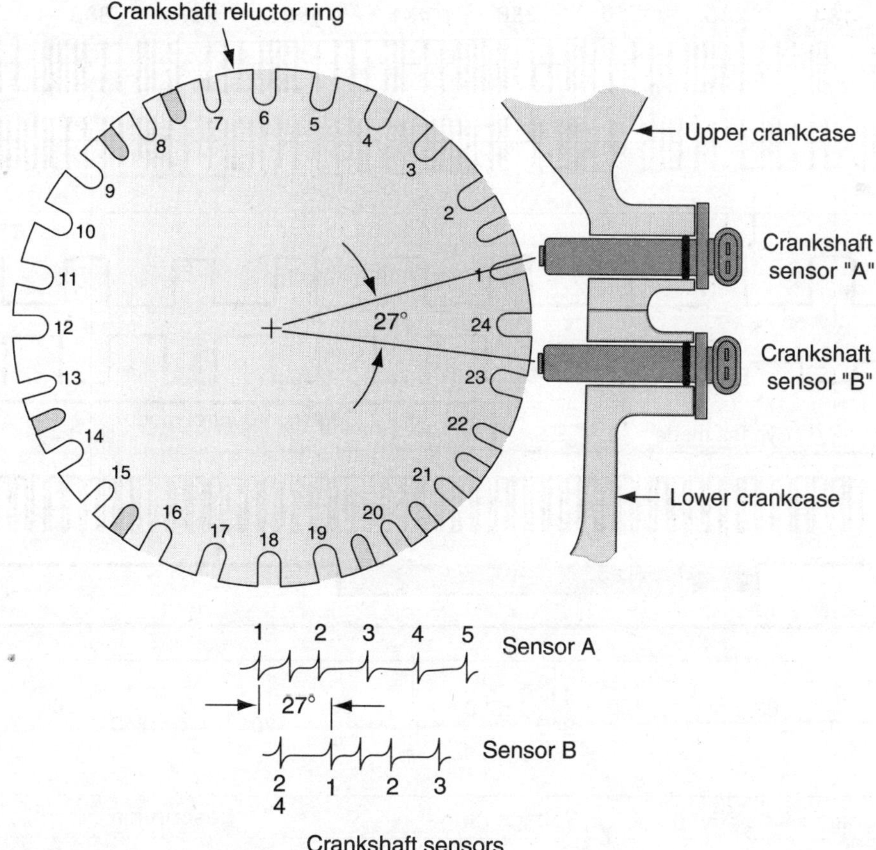

FIGURE 12-23 *A and B sensors in a Northstar engine.*

much quicker starting than other EI systems that require the crankshaft to rotate one or two times before the coils are sequenced.

System Operation

Once the engine starts, the PCM switches from the bypass mode to the ignition control mode. The ICM uses the A and B crankshaft sensor signals to determine the exact crankshaft position and rpm, and the ICM relays this information to the PCM with 4X reference and 24X voltage signals. The PCM scans all the other input sensor signals and calculates the precise spark advance required by the engine. The PCM sends an ignition control signal to the ICM that informs the ICM to turn off the appropriate coil primary at the proper time to supply the correct spark advance. The reference cam low wire is a ground wire between the ICM and the PCM (Figure 12-25). If the engine detonates, the knock sensor signal informs the PCM to reduce the spark advance.

The camshaft position sensor is located in the rear cylinder bank in front of the exhaust camshaft sprocket. A reluctor pin in the sprocket rotates past the sensor, and this sensor produces one high and one low voltage signal every camshaft revolution or every two crankshaft revolutions (Figure 12-26). The PCM uses the camshaft position sensor signal to sequence the injectors properly.

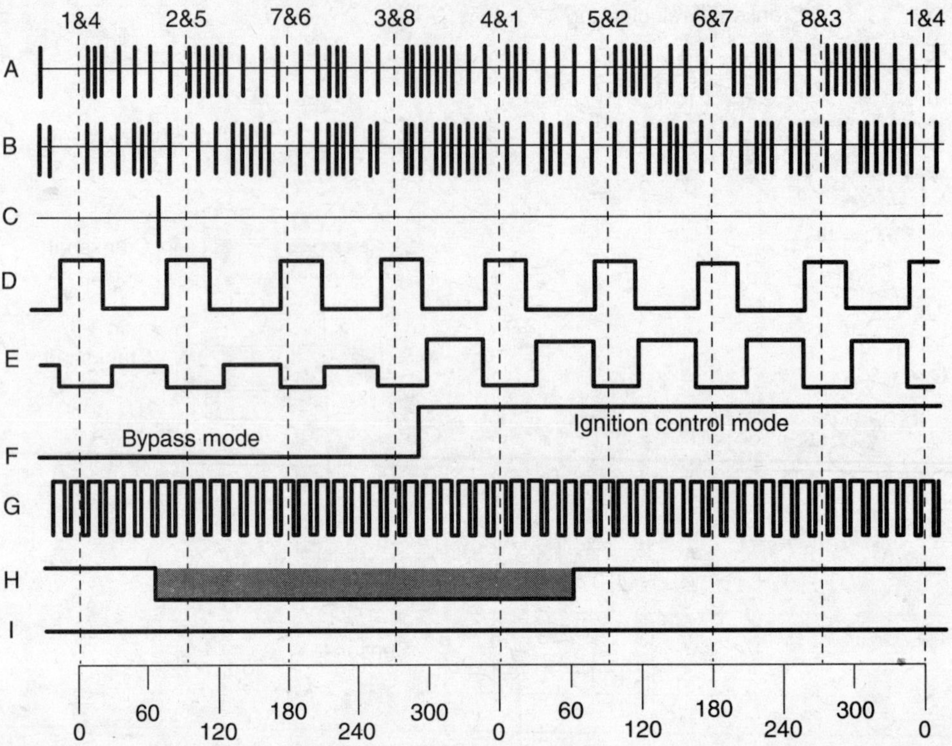

Signal	Name	Voltage range	Description
A	Crankshaft position "A" sensor	+/– 100V AC	Voltage and frequency varies with rpm
B	Crankshaft position "B" sensor	+/– 100V AC	Voltage and frequency varies with rpm
C	Camshaft position sensor	+/– 100V AC	Voltage and frequency varies with rpm (signal occurs every 720°)
D	4X reference HI	0-5V DC	Key "ON", engine "OFF"= signal is HI HI to LO occurs at first SYNC
E	Ignition control	0-5V DC	PCM send signal to ICM (falling edge signal ICM to stop pri. current)
F	Bypass	0-5V DC	Key "ON", engine "OFF"= signal is LO LO to HI occurs with PCM control
G	24X crank	0-5V DC	This signal remains HI if fault is found with A, B, or C signals
H	1/2X cam HI	0-5V DC	PCM uses this signal for fuel control
I	Ref LO/Cam LO	0V DC	Ground reference between PCM and ICM

Figure 12-24 *Operation of the EI fast-start system used on Northstar engine.*

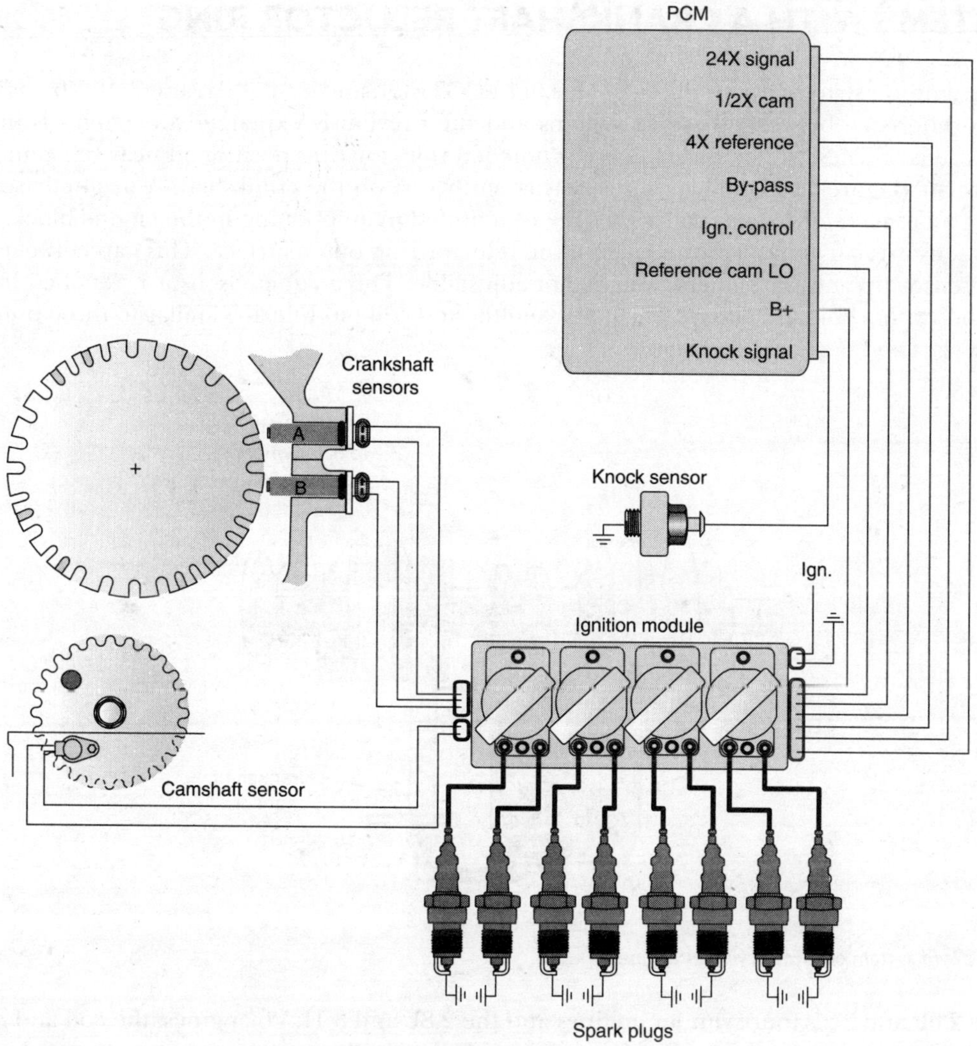

PCM
24X signal
1/2X cam
4X reference
By-pass
Ign. control
Reference cam LO
B+
Knock signal
Crankshaft sensors
A
B
Knock sensor
Ign.
Ignition module
Camshaft sensor
Spark plugs

Figure 12-25 *Complete EI fast-start system with A and B sensors.*

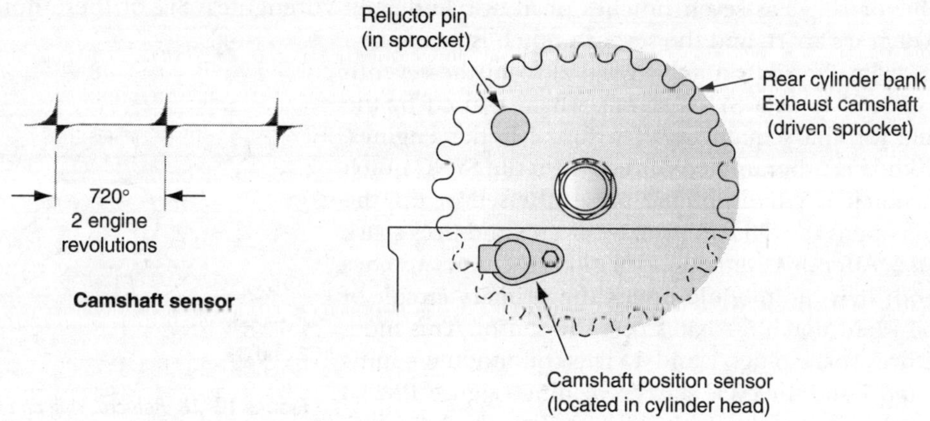

Figure 12-26 *Camshaft position sensor.*

EI SYSTEMS WITH A CRANKSHAFT RELUCTOR RING

Electronic ignition systems are used on GM's 2.0L, ECOTEC4, and 2.8L, 3.1L and 3.4L V6 engines. The main difference between these EI systems and the previously explained EI systems is in the crankshaft sensor. These other systems have a notched reluctor ring positioned near the center of the crankshaft (Figure 12-27). This ring is permanently cast on the crankshaft. A magnetic sensor containing a permanent magnet and a winding is mounted in an opening in the engine block. The tip of this sensor is 0.050 in. (1.27 mm) from the reluctor ring outer surface. This gap between the magnetic sensor tip and the reluctor ring is not adjustable. The magnetic sensor is retained in the engine block with a bolt and clamp. The coil assembly and coil module are similar to those used on other slow-start and fast-start EI systems.

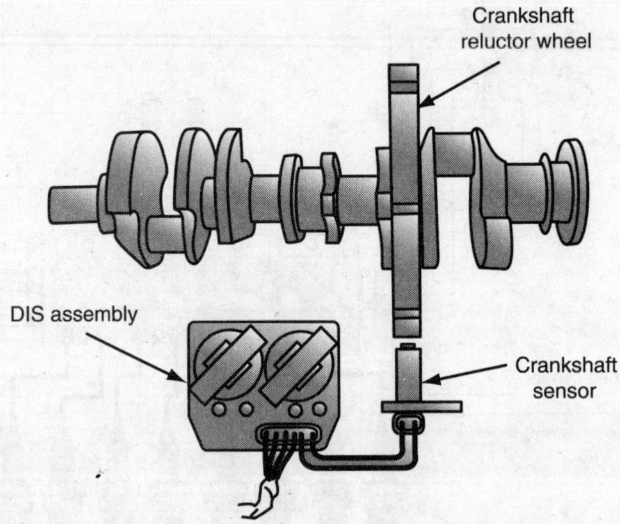

FIGURE 12-27 *EI system on a four-cylinder engine.*

On the 2.0L and 2.2L four-cylinder engines and the 2.8L and 3.1L V6 engines, the coil and module assembly is positioned on one side of the engine block, and the magnetic sensor is located in the opposite side of the block.

The reluctor ring has seven notches on four-cylinder or V6 engines. Six of these notches are spaced 60 degrees apart, and the seventh notch is positioned 10 degrees from the sixth notch. A signal from the seventh notch is referred to as a SYNC signal, which is used by the coil module for coil sequencing. On four-cylinder engines, the coil module is programmed to recognize the SYNC notch and count notch 1. When notch 2 passes the sensor tip, the coil module opens the 2-3 coil primary circuit and fires spark plugs 2 and 3. After this event, the coil module counts notches 3 and 4 and then the module opens the primary circuit of the 1-4 coil when notch 5 rotates past the sensor. This module action fires spark plugs 1 and 4. The coil module counts notches 6 and 7 and the cycle starts repeating (Figure 12-28). During engine starting, the 2-3 coil fires before the 1-4 coil.

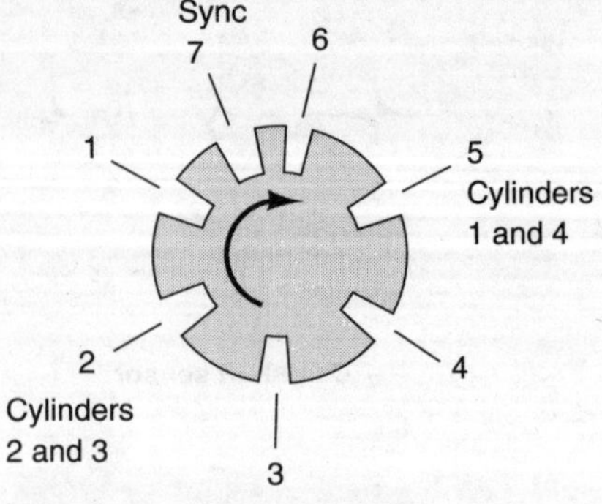

FIGURE 12-28 *Reluctor ring and firing order for a 4-cylinder engine.*

On the V6 engines, the coil module recognizes the SYNC notch and counts notch 1. When the signal from notch 2 is received, the coil module opens the primary circuit of the 2-5 coil which fires spark plugs 2 and 5 (Figure 12-29). Notch 3 is counted next, and the signal from notch 4 is then used to open the primary circuit of the 3-6 coil and fire spark plugs 3 and 6. As the sequence continues, notch 5 is counted and the signal from notch 6 is then used to open the primary circuit of the 1-4 coil and fire spark plugs 1 and 4. The cycle repeats as the crankshaft continues to rotate. During engine starting, the 2-5 coil fires first.

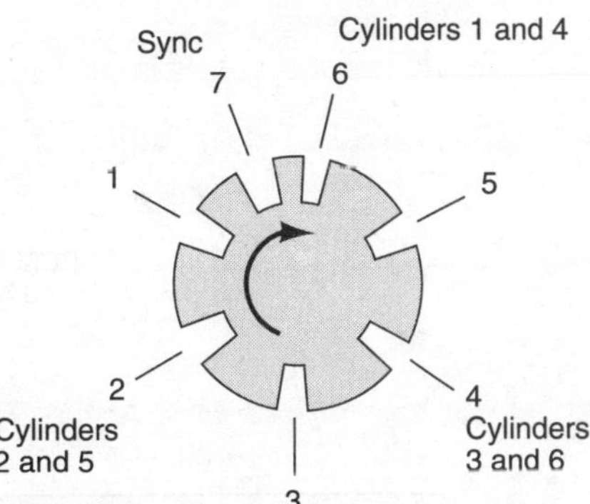

FIGURE 12-29 *Reluctor ring and firing order for a V6 engine.*

When the engine is running, a low-voltage signal is sent via the reference wire from the coil module to the PCM when the notch that is 60 degrees ahead of when the cylinder event notch passes the sensor. When the cylinder event notch passes the sensor, the reference signal changes to high voltage. This reference signal informs the PCM regarding crankshaft position and speed. After a reference signal is received, the PCM scans the inputs and determines the spark advance required by the engine. When this calculation is completed in a few milliseconds, the PCM sends an EST signal to the coil module to open the primary circuit of the next coil at the correct instant to provide the required spark advance (Figure 12-30). The PCM can affect the spark advance during engine starting on these EI systems. If an engine with EI has multiport fuel injection or throttle body injection, a cam sensor signal is not required for injector sequencing.

Ford's EI System with a Crankshaft Reluctor Ring

Ford uses a system similar to GM. However the reluctor ring has many more slots. The crankshaft sensor for their 4.6L V8 engine is a variable reluctance sensor which is triggered by a 36 minus 1 (or 35) tooth trigger wheel located inside the front cover of the engine (Figure 12-31). The sensor provides two types of information: crankshaft position and engine speed.

The system utilizes four ignition coils, two in each housing (Figure 12-32). Each coil terminal has two cylinder numbers on them. This allows for interchangeability.

The trigger wheel has a tooth every 10 degrees with one tooth missing. When the part of the wheel that is missing, a tooth passes by the sensor, and there is a longer-than-normal pause between signals from the sensor. The ignition control module recognizes this and is able to identify this long pause as the location of piston number one (Figure 12-33).

Chrysler's EI System with a Crankshaft Reluctor Ring

Again, most systems that use a crankshaft reluctor ring are quite similar in construction and operation. Chrysler's is like the others but uses a different number of teeth on the reluctor, a camshaft sensor, and a camshaft reluctor. Therefore, the signals received by the control module are also different.

The crankshaft timing sensor is mounted in an opening in the transaxle bell housing (Figure 12-34). The inner end of this sensor is positioned near a series of notches and slots that are integral with the transaxle drive plate (Figure 12-35).

A bolt retains the crankshaft timing sensor to the bell housing. A group of four slots is located on the transaxle drive plate for each pair of engine cylinders. Thus, a total of twelve slots is positioned around the drive plate. The slots in each group are positioned 20 degrees apart. When the slots on the transaxle drive plate rotate past the crankshaft timing sensor, the voltage signal from the sensor

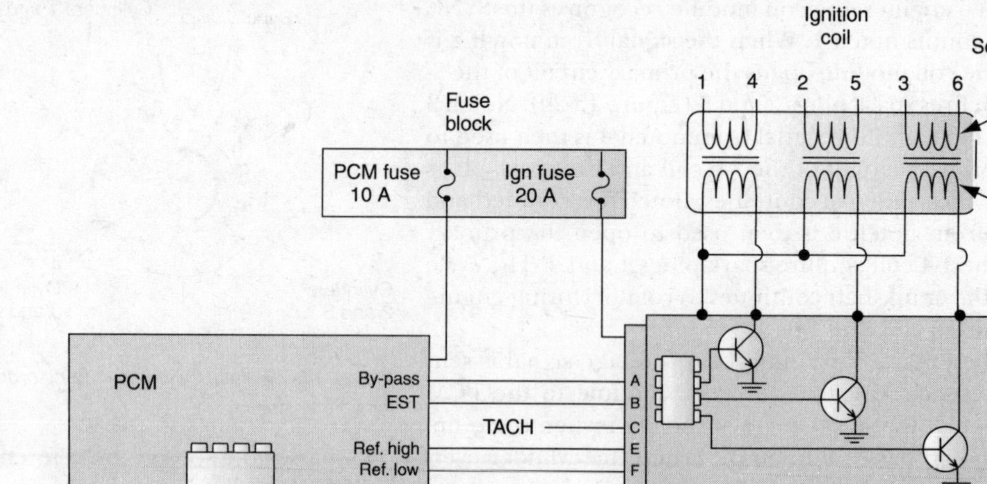

FIGURE 12-30 *Schematic of the EI system for a V6 engine.*

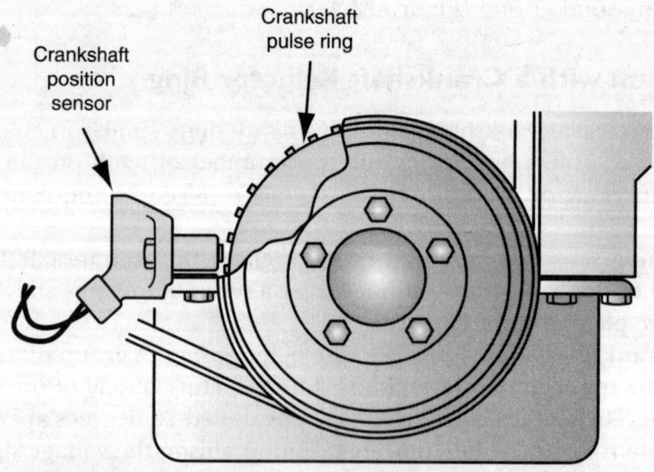

FIGURE 12-31 *Location of a crankshaft position sensor on a Ford 4.6L engine.*

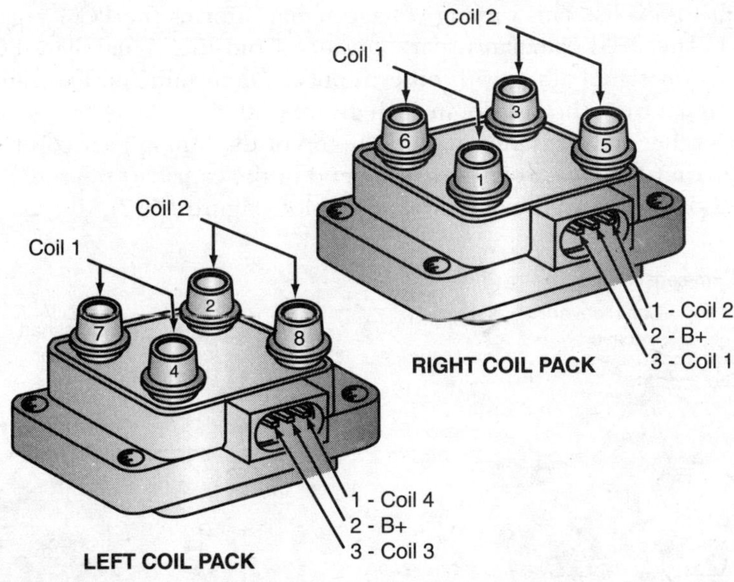

FIGURE 12-32 *Ignition coils for a Ford 4.6L engine.*

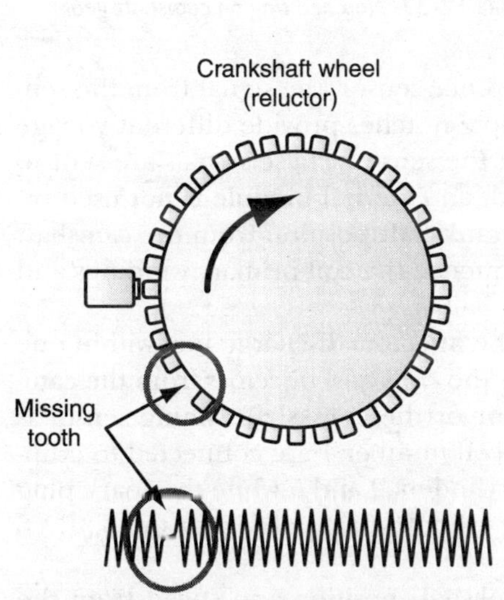

FIGURE 12-33 *Sensor activity to monitor engine speed and crankshaft position, as well as the location of piston number one.*

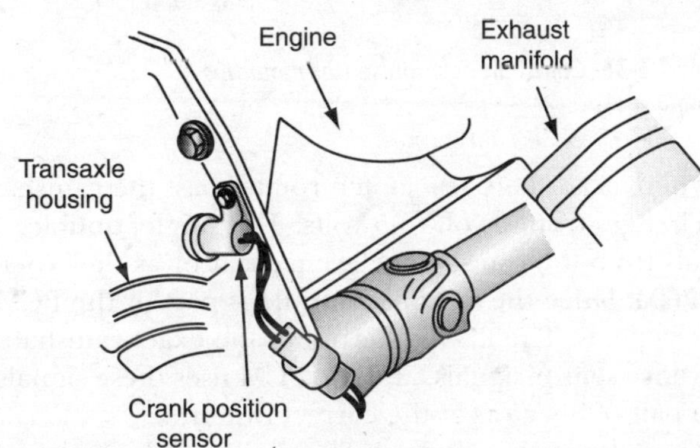

FIGURE 12-34 *Crankshaft position sensor mounted in a transaxle.*

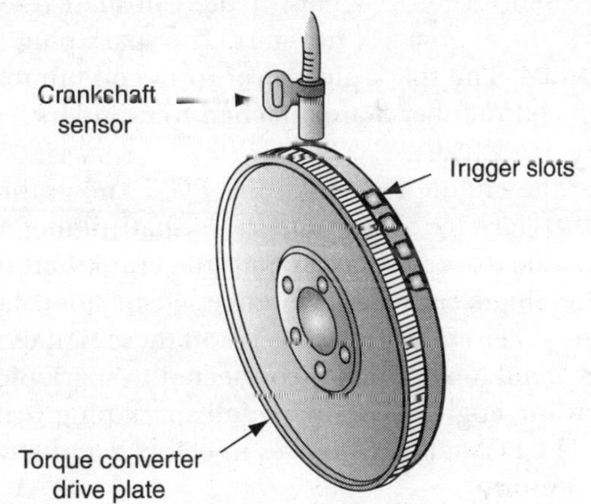

FIGURE 12-35 *Crankshaft timing sensor with the transaxle drive plate.*

changes from 0 volt to 5 volts. This varying voltage signal informs the PCM regarding crankshaft position and speed. The PCM calculates spark advance from this signal. The PCM also uses the crankshaft timing sensor signal along with other inputs to determine air-fuel ratio. Base timing is determined by the signal from the last slot in each group of slots.

The camshaft reference sensor is mounted in the top of the timing gear cover (Figure 12-36). A notched ring on the camshaft gear rotates past the end of the camshaft reference sensor. This ring contains two single slots, two double slots, and a triple slot (Figure 12-37).

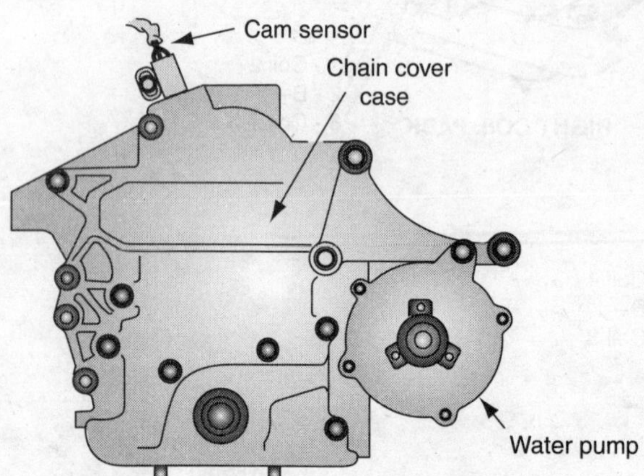

FIGURE 12-36 *Camshaft position sensor mounting in timing cover.*

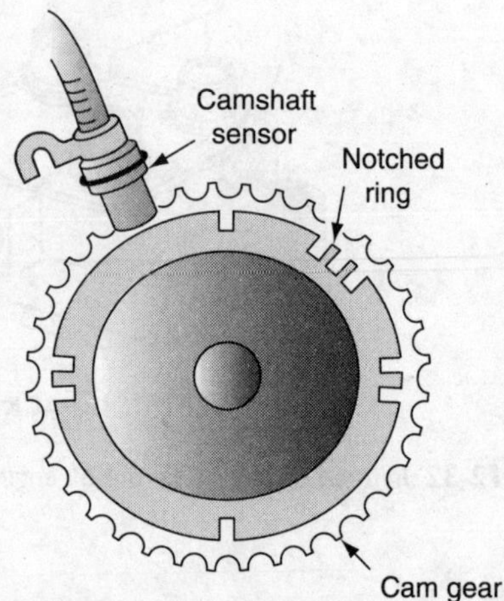

FIGURE 12-37 *Notched ring on camshaft gear.*

When a camshaft gear notch rotates past the camshaft reference sensor, the signal from the sensor changes from 0 volt to 5 volts. The single, double, and triple notches provide different voltage signals from the camshaft reference sensor as they rotate past the sensor. These signals are sent to the PCM. Since the ignition module is part of the PCM board, an external module is not used on these systems. The PCM determines the exact camshaft and crankshaft position from the camshaft reference sensor signals, and the PCM uses these signals to sequence the coil primary windings and each pair of injectors at the correct instant.

When the engine starts cranking, the spark plugs fire and the injectors discharge fuel within one crankshaft revolution. The PCM determines when to sequence the coils and injectors from the camshaft reference sensor signals. If the camshaft reference sensor or the crankshaft timing sensor is defective, the engine will not start. The spark plug wires from coil number 1 are connected to cylinders 1 and 4. The spark plug wires from coil number 2 go to cylinders 2 and 5 while the spark plug wires on coil number 3 are attached to cylinders 3 and 6. The cylinder firing order for the 3.3L V6 engine is 1-2-3-4-5-6.

Once the engine is started, the PCM knows the exact crankshaft position and speed from the camshaft reference sensor and crankshaft timing sensor signals. The leading edges of the slots in the transaxle driveplate rotate past the crankshaft timing sensor at 9, 29, 49, and 69 degrees BTDC. When the single camshaft reference sensor slot rotates past the sensor, one high and one low digital signal are received by the PCM. When these signals are received, the PCM is programmed to fire the number 2 coil next, which is connected to spark plugs 2 and 5 (Figure 12-38).

When the engine is cranking, all spark plug firings are at 9 degrees BTDC on the compression stroke. The PCM also sequences injectors 2 and 3 when the single slot rotates past the camshaft reference sensor.

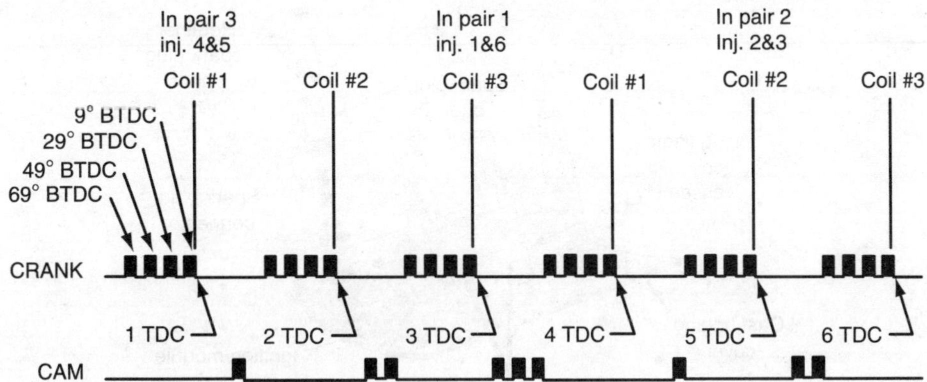

FIGURE 12-38 *EI system coil firing and injector sequencing.*

When the double notch rotates past the camshaft reference sensor, the PCM is programmed to fire coil 3 connected to spark plugs 3 and 6, as well as sequence injectors 1 and 6. When the triple notch rotates past the camshaft reference sensor, the PCM is programmed to fire coil 1 connected to spark plugs 1 and 4 and sequence injectors 4 and 5.

Since Chrysler engines are now equipped with sequential fuel injection, the PCM grounds each injector individually, but the proper injector sequencing is determined from the camshaft reference sensor signals.

EI SYSTEMS WITH COILS CONNECTED DIRECTLY TO SPARK PLUGS

These EI systems have the same reluctor ring and magnetic sensor as other EI systems. However, on these EI systems, the spark plug wires are eliminated and the coil secondary terminals are connected directly to the spark plugs. Since the spark plug wires are eliminated, the chance of high-voltage leaks is reduced. Figure 12-39 shows a typical coil-on-plug, or COP, system. There are two distinct types of COP ignitions. One is basically a waste spark system with the coils mounted over the plugs using one coil per pair of cylinders. The other style COP uses a coil mounted over the spark plug for each cylinder. Some of these systems have a module integral with the coil, some have a module that controls all the coil primaries, and some are controlled directly by the PCM. One of the older styles of EI is shown in Figure 12-40. This system is a COP/waste spark ignition used on the 2.3/2.4L SOHC/DOHC GM engine family. This ignition system is a variation of the waste spark system. The ignition module and coils are mounted under a plate that is positioned between the cam covers on top of the engine. Each coil is connected to a pair of spark plugs. The spark plug pairs are 1-4 and 2-3. Since the coil module contacts the mounting plate, it acts as a heat shield. The mounting plate must be

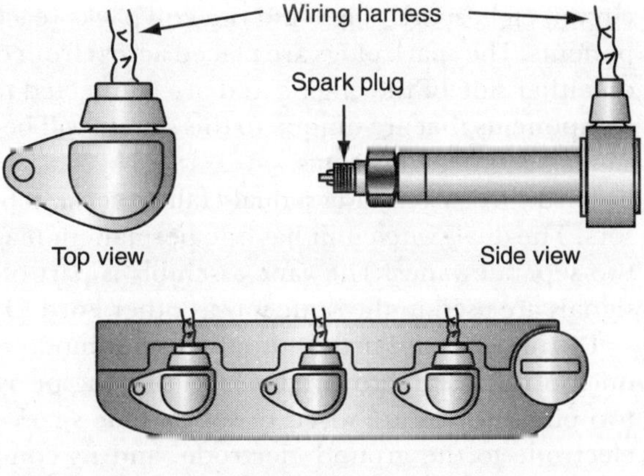

FIGURE 12-39 *COP ignition system. Coil is mounted directly over the spark plug.*

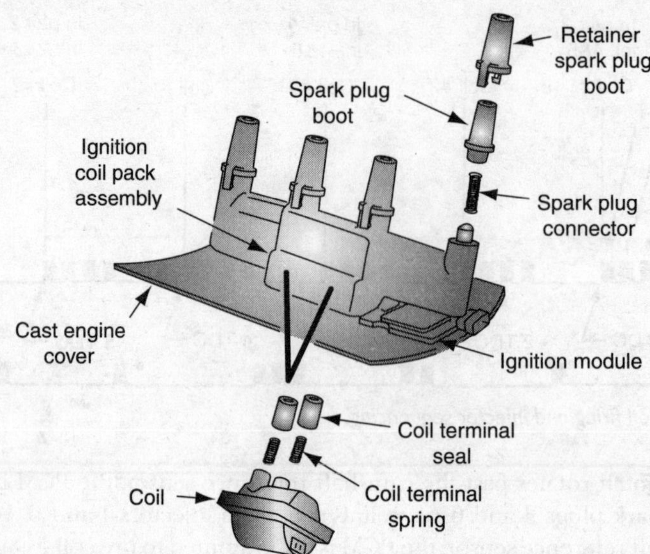

FIGURE 12-40 *The coil module, coil assemblies, and cover plate for an EI system with plugs connected directly to the ignition coils.*

grounded to the engine to provide ignition operation. The operation and electrical connections for these EI systems are similar to the EI system operations explained previously (Figure 12-41).

Figure 12-42 shows an import COP ignition with an ignition module that controls the individual coils for each cylinder. Figure 12-43 shows a COP ignition system with the module function taken over by the PCM. The basic advantage of COP is that there are no plug wires to wear out or be damaged, and these systems are much less likely to be affected by moisture than systems using plug wires.

DUAL SPARK PLUG EI SYSTEMS

Some EI systems fire two spark plugs at each cylinder. These systems are known as dual plug (DP) systems. Commonly found on four-cylinder engines, the system is comprised of a dual plug inhibit circuit, eight spark plugs, and two coil packs (each one containing two coils) as well as other EI components. The spark plugs are placed across from each other in the cylinder. The coil packs are placed on either side of the engine and are connected to the plugs on that side (Figure 12-44). Only those components that are unique to this system will be discussed here because the basics of the system are similar to other EI systems.

Ford's DP system uses a dual Hall effect switch (Figure 12-45) that contains the CID and PIP sensors. The dual switch unit has one permanent magnet, two Hall devices, and a rotating assembly with two separate vanes. The vane assembly is part of the crankshaft pulley assembly. The CID and PIP signals are used in the same way as other Ford EI systems.

During engine startup, the dual plug mode of operation is inhibited and only the spark plugs on the right side are fired. Once the engine is running, both sets of plugs fire. Each coil fires two plugs, which are wired in series. One spark plug in each cylinder always fires from the center electrode to the ground electrode, and its companion plug fires from the ground to the center electrode. Because of the way the coils are wired, the two spark plugs in a cylinder fire in opposite directions.

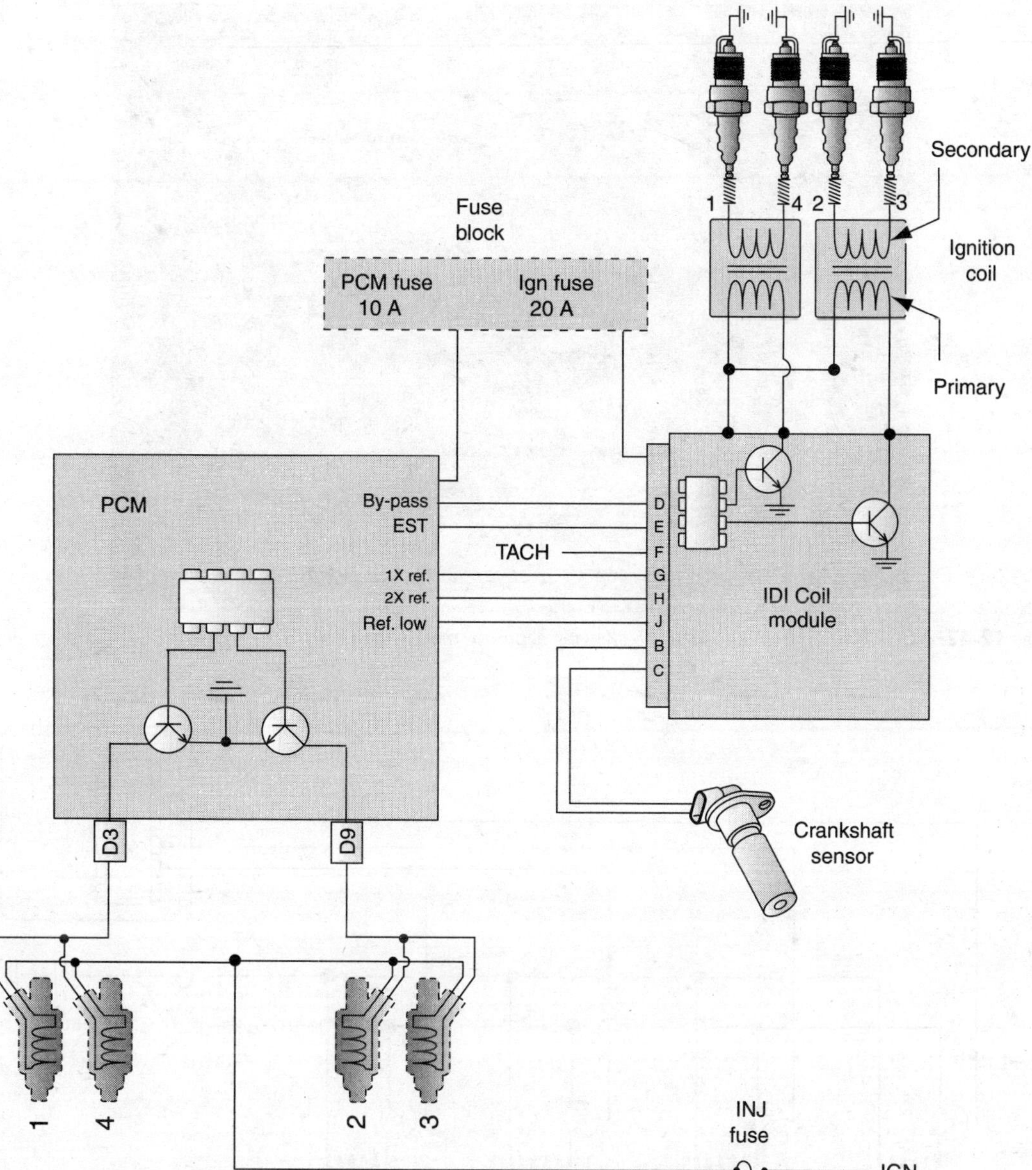

FIGURE 12-41 *Schematic for the waste-spark EI system with coils mounted over the spark plugs.*

Coil-On-Plug/Coil-Near-Plug Systems

The coil-on-plug (COP) (Figure 12-46) and coil-near-plug (CNP) (Figure 12-47) systems have emerged on more vehicles during the past few years. These systems are nothing more than an enhanced version of the distributorless systems. The major exception is that there is no waste spark. The coils fire only once for their respective cylinders. One coil is fired at a time, and only when the cylinder is on its compression stroke. The ignition coils are mounted on or near the spark plug for each cylinder of the engine. For example, most systems contain four individual coils on a four-cylinder engine, six coils on a six-cylinder engine, and eight coils on an eight-cylinder engine.

FIGURE 12-42 *A COP ignition from an Isuzu V-6 showing separate module and coils.*

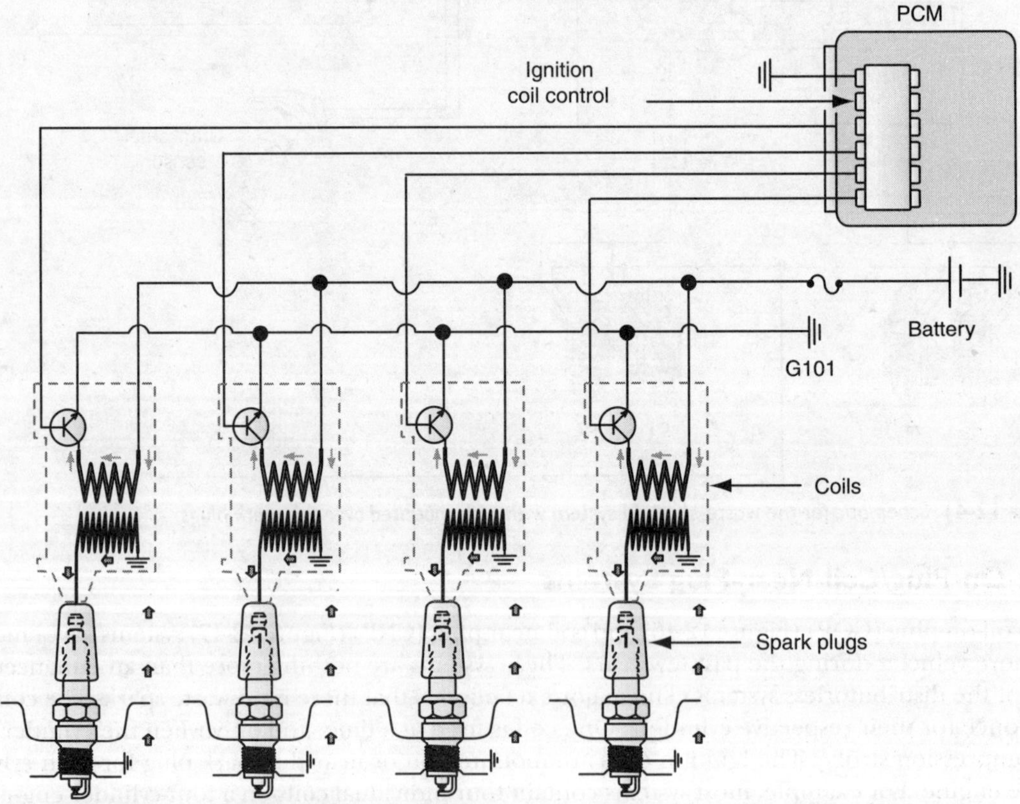

FIGURE 12-43 *A COP ignition controlled entirely by the PCM.*

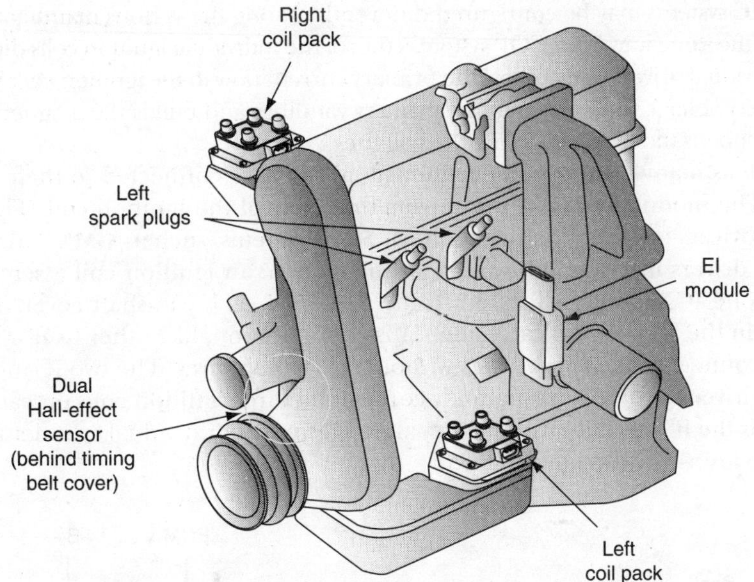

FIGURE 12-44 *Location of components in Ford's DP EI system.*

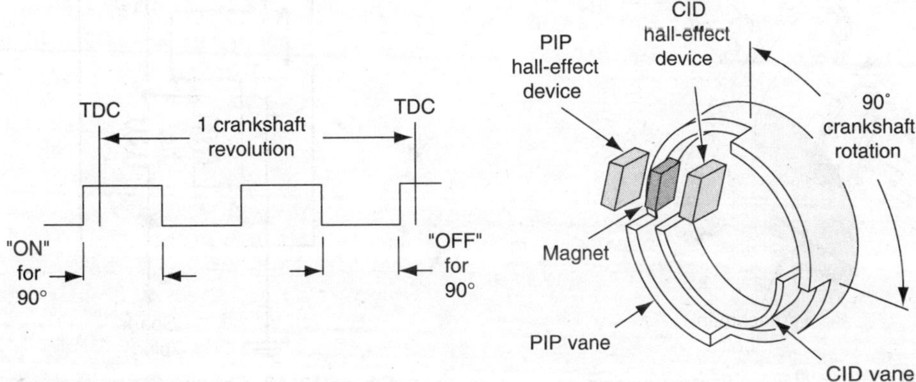

FIGURE 12-45 *PIP signal.*

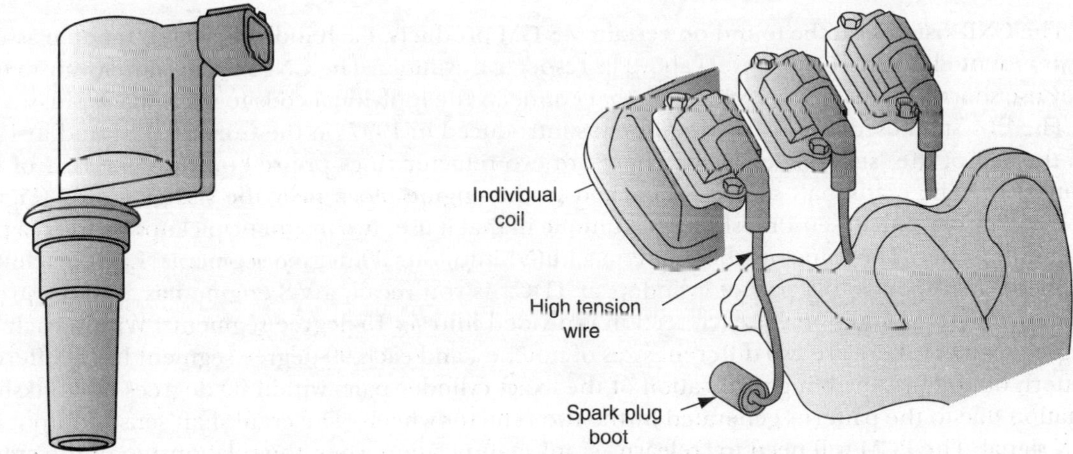

FIGURE 12-46 *A coil-on-plug assembly.*

FIGURE 12-47 *A coil-near-plug ignition assembly.*

Although the IC systems may be configured differently among the various manufacturers, they will all generally operate the same way. Ford COP systems control the individual ignition coils directly by the PCM. The PCM has individual drivers that control the primary current flow to the ignition coil. When the primary is turned on, battery voltage flows through the primary windings and builds the magnetic field. When the driver in the PCM opens the primary circuit, the coil fires.

On GM as well as many import systems, individual coils are connected to their own IC modules (Figure 12-48). The modules contain the drivers that control the ignition coil (Figure 12-49). The switching of the drivers is a function of the PCM. Some systems, such as GM's 3.5L V-6 engine, may integrate several drivers in a single housing. In this system, an ignition coil assembly consisting of three coils, and one IC module is located in the center of each camshaft cover. There are two of these assemblies in the V-6, one on each side. This configuration, like other COP systems, allows the ignition coils to connect to the spark plugs without spark plug wires. The two IC modules each have three individual driver circuits that separately control the three ignition coils on each cylinder bank. The PCM controls the IC modules using six separate IC circuits. Individual cylinder timing and firing order sequencing are controlled by the PCM.

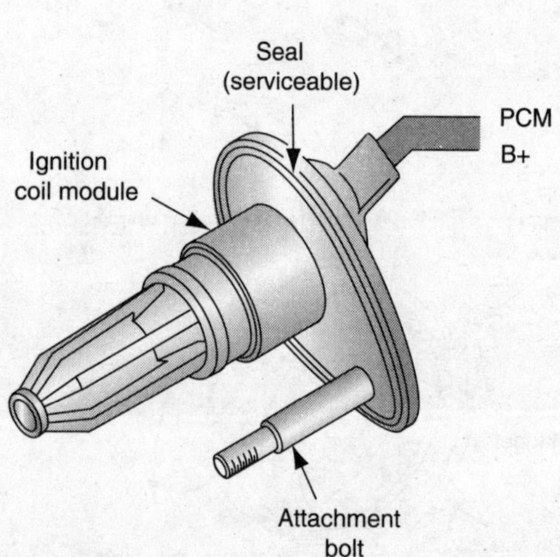

FIGURE 12-48 *Coil-on-plug ignition coil/module assembly.*

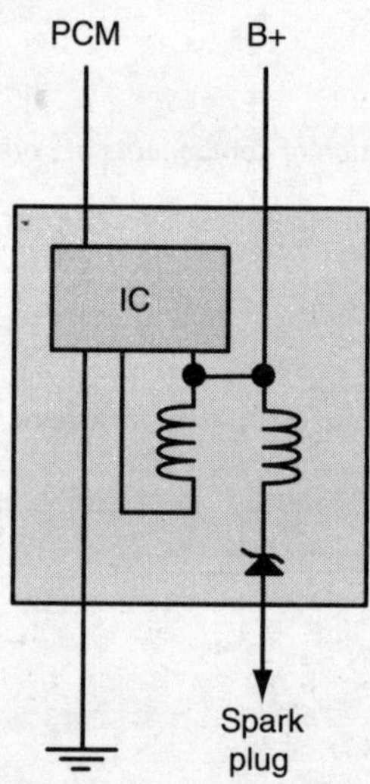

FIGURE 12-49 *Circuit for coil-on-plug control module.*

The CNP systems can be found on certain V-8 GM products. Each individual coil/module assembly is mounted on the rocker covers above its respective cylinder. The CNP systems differ only in that they use short secondary spark plug wire that connects the individual coils to their spark plugs.

The EI system used on GM V-8 engines was introduced in 1997 on the Corvette LS1 and in 1999 on the rest of the "small block" V-8s. There are two reluctor rings pressed on near the rear of the crankshaft. The crankshaft sensor is attached to the engine block near the starter motor (Figure 12-50). The crankshaft sensor is somewhat unique in that it uses two magnetic pickups between a permanent magnet. The reluctor wheels are machined into four 90 degree segments. Each machined segment corresponds to a pair of cylinders at TDC. As you recall, a V-8 engine has a power stroke every 90 degrees. Additionally, each section is divided into six 15-degree segments. Within each 90-degree segment there are two different sizes of notches, and each 90-degree segment has a different pattern of notches, enabling verification of the exact cylinder pairs within 90 degrees of crankshaft rotation due to the patterns generated by the two reluctor wheels. The crankshaft sensor output is a 24X signal. The PCM will need to "relearn" crankshaft position when the relationship of the crank-

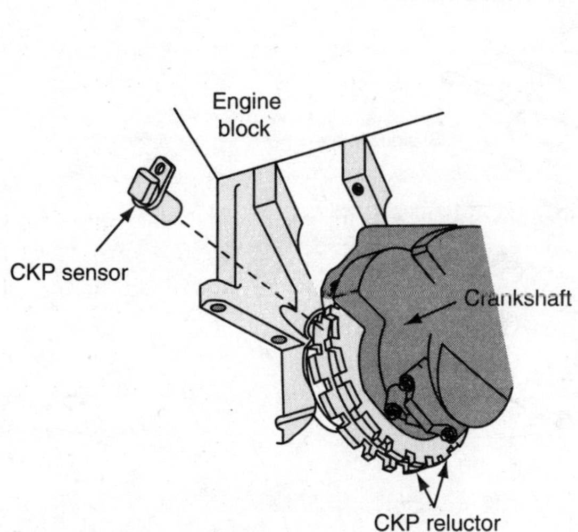

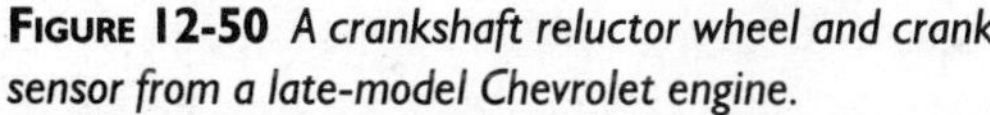

FIGURE 12-50 *A crankshaft reluctor wheel and crank sensor from a late-model Chevrolet engine.*

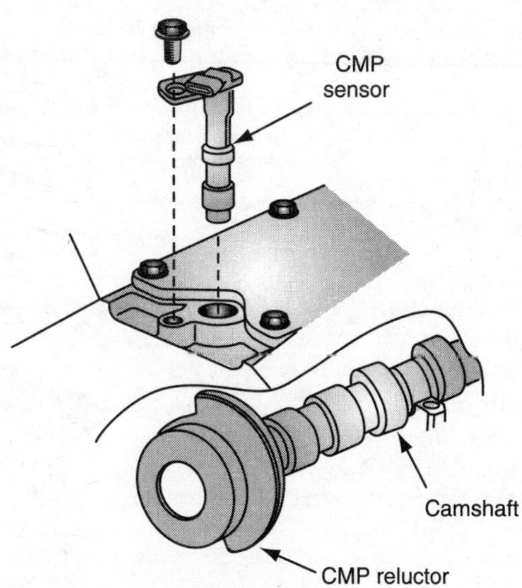

FIGURE 12-51 *A camshaft sensor and camshaft with reluctor wheel from a late-model Chevrolet engine.*

shaft and crankshaft sensor are disturbed, such as when the engine, crankshaft, or sensor is replaced on this system.

The camshaft sensor (Figure 12-51) is also a magneto resistive sensor that produces a digital on/off pulse once per camshaft revolution. The cam sensor is located near the rear center of the block and extends into the engine to read the cam reluctor wheel. The cam sensor reluctor wheel can be part of the cam itself, or it can be pressed onto the cam gear. The configuration of the camshaft sensor is such that it can send a valid signal before the engine starts.

The PCM is in control of the ignition system with input from several sensors such as the throttle position (TP) sensor, ECT, the MAF, IAT, KS, VSS, and others.

Compression Sense Ignition

One of the latest developments in ignition systems is the compression sense ignition. This ignition system offers sequential fuel injection and waste spark ignition without a camshaft position sensor on GM's ECOTEC engines (Figure 12-52). Compression sense ignition utilizes the basic waste spark ignition systems, which, as you remember, fires two spark plugs in series. One cylinder of the firing pair is on compression, and the waste spark is fired in the exhaust stroke. The spark plug in the exhaust stroke takes less energy to fire (3–4 kV) than the spark plug under compression pressure (9–12 kV). The compression sense ignition module is able to determine which plug took the most energy to fire, along with the direction of current flow and uses this information as a substitute for a cam sensor signal (Figure 12-53 and Figure 12-54). There are times that the cam signal may not be reliable, such as during deceleration. During these times, the PCM can synchronize the injection based on the last good signal received. If there is an ignition problem, the cam signal may not be usable; in this event, the PCM will fire injectors 1-4 and 2-3 as a batch-fire multiport injection system.

Ion Sensing Ignition

Delphi has developed an ion sensing ignition that is utilized by coil-over-plug style of EI. The spark plug in ion sensing ignition is actually used as a sensor inside the combustion chamber. The system

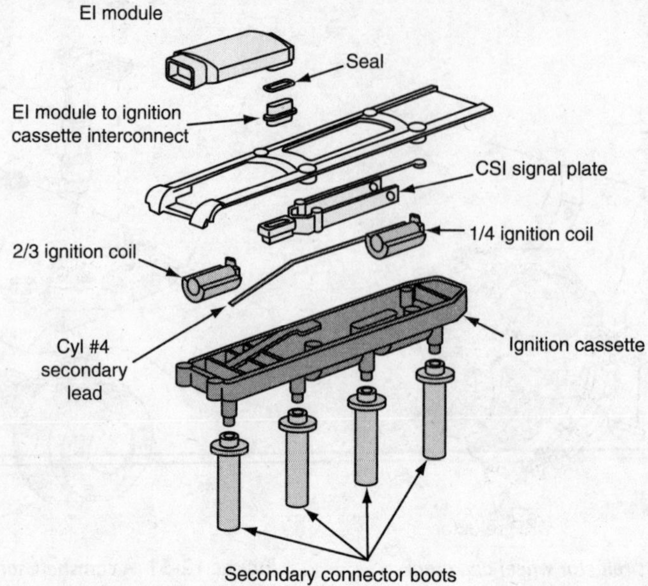

FIGURE 12-52 *The compression sense ignition cassette.*

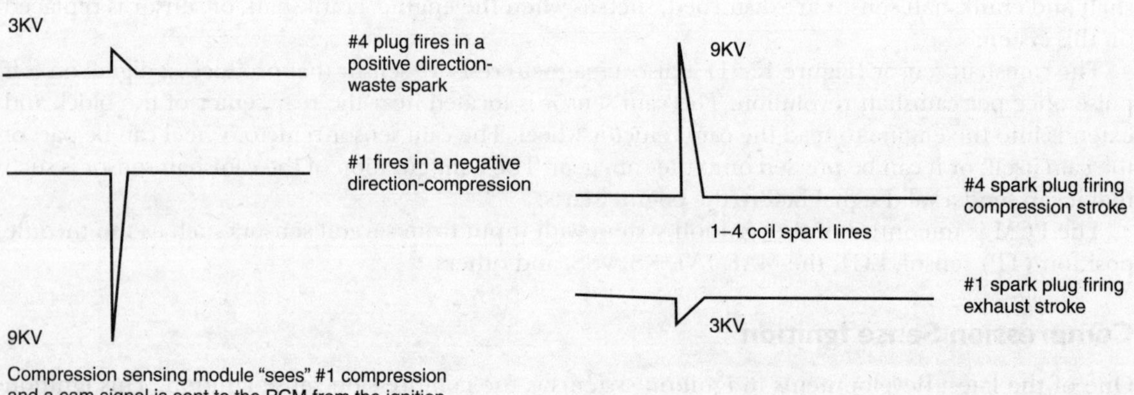

FIGURE 12-53 *The module knows cylinder #1 is on compression because the required firing voltage is higher than the companion #4 cylinder. The ignition module can then send a cam signal to the PCM.*

FIGURE 12-54 *In this example, the module knows cylinder #4 is on compression because the required firing voltage is higher than the companion #1 cylinder.*

works by applying a voltage across the spark plug gap immediately after the spark plug firing, while the spark gap is still ionized (Figure 12-55). The capacitor is charged by the spark plug firing voltage. The ignition module has the ability to analyze the characteristics of the current flow across the gap and inferring information regarding misfire, air-fuel ratio, pre-ignition, and spark knock. The information can be used to eliminate the use of a knock sensor. Beginning in 2004, some Saab vehicles use ion sensing ignition to eliminate the front oxygen sensor.

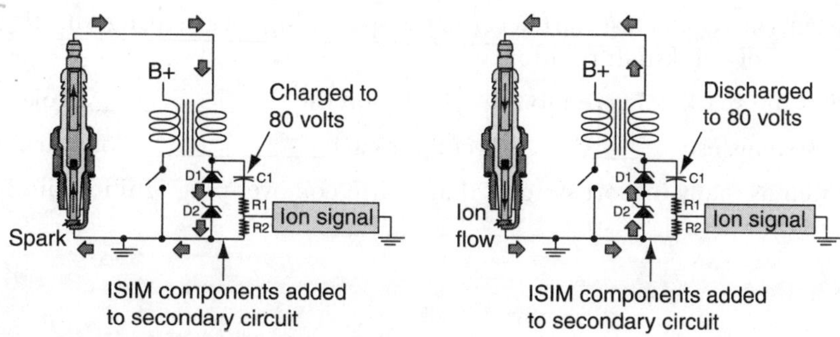

Figure 12-55 *Delphi's Ion sensing ignition module.*

Review Questions

Short Answer Essay

1. Name four different types of primary triggering units commonly used in ignition systems.
2. Name the three advantages of EI over DI.
3. Explain the necessary requirements of the ignition system.
4. Name the advantage of using the old distributor location for a cam sensor.
5. Give some examples of information that a computer uses to determine the ideal amount of ignition timing advance for a particular operating condition.
6. Explain the advantage of compression sense ignition.
7. What is the purpose of the 18X crankshaft sensor?
8. What does the term "waste spark" mean?
9. Explain the basic operation of the ion sensing ignition.
10. Describe the pickup and triggering mechanism on an EI system with a reluctor ring mounted near the center of the crankshaft.

Fill-in-the Blanks

1. The computer, ____________ ____________ and ____________ sensors combine to control spark timing and advance.
2. The timing and sequencing of the ignition coil action is determined by the ____________ ____________and input from a ____________ device.
3. The ____________ ____________ electronic ignition system used in GM's Northstar system uses two crankshaft sensors.
4. The CID is a ____________ ____________ switch assembly placed in the distributor bore and is driven by the camshaft.
5. Ford's 4.6 L V-8 uses a ____________ ____________ ____________ which is triggered by a 36-minus-one (or 35) tooth trigger wheel located inside the front cover of the engine.
6. Some Chrysler EI systems use a crankshaft ____________ ____________ mounted in an opening in the transaxle bell housing.

7. Some EI systems are called fast start because the spark plugs begin firing within ______________ ______________ of crankshaft rotation.
8. Waste spark is the spark delivered to the cylinder on the ______________ stroke.
9. Waste spark systems use ______________ coil for each ______________ of spark plugs.
10. On GM as well as many import systems that utilize coil-over-plug ignition, individual coils are connected to their own ______________ ______________.

Multiple Choice

1. *Technician A* says that the primary circuit of the ignition coil operates basically the same in EI and DI systems.

   Technician B says that the secondary circuit operates basically the same in EI and DI.

   Who is correct?

   A. Technician A | C. Both technicians
   B. Technician B | D. Neither technician

2. *Technician A* says the permanent magnet sensor is basically a magnet and a coil of wire.

   Technician B says these sensors produce a D/C signal.

   Who is correct?

   A. Technician A | C. Both technicians
   B. Technician B | D. Neither technician

3. All of the following are examples of advantages of EI ***except:***

   A. Flexibility in mounting locations
   B. Reduced radio frequency interference
   C. Elimination of distributor cap buildups of water and nitric acid
   D. Reduced spark burn time

4. While discussing waste spark ignition,

   Technician A says there are two spark plugs connected in series.

   Technician B says the two spark plugs are in companion cylinders that are at TDC at the same time.

   Who is correct?

   A. Technician A | C. Both technicians
   B. Technician B | D. Neither technician

5. *Technician A* says that the camshaft position sensor for an EI system can be located in the space that had been occupied by the distributor and driven by the camshaft.

   Technician B says the camshaft sensor can be located in the front cover.

   Who is correct?

   A. Technician A | C. Both technicians
   B. Technician B | D. Neither technician

6. While discussing EI systems that use a crankshaft reluctor ring,
   Technician A says the tip of the sensor is 0.5 inches from the cast reluctor.
   Technician B says the gap can be adjusted on these engines.
   Who is correct?
   A. Technician A C. Both technicians
   B. Technician B D. Neither technician
7. *Technician A* says some coil on plug systems has an ignition module that is part of the PCM.
   Technician B says some coil on plug ignition systems has a separate ignition module built into each coil assembly.
   Who is correct?
   A. Technician A C. Both technicians
   B. Technician B D. Neither technician
8. *Technician A* says that some Chevrolet V-8s uses three crankshaft reluctor rings pressed onto the crankshaft.
   Technician B says this crankshaft sensor produces a 24X signal.
   Who is correct?
   A. Technician A C. Both technicians
   B. Technician B D. Neither technician
9. *Technician A* says that the compression sensing ignition does not need a camshaft position sensor.
   Technician B says that compression sensing ignition does not need a crankshaft position sensor.
   Who is correct?
   A. Technician A C. Both technicians
   B. Technician B D. Neither technician
10. *Technician A* says the ion sensing ignition system is based on the coil-over-plug system.
    Technician B says that ion sensing ignition uses the spark plug itself as a sensor.
    Who is correct?
    A. Technician A C. Both technicians
    B. Technician B D. Neither technician

EMISSION CONTROL SYSTEMS 13

Upon completion and review of this chapter, you should be able to:

- Explain why hydrocarbon (HC) emissions are released from an engine's exhaust.
- Explain how carbon monoxide (CO) emissions are formed in the combustion chamber.
- Describe oxygen (O_2) emissions in relation to air-fuel ratio.
- Describe how carbon dioxide (CO_2) is formed in the combustion chamber.
- Describe how oxides of nitrogen (NO_x) are formed in the combustion chamber.
- Describe the operation of an evaporative control system during the canister purge and nonpurge modes.
- Explain the purpose of the positive crankcase ventilation (PCV) system.
- Describe the operation of the PCV system at idle speed, part throttle, and heavy load conditions.
- Describe the operation of the detonation sensor and electronic spark control module.
- Describe the operation of a port exhaust gas recirculation (EGR) valve.
- Explain the design and operation of a positive backpressure EGR valve.
- Describe the design and operation of a negative backpressure EGR valve.

- Explain the operation of a digital EGR valve.
- Explain the operation of a linear EGR valve.
- List and describe the various controls commonly used in EGR systems.
- Define the purpose of a catalytic converter.
- Explain how a catalytic converter works.
- Describe the operation of a secondary air injection system.
- Describe Tier 2 emissions.

INTRODUCTION

Emission controls on cars and trucks have one purpose—to reduce the amount of pollutants and environmentally damaging substances released by the vehicles. The consequences of the pollutants are grievous. The air we breathe and the water we drink have become contaminated with chemicals that adversely affect our health. It took many years for the public and the industry to address the problem of these pollutants. Not until smog became an issue did anyone in power really care and do something about these pollutants.

Smog not only appears as dirty air, it is also an irritant to your eyes, nose, and throat. The components necessary to form photochemical smog are HC and NO_x exposed to sunlight in stagnant air. When there is enough HC in the air, it reacts with the NO_x in the air. The energy of sunlight causes these two chemicals to react and form photochemical smog.

LEGISLATIVE HISTORY

The first Clean Air Act prompted Californians to create the California Air Research Board (CARB). California ARB's purpose was to implement strict air standards. These became the standard for federal mandates. One of the approaches to clean the air by the ARB was to start **periodic motor vehicle inspection (PMVI)**. The purpose for the PMVI is to inspect a vehicle's emission controls once a year. This inspection includes a tailpipe emissions test and an underhood inspection. The tailpipe test certifies that the vehicle's exhaust emissions are within the limits set by law. The underhood and/or vehicle inspection verifies that the pollution control equipment has not been tampered with or disconnected.

California is not the only state that requires annual emissions testing. Many states have incorporated an emissions test with their annual vehicle registration procedures. Most states either already have or are planning to implement some type of emission testing program such as the I/M 240, ASM, OBD II monitor, or similar program. The I/M 240 and ASM tests are performed with the vehicle under a variety of loads at various speeds, depending on the type of test being performed. These types of tests are more accurate than exhaust emission readings taken at idle in obtaining actual emission performance results.

The Acceleration Simulation Mode (ASM) test, which incorporates steady state and transient testing, varies depending on specific state requirements. The ASM tests at a certain percentage of engine load for a defined number of seconds at a specified steady speed and a 90-second transient test.

The On-Board Diagnostics generation two (OBD II) emission monitor test is performed in conjunction with an exhaust emissions test or as a stand-alone test. As time goes on, more states will likely begin to use the OBD II test in lieu of the I/M 240 or ASM-type tests. The ability of the OBD II system to reveal engine data, performance, and emission control-related history was implemented on all domestic vehicles in 1996. However, a few models had some OBD II capability in 1994 and 1995. The diagnostic trouble codes (DTC) as well as systems monitor data and history are retrieved by connecting a scanner to the under-dash diagnostic connector. When a repeated emissions-related failure occurs within a specific period of time, the PCM will turn on the malfunction indicator lamp (MIL) to warn the driver of a problem. A DTC is then stored in memory and is used to identify the system at fault.

The **Inspection/Maintenance (I/M)** 240 test requires the use of a chassis (road) dynonameter, commonly called a *dyno.* While on the dyno, the vehicle is operated for 240 seconds and under different load conditions. The test drive on the dyno simulates both in-traffic and highway driving and stopping. The emissions tester tracks the exhaust quality through these conditions.

The I/M 240 program also includes a functional test of the evaporative emission control devices and a visual inspection of the total emission control system. If the vehicle fails the test, it must be repaired and certified before it can be registered.

This same source also states that passenger cars are responsible for 17.8 percent of the total hydrocarbon emissions, 30.9 percent of the total carbon monoxide emissions, and 11.1 percent of the oxides of nitrogen emissions. After 30 years of emission regulations, these figures remain staggering! Imagine what these figures would be if automotive and industrial emissions had remained unregulated during the last 30 years!

There are three main automotive pollutants: hydrocarbons (HC), carbon monoxide (CO), and oxides of nitrogen (NO_x). Particulate emissions are also present in diesel engine exhaust. HC emissions are caused largely by unburned fuel from the combustion chambers. HC emissions can also originate from evaporative sources such as the gasoline tank. CO emissions are a byproduct of the combustion process, resulting from incorrect air-fuel mixtures. NO_x emissions are caused by nitrogen and oxygen uniting at cylinder temperatures above 2,500°F (1,371°C).

Emission standards have been one of the driving forces behind many of the technological changes in the automotive industry. Catalytic converters and other emission systems were installed to meet emission standards. Computer-controlled carburetors and fuel injection systems were installed to provide more accurate control of the air-fuel ratio to reduce emission levels and allow the catalytic converter to operate efficiently.

During the 1990s, emission standards in the United States have become increasingly stringent. New engine systems and technology are being developed to keep pace with the demands of emerging stringent emission standards. Since approximately 90 percent of hydrocarbon emissions occur before the catalytic converter is hot enough to provide proper HC oxidation, engineers are designing catalytic converters that are heated from the vehicle electrical system. Since these heaters have high current flow requirements, some charging system modifications may be necessary. This is just one of the many changes in emission systems that we will likely see in the near future.

Low-Emission Vehicles (LEV)

Emission Standard Level (listed from least clean to cleanest)

- Tier 1—had varying emission level vehicles before 2004.
  - Less stringent emission standards
- Transitional Low Emission
  - Vehicle more stringent than Tier 1 standards for hydrocarbons (HC)
- Low-Emission Vehicle

- More stringent than TLEV standards for both hydrocarbons (HC) and nitrogen oxides (NO_x)
- Ultra Low-Emission Vehicle
  - More stringent than LEV standards for HC
- Super Ultra Low-Emission Vehicle
  - Even more stringent standards than ULEV for both HC and NO_x
- Zero-Emission Vehicle
  - The strictest emission standard, permitting no emissions

Tier 2

Tier 2 emission standards will result in cars, minivans, SUVs, and pickup trucks that are 77 to 95 percent cleaner than those on the road today. That is the equivalent of removing 164 million of today's cars from the road. Tier 2 standards were optional in model years 2001 through 2003 and were required to be phased in beginning in 2004. In 2009, all new cars and trucks must meet Tier 2 standards. For the first time ever, the Tier 2 standards require larger passenger vehicles, such as minivans, SUVs, and pickup trucks, to meet the same emission standards as cars.

Tier 2 emission standards are categorized by a system of bins (Figure 13-1). Originally, during the phase-in of the tougher standards in 2004, there were 11 bins. Bins 9–11 were eliminated in 2006 for cars and 2008 for light-duty trucks. Bin 1 is the zero emissions vehicles (ZEV), the cleanest vehicles, and bin 11 was the dirtiest vehicle that could still be certified for the U.S. market. This leaves some room for manufacturers to sell larger dirtier vehicles; however, manufacturers must meet an average emission level that corresponds roughly to bin 5. This means that a manufacturer could sell cars after 2008 from bin 8 but has to sell enough cars below bin 5 to average a bin 5 emissions level across their product line.

Emission bins		Carbon monoxide (CO) g/mile	Oxides of nitrogen (NO_x) g/mile	Hydrocarbons (HC) g/mile	Particulates g/mile
These bins eliminated for cars in 2006	11	7.3	0.9	.032	0.12
	10	4.2	0.6	.027	0.08
	9	4.2	0.3	.018	0.06
	8	4.2	0.2	.018	0.02
	7	4.2	0.15	.018	0.02
	6	4.2	0.10	.018	0.01
Average	5	4.2	0.07	.018	0.01
	4	2.1	0.04	.011	0.01
	3	2.1	0.03	.011	0.01
	2	2.1	0.02	.004	0.01
	1	0.0	0.00	0.00	0.00

FIGURE 13-1 *Tier 2 emission bins. Manufacturers can certify vehicles in any of the bins, provided their average stays in or below bin 5.*

In order to meet these new standards, special equipment has been placed on vehicles, particularly in diesel engines to reduce particulate matter. Tier 2 emission standards also called for reductions in sulfur content of gasoline and diesel fuel. Sulfur content was reduced over 97 percent in 2006. Sulfur can shorten the effective life of catalytic converters for gasoline engines and particulate filters in diesels. The goal is to have one emission standard for gasoline and diesel-fueled vehicles.

DEVELOPMENT OF EMISSION CONTROL DEVICES

In late 1959, California established the first standards for automotive emissions. In 1967, the Federal Clean Air Act was amended to provide for federal standards to apply to motor vehicles.

The first source of emissions to be brought under control was the crankcase. Positive crankcase ventilation (PCV) systems that route crankcase vapors back to the engine's intake manifold were developed and incorporated into 1961 cars and light trucks sold in California. These systems were installed on all cars nationwide beginning with the 1963 models.

Control of unburned hydrocarbons and carbon monoxide in the engine's exhaust was the next major development. An **air injection reactor (AIR)** system was built into cars and light trucks sold in California in 1966. Other systems, including the controlled combustion system, were developed and used nationwide in 1968. Further improvements in the following years improved combustion to reduce hydrocarbon and carbon monoxide emissions.

Fuel vapors from the gasoline tank and the carburetor float bowl were brought under control with the introduction of evaporation control systems. These systems were first installed in 1970 model cars sold in California and in most domestic-made cars beginning with 1971 models.

Most vehicle manufacturers started to provide emission control systems that reduced oxides of nitrogen as early as 1970. The exhaust gas recirculation system used on some 1972 models was used extensively for 1973 models when federal standards for oxides of nitrogen took effect.

One of the most important developments for lowering emission levels has been the availability and use of unleaded gasolines. Beginning with 1971, engines were designed to operate on unleaded fuels. In 1975, unleaded fuel became mandatory in new cars.

The catalytic converter, a later development, provided a means for oxidizing the carbon monoxide and hydrocarbon emissions in the engine exhaust. Beginning with the 1975 model year, passenger cars and light trucks have been equipped with converters.

Three basic types of emission control systems are used in modern vehicles: evaporative control systems, precombustion, and post-combustion.

The **evaporative emission control (EVAP)** system is a sealed system. It traps the fuel vapors (HC) that would normally escape from the fuel tank into the air.

Most of the pollution control systems used today prevent emissions from being created in the engine either during or before the combustion cycle. The common **precombustion control** systems are as follows:

- Positive Crankcase Ventilation (PCV). The PCV system removes pollutants that blow by the pistons into the crankcase and recirculates them into the induction system.
- Engine Modification Systems. These systems improve combustion and reduce HC and CO in the exhaust. They include a heated primary air system, air-fuel control changes, engine breathing refinements, and some spark timing controls.
- Exhaust Gas Recirculating (EGR) Systems. EGR reduces NO_x by diluting the air-fuel mixture with some exhaust gas, which does not burn.

Post-combustion control systems clean up the exhaust gases after the fuel has been burned. Secondary air or air injector systems put fresh air into the exhaust to reduce HC and CO to harmless water vapor and carbon dioxide by chemical (thermal) reaction with oxygen in the air. Catalytic converters help this process. Most catalysts now reduce NO_x as well as HC and CO.

POLLUTANTS

The gases that are of most concern to environmentalists, engineers, and technicians are HC, CO,

NO_x, CO_2, and O_2. The latter two are not really pollutants but are monitored because they are indicators of combustion efficiency.

Hydrocarbons

Hydrocarbon (HC) emissions are unburned fuel and are caused by incomplete combustion. Even an engine in good condition with satisfactory ignition and fuel systems produces some HC. When the flame front in the combustion chamber approaches the cooler cylinder wall, the flame front quenches leaving some unburned HC.

An excessively lean air-fuel ratio also results in cylinder misfiring and high HC emissions. A very rich air-fuel ratio also causes higher-than-normal HC emissions. At the stoichiometric air-fuel ratio, HC emissions are low. Evaporative emissions from fuel tanks and evaporative systems are also a source of HC emissions.

Because of the catayltic converter, the HC reading at the tailpipe is very low if the engine, ignition, fuel, and emission systems are in normal working condition. When a cylinder misfires, all the unburned gas in the cylinder is delivered to the exhaust system, resulting in a high HC reading. Cylinder misfiring and high HC readings may be caused by ignition defects, such as defective spark plugs, spark plug wires, coil, and distributor cap or rotor. Low cylinder compression also causes high HC emissions.

Excessive HC emissions may be caused by:

- Ignition system misfiring
- Improper ignition timing
- Excessively lean mixture
- Low cylinder compression
- Defective valves, guides, or lifters
- Defective rings, pistons, or cylinders
- Vacuum leaks
- Plugged PCV system
- Excessively rich air-fuel ratio
- Stuck open heat riser valve
- AIR pump inoperative or disconnected
- Engine oil diluted with gasoline

Carbon Monoxide

Carbon monoxide (CO) is a byproduct of combustion. CO is a poisonous chemical compound of carbon and oxygen. It forms in the engine when there is not enough oxygen to combine with the hydrocarbons during combustion. When there is enough oxygen in the mixture, carbon dioxide (CO_2) is formed. CO_2 is not a pollutant and is the gas used by plants to manufacture oxygen. CO is primarily found in the exhaust but can also be in the crankcase. CO is odorless and tasteless, but in concentrated form it is toxic.

CO emissions are caused by a lack of air or too much fuel in the air-fuel mixture. CO will not occur if combustion does not take place in the cylinders. Therefore, the presence of CO means combustion is taking place. As the air-fuel ratio becomes richer, the CO levels increase (Figure 13-2). At the stoichiometric air-fuel ratio, the CO emissions are very low. If the air-fuel ratio is leaner than stoichiometric, the CO emissions remain very low. Therefore, CO emissions are a good indicator of a rich air-fuel ratio but are not an accurate indication of a lean air-fuel ratio. When cylinder misfiring occurs, there is less total combustion in the engine cylinders. Since CO is a byproduct

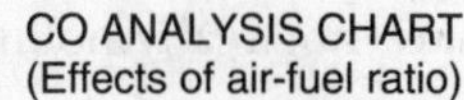

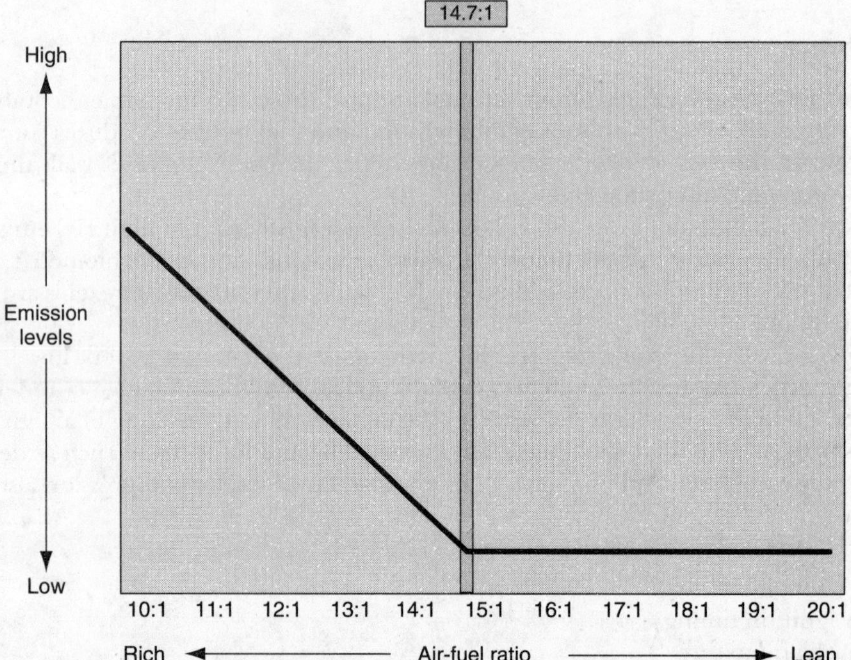

FIGURE 13-2 *CO emissions in relationship to air-fuel ratio.*

of combustion, cylinder misfiring does not increase CO emissions. If a cylinder is misfiring, CO emissions may decrease slightly.

Excessive CO emissions may be caused by:

- Rich air-fuel mixtures
- Dirty air filter
- Faulty injectors
- Higher-than-normal fuel pressures
- Defective system input sensor
- Plugged PCV system
- Excessively rich air-fuel ratio
- Stuck open heat riser valve
- Inoperative or disconnected AIR pump
- Engine oil diluted with gasoline.

Oxides of Nitrogen

This pollutant is actually various compounds of nitrogen and oxygen. Both of these gases are present in the air used for combustion. The formation of **oxides of nitrogen (NO_x)** is the result of high combustion temperatures. When combustion temperature reaches more than 2,500°F (1,370°C), the N and the O_2 in the air combine to form these oxides of nitrogen. NO_x emissions are a major contributor to the problem of smog. Since outside air is 78 percent N, the gas cannot be prevented from entering the combustion chamber. The key to controlling NO_x is to prevent N from joining with O_2 during the combustion process.

The "x" in NO_x stands for the proportion of oxygen mixed with a nitrogen atom. The "x" is a variable, which means it could be the number 1, 2, 3, and so on, therefore, the term NO_x refers to many different oxides of nitrogen (NO, NO_2, NO_3, and so on). Most of the NO_x emissions from an engine are NO, or nitrous oxide. When NO is released in the air, NO seeks, finds, and combines with an oxygen atom to form nitrous dioxide (NO_2). NO_2 is a very toxic gas and contributes to the formation of smog, ozone, and acid rain.

Higher-than-normal NO_x emissions may be caused by:

- An overheated engine
- Lean air-fuel mixtures
- Vacuum leaks
- Overadvanced ignition timing
- Defective EGR system
- Compression too high

Oxygen

A certain amount of oxygen is required for proper catalytic converter operation. O_2 is not a pollutant, therefore its presence in the exhaust does not pose any threat to our environment. However, too much oxygen in the exhaust does indicate that an improper mixture was in the cylinders or poor combustion has occurred in the engine. An improper air-fuel mixture will also cause a high reading of oxygen.

If the air-fuel ratio is rich, all the oxygen in the air is mixed with fuel and the O_2 levels in the exhaust are very low. When the air-fuel ratio is lean, there is not enough fuel to mix with all the air entering the engine, and O_2 levels in the exhaust are higher (Figure 13-3). Therefore, O_2 levels

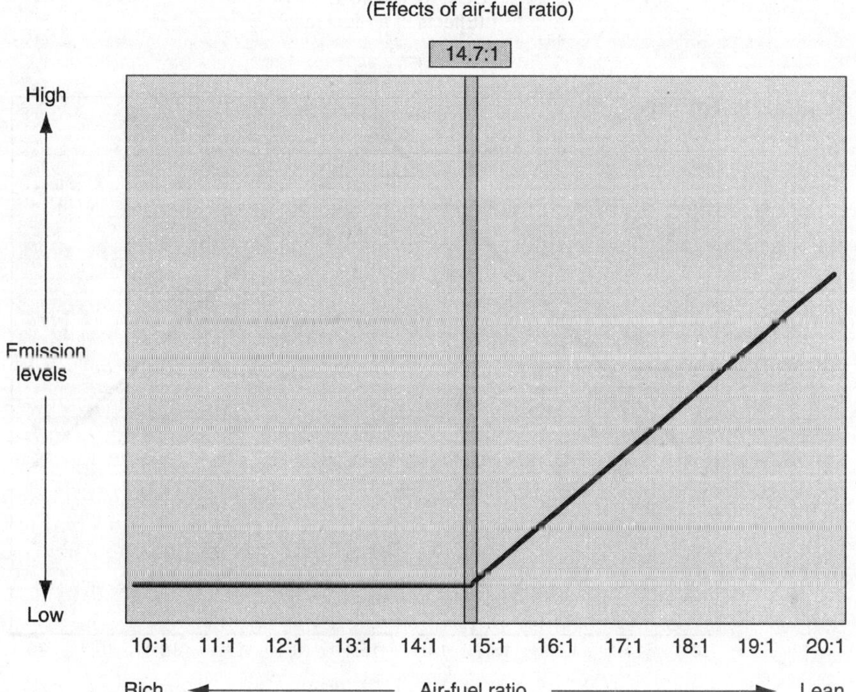

FIGURE 13-3 *O_2 levels in relationship to air-fuel ratio.*

are a good indicator of a lean air-fuel ratio, and they are minimally affected by catalytic converter operation.

Lower-than-normal O_2 emissions may be caused by:

- Rich air-fuel mixture
- Dirty air filter
- Faulty injectors
- Higher-than-normal fuel pressures
- Defective system input sensor
- Restricted PCV system
- Charcoal canister purging at idle and low speeds

Higher-than-normal O_2 emissions may be caused by:

- An engine misfire
- Lean air-fuel mixtures
- Vacuum leaks
- Lower-than-specified fuel pressures
- Defective fuel injectors
- Defective system input sensor
- Engine mechanical problems

Carbon Dioxide

CO_2 is also not a pollutant; however, it has been linked to the "greenhouse effect." An ideal byproduct of combustion is CO_2. Therefore, large amounts of this gas are desired. If the air-fuel ratio goes from 9:1 to 14.7:1, the CO_2 levels gradually increase from approximately 6 percent to 13.5 percent (Figure 13-4).

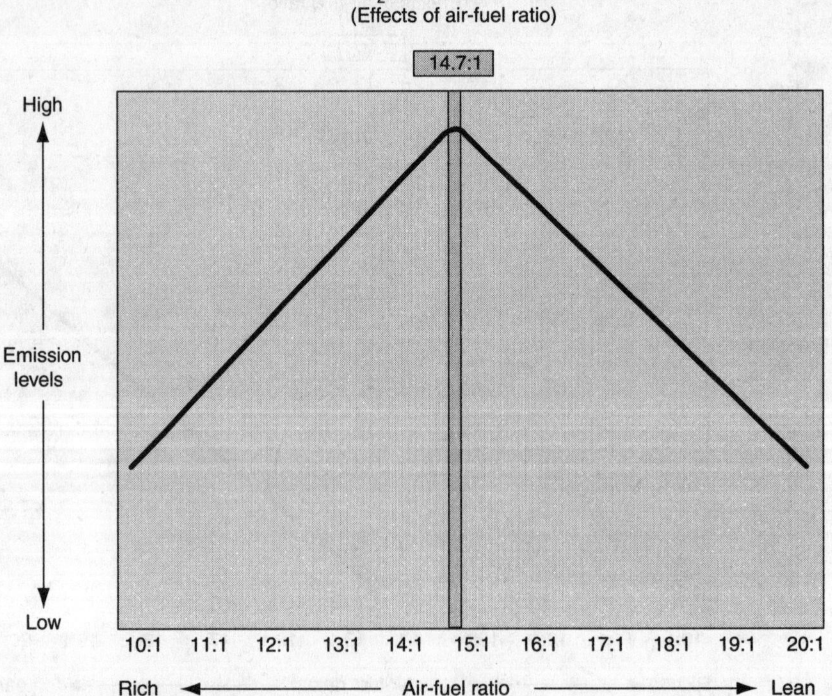

FIGURE 13-4 *CO_2 levels in relationship to air-fuel ratio.*

CO_2 levels are highest when the air-fuel ratio is slightly leaner than stoichiometric. At the stoichiometric air-fuel ratio, CO_2 levels begin to decrease.
Lower-than-normal CO_2 emissions may be caused by:

- Leaking exhaust system
- Improper air-fuel mixture
- An engine misfire
- Insufficient combustion
- Engine mechanical problems

EVAPORATIVE EMISSION CONTROL SYSTEMS

If gasoline is allowed to evaporate into the air, it becomes a significant source of hydrocarbon emissions (HC). Before the implementation of evaporative controls, it was determined that 20 percent of the vehicle's total emissions were occurring even while the vehicle was sitting in the driveway. Evaporative emissions were implemented in 1968. Prior to evaporative emission controls, the fuel tank and the carburetor were simply vented to the atmosphere. Of course, the fuel tank does have to be vented and/or the pressure relieved depending on conditions. Warm fuel will cause pressure to build inside the tank, or as fuel is used, a vacuum would develop inside that the fuel pump would not be able to overcome. To solve this problem, the tank is connected to and vented into a charcoal canister, which stores the vapors released until the vehicle is started and warm. The vapors are then drawn out of the canister by vacuum and burned in the engine. To help control the expansion of the fuel tank when warm, the tank is designed to never be totally full of fuel. The evaporative emissions system is monitored by the PCM to determine if the fuel system is sealed and HC vapors are not escaping.

Basically, there are two different evaporative emission systems (EVAP) that you may encounter on fuel injected vehicles. The first is just a basic EVAP as shown in Figure 13-5. The computer controls the purge valve by pulse width modulation of the purge solenoid whenever conditions are appropriate as explained later. The basic EVAP system does not use computerized monitoring for leaks in the system, although some of the basic systems did monitor purge valve operation by use of a diagnostic switch on the engine side of the purge valve. The computer knew if the purge valve was operating because the diagnostic switch would close.

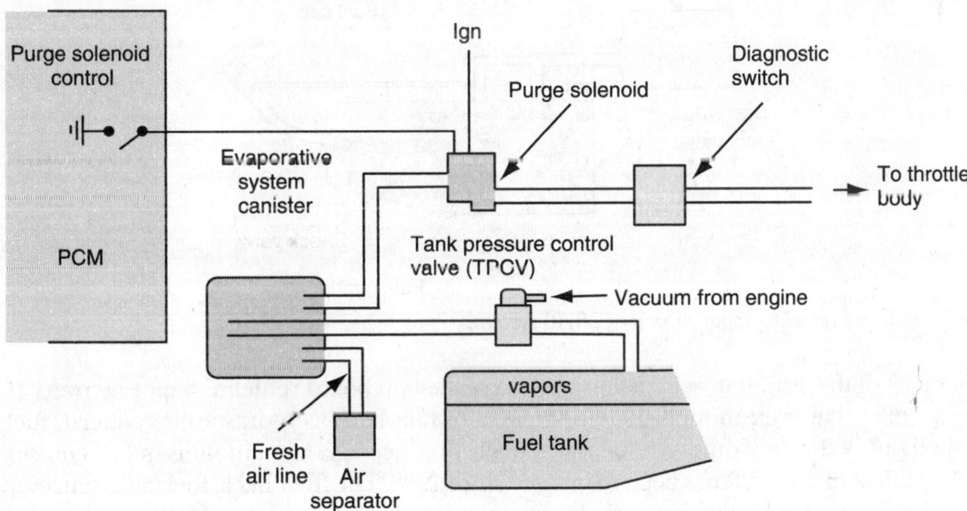

FIGURE 13-5 *Basic EVAP system components.*

The second and more recent EVAP system is the **enhanced EVAP**. The vent valve and tank pressure sensor were added for diagnostic purposes, and the fuel level sensor was added to the list of input sensors to the PCM. With enhanced EVAP, the PCM conducts several tests to determine if the system is operational and there are no leaks (Figure 13-6). Modern evaporative emission systems must be able to detect a leak as small as 0.020 inch in diameter and use this test to confirm that there are no leaks present (Figure 13-7).

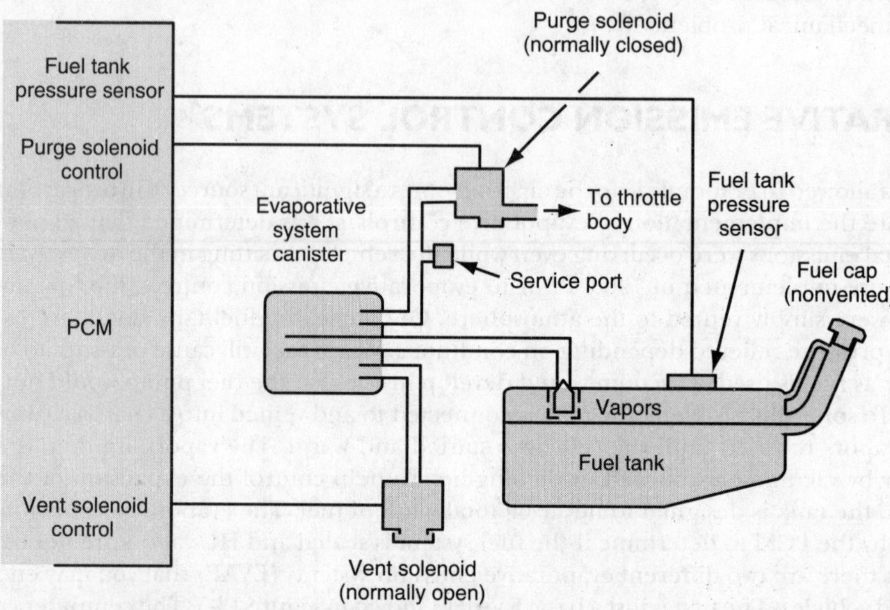

FIGURE 13-6 *The enhanced EVAP system. The purge-solenoid, the evaporative system canister, the vent solenoid, the fuel tank pressure sensor, and the fuel cap are highlighted in blue.*

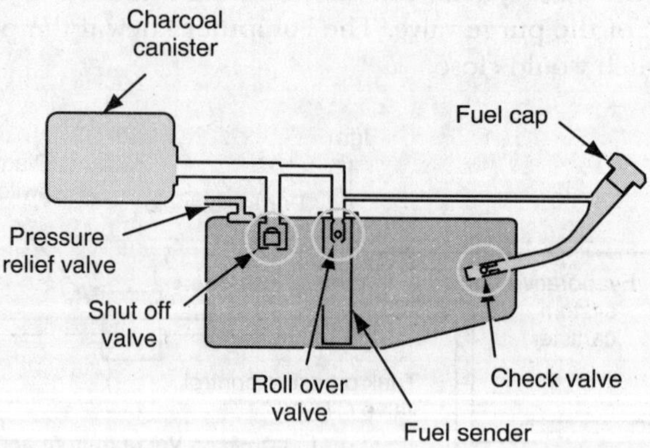

FIGURE 13-7 *On-board refueling vapor recovery (ORVR) system.*

Another part of the evaporative emission system is called on-board refueling vapor recovery (ORVR). It was determined that even though the evaporation of fuel had been drastically reduced, fuel vapors being pushed out of the tank during refueling actually produced greater amounts of HC emissions than burning the tank of fuel. ORVR has been mandated since 1998. The filler neck, fuel tank vent, evaporative canister, and rollover check valve were all changed to provide this capability. Major components of the evaporative emission system are:

For all systems

- Charcoal canister in which to store the HC vapors until burned
- Filler cap with vacuum and pressure relief valves (Figure 13-8)
- Fuel tank with a domed area to provide for expansion of fuel. The tank cannot be completely filled to help store vapors.
- Purge valve or solenoid to allow for the drawing of the fuel vapor into the engine
- Fuel tank pressure control valve (TPCV)
- Hoses and tubing to connect the system components

For enhanced systems (OBD II)

- Vent valve to control the flow of fresh air into the system
- Vacuum pressure sensor mounted on the tank
- Small filler neck that contains a check valve (ORVR-equipped vehicles)
- Check and one-way valves to keep liquid and vapor separated (Figure 13-9)
- Fuel level sensor
- An EVAP pump, used on some vehicles to pressurize the system while the fuel tank pressure sensor monitors for leaks

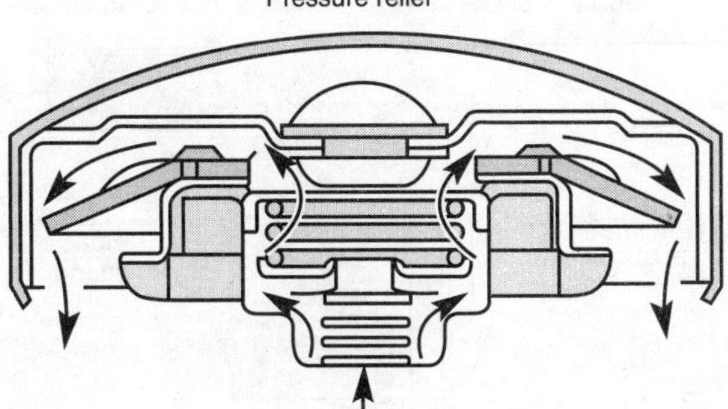

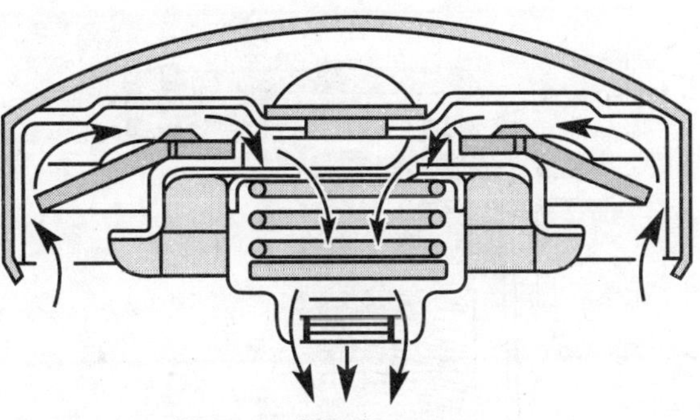

FIGURE 13-8 *Sealed fuel tank cap.*

Please note that there are many various systems in existence, and always make sure to check specific information on the vehicle before starting work on any system.

The **charcoal canister** is the heart of the EVAP system. The charcoal canister can be located in the engine compartment or near the fuel tank. The location near the fuel tank is especially true if the vehicle has the ORVR refueling vapor recovery system. The canister has to be large enough on these vehicles to store the vapors from refueling. Charcoal has the ability to store the vapors and then release them when the PCM determines that the engine can handle the extra fuel load, usually after the engine is warm (Figure 13-10). When the PCM decides to purge the canister, fresh air is allowed into the canister and vacuum is applied from the engine through the purge valve or solenoid.

The **purge valve** has undergone many changes since the inception of EVAP. Earlier purge valves were vacuum operated without computer control, but modern purge valves are computer controlled to allow more precise control of the vapors according to the many sensor inputs at the PCM (Figure 13-11). The purge solenoid can also be remotely mounted from the purge valve. The canister purge valve is normally closed. It opens the inlet to the purge outlet when vacuum is applied to the valve. Purging is done only when conditions warrant. Some of the conditions typically include such items as:

- 150 seconds since the PCM entered closed loop
- Coolant temperature above 176°F
- PCM not enabling injector shutdown, such as during a traction control
- Vehicle speed above 20 mph
- Engine speed above 1,100 rpm

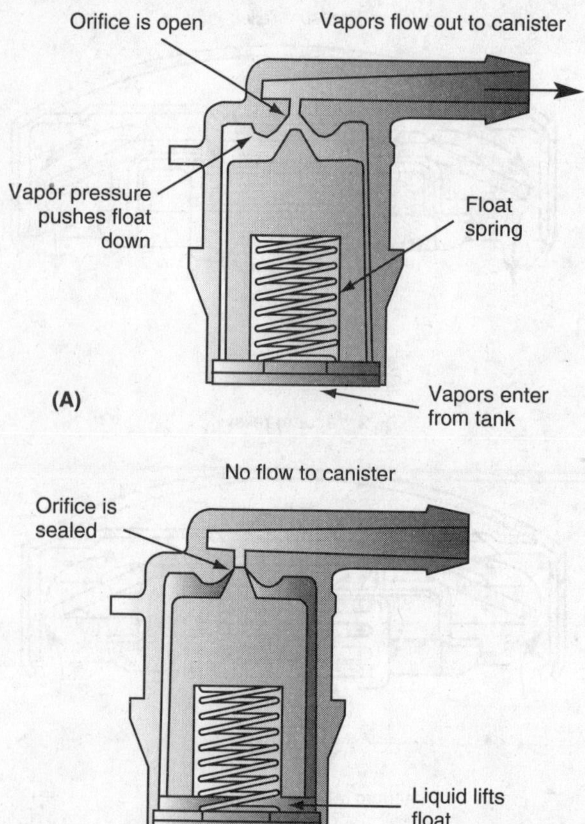

FIGURE 13-9 *(A) Normal operation of vapor separator, (B) with liquid in separator.*

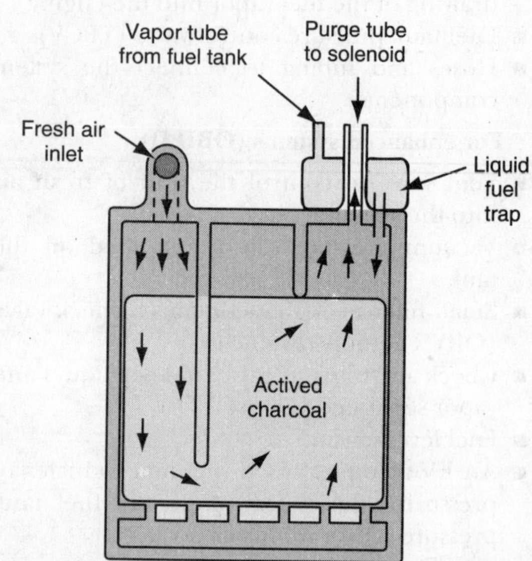

FIGURE 13-10 *Typical charcoal canister.*

FIGURE 13-11 *Computer-operated canister purge solenoid located on the canister.*

- Temperature sensor not indicating overheating
- Low coolant not indicated

The conditions that purge occur will of course vary from vehicle to vehicle.

The **vent valve** is opened to allow fresh air through the charcoal canister. Early canisters did not use a vent valve; the vent was left open to the atmosphere. The vent valve is only used for OBD II diagnostics. The vent valve can be closed with the purge valve open while the PCM monitors the fuel tank pressure sensor for vacuum. Vacuum should build with the vent closed and the purge open. The vent is checked for blockage during normal purging by checking for excessive vacuum with the vent valve commanded open. If there is vacuum drawn on the fuel tank with the vent and purge valves open, then the vent must be blocked. Finally, the purge valve can be checked for leaks by closing both the purge and vent valves and determining if a vacuum begins to build. If it does, the purge valve is leaking.

The most recent use of the vent valve and tank pressure sensor on EVAP systems on some 2003 and 2004 vehicles is the **engine off natural vacuum (EONV)** test. The system runs a pressure and vacuum test based on the natural volatility of the fuel. After driving, the fuel will be warm. If the vent to the tank is closed, the fuel pressure will build in a predictable way according to the ambient temperature. After the fuel starts to cool down, again with the vent closed, there will be a natural vacuum build within the tank that the system can measure. The PCM can use this information to determine if there are any small leaks in the system. If the fuel is too volatile, as determined by the rise in pressure after the engine is turned off, the test is canceled.

The **fuel tank pressure sensor** is mounted on the fuel tank and can measure vacuum and pressure at the tank. The fuel tank pressure sensor is a PCM input.

The **fuel tank level sensor** is actually the same sensor used for the fuel gauge but on OBD II vehicles is used to determine whether the fuel tank pressure or vacuum test should be run. If the tank is very full or near empty, the test will not run. The fuel tank sensor can also be checked at startup and during driving to detect refueling which could upset the results of the leak test.

The **fuel pressure control valve** is designed to control fuel tank pressure while the vehicle is sitting still. Vapors are stored in the tank with the valve closed. If tank pressure builds too high, the valve opens and lets the vapor into the canister. When the engine is running, the valve has vacuum applied, opening the valve and allowing vapors to be stored in the canister until purging.

Some systems use a **leak detection pump (LDP)** that pressurizes the system and checks for leaks, along with the fuel tank pressure sensor.

PRECOMBUSTION SYSTEMS

Systems designed to prevent or limit the amount of pollutants produced by an engine are called precombustion emission control devices. Although there are specific systems and engine designs that are classified this way, anything that makes an engine more efficient can be categorized as a precombustion emission control. The specific systems discussed in this chapter are the:

Engine design changes
PCV system
Spark control systems
EGR systems

ENGINE DESIGN CHANGES

In recent years, the basic engine has seen many technological changes. For the most part, the basics of operation have not been changed. Engineers have worked overtime in an attempt to squeeze as much out of small engines as they can. Many of these changes have not only increased the efficiency of the engines but have decreased the pollutants released by the engines. Also, some of the changes were only necessary or brought about to accommodate changes in the engine's fuel and/or ignition systems.

Better Sealing Pistons

One of the first areas of concern for engineers and emission control devices was the crankcase of an engine. PCV systems relieve the crankcase of unwanted gases and pressure. The PCV did not solve the problem of these pressurized gases blowing by the piston rings. Not only do these blowby gases represent a problem for the engine's lubrication, but they are an indication of wasted energy as well. The blowby gases start out to be fuel-air mixture. The mixture leaks past the piston rings during the compression and power strokes of the engine. Instead of being used to produce energy, this sampling of mixture is used only to dilute the oil. Blowby gases can and are being reduced in some engines through the use of better sealing piston rings and improved cylinder wall surfaces. Many of these better sealing piston rings also have frictional qualities that make them less of a drag. This increases fuel economy and engine power.

Combustion Chamber Designs

Combustion chamber design has seen many changes. The aim of these changes is to reduce or eliminate the quench area of the combustion chamber. The quench area (Figure 13-12) is any place in the chamber where the flame front of combustion is cooled as it tries to move into a small area. By removing the quench areas in a combustion chamber, HC and CO emissions can be reduced. Another change in the design of combustion chambers has been the locating of the spark closer to the center of the chamber. This provides for a more even burn and allows for leaner air-fuel mixtures. Manufacturers have also worked with designs that cause controlled turbulence in the chamber (Figure 13-13). This turbulence improves the mixing of the fuel with the air which results in improved combustion.

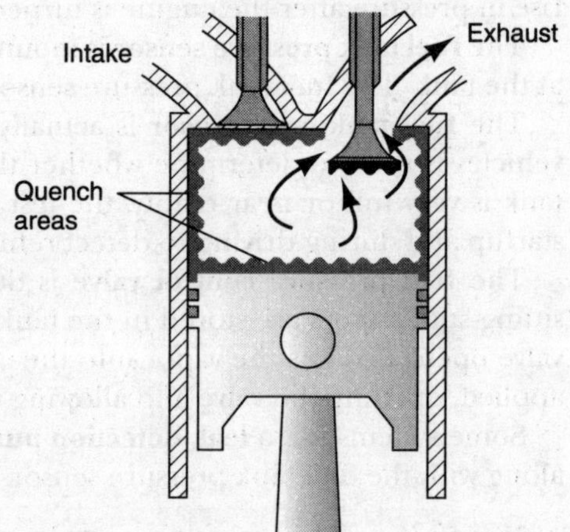

FIGURE 13-12 *Unburned fuel is left on all surface areas.*

Lower Compression

Combustion chamber designs have also affected the compression ratios of engines. By keeping the compression ratio low, combustion temperatures can be kept below the point where NO_x is formed. Initially, when compression ratios dropped, engine performance and fuel economy also dropped. With the application of new technology, engine performance and fuel economy have greatly improved in spite of the lower compression ratios. These other technological changes have also allowed for compression ratios to come back up on some high-performance engines.

Decreased Friction

Power losses through friction are a major contributor to the overall inefficiency of a gasoline engine. The friction of all of the moving parts of an engine results in a large loss of useable power and energy. By reducing the friction at key points within the engine, engineers have reduced the amount of power

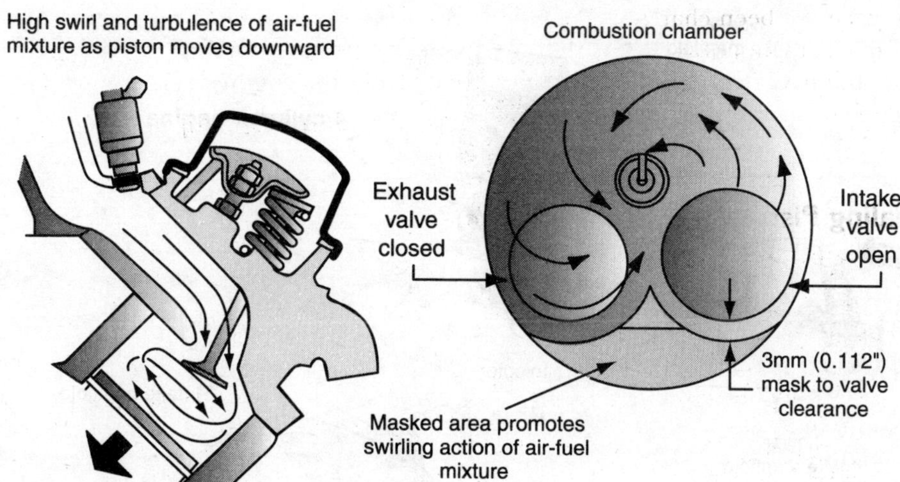

FIGURE 13-13 *Combustion chamber designed to control turbulence.*

lost. By regaining power, fuel economy and engine performance are increased. Emissions are also reduced because less fuel is burned to produce the same amount of useable power. Improved engine oils, new component materials, and weight reductions have had the biggest impact on reducing friction.

Unleaded Fuel

Leaded fuels are no longer used in automobiles because they poison catalytic converters and lead emitted in the exhaust poisons the atmosphere. Lead was added to fuels to increase their octane rating. Lead also served as a cushion between the engine's valve and valve seats. Unleaded fuel does not offer this cushioning. Therefore, engines are built with hardened valve seats. This change has been in place for many years. However, engineers are still working to design valves and valve seats that maintain their seal after hundreds of thousands of miles. By maintaining a proper seal at the valves, engines can run more efficiently for many miles of use.

Intake Manifold Designs

Intake manifolds have been designed to distribute equal amounts of air to each cylinder. Most of the design changes to intake manifolds have been afforded by the use of port fuel injection (Figure 13-14). The use of plastics in the manufacture of intake manifolds have allowed for smoother runners and better heat control of the air. Intake manifolds can be designed to be more efficient at low engine speeds, high engine speeds, or both. Again, increased efficiency results in decreased emissions.

Improved Cooling Systems

Today's engines have a higher normal operating temperature than older engines. The higher engine temperature reduces HC and CO emissions. However, the higher temperature also makes the formation of NO_x harder to control. Most engine cooling systems have been designed to run at high temperatures but are prevented from becoming too hot. This prevention reduces NO_x. The high engine temperature results in increased efficiency because the engine parts around the combustion chamber are hotter. This means less heat from combustion is absorbed by the metal engine parts leaving more heat for power conversion. Today's engine control systems incorporate many features

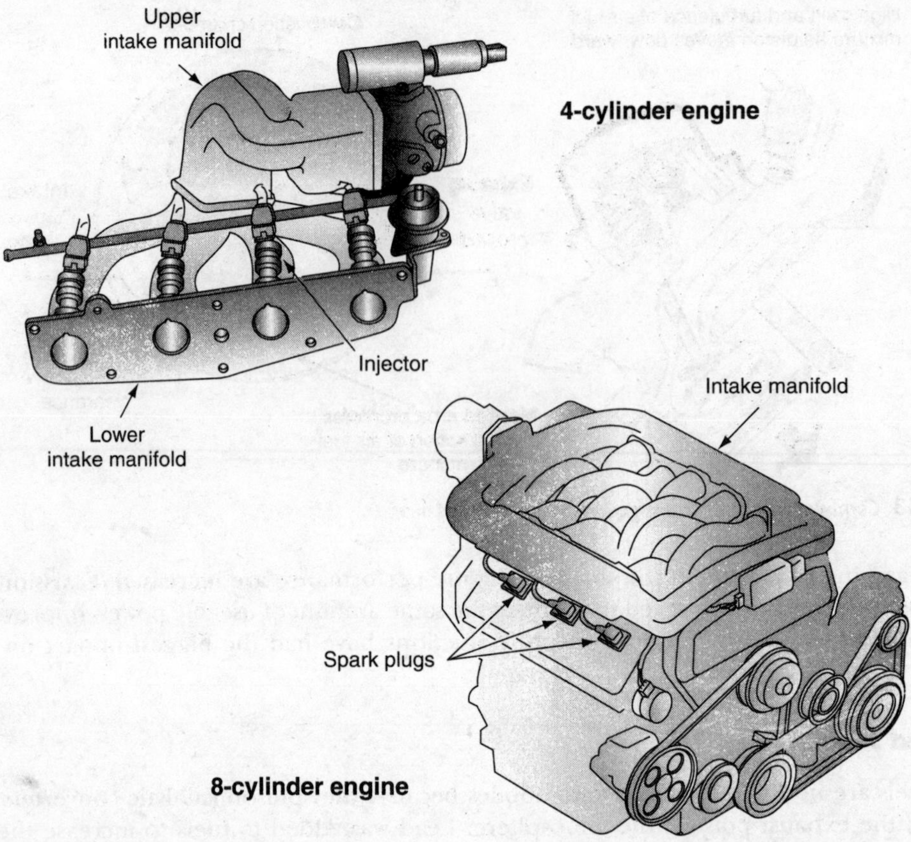

FIGURE 13-14 *A tuned intake manifold.*

that change air-fuel mixture, ignition timing, and idle speed to control the temperature of the engine.

PCV SYSTEMS

During the last part of the engine's combustion stroke, some unburned fuel and products of combustion—water vapor, for instance—leak past the engine's piston rings into the crankcase. This leakage into the engine crankcase is called **blowby**. Blowby must be removed from the engine before it condenses in the crankcase and reacts with the oil to form sludge. Sludge, if allowed to circulate with engine oil, corrodes and accelerates the wear of pistons, piston rings, valves, bearings, and other internal working parts of the engine. Blowby gases must also be removed from the crankcase to prevent premature oil leaks. Because these gases enter the crankcase by the pressure formed during combustion, they pressurize the crankcase. The gases exert pressure on the oil pan gasket and crankshaft seals. If the pressure is not relieved, oil is eventually forced out of these seals.

Because the air-fuel mixture in an engine never completely burns, blowby also carries some unburned fuel into the crankcase. If not removed, the unburned fuel dilutes the crankcase oil. When oil is diluted with gasoline, it does not lubricate the engine properly, causing excessive wear.

Combustion gases that enter the crankcase are removed by a positive crankcase ventilation system that uses engine vacuum to draw fresh air through the crankcase. This fresh air dissipates the harmful gases and enters through the air filter or through a separate PCV breather filter located on the inside of the air filter housing.

Because the vacuum supply for the PCV system is from the engine's intake manifold, the airflow through this system must be controlled in such a way that it varies in proportion to the regular air-fuel ratio being drawn into the intake manifold. Otherwise, the additional air that is drawn into the system would cause the air-fuel mixture to become too lean for efficient engine operation. Therefore, a PCV valve is placed in the flow just before the intake manifold to regulate the flow according to vacuum.

The positive crankcase ventilation system has two major functions. It prevents the emission of blowby gases from the engine crankcase to the atmosphere. These gases were once vented through a road draft tube. Now they are recirculated to the engine intake and burned during combustion. It also scavenges the crankcase of vapors that could dilute the oil and cause it to deteriorate or that could build undesirable pressure in the crankcase. Fresh air from the air cleaner mixes with these vapors and makes them flow to the intake.

The PCV system benefits the vehicle's driveability by eliminating harmful crankcase gases, reducing air pollution, and promoting fuel economy. An inoperative PCV system could shorten the life of the engine by allowing harmful blowby gases to remain in the engine, causing corrosion and accelerating wear.

The PCV valve is usually mounted in a rubber grommet in one of the valve covers. A hose is connected from the PCV valve to the intake manifold. A clean air hose is connected from the air cleaner to the opposite rocker arm cover. A filter is positioned in the air cleaner end of the clean air hose (Figure 13-15). On some systems, the PCV valve is mounted in a vent module and the clean air filter is located in this module (Figure 13-16).

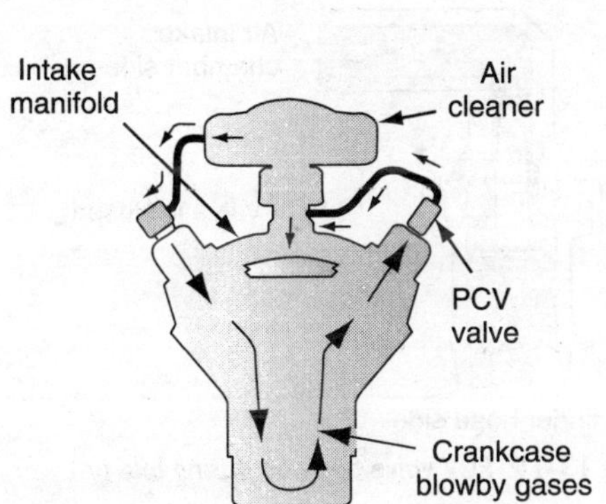

FIGURE 13-15 *Typical PCV system.*

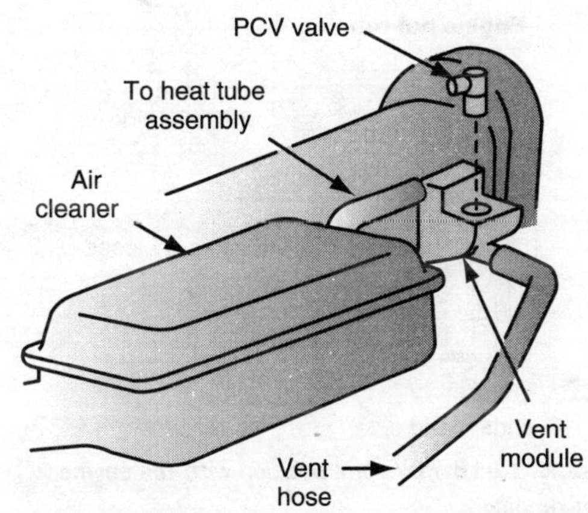

FIGURE 13-16 *PCV valve mounted in a vent module.*

When the engine is running, intake manifold vacuum is supplied to the PCV valve. This vacuum moves air through the clean air hose into the rocker arm cover. From this location, air flows through cylinder head openings into the crankcase where it mixes with blowby gases that escape from the combustion chamber past the piston rings. The mixture of blowby gases and air flows up through cylinder head openings to the rocker arm cover and PCV valve. Intake manifold vacuum moves the blowby gas mixture through the PCV valve into the intake manifold (Figure 13-17). The blowby gases are then moved through the intake valves into the combustion chambers where they are burned.

On many engines, the PCV system delivers blowby gases to one location in the intake manifold. This type of system may not deliver these gases equally to all the cylinders. This action may result in an air-fuel ratio variation between the cylinders which results in rougher idle operation. Some engines, such as the Ford's 4.6L V8, have passages from the PCV valve through the intake manifold to supply blowby gases equally to each cylinder resulting in smoother idle operation.

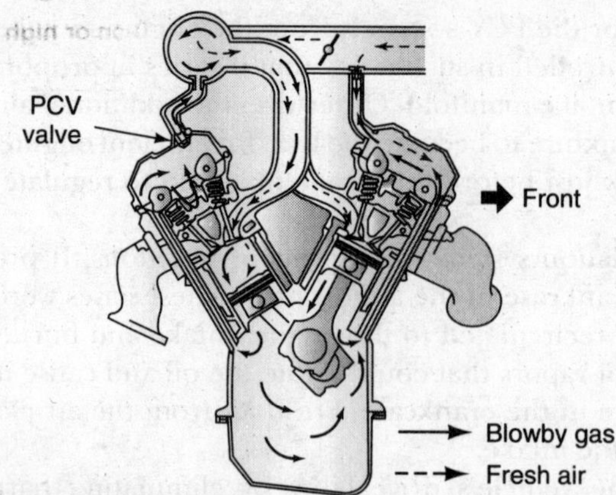

FIGURE 13-17 *Operation of PCV system.*

A PCV valve contains a tapered valve. When the engine is not running, a spring keeps the tapered valve seated against the valve housing (Figure 13-18). During idle or deceleration, the high intake manifold vacuum moves the tapered valve upward against the spring tension. Under this condition, there is a small opening between the tapered valve and the PCV valve housing (Figure 13-19). Since the engine is not under heavy load during idle or deceleration operation, blowby gases are minimal, and the small PCV valve opening is adequate to move the blowby gases out of the crankcase.

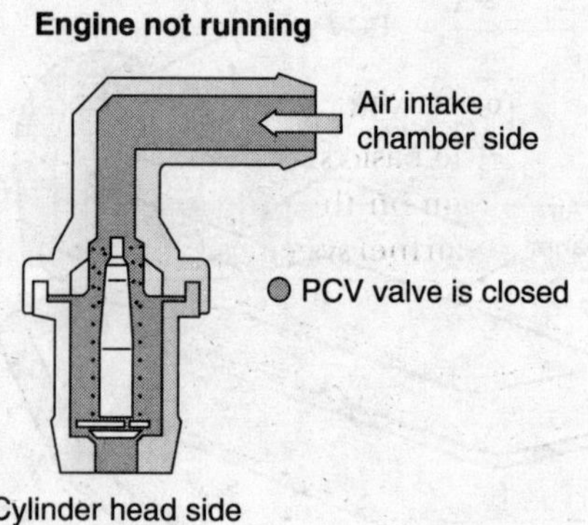

FIGURE 13-18 *PCV valve position with the engine not running.*

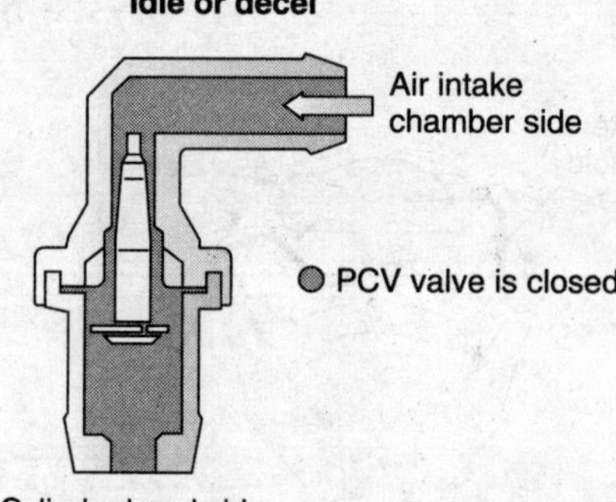

FIGURE 13-19 *PCV valve position during idle or deceleration.*

Intake manifold vacuum is lower during part-throttle operation than during idle operation. Under this condition, the spring moves the tapered valve downward to increase the opening between this valve and the PCV valve housing (Figure 13-20). Since engine load is higher at part-throttle operation than at idle operation, blowby gases are increased. The larger opening between the tapered valve and the PCV valve housing allows all the blowby gases to be drawn into the intake manifold.

When the engine is operating under heavy load conditions with a wide throttle opening, the decrease in intake manifold vacuum allows the spring to move the tapered valve further downward in the PCV valve (Figure 13-21). This action provides a larger opening between the tapered valve and the PCV valve housing. Since higher engine load results in more blowby gases, the larger PCV valve opening is necessary to allow these gases to flow through the valve into the intake manifold.

When worn rings or scored cylinders allow excessive blowby gases into the crankcase, the PCV valve opening may not be large enough to allow these gases to flow into the intake manifold. Under

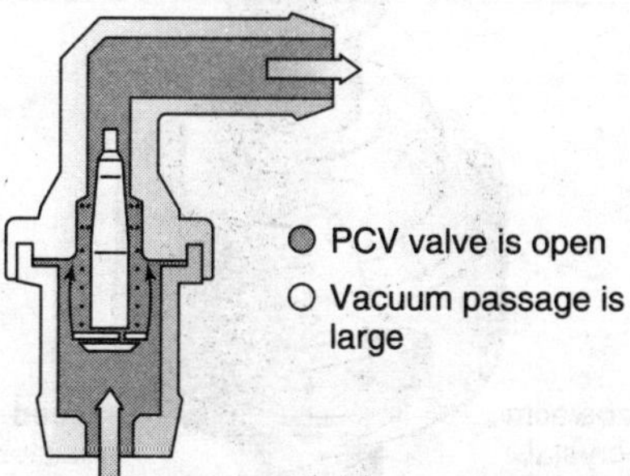

FIGURE 13-20 *PCV valve position during part-throttle operation.*

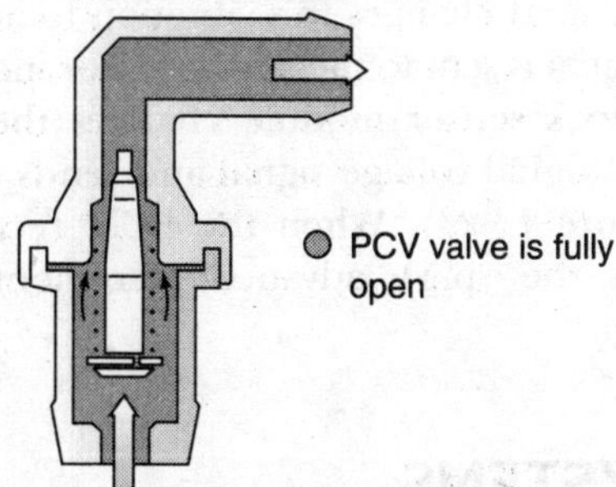

FIGURE 13-21 *PCV valve position during hard acceleration or heavy load.*

this condition, the blowby gases create a pressure in the crankcase, and some of these gases are forced through the clean air hose and filter into the air cleaner. When this action occurs, there is oil in the PCV filter and air cleaner. This same action occurs if the PCV valve is restricted or plugged.

If the PCV valve sticks in the wide-open position, excessive airflow through the valve causes rough idle operation. If a backfire occurs in the intake manifold, the tapered valve is seated in the PCV valve as if the engine is not running. This action prevents the backfire from entering the engine where it could cause an explosion.

Fixed Orifice Tube PCV System

Some engines are equipped with a PCV system that does not use a PCV valve. Rather, the blowby gases are routed into the intake manifold through a fixed orifice tube. The basic system works the same as if it had a valve except that the system is regulated only by the vacuum on the orifice. The size of the orifice limits the amount of blowby flow into the intake. The engine's airfuel system is calibrated for this calibrated air leak. Since the action of the PCV allows unmetered air into the intake, the air-fuel system must be set for this amount of extra air.

SPARK CONTROL SYSTEMS

Spark control systems have been in use since the earliest gasoline engines. It was discovered that the proper timing of the ignition spark helped to reduce exhaust emissions and develop more power output. Incorrect timing affects the combustion process. Incomplete combustion results in HC emissions. High CO emissions can also result from incorrect ignition timing. Advanced timing can also increase the production of NO_x. When timing is too far advanced, combustion temperatures rise. For every one degree of overadvance, the temperature increases by 125°F. Throughout the years, each car manufacturer developed slightly different spark timing controls according to engine requirements and emission standards for each model year, but the systems and devices all operate on the same principles.

Knock Sensor and Knock Sensor Module

Many engines with an EFI have a knock sensor or sensors. The knock sensors may be mounted in the block, cylinder head, or intake manifold. A piezoelectric sensing element is mounted in the knock sensor, and a resistor is connected parallel to this sensing element (Figure 13-22). When the engine detonates, a vibration occurs in the engine. The piezoelectric sensing element changes this vibration to an analog voltage, and this signal is sent to the knock sensor module.

The knock sensor module changes the analog voltage signal to a digital voltage signal and sends this signal to the PCM (Figure 13-23). When the PCM receives this signal, it reduces the spark advance incrementally to prevent detonation.

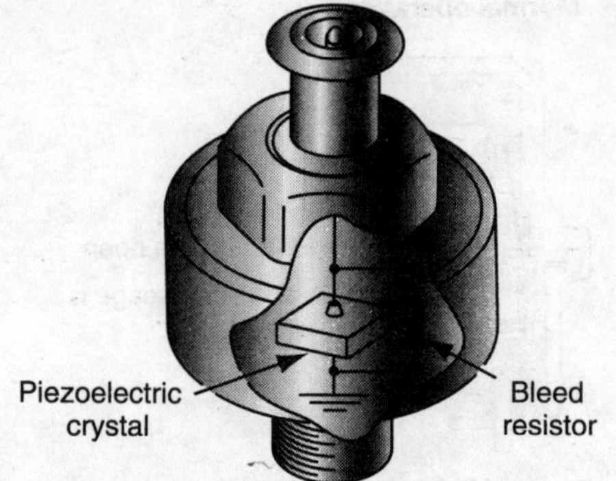

FIGURE 13-22 *Detonation sensor.*

EGR SYSTEMS

Exhaust gas recirculating systems reduce the amount of oxides of nitrogen emitted. The EGR system dilutes the air-fuel mixture with controlled amounts of exhaust gas. Since exhaust gas does not burn, this reduces the peak combustion temperatures. At lower combustion temperatures, very little of the nitrogen in the air combines with oxygen to form NO_x. Most of the nitrogen is simply carried out with the exhaust gases. For driveability, it is desirable to have the EGR valve opening (and the amount of gas flow) proportional to the throttle opening. Driveability is also improved by shutting off the EGR when the engine is started up cold, at idle, and at full throttle. Since the NO_x control requirements vary on different engines, there are several different systems with various controls to provide these functions.

Modern EGR systems have to be monitored by the OBD II system for operation. Older EGR systems that used a heated intake manifold such as TBI-equipped vehicles, tap into the exhaust crossover to place a metered amount of exhaust into the intake charge to lower the combustion chamber temperature. Since port fuel vehicles do not have to use a heated intake manifold, the EGR exhaust must be piped directly from the exhaust.

Figure 13-24 shows a basic vacuum operated flow control valve. A small exhaust crossover passage in the intake manifolds of some TBI vehicles admits exhaust gases into the intake manifold air fuel passages when it is opened. On vehicles without a heated exhaust manifold the exhaust may be routed

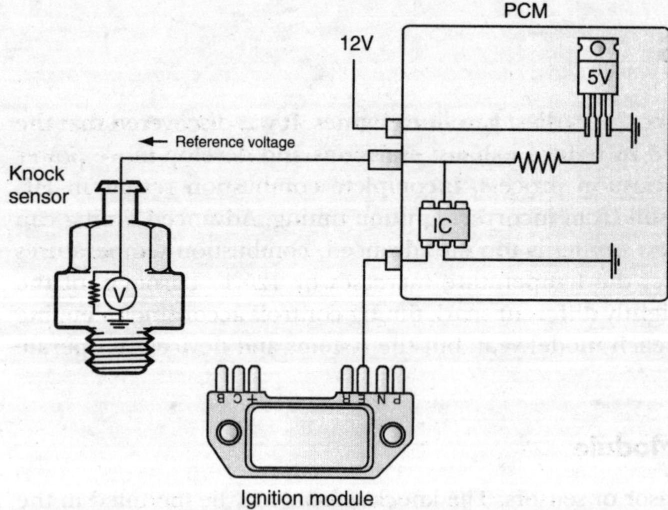

FIGURE 13-23 *The PCM uses the knock sensor to modify timing and prevent spark knock.*

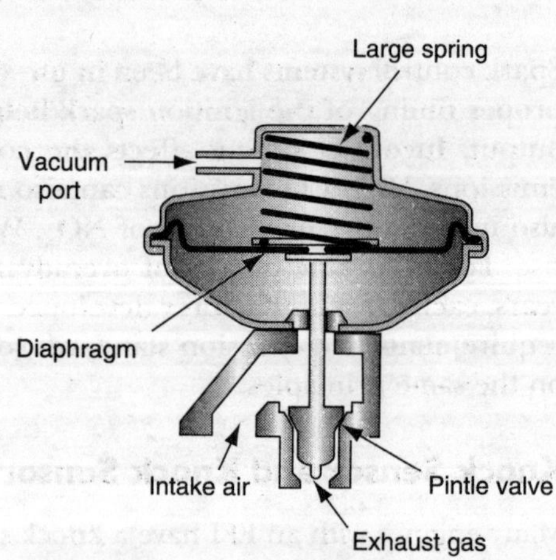

FIGURE 13-24 *Typical vacuum-operated EGR valve.*

to the EGR valve via a special tube. Opening the EGR valve by control vacuum at the diaphragm allows exhaust gases to flow through the valve and back to another port of the spacer (Figure 13-25). Here, the exhaust gas mixes with the incoming air-fuel mixture and then enters the intake manifold. The effect is to dilute or lean-out the mixture so that it still burns completely but with a reduction in combustion chamber temperatures.

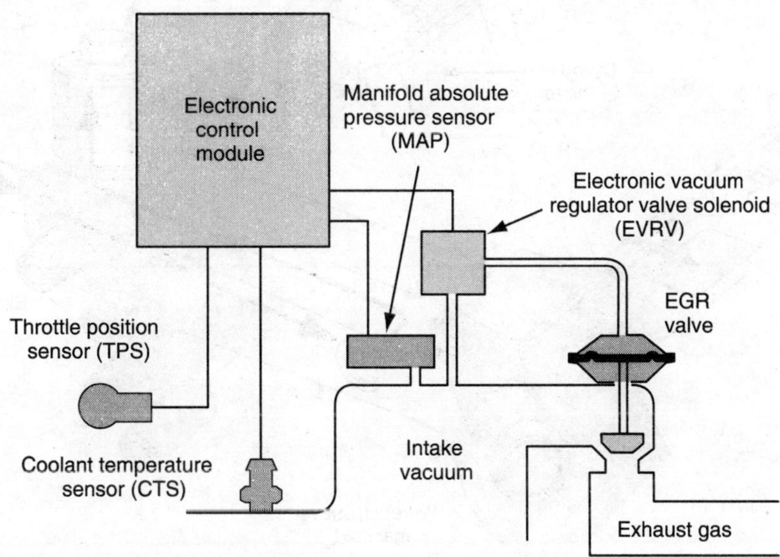

FIGURE 13-25 *A computer-controlled EGR system.*

On some engines, such as the GM's Northstar 4.6L V8, the exhaust gas from the EGR system is distributed through passages in the cylinder heads and distribution plates to each intake port (Figure 13-26). The distribution plates are positioned between the cylinder heads and the intake manifold.

Since the exhaust gas from the EGR system is distributed equally to each cylinder, smoother engine operation results. Exhaust gases in the Northstar 4.6L V8 engine flow through passages in the crossover water pump housing where they are cooled by engine coolant. This cooling action lowers the exhaust gases below their carbon-forming temperature prior to routing these gases into the cylinder distribution passages, which reduces carbon deposits in the EGR system.

The vacuum-controlled EGR is opened by vacuum and is closed by a spring. The vacuum used on modern EGR valve systems is computer controlled (Figure 13-25). The duty cycle of the vacuum solenoid can be changed to regulate the opening of the valve. The TPS, CTS, and MAP sensors are all monitored to determine if and how much EGR is needed to limit NO_x production. Manifold vacuum that is pulse width modulated (PWM) through a solenoid called the **electronic vacuum regulator valve (EVRV)** is used to open the EGR valve. The PCM on OBD II vehicles must also determine that the EGR valve has opened when commanded and that EGR is flowing into the intake manifold. One strategy to do this monitors the MAP sensor to sense a change in the intake manifold pressure. Other valves may use temperature sensors or dedicated vacuum sensors to perform this function. Make sure to check with service literature before starting work on any system.

Figure 13-27 shows a **delta pressure feedback EGR sensor (DPFE)** system. When the EGR valve is open, there is a difference in pressure between the exhaust and intake side of a metering orifice. The DPFE sensor relays this information to the PCM. The PCM can then use this information to verify EGR valve opening, and/or modify the amount of opening to match the engine's needs.

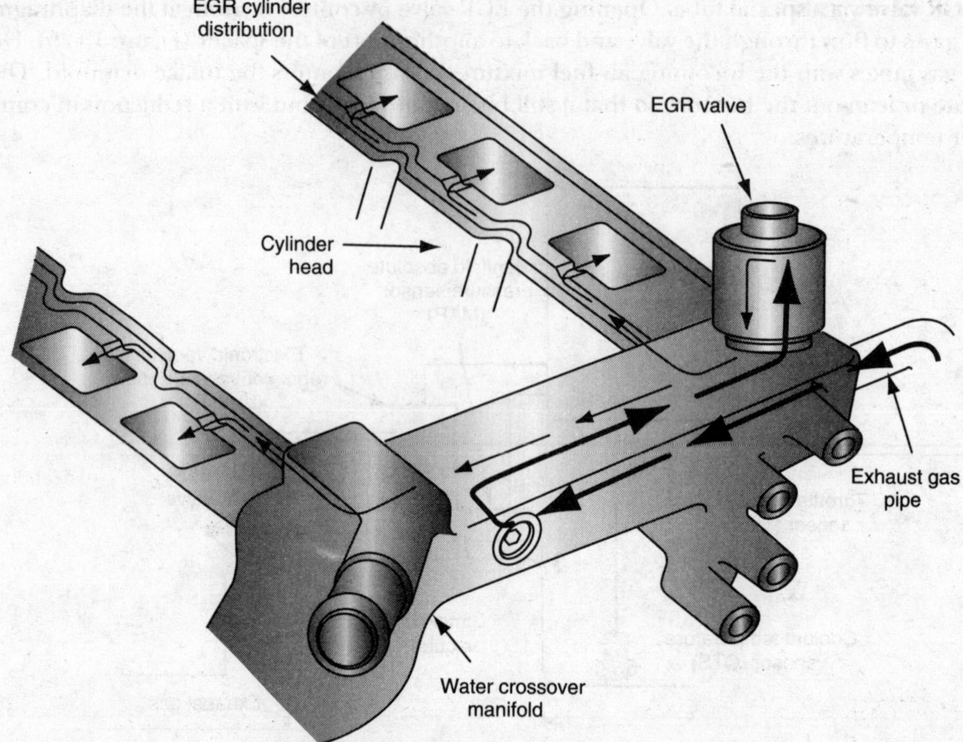

FIGURE 13-26 *A GM Northstar engine with EGR passages to each intake port.*

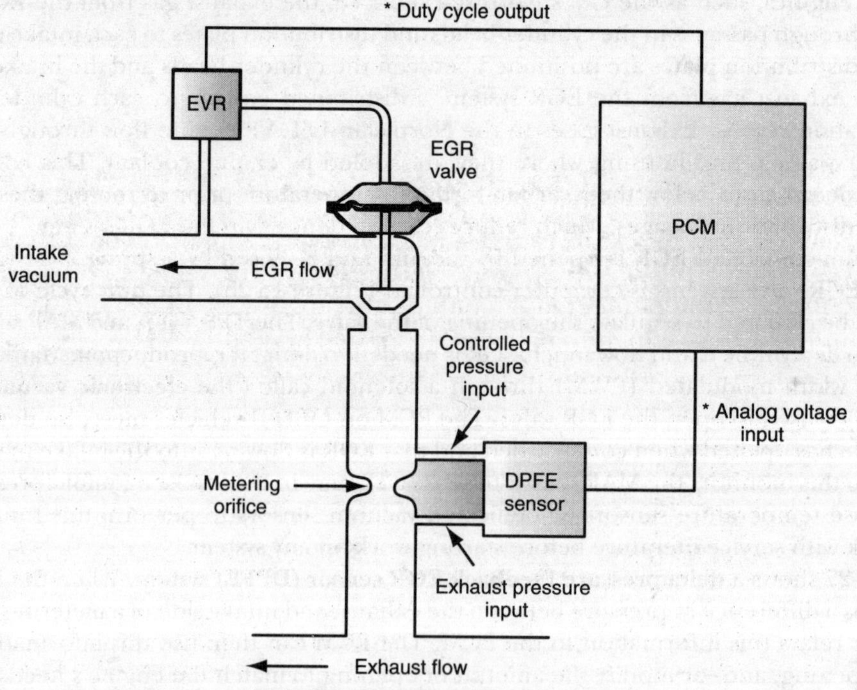

FIGURE 13-27 *A DPFE sensor EGR circuit with an electronic vacuum regulator (EVR).*

Types of EGR Valves

Digital EGR Valve. A digital EGR valve contains up to three electric solenoids that are operated directly by the PCM (Figure 13-28). Each solenoid contains a moveable plunger with a tapered tip that seats in an orifice. When any solenoid is energized, the plunger is lifted and exhaust gas is allowed to recirculate through the orifice into the intake manifold. The solenoids and orifices are different sizes. The PCM can operate one, two, or three solenoids to supply the amount of exhaust recirculation required to provide optimum control of NO_x emissions.

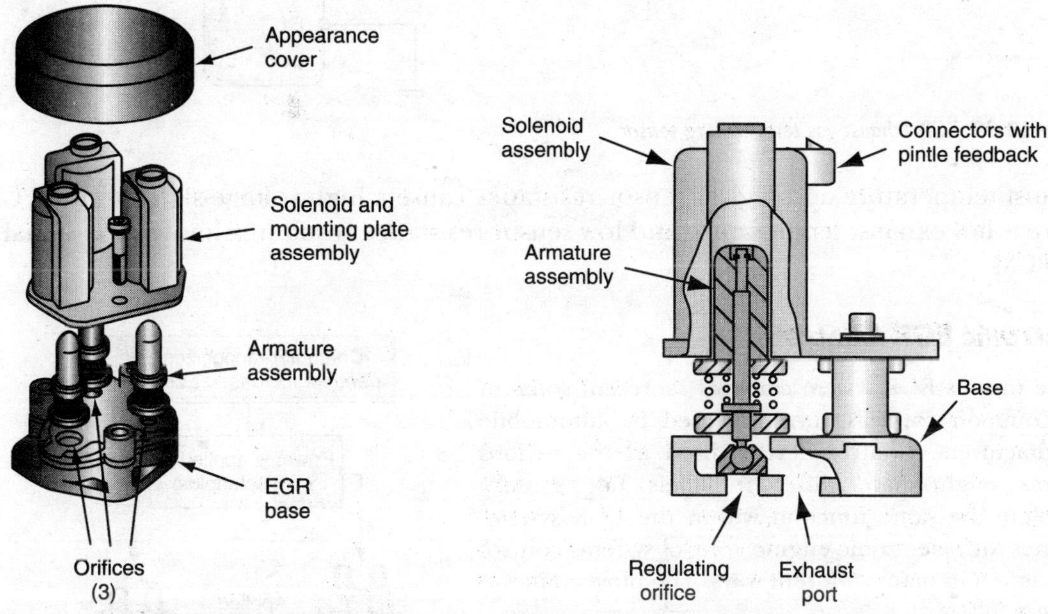

FIGURE 13-28 *A digital EGR valve with three solenoids.*

FIGURE 13-29 *Linear EGR valve operation.*

Linear EGR Valve. The linear EGR valve contains a single electric solenoid that is operated by the PCM. A tapered pintle is positioned on the end of the solenoid plunger. When the solenoid is energized, the plunger and tapered valve are lifted and exhaust gas is allowed to recirculate into the intake manifold (Figure 13-29). The EGR valve contains an EGR valve position (EVP) sensor, which is a linear potentiometer. The signal from this sensor varies from approximately 1 volt with the EGR valve closed to 4.5 volts with the valve wide open.

The PCM pulses the EGR solenoid winding on and off with a pulse width modulation principle to provide accurate control of the plunger and EGR flow. The EVP sensor acts as a feedback signal to the PCM to inform the PCM if the commanded valve position was achieved.

EGR Valve with Exhaust Gas Temperature Sensor. Some EGR valves, particularly on vehicles sold in California, contain an exhaust gas temperature sensor. This sensor contains a thermistor that changes resistance in relation to temperature. An increase in exhaust temperature decreases the sensor resistance. Two wires are connected from the exhaust gas temperature sensor to the PCM (Figure 13-30). The PCM senses the voltage drop across this sensor. Cool

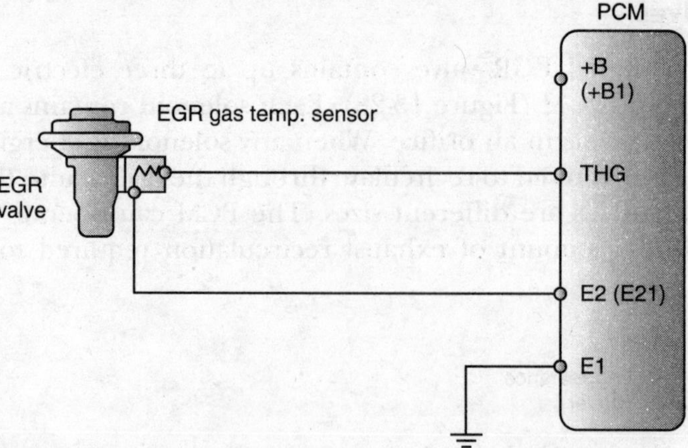

FIGURE 13-30 *EGR exhaust gas temperature sensor.*

exhaust temperature and higher sensor resistance cause a high-voltage signal to the PCM, whereas hot exhaust temperature and low sensor resistance result in a low-voltage signal to the PCM.

Electronic EGR Controls

These various EGR system controls represent some of the common controls currently used by automobile manufacturers. Control devices used in the various systems might have different labels but actually complete the same function within the EGR system. Engines with electronic engine control systems control EGR action in many different ways. The most common of these follow.

Twin Solenoid EGR System. The EGR valve within this system resembles and is operated in a manner similar to the conventional EGR valves. This system uses sensors, solenoids, and an electronic control assembly to modulate and control EGR system components. A sensor mounted on the valve stem sends an electronic signal to the on-board computer, which in turn tells how far the EGR valve is opened.

This system is often controlled by two solenoids (Figure 13-31). The solenoids respond to voltage signals from the on-board computer. An EGR vent solenoid, normally an open vent solenoid valve, closes when it is energized. An EGR control solenoid, normally a closed solenoid valve, opens when it is energized.

Voltage signals from the on-board computer can trigger the solenoids to increase EGR flow by applying vacuum to the EGR valve, maintain EGR flow by trapping

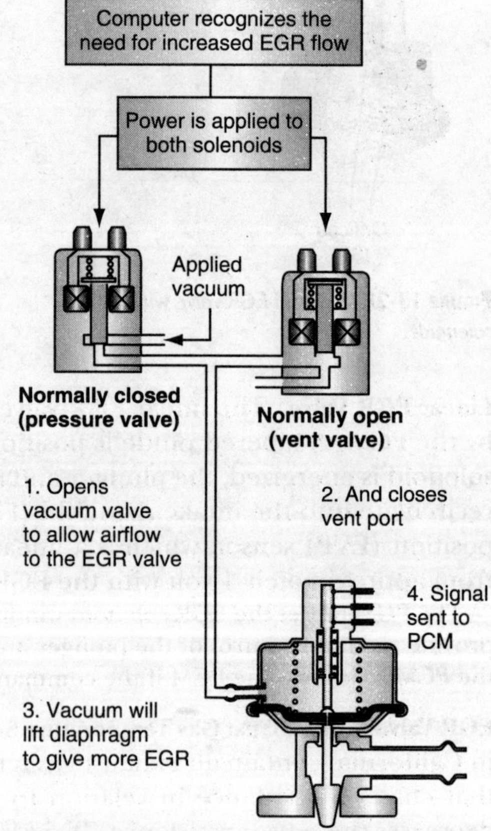

FIGURE 13-31 *Computer-activated solenoids control the vacuum to the EGR valve.*

vacuum in the system, or decrease EGR flow by venting EGR vacuum. In actual operation, both solenoids constantly shift between the three operating conditions mentioned as engine operating conditions change.

EGR Vacuum Regulator (EVR). In many EGR systems the PCM operates a normally closed EGR vacuum regulator solenoid (Figure 13-32), which supplies vacuum to the EGR valve. If the EVR solenoid is not energized, the solenoid plunger tip is seated in the vacuum passage and shuts off vacuum to the EGR valve. When the EVR solenoid plunger is shutting off vacuum to the EGR valve, any vacuum in the EGR valve and hose is vented through the EVR solenoid to prevent vacuum from being locked in the system, which could hold the EGR valve open.

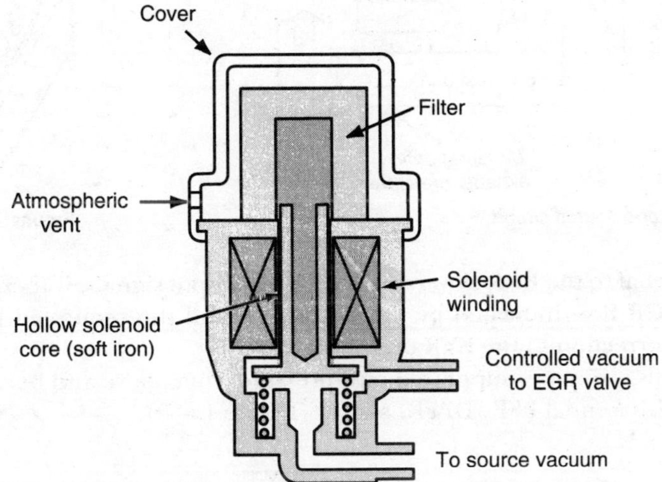

Figure 13-32 *Electronic vacuum regulator (EVR) operation.*

When the PCM inputs indicate the EGR valve should be open, the PCM provides a ground for the EVR solenoid winding. This action moves the solenoid plunger and opens the vacuum passage through the solenoid to the EGR valve. In some systems, the PCM pulses the EVR on and off to supply the precise vacuum and EGR valve opening required by the engine.

The PCM uses inputs such as engine temperature, throttle position, and vehicle speed to operate the EGR valve. The PCM will not energize the EVR solenoid if the engine coolant temperature is below a preset value. The EGR valve is opened by the PCM when the vehicle is operating at normal temperature in the cruising speed range. When the vehicle is operating at low speed or near wide-open throttle, the PCM does not open the EGR valve. If the EGR valve is open while the engine is idling or operating at low rpm, engine operation is erratic.

EGR System with Pressure Feedback Electronic (PFE) Sensor. Some EGR systems have a pressure feedback electronic sensor. These systems have an orifice located in the exhaust passage below the EGR valve. A small pipe connected from this orifice chamber supplies exhaust pressure to the PFE sensor (Figure 13-33).

The PFE sensor changes the exhaust pressure signal to a voltage signal that is sent to the PCM. Three wires are connected from the PFE sensor to the PCM (Figure 13-34). These wires include ground, 5 volt reference, and signal wires. The exhaust pressure in the orifice chamber is proportional to the EGR valve flow. The PFE signal informs the PCM regarding the amount of EGR flow, and the

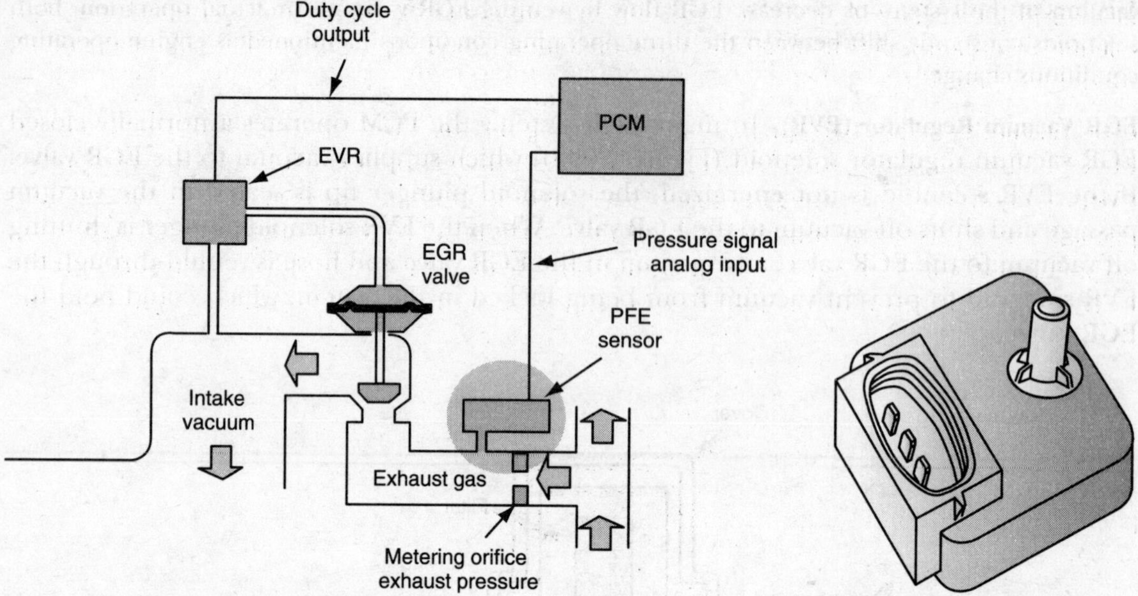

FIGURE 13-33 *PFE sensor and related circuit.*

FIGURE 13-34 *PFE sensor.*

PCM compares this signal to the EGR flow requested by the input signals. If there is some difference between the actual EGR flow indicated by the PFE signal and the requested EGR flow, the PCM makes the necessary correction to the EVR output signal.

In some EGR systems, two pipes supply exhaust pressure from above and below the orifice under the EGR valve to the differential PFE (DPFE) sensor (Figure 13-35).

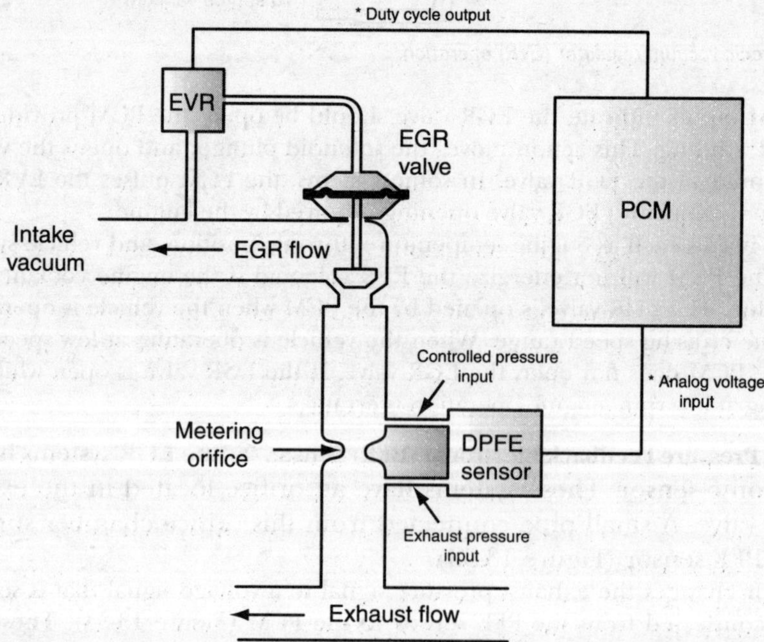

FIGURE 13-35 *Differential PFE with dual exhaust pressure pipes connected above and below the EGR orifice to the DPFE.*

EGR System with Pressure Transducer (EPT). Some EGR systems have a pressure transducer connected in the vacuum hose to the EVR solenoid. A small pressure pipe is connected from the exhaust passage under the EGR valve to the EGR pressure transducer. The exhaust pressure is supplied to a bleed valve diaphragm in the EPT, and ported vacuum from a port above the throttle is connected through a hose to the upper side of this diaphragm.

When the engine is operating at low rpm, the exhaust pressure is reduced. Under this condition, the exhaust pressure does not move the bleed valve in the EPT, and the vacuum to the EVR is bled off through the open bleed valve in the modulator. At a preset engine rpm, the combination of exhaust pressure below the EPT diaphragm and vacuum above the diaphragm moves the diaphragm upward and closes the bleed valve. When this action occurs, vacuum is supplied through the EPT to the EVR solenoid (Figure 13-36). The PCM operates the EVR solenoid as explained previously.

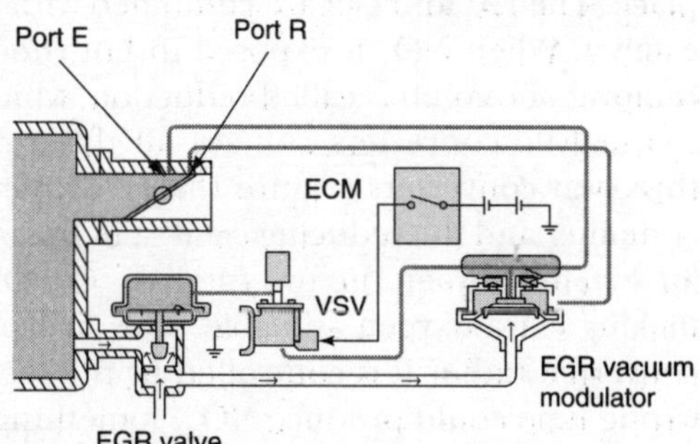

FIGURE 13-36 *EGR system with exhaust pressure transducer.*

POST-COMBUSTION SYSTEMS

Post-combustion emission control devices clean up the exhaust after the fuel has been burned but before the gases exit the vehicle's tailpipe. An excellent example of this is the catalytic converter. A converter is one of the most effective emission control devices on a vehicle for reducing HC, CO, and NO_x.

Another post-combustion system is the secondary air or air injection system. This system forces fresh air into the exhaust stream to reduce HC and CO emissions.

CATALYTIC CONVERTERS

Catalytic converters are the most effective devices for controlling exhaust emissions. Until 1975, car makers had done a somewhat effective job of controlling emissions by the use of other systems—auxiliary air injection systems, exhaust gas recirculation systems, and positive crankcase ventilation. But controlling emissions with these systems alone also meant lean mixtures and exotic ignition timing that often severely penalized power and fuel economy. When catalytic converters were introduced, much of the emission control could be taken out of the engine and moved into the exhaust system. This change allowed manufacturers to retune the engine for better performance and improved fuel economy.

Many changes will be necessary in vehicles, engines, and emission systems to meet emission standards. Since approximately 90 percent of HC emissions occur before the catalytic converter is hot enough to provide for proper HC oxidation, engineers are designing catalytic converters that are heated from the vehicle's electrical system. Since these heaters have high current flow requirements, some charging system modifications may be necessary.

A catalytic converter contains a ceramic element coated with a catalyst. A catalyst is something that causes a chemical reaction without being part of the reaction. A catalytic converter causes a chemical change to take place in the passing exhaust gases. Most of the harmful gases are changed to harmless gases.

Three different materials are used as the catalyst in automotive converters: platinum, palladium, and rhodium. Platinum and palladium are the oxidizing elements of a converter. When HC and CO are exposed to heated surfaces covered with platinum and palladium, a chemical reaction takes place. The HC and CO are combined with oxygen to become H_2O and CO_2. Rhodium is a reducing catalyst. When NO_x is exposed to hot rhodium, oxygen is removed and NO_x becomes just N. The removal of oxygen is called reduction, which is why rhodium is a reducing catalyst.

Catalytic converters contain all three catalysts and reduce HC, CO, and NO_x and are called three-way converters (Figure 13-37). Three-way converters have the oxidizing catalysts in part of the container and the reducing catalyst in the other (Figure 13-38). Fresh air is injected by the secondary air system between the two catalysts. On OBD I systems this air helps the oxidizing catalyst work by making extra oxygen available. The air from the secondary air system is not always forced into the converter, rather it is controlled by the secondary air system. Fresh air added to the exhaust at the wrong time could produce NO_x, something the catalytic converter is trying to destroy.

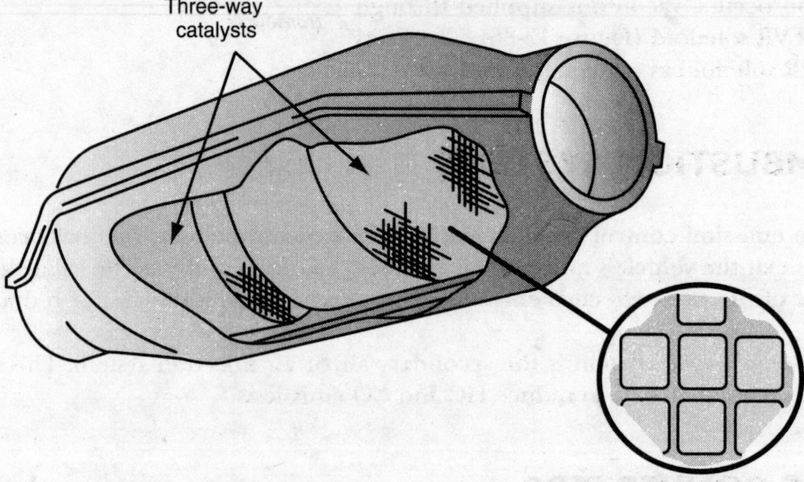

FIGURE 13-37 *A typical three-way catalytic converter (TWC).*

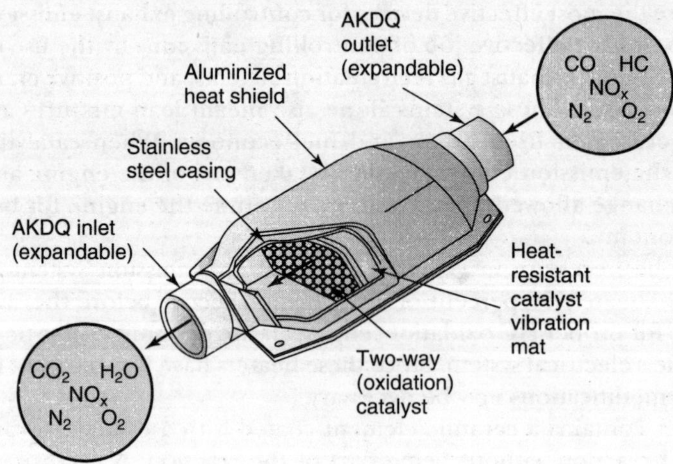

FIGURE 13-38 *The action of a three-way catalytic converter.*

AIR INJECTION SYSTEMS

One of the earliest methods used to reduce the amount of hydrocarbons and carbon monoxide in the exhaust was to force fresh air into the exhaust system after combustion. This additional fresh air causes further oxidation and burning of the unburned hydrocarbons and carbon monoxide. The process is much like blowing on a dwindling fire. Oxygen in the air combines with the HC and CO to continue the burning that reduces the HC and CO concentrations. This allows them to oxidize and produce harmless water vapor and carbon dioxide. In this section, we will look at both systems, the typical older system first and then the latest system types. Remember that there are many variations to all of these systems, and this information is not meant to substitute for factory service information.

Pump Type

A typical system with an air pump is shown in Figure 13-39. On some engines, air from the air injection system is used to pressure purge the charcoal canister in addition to reacting with the exhaust gases. The typical pump-type air injection system includes the following.

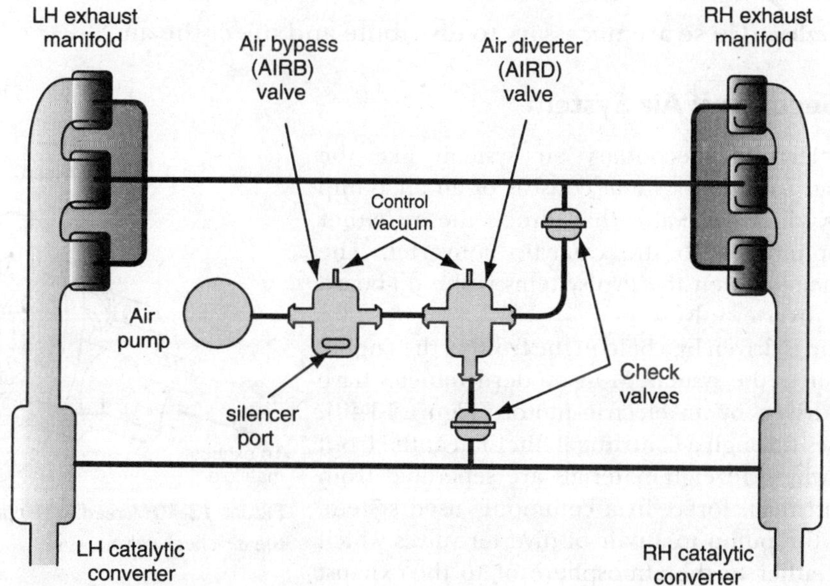

FIGURE 13-39 *A typical OBD I AIR injection system.*

Air Pump. The air pump produces pressurized air that is sent to the exhaust manifold and to the catalytic converter. The air pump is driven by a belt from the crankshaft.

Air Control Valve (or Air-Switching Valve). This vacuum-operated valve is used to route the air from the pump either to the exhaust manifold or to the catalytic converter. During engine warmup, the valve directs the air into the exhaust manifold. Once the engine is warm, the extra air in the manifold would affect EGR operation so the air control valve directs the air to the converter where it aids the converter in oxidizing emissions.

Thermal Vacuum Switch. This switch controls the vacuum to the air control valve. When the coolant is cold, it signals the valve to direct air to the exhaust manifold. Then when the engine warms to normal operating temperature, the thermal vacuum switch signals the air control valve to reroute the air to the converter.

Air Bypass Valve (or Diverter Valve). This device is located between the air pump and the air control valve, or sometimes it is combined with the air control valve to make one component. The air bypass valve diverts or detours air during deceleration. Excess air in an exhaust rich with fuel can produce a backfire or explosion in a muffler. A vacuum signal operates the bypass valve during deceleration, and compressed air is diverted to the atmosphere. The diverter valve prevents backfiring in the exhaust system during sudden deceleration. A very rich mixture is present the moment the throttle closes. The HCs in the exhaust can burn with the air from the air pump, causing a backfire. To prevent this, the air from the air pump is quickly diverted to the atmosphere.

One-Way Check Valves. These valves allow air into the exhaust but prevent exhaust from entering the pump in the event the drive belt breaks. Their location in the system is behind the air control valve and before the exhaust manifold and catalytic converter.

Hoses and Nozzles. These are necessary to distribute and inject the air.

Electronic Secondary Air System

The typical electronic secondary air system, like the conventional air injection system, consists of an air pump to a secondary air bypass valve that directs the air either to the atmosphere or to the catalytic converter. The major difference between the two systems is the on-board computer and diverter valve.

The air pump is driven by a belt on the front of the engine and supplies air to the system. Most modern vehicles have an air pump driven by an electric motor (Figure 13-40). Intake air passes through a centrifugal filter fan at the front of the pump where foreign materials are separated from the air by centrifugal force. In a commonly used system, air flows from the pump to a pair of diverter valves which direct the air either to the atmosphere or to the exhaust manifold (Figure 13-41). On older systems, the valves direct the air either to the exhaust manifold or to the catalytic converter. Therefore, secondary airflow can be directed to three points:

1. Vented (or bypassed) to the atmosphere via the air filter
2. Upstream to the exhaust manifold
3. Downstream to the catalytic converter (on older vehicles)

Late-model vehicles have an electric AIR pump system (Figure 13-42). The pump is activated by a solid state relay which is controlled by the PCM. The air injection bypass solenoid is also controlled by the PCM. The bypass

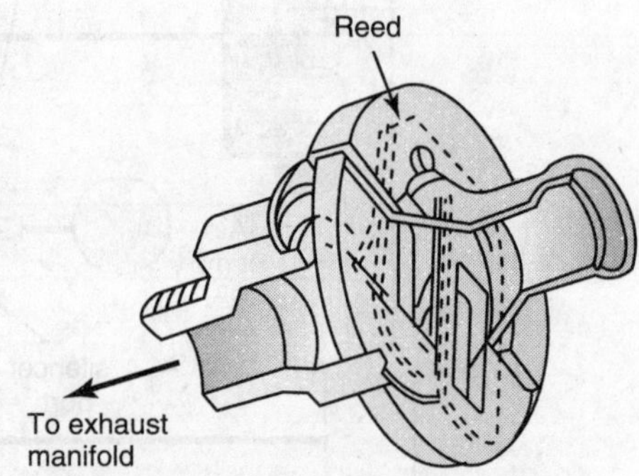

FIGURE 13-40 *A reed valve opens and closes the air-check valve.*

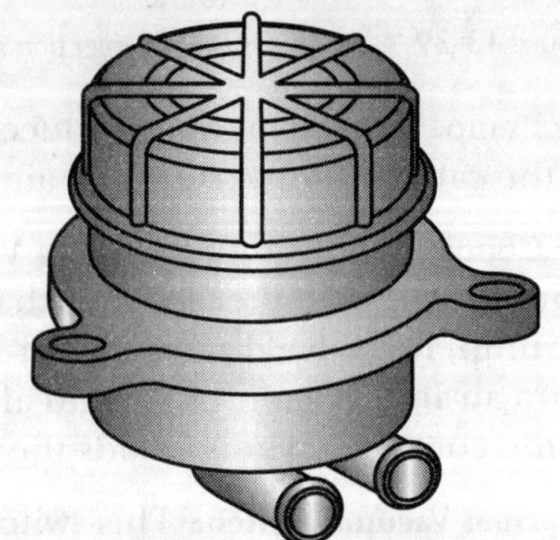

FIGURE 13-41 *Some AIR systems use an electric pump.*

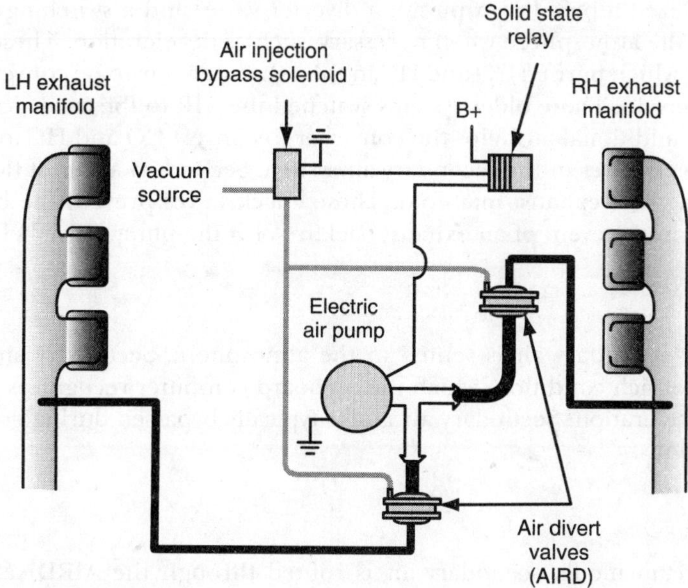

FIGURE 13-42 *Late-model air system.*

solenoid directs vacuum to the AIRD valves which opens the normally closed valves (Figure 13-43). Air from the AIR system helps to warm up the catalytic converter and oxygen sensors by burning HC and CO in the exhaust system. Once the catalytic converter is warm, the PCM shuts the pump down.

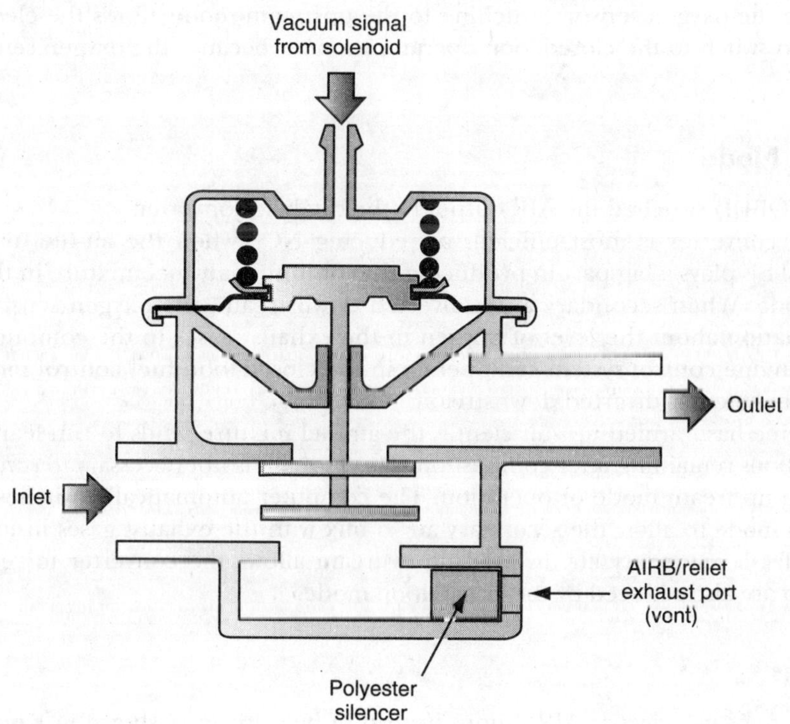

FIGURE 13-43 *AIRD valve.*

Older systems utilized a belt-driven pump, a diverter valve, and a switching valve. The diverter valve diverted air to the atmosphere when necessary, such as deceleration. These older systems had upstream operation, which burned CO and HC in the exhaust to warm the converter and O_2 sensors, just as the new systems do. These older systems switched the AIR to the catalytic converter after the engine is warm. The additional air helps the converter to convert CO and HC to water and CO_2.

There are two check valves in the secondary air system. Secondary air must flow through a check valve before it reaches the exhaust manifold. These check valves prevent the backflow of exhaust gases into the pump in the event of an exhaust backfire or if the pump drive belt fails.

Bypass Mode

In the bypass mode, secondary air is vented to the atmosphere. Secondary air may be vented or bypassed due to a fuel-rich condition, which the on-board computer recognizes as a problem in the system or during deceleration. Secondary air is also typically bypassed during cold engine cranking and cold idle conditions.

Upstream Mode

During the downstream mode, secondary air is routed through the AIRD valves to the exhaust manifold. The upstream mode is actuated when the computer senses a warm crank or startup condition. The secondary airflow remains upstream for 1 to 3 minutes after startup to help control emissions.

The air-fuel mixture at startup is typically very rich. This rich mixture results in unburned HC and CO in the exhaust after combustion. By switching to the upstream mode, the hot HC and CO mix with the incoming secondary air and are burned up.

This reburning of HC and CO compounds causes the exhaust gases to become hotter, which in turn heats up the oxygen sensor. Switching to the upstream mode allows the electronic engine control system to switch to the closed-loop operation sooner because the oxygen sensor is ready to function sooner.

Downstream Mode

Older vehicles (OBDI) switched the AIR output to the catalytic converter.

The catalytic converter is most efficient at reducing NO_x when the air-fuel mixture is near stoichiometric. This plays a big part in producing that optimum air-fuel mixture in the closed-loop fuel control mode. When secondary air is diverted downstream, the oxygen sensor can provide accurate information about the level of oxygen in the exhaust gases to the computer. Therefore, the electronic engine control system can operate in the closed-loop fuel control mode only when the secondary air system is diverted downstream.

After the engine has warmed up sufficiently, the air-fuel mixture tends to run lean leaving fewer excess hydrocarbons remaining after combustion. Therefore, it is not necessary to run the secondary air system in the upstream mode of operation. The computer automatically switches the system to the downstream mode to allow the secondary air to mix with the exhaust gases inside the catalytic converter. The fresh secondary air diverted downstream allows the converter to reduce the NO_x emissions, which are also reduced by the closed-loop mode.

Later Systems

Many OBD II systems use electric AIR pumps instead of belt driven as shown in Figure 13-44. Also, many systems do not switch to the catalytic converter to help oxidize HC and CO, but only rely on the

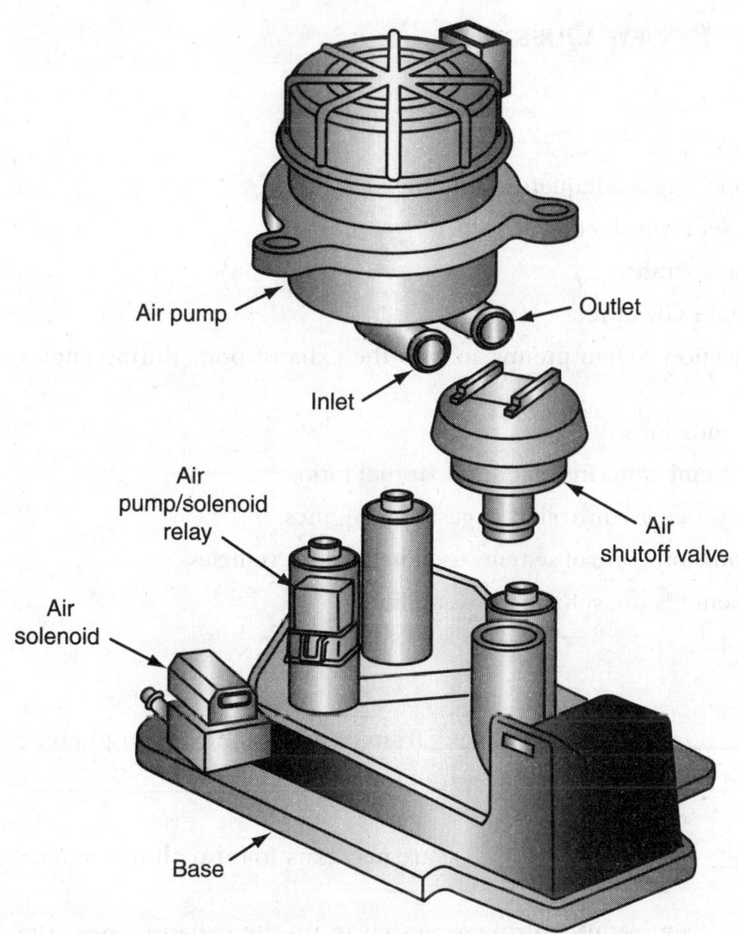

FIGURE 13-44 *Electric AIR pump and components.*

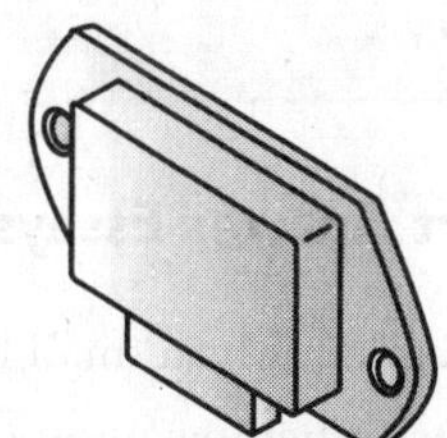

FIGURE 13-45 *Solid state relay.*

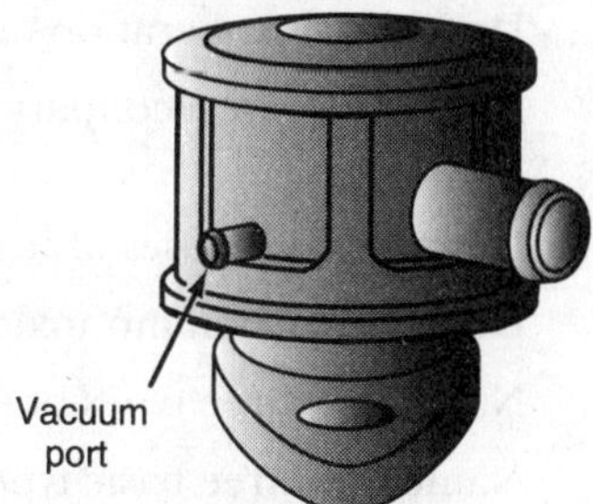

FIGURE 13-46 *Diverter valve.*

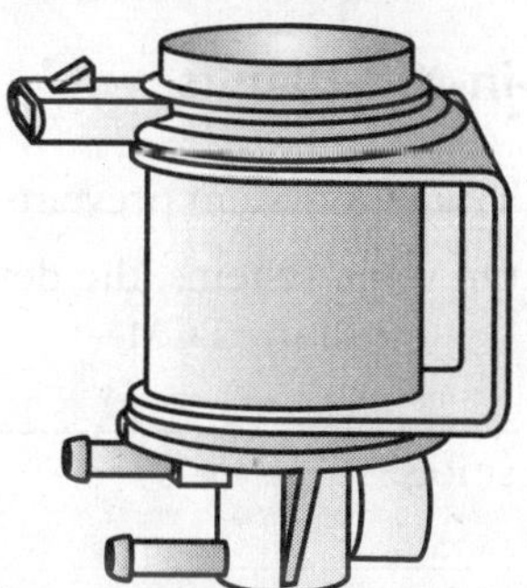

FIGURE 13-47 *Secondary air injection bypass solenoid.*

AIR system to help heat the converter for maximum efficiency. These pumps only run for about 100 to 150 seconds depending on application and only when the engine is below operating temperature.

Solid State Relay

Since the electric air pumps can drawn up to 35 amps, they require a relay for operation (Figure 13-45).

Diverter Valve

The diverter valve shuts off the flow of air to the exhaust manifolds when the air pump is off (Figure 13-46).

Secondary AIR Injection Bypass Solenoid

The PCM utilizes the secondary AIR injection bypass solenoid to control vacuum to the diverter valve, thus closing the valve (Figure 13-47).

REVIEW QUESTIONS

Short Answer Essays

1. Explain why a small PCV valve opening is adequate at idle speed.
2. Describe how photochemical smog is produced.
3. Explain how a detonation sensor operates.
4. Describe the operation of a digital EGR valve.
5. Explain why a secondary air injection system pumps air into the exhaust ports during engine warmup.
6. Describe the causes of high HC emissions.
7. Describe carbon monoxide (CO) emissions in relation to air-fuel ratio.
8. Name the three types of emissions being controlled in gasoline engines.
9. Name the three basic types of emission control systems used in modern vehicles.
10. List three ways the PCV system benefits the vehicle's driveability.

Fill-in-the-Blanks

1. The PCV system prevents ____________ ____________ from escaping to the atmosphere.
2. On some systems, the detonation sensor signal is sent through the ____________ ____________ to the PCM.
3. ____________, ____________ and ____________ are necessary to form photochemical smog.
4. ____________ ____________ emission control systems clean up the exhaust gases after the fuel has been burned.
5. In a secondary air injection system, the airflow from the pump is directed into the ____________ with the engine at normal operating temperature.
6. HC emissions may come from the tailpipe or ____________ sources.
7. A lean air-fuel ratio causes HC emissions to ____________.
8. CO emissions are a good indicator of a ____________ air-fuel ratio.
9. ____________ emissions are formed by high combustion temperatures.
10. NO_x, HC, and CO are changed into harmless gases by the ____________ in the catalytic converter.

Multiple Choice

1. *Technician A* says CARB is an abbreviation for California Air Research Board.
   Technician B says that PMVI is to inspect a vehicle's emission controls twice a year.
   Who is correct?
   A. Technician A
   B. Technician B
   C. Both technicians
   D. Neither technician

2. *Technician A* says most manufacturers started adding controls to reduce oxides of nitrogen (NO_x) as early as 1960.

   Technician B says that the first catalytic converters were designed to oxidize CO and HC.

   Who is correct?

   A. Technician A C. Both technicians
   B. Technician B D. Neither technician

3. *Technician A* says that Hydrocarbons (HC) result from unburned fuel and result from incomplete combustion.

   Technician B says CO is formed with a mixture that is too rich.

   Who is correct?

   A. Technician A C. Both technicians
   B. Technician B D. Neither technician

4. *Technician A* says NO_x is formed at temperatures over 1,500° F.

   Technician B says that NO_x is formed when an engine overcools, due to a stuck open thermostat.

   Who is correct?

   A. Technician A C. Both technicians
   B. Technician B D. Neither technician

5. *Technician A* says if gasoline is allowed to evaporate into the air, it becomes a significant source of CO emissions.

   Technician B says that before evaporative controls (EVAP) 20 percent of th total emissions from a vehicle occurred while it was sitting in the driveway

   Who is correct?

   A. Technician A C. Both technicians
   B. Technician B D. Neither technician

6. *Technician A* says early purge valves were vacuum controlled.

   Technician B says modern purge valves are computer controlled.

   Who is correct?

   A. Technician A C. Both technicians
   B. Technician B D. Neither technician

7. All of the following are precombustion emission controls ***except:***

   A. Catalytic converter C. spark control systems
   B. PCV system D. EGR systems

8. *Technician A* says that lower compression ratios bring down NO_x emsission.

   Technician B says that lower compression ratios improve performance and fuel milage.

   Who is correct?

   A. Technician A C. Both technicians
   B. Technician B D. Neither technician

9. *Technician A* says PCV systems are used to control engine blowby.

   Technician B says that PCV systems also control sludge.

   Who is correct?

A. Technician A C. Both technicians
B. Technician B D. Neither technician

10. *Technician A* says that EGR systems reduce the amount of HC emission.

 Technician B says that EGR systems utilize controlled amounts of exhaust gases to cool combustion temperatures.

 Who is correct?

 A. Technician A C. Both technicians
 B. Technician B D. Neither technician

RELATED SYSTEMS

14

Upon completion and review of this chapter, you should be able to:

- List the basic systems that make up an automobile and name their major components and functions.
- Describe the various clutch components and their functions.
- Explain the design characteristics of the gears used in manual transmission and transaxles.
- Explain the fundamentals of torque multiplication and overdrive.
- Explain the basic design and operation of standard and lockup torque converters.
- Explain the function and operation of a differential and drive axles.
- Describe how an automotive airconditioning system operates.
- Understand how cruise or speed control operates and the differences of various systems.
- Consider the use and value of engine cooling fans.
- Identify the major components of a typical drum brake and describe its functions.
- Describe the components of a hydraulic brake system and its operation.
- Briefly describe the operation of drum and disc brakes.
- Describe the main purposes of the steering and suspension systems.

INTRODUCTION

Although the main emphasis of this book is on the engine and its systems, there are other systems that affect the way a vehicle or engine runs or appears to run. The engine is the power source for a car or truck; poor driveability can result from problems other than the engine. To better understand this, let's define driveability. Good driveabilty requires the following conditions:

1. The engine must start quickly.
2. The engine must idle smoothly.
3. The engine's idle speed must be constant to prevent stalling or racing of the engine.
4. The engine must accelerate smoothly and without hesitation.
5. The engine must run smoothly at all speeds.
6. Normal amounts of fuel should be used by the engine.
7. Exhaust emissions should be at a minimum, and there should be no noticeable smoke from the tailpipe.

Most of these conditions do only concern the engine. Some are affected by other systems. For example, if a car has a flat tire, it will not accelerate smoothly or quickly. This may seem ridiculously simple, but you would be surprised at how often simple problems are the cause of driveability problems.

In this chapter, we will look at the components and systems that affect driveability. Most of these systems have the purpose of moving the car down the road, comfortably and safely.

The engine provides the power to drive the wheels of the vehicle. All automobile engines, both gasoline and diesel, are classified as internal combustion engines because the combustion or burning that creates energy takes place inside the engine. The combustion process is the burning of an air and fuel mixture. As a result of combustion, large amounts of pressure are generated in the engine. This pressure or energy is used to power the car. The engine must be built strong enough to hold the pressure and temperatures formed by combustion.

The drivetrain is made up of all components that transfer power from the engine to the driving wheels of the vehicle. The exact components used in a vehicle's drivetrain depend on whether the vehicle is equipped with rear-wheel drive, front-wheel drive, or four-wheel drive (Figure 14-1).

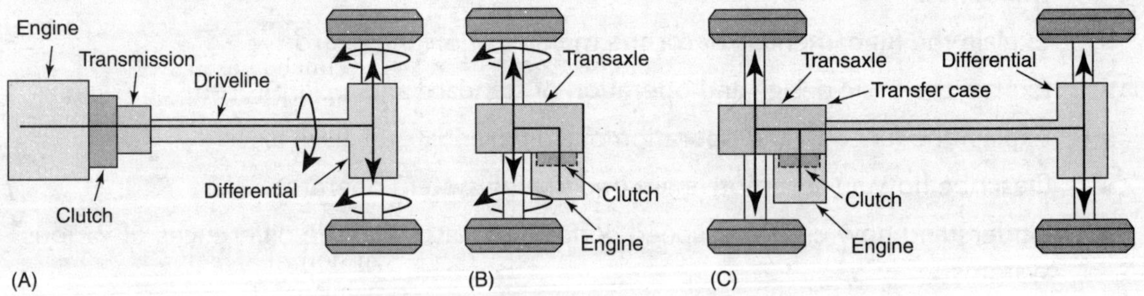

FIGURE 14-1 *Typical drivetrains (A) rear-wheel drive, (B) front-wheel drive, and (C) four-wheel drive.*

Power flow through the drivetrain of a rear-wheel-drive vehicle passes through the clutch or torque converter, manual or automatic transmission, and the driveline. Then it goes through the rear differential, the rear-driving axles, and onto the rear wheels.

Power flow through the drivetrain of a front-wheel-drive vehicle passes through the clutch or torque converter, manual or automatic transmission, then through a front differential, the driving axles, and onto the front wheels.

Four-wheel drive, or all-wheel drive, vehicles combine features of both rear- and frontwheel-drive systems so that power can be delivered to all wheels either on a permanent or on-demand basis.

CLUTCHES

Clutches are used on vehicles with manual transmissions or transaxles. The clutch is used to mechanically connect the engine's flywheel to the transmission or transaxle input shaft (Figure 14-2). It does this through the use of a special friction plate that is splined to the input shaft. When the clutch is engaged, the friction plate contacts the flywheel, transferring power through the plate to the input shaft.

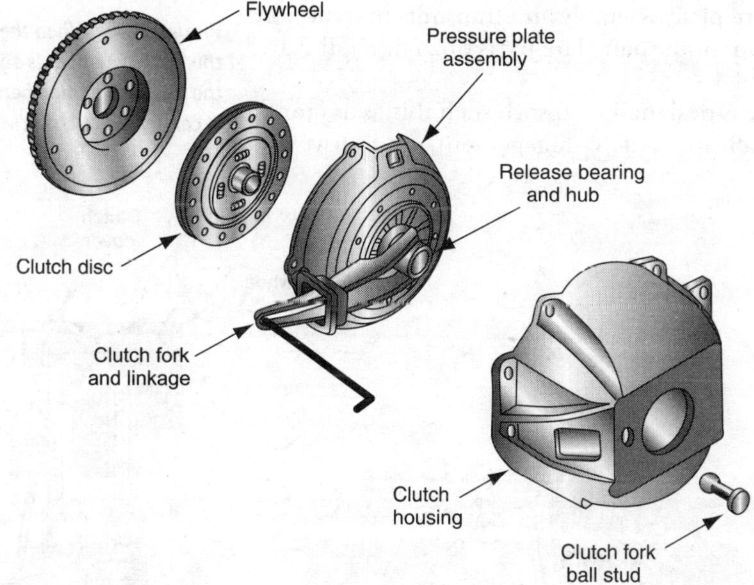

FIGURE 14-2 *Parts of a clutch assembly.*

When stopping, starting, and shifting from one gear to the next, the clutch is disengaged by pushing down on the clutch pedal. This moves the clutch plate away from the flywheel. Power flow stops at the pressure plate. The driver can then shift gears without damaging the transmission or transaxle. Allowing the clutch pedal to come up re-engages the clutch. This allows power to flow from the engine through the transmission.

All manual transmissions require a clutch to engage or disengage the transmission. If the vehicle had no clutch and the engine was always connected to the transmission, the engine would stop every time the vehicle was brought to a stop. The clutch allows the engine to idle while the vehicle is stopped. It also allows for easy shifting between gears.

The clutch engages the transmission gradually by allowing a certain amount of slippage between the input and the output shafts on the clutch. The basic principle of engaging a clutch is demonstrated in Figure 14-3. The flywheel and the pressure plate are the drive or driving members of the clutch. The driven member splined to the transmission input shaft is the **clutch disc**, also called the friction disc. As long as the clutch is disengaged (clutch pedal depressed), the drive members turn independently of the driven member and the engine is disconnected from the transmission. However, when the clutch is engaged (clutch pedal released), the pressure plate moves in the direction of the arrows and the clutch disc is bound between the two revolving drive members and forced to turn at the same speed.

The **flywheel** is the main driving member of the clutch. The rear surface of the flywheel is a friction surface machined very flat to assure smooth clutch engagement.

A bore in the center of the flywheel and crankshaft holds the **pilot bushing**, which supports the front end of the transmission input shaft and maintains alignment with the engine's crankshaft. Sometimes a ball or roller needle bearing is used instead of a pilot bushing.

The clutch disc receives the driving motion from the flywheel and pressure plate assembly and transmits that motion to the transmission input shaft. The parts of a clutch disc are shown in Figure 14-4.

The clutch disc is designed to absorb such things as crankshaft vibration, abrupt clutch engagement, and driveline

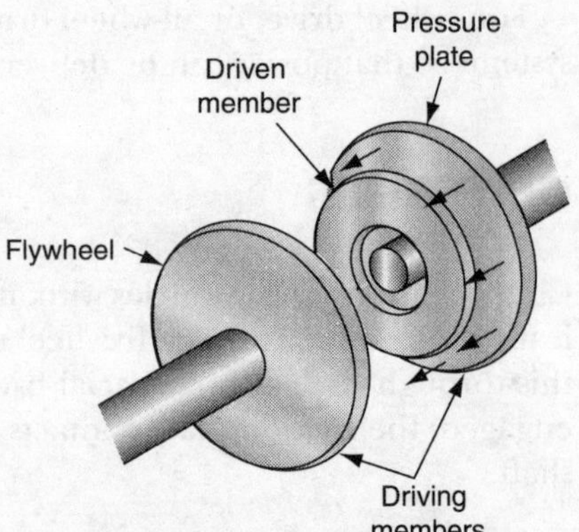

Figure 14-3 *When the clutch is engaged, the driven member is squeezed between the two driving members. The transmission is connected to the driven member.*

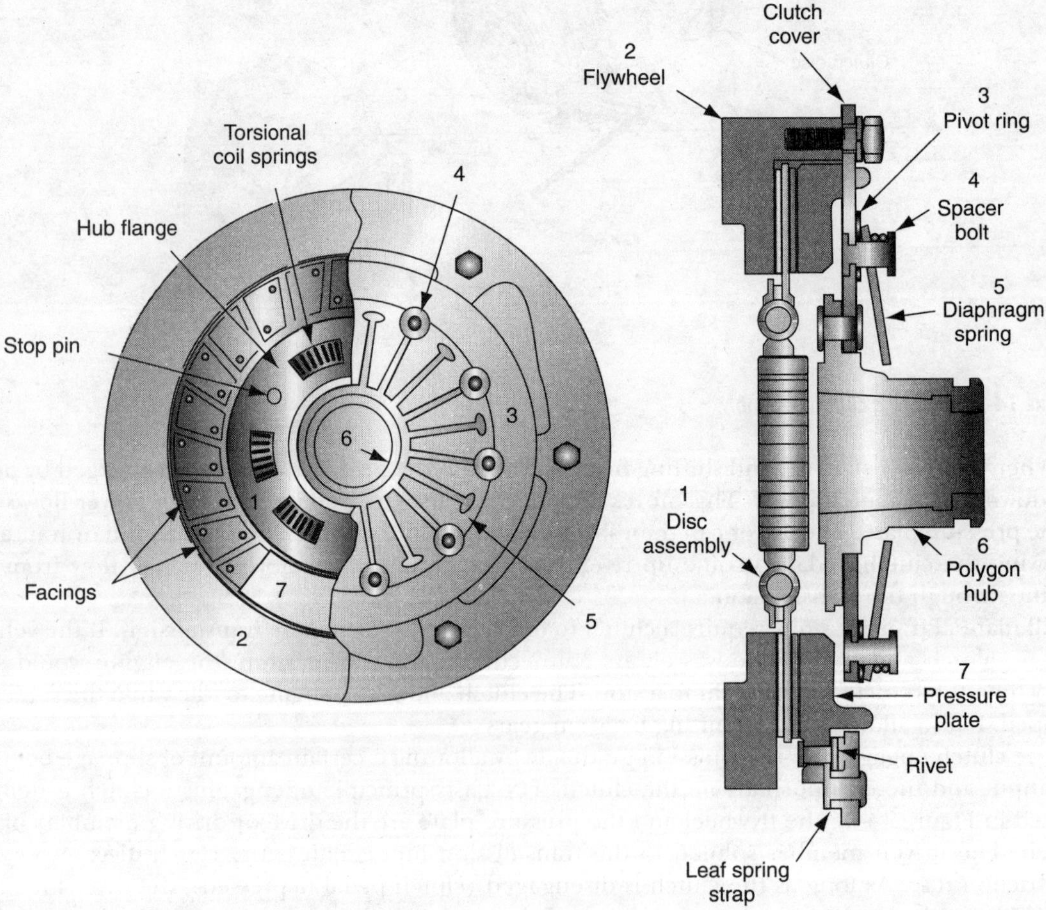

Figure 14-4 *Parts of a clutch assembly.*

shock. Torsional coil springs allow the disc to rotate slightly in relation to the pressure plate while they absorb the torque forces. The number and tension of these springs is determined by engine torque and vehicle weight. Stop pins limit this torsional movement to approximately 3/8 inch.

The purpose of the pressure plate assembly is two-fold. First, it must squeeze the clutch disc onto the flywheel with sufficient force to transmit engine torque efficiently. Second, it must move away from the clutch disc so that the clutch disc can stop rotating even though the flywheel and pressure plate continue to rotate.

The **clutch release bearing** is usually a sealed, prelubricated ball bearing (Figure 14-5). Its function is to smoothly and quietly move the pressure plate release levers or diaphragm spring through the engagement and disengagement process.

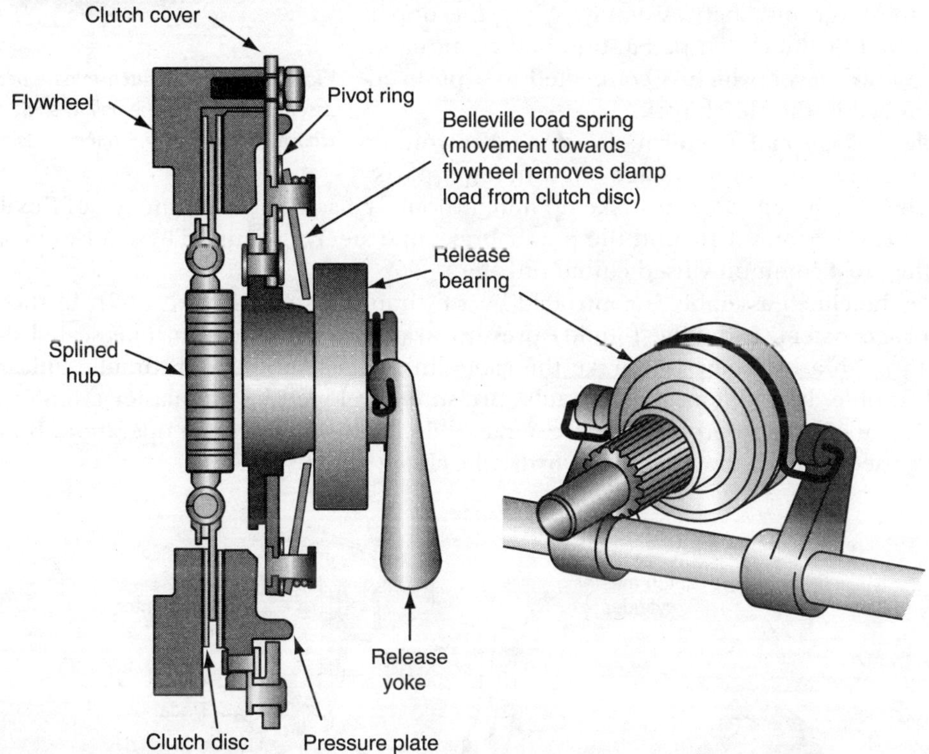

FIGURE 14-5 *Typical clutch-release bearing.*

The release bearing is mounted on an iron casting called a hub, which slides on a hollow shaft at the front of the transmission housing. This hollow shaft, shown in Figure 14-6, is part of the transmission bearing retainer.

To disengage the clutch, the release bearing is moved forward on its shaft by the **clutch fork**. As the release bearing contacts the release levers or diaphragm spring of the pressure plate assembly, it begins to rotate with the rotating pressure plate assembly. As the release bearing continues forward, the clutch disc is disengaged from the pressure plate and flywheel.

To engage the clutch, the release bearing slides to the rear of the shaft. The pressure plate moves forward and traps the clutch disc against the flywheel to transmit engine torque to the transmission input shaft. Once the clutch is fully engaged, the release bearing is normally stationary.

The clutch linkage is a series of parts that connects the clutch pedal to the clutch fork. It is through the clutch linkage that the operator controls the engagement and disengagement of the clutch assembly smoothly and with little effort.

Clutch linkage can be mechanical or hydraulic. Mechanical clutch linkage can be divided into two types: shaft and lever linkage and cable linkage. The shaft and lever clutch linkage consists of the various shafts, levers, adjustable rods, and pivots that transmit clutch pedal motion to the clutch fork. A rod connects the clutch pedal to the lever and shaft assembly. When the upper lever is moved by the clutch pedal, the shaft rotates and moves the lower lever, which is connected to a pushrod that is attached to the clutch fork.

FIGURE 14-6 *The clutch-release bearing assembly slides on the hollow shaft of the front transmission bearing retainer housing.*

A cable linkage can perform the same controlling action as the shaft and lever linkage but with fewer parts. The clutch cable system does not take up much room. It also has the advantage of flexible installation so it can be routed around the power brake and steering units. These advantages help to make it the most commonly used clutch linkage.

Usually, the clutch assembly is controlled by a hydraulic system (Figure 14-7). In the hydraulic clutch linkage system, hydraulic (liquid) pressure transmits motion from one sealed cylinder to another through a hydraulic line. Like the cable linkage assembly, the hydraulic linkage is compact and flexible. In addition, the hydraulic pressure developed by the master cylinder decreases required pedal effort and provides a precise method of controlling clutch operation. Brake fluid is commonly used as the hydraulic fluid in hydraulic clutch systems.

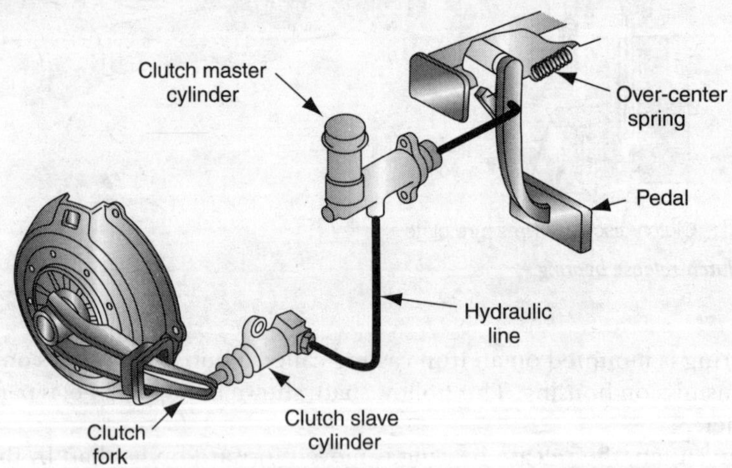

FIGURE 14-7 *Typical hydraulic clutch linkage arrangement.*

When the clutch pedal is depressed, the movement of the piston develops hydraulic pressure that is displaced from the master cylinder through a tube into the slave cylinder. The slave cylinder piston movement is transmitted to the clutch fork, which disengages the clutch.

When the clutch pedal is released, the piston is forced back to the engaged position by the master cylinder piston return spring. External springs move the slave cylinder pushrod and piston back to the engaged position. Fluid pressure returns through the hydraulic tubing to the master cylinder assembly. There is no hydraulic pressure in the system when the clutch assembly is in the engaged position.

MANUAL TRANSMISSIONS

The transmission or transaxle is a vital link in the powertrain of any modern vehicle. The purpose of the transmission or transaxle is to use gears of various sizes to give the engine a mechanical advantage over the driving wheels. During normal operating conditions, power from the engine is transferred through the engaged clutch to the input shaft of the transmission or transaxle. Gears in the transmission or transaxle housing alter the torque and speed of this power input before passing it on to other components in the powertrain. Without the mechanical advantage the gearing provides, an engine can generate only limited torque at low speeds. Without sufficient torque, moving a vehicle from a standing start would be impossible.

In any engine, the crankshaft always rotates in the same direction. If the engine transmitted its power directly to the drive axles, the wheels could be driven only in one direction. Instead, the transmission or transaxle provides the gearing needed to reverse direction so the vehicle can be driven backward.

Vehicles propelled by the rear wheels normally use a transmission. Transmission gearing is located within an aluminum casting called the transmission case assembly (Figure 14-8). The transmission case assembly is attached to the rear of the engine, which is normally located in the front of the vehicle. A drive shaft links the output shaft of the transmission with the differential and drive axles located in a separate housing at the rear of the vehicle (Figure 14-9). The differential splits the driveline power and redirects it to the two rear drive axles, which then pass it onto the wheels. For many years, rear-wheel drive systems were the conventional method of propelling a vehicle.

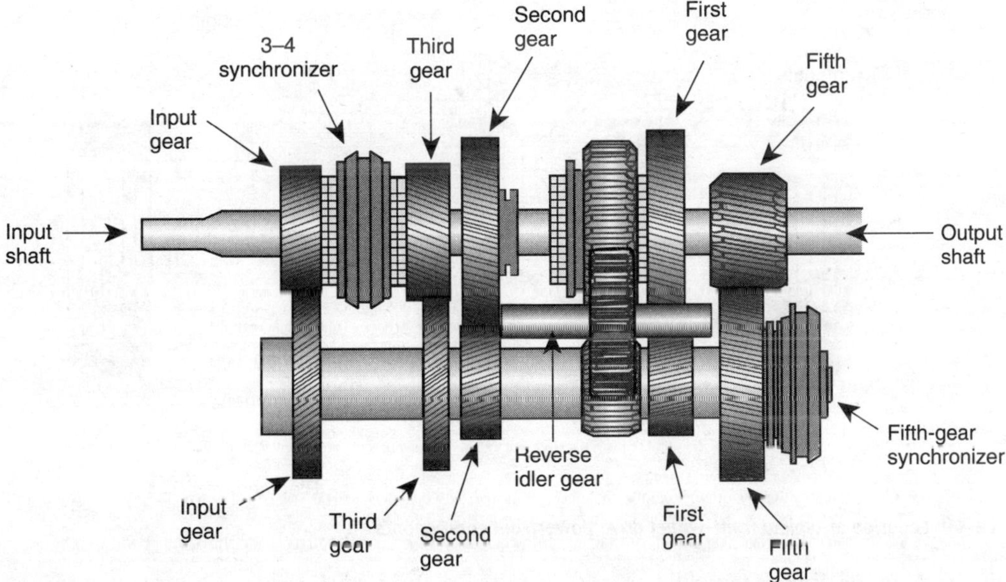

FIGURE 14-8 *Typical five-speed manual transmission with the mainshaft (speed) gears, counter-shaft cluster gears, and shaft forks visible through the case cutaway.*

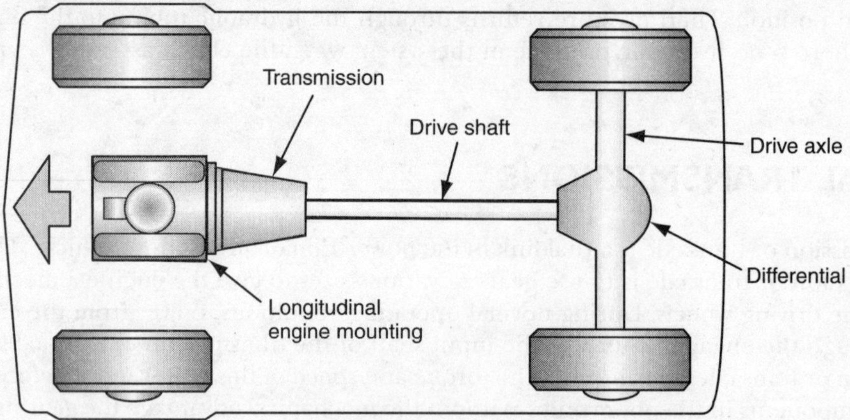

FIGURE 14-9 *Location of typical rear wheel powertrain components.*

Front-wheel drive vehicles are propelled by the front wheels. For this reason, they must use a drive design different from that of a rear-wheel drive vehicle. The transaxle is the special power transfer unit commonly used on front-wheel drive vehicles. A transaxle combines the transmission gearing, differential, and drive axle connections into a single case aluminum housing located in front of the vehicle (Figure 14-10). This design offers many advantages. One major advantage is the good traction on slippery roads due to the weight of the powertrain components being directly over the driving axles of the vehicle.

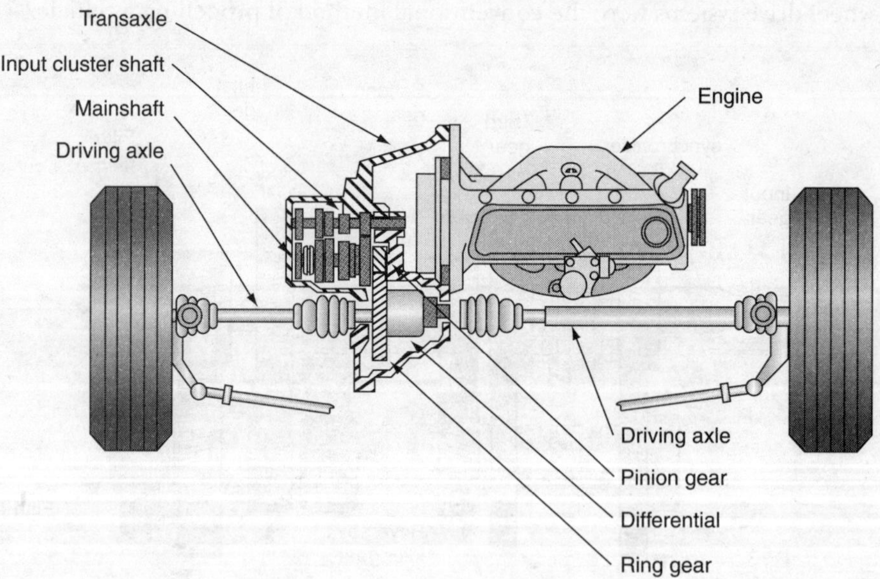

FIGURE 14-10 *Location of typical front-wheel drive powertrain components.*

Four-wheel drive vehicles typically use a transmission and transfer case. The transfer case mounts on the side or back of the transmission. A chain or gear drive inside the transfer case receives power from the transmission and transfers it to two separate drive shafts. One drive shaft connects to a differential on the front drive axle. The other drive shaft connects to a differential on the rear drive axle.

Most manual transmissions and transaxles are constant mesh, fully synchronized units. Constant mesh means that regardless of the vehicle being stationary or moving, the gears within the unit are constantly in mesh. Fully synchronized means that the unit uses a mechanism of brass rings and clutches to bring rotating shafts and gears to the same speed before shifts occur. This promotes smooth shifting. In a vehicle equipped with a four-speed manual shaft transmission or transaxle, all four forward gears are synchronized. Reverse gearing may or may not be synchronized, depending on the type of transmission or transaxle.

TORQUE CONVERTERS

An automatic transmission eliminates the use of a mechanical clutch and shift lever. In place of a clutch, it uses a fluid coupling called a **torque converter** to transfer power from the engine's flywheel to the transmission input shaft. The torque converter allows for smooth transfer of power at all engine speeds (Figure 14-11).

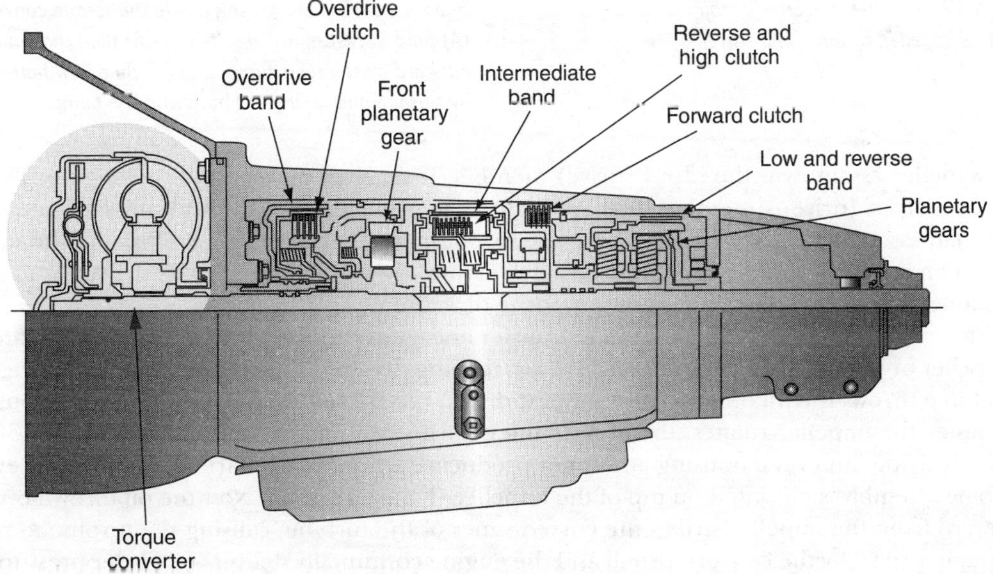

Figure 14-11 *Typical torque converter and automatic transmission.*

The torque converter operates through hydraulic force provided by automatic transmission fluid. The torque converter changes or multiplies the twisting motion of the engine crankshaft and directs it through the transmission.

The torque converter automatically engages and disengages power from the engine to the transmission in relation to engine rpm. With the engine running at the correct idle speed, there is not enough fluid flow for power transfer through the torque converter. As engine speed is increased, the added fluid flow creates sufficient force to transmit engine power through the torque converter assembly to the transmission.

A standard torque converter consists of three elements (Figure 14-12): the impeller, the stator assembly, and the turbine.

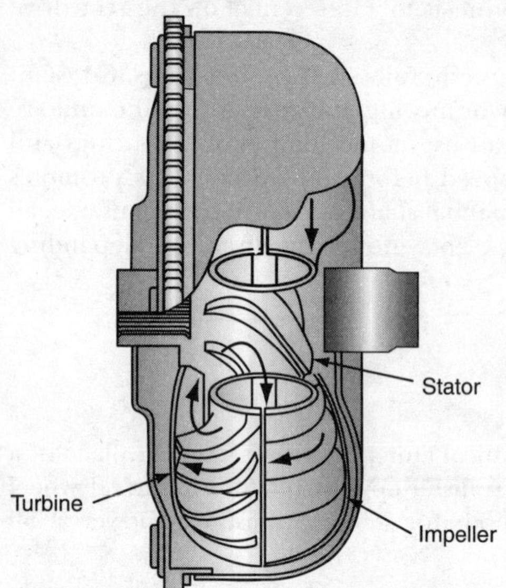

FIGURE 14-12 *A torque converter's major internal parts are its impeller, turbine, and stator.*

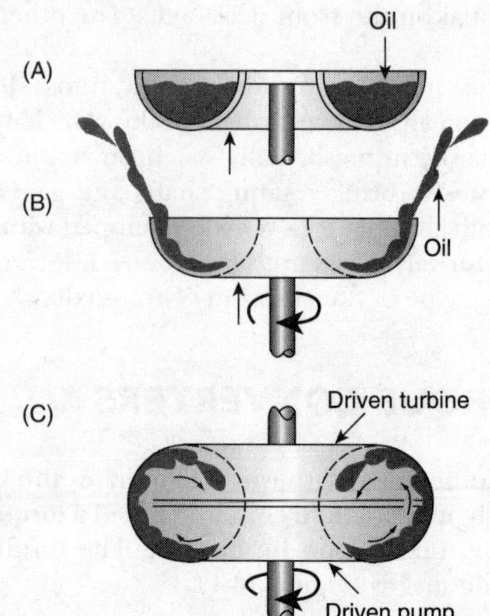

FIGURE 14-13 *Fluid travels inside the torque converter: (A) fluid at rest in impeller/pump, (B) fluid thrown up and outward by spinning pump, and (C) fluid flow harnessed by turbine and redirected back into the pump.*

The **impeller** assembly is the input (drive) member. It receives power from the engine. The **turbine** is the output (driven) member. It is applied to the input shaft of the transmission and to the turbine shaft assembly. The **stator** assembly is the reaction member or torque multiplier. The stator is supported on a roller race which operates as an overrunning clutch and permits the stator to rotate freely in one direction and lock up in the opposite direction.

Transmission oil is used as the medium to transfer energy in the T/C. Figure 14-13A illustrates the T/C impeller or pump at rest. Figure 14-13B shows it being driven. As the pump impeller rotates, centrifugal force throws the oil outward and upward due to the curved shape of the impeller housing.

The faster the impeller rotates, the greater the centrifugal force becomes. In Figure 14-13B, the oil is simply flying out of the housing and is not producing any work. To harness some of this energy, the turbine assembly is mounted on top of the impeller (Figure 14-13C). Now the oil thrown outward and upward from the impeller strikes the curved vanes of the turbine, causing the turbine to rotate. An oil pump driven by the converter shell and the engine continually delivers oil under pressure into the T/C through a hollow shaft at the center axis of the rotating torque converter assembly. A seal prevents the loss of fluid from the system.

With the transmission in gear and the engine at idle, the vehicle can be held stationary by applying the brakes. Since the impeller is driven by engine speed, it turns slowly creating little centrifugal force within the torque converter. Therefore, little or no power is transferred to the transmission.

When the throttle is opened, engine speed, impeller speed, and the amount of centrifugal force generated in the torque converter increase dramatically. Oil is then directed against the turbine blades, which transfer power to the turbine shaft and transmission.

Types of Oil Flow

Two types of oil flow take place inside the torque converter: rotary and vortex flow (Figure 14-14). Rotary oil flow is the oil flow around the circumference of the torque converter caused by the rota-

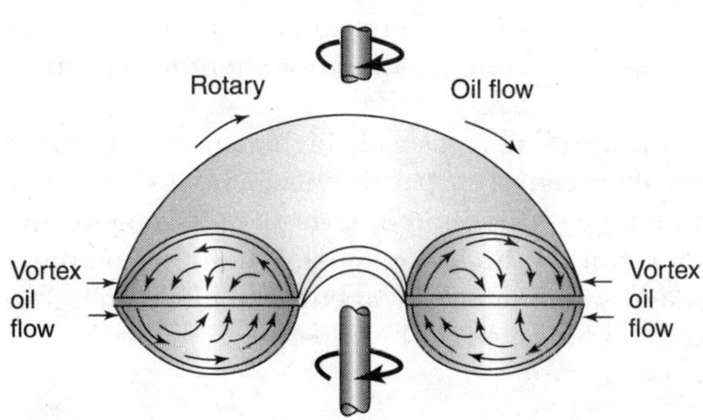

FIGURE 14-14 *Rotary and vortex oil flow in the torque converter.*

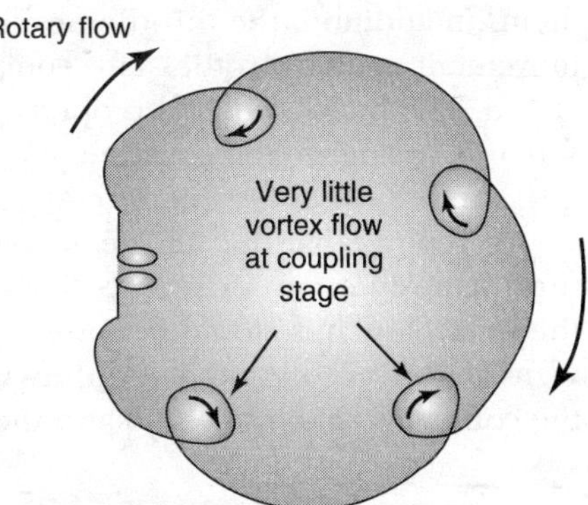

FIGURE 14-15 *Rotary flow is at its greatest at the coupling stage.*

tion of the torque converter on its axis. Vortex oil flow is the oil flow occurring from the impeller to the turbine and back to the impeller.

Figure 14-15 also shows the oil flow pattern as the speed of the turbine approaches the speed of the impeller. This is known as the **coupling point**. The turbine and the impeller are running at essentially the same speed. They cannot run at exactly the same speed due to slippage between them. The only way they can turn at exactly the same speed is by using a lockup clutch to mechanically tie them together. Torque converter multiplication can only occur when the impeller is rotating faster than the turbine.

As the vehicle begins to move, the stator stays in its stationary or locked position because of the difference between the impeller and turbine speeds.

As vehicle road speed increases, turbine speed increases until it approaches impeller speed. Oil exiting the turbine vanes strikes the back face of the stator, causing the stator to rotate in the same direction as the turbine and impeller.

If the vehicle slows, engine speed also slows along with turbine speed. This decrease in turbine speed allows the oil flow to change direction. It now strikes the front face of the stator vanes, halting the turning stator and attempting to rotate it in the opposite direction.

As this happens, the stator is locked in position. In a stationary position, the stator now redirects the oil exiting the turbine so that torque is again multiplied.

Lockup Torque Converters

A lockup torque converter eliminates the 10 percent slip that takes place between the impeller and turbine at the coupling stage of operation. The engagement of a clutch between the engine crankshaft and the turbine assembly has the advantage of improving fuel economy and reducing torque converter operational heat and engine speed.

The lockup torque converter clutch assembly is controlled by the powertrain control module (PCM). When the computer receives electronic signals from the different sensors confirming the requirements for lockup have been met, lockup clutch engagement begins. These sensors include an engine coolant sensor, vehicle speed sensor, engine vacuum sensor, and throttle position sensor

The system operates in the following manner. The engine operates for more than 5 minutes and the engine coolant temperature sensor reports 150°F. Engagement could take place if all the other sensors agree. However, the vehicle operates in congested traffic at speeds varying from 15 to 35 mph and the converted clutch engagement speed is approximately 40 mph. Under these operating conditions, the vehicle speed sensor reports that the vehicle speed is too low for clutch converter engagement. In addition, the throttle position sensor reports to the computer the unsteady up-and-down movement of the throttle. The computer interprets this as a reason not to engage the converter clutch. The brake switch also opens periodically. Thus, the computer does not energize the clutch solenoid to engage the converter clutch.

If the vehicle breaks out of congested traffic and is traveling at a steady higher speed, the speed sensor reports that the vehicle is at a speed higher than converter clutch engagement speed. The throttle position sensor reports that the throttle is in a steady position in favor of engagement, and the brake switch is closed because the driver's foot is not on the brake pedal. When the computer scans all the sensors and determines that all sensor and switch signals favor engagement, it energizes the converter clutch solenoid and the converter clutch is engaged for lockup operation.

AUTOMATIC TRANSMISSIONS

Many rear-wheel drive and four-wheel drive vehicles are equipped with automatic transmissions. Automatic transaxles, which combine an automatic transmission and final drive assembly in a single unit, are used on front-wheel drive, all-wheel drive, and some rear-wheel drive vehicles (Figure 14-16).

An automatic transmission or transaxle selects gear ratios according to engine speed, powertrain load, vehicle speed, and other operating factors. Little effort is needed on the part of the driver because both upshifts and downshifts occur automatically. A driver-operated clutch is not needed to change gears, and the vehicle can be brought to a stop without shifting to neutral. This is a great convenience, particularly in stop-and-go traffic. The driver can also manually select a lower forward gear, reverse, neutral, or park. Depending on the forward range selected, the transmission can provide engine braking during deceleration.

Until recently, all automatic transmissions were controlled by hydraulics. However, new systems now feature computer-controlled operation of the torque converter and transmission. Based on input data supplied by electronic sensors and switches, the computer sets the torque converter's operating mode, controls the transmission's shifting sequence, and, in some cases, regulates transmission oil pressure.

Most automatic transmissions rely on planetary gearsets to transfer power and multiply engine torque to the drive axle. Compound gearsets combine two simple planetary gearsets so that load can be spread over a greater number of teeth for strength and also to obtain the largest number of gear ratios possible in a compact area.

A simple planetary gearset consists of three parts: a sun gear, a carrier with planetary pinions mounted to it, and an internally toothed ring gear or annulus. The sun gear is located in the center of the assembly (Figure 14-17). It can be either a spur or helical gear design. It meshes with the teeth of the planetary pinion gears. Planetary pinion gears are small gears fitted into a framework called the planetary carrier. The planetary carrier is designed with a shaft for each of the planetary pinion gears.

The planetary pinions surround the sun gear's center axis and they themselves are surrounded by the annulus or ring gear, which is the largest part of the simple gearset. The ring gear acts like a band to hold the entire gearset together and provide great strength to the unit.

Any one of the three members can be used as the driving or input member. At the same time, another member might be kept from rotating and thus becomes the held or stationary member. The third member then becomes the driven or output member. Depending on which member is the driver, which is held, and which is driven, either a torque increase or a speed increase is produced by the planetary gearset. Output direction can also be reversed through various combinations.

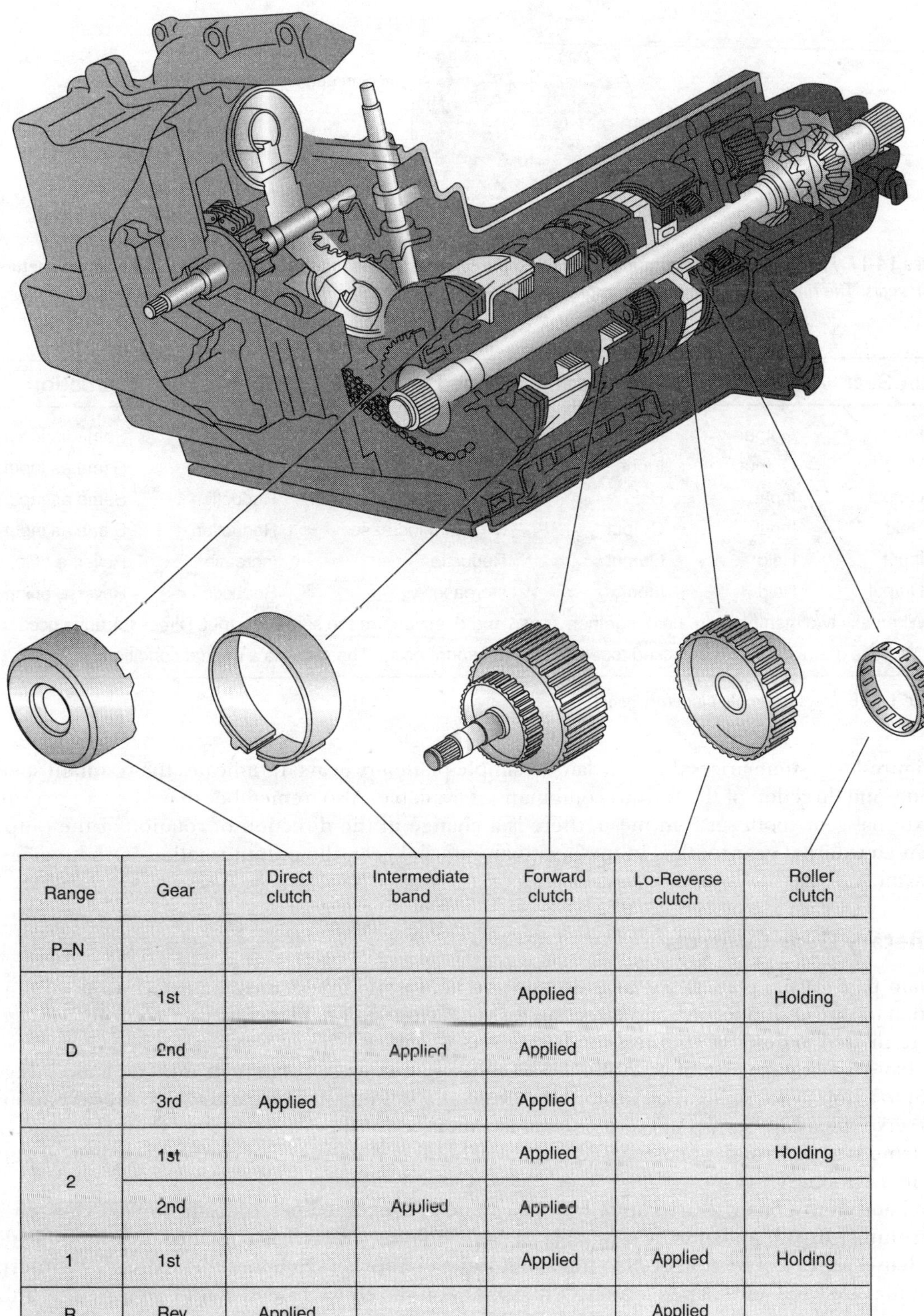

Range	Gear	Direct clutch	Intermediate band	Forward clutch	Lo-Reverse clutch	Roller clutch
P–N						
D	1st			Applied		Holding
	2nd		Applied	Applied		
	3rd	Applied		Applied		
2	1st			Applied		Holding
	2nd		Applied	Applied		
1	1st			Applied	Applied	Holding
R	Rev	Applied			Applied	

FIGURE 14-16 *Interior view of a typical transaxle.*

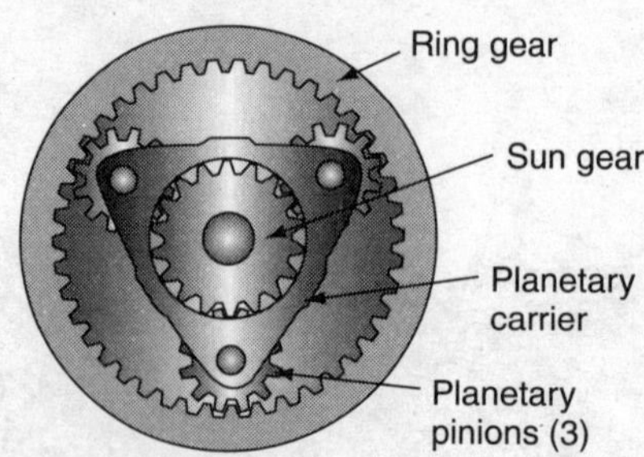

FIGURE 14-17 *Planetary gear configuration is similar to the solar system, with the sun gear surrounded by the planetary pinion gears. The ring gear surrounds the complete gearset.*

Sun Gear	Carrier	Ring Gear	Speed	Torque	Direction
1. Input	Output	Held	Maximum reduction	Increase	Same as input
2. Held	Output	Input	Minimum reduction	Increase	Same as input
3. Output	Input	Held	Maximum increase	Reduction	Same as input
4. Held	Input	Output	Minimum increase	Reduction	Same as input
5. Input	Held	Output	Reduction	Increase	Reverse of input
6. Output	Held	Input	Increase	Reduction	Reverse of input
7. When any two members are held together, speed and direction are the same as input. Direct 1:1 drive occurs.					
8. When no member is held or locked together, output cannot occur. The result is a neutral condition.					

FIGURE 14-18 *Laws of simple planetary gears.*

Figure 14-18 summarizes the basic laws of simple planetary gears. It indicates the resultant speed, torque, and direction of the various combinations available. Also, remember that when an external-to-external gear tooth set is in mesh, there is a change in the direction of rotation at the output. When an external gear tooth is in mesh with an internal gear, the output rotation for both gears is the same.

Planetary Gear Controls

Certain parts of the planetary gear train must be held while others must be driven to provide the needed torque multiplication and direction for vehicle operation. Planetary gear controls is the general term used to describe transmission bands, servos, and clutches.

A **band** is a braking assembly positioned around a stationary or rotating drum. The band brings a drum to a stop by wrapping itself around the drum and holding it. The band is hydraulically applied by a servo assembly. Connected to the drum is a member of the planetary gear train. The purpose of a band is to control the planetary gear train by holding the drum and connecting planetary gear member stationary.

In contrast to a band, which can only hold a planetary gear member, transmission clutches, either overrunning or multiple-disc, are capable of both holding and driving members. A **multiple-disc clutch** uses a series of friction discs to transmit torque or apply braking force. The discs have internal teeth that are sized and shaped to mesh with splines on the clutch assembly hub. In turn, this hub is connected to a planetary gear train component so gearset members receive the desired braking or transfer force when the clutch is applied or released.

Multiple-disc clutches have a large drum-shaped housing that can be either a separate casting or part of the existing transmission housing (Figure 14-19). This drum housing holds all other clutch components: the cylinder, hub, piston, piston return springs, seals, pressure plate, **clutch pack**, and snap rings.

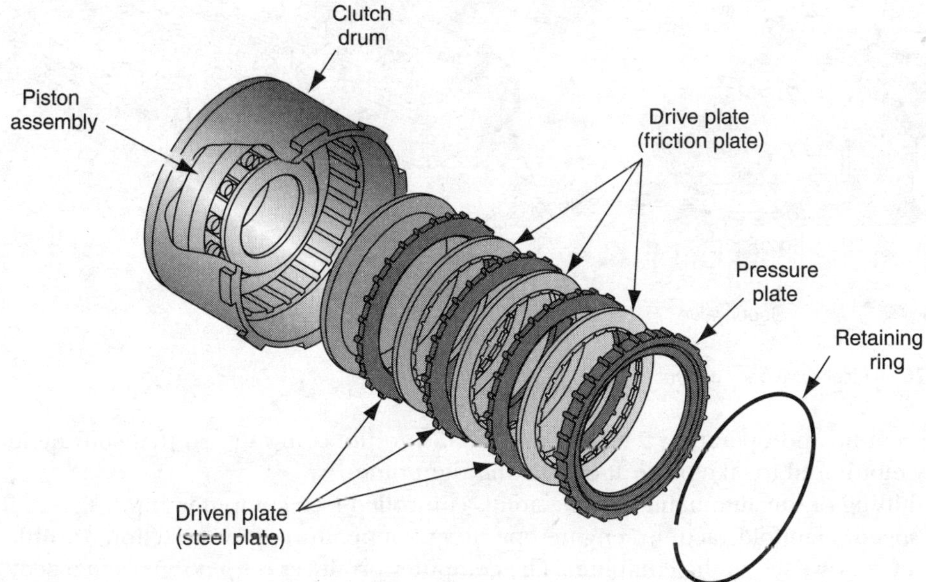

FIGURE 14-19 *Exploded view of a multiple-disc clutch assembly.*

Hydraulic Systems

A hydraulic system uses a liquid to perform work. In an automatic transmission, this liquid is automatic transmission fluid (ATF). An automatic transmission uses ATF fluid pressure to control the action of the planetary gearsets. This fluid pressure is regulated and directed to change gears automatically through the use of various pressure regulators and control valves.

The **valve body** can be best understood as the control center of an automatic transmission (Figure 14-20). The purpose of the valve body is to sense the load on the vehicle's engine and drivetrain and the operator's driving requirements.

Many very precisely machined holes are located in the valve body to accommodate the various valves. The purpose of a valve is to start, stop, or direct and regulate fluid flow. The movement of the valves engages and disengages the gears. The choice of gear is determined by the driver and the placement of the shift lever. The automatic shifts are determined by vehicle speed and load.

Electronic Controls

Shifting in an automatic transmission is controlled by a hydraulic system. Most late-model automatic transmissions use electronics to control shifting with the hydraulic system. In a hydraulic system, an intricate network of valves and other components use hydraulic pressure to control the operation of planetary gearsets. These gearsets generate the three, four, or five forward speeds, neutral, park, and reverse gears normally found on automatic transmissions. Electronic shifting systems use electric solenoids to control shifting mechanisms. Electronic shifting is precise and can be varied to suit certain operating conditions. Electronic control is superior because information about the engine, fuel,

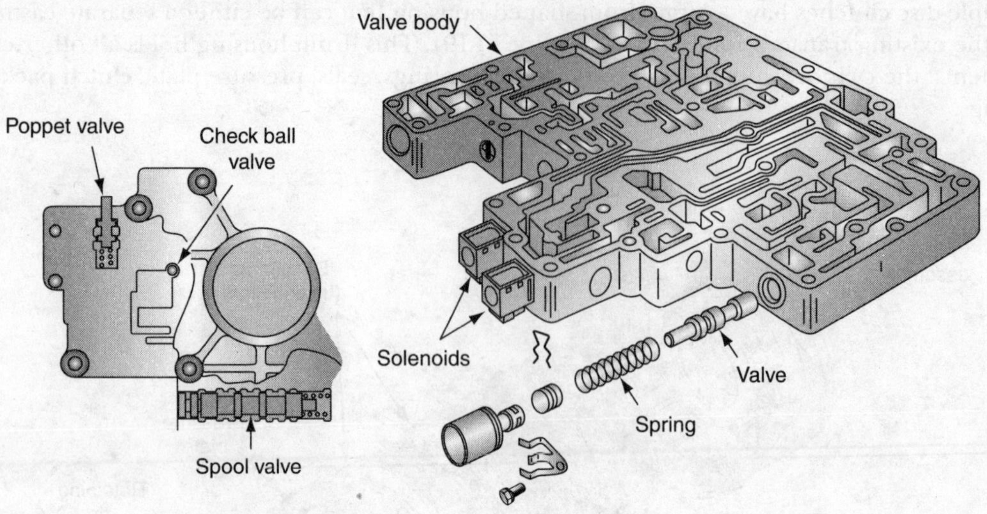

FIGURE 14-20 *Typical valve body assembly.*

ignition, vacuum, and operating temperature is fed into the computer so that shifting and lockup are closely monitored to take place at exactly the right time.

When shifting of the automatic transmission is controlled by a computer, input signals for engine and road speed, manifold vacuum, engine operating temperature, gear selection, throttle position, and other factors are fed to the computer. The computer produces output signals that activate relays, which in turn operate electrical solenoid valves. Instead of hydraulic pressures and springs, the motion of the solenoids controls the position of the valves. When activated, a solenoid moves its valve to control fluid pressure in a valve body (Figure 14-21).

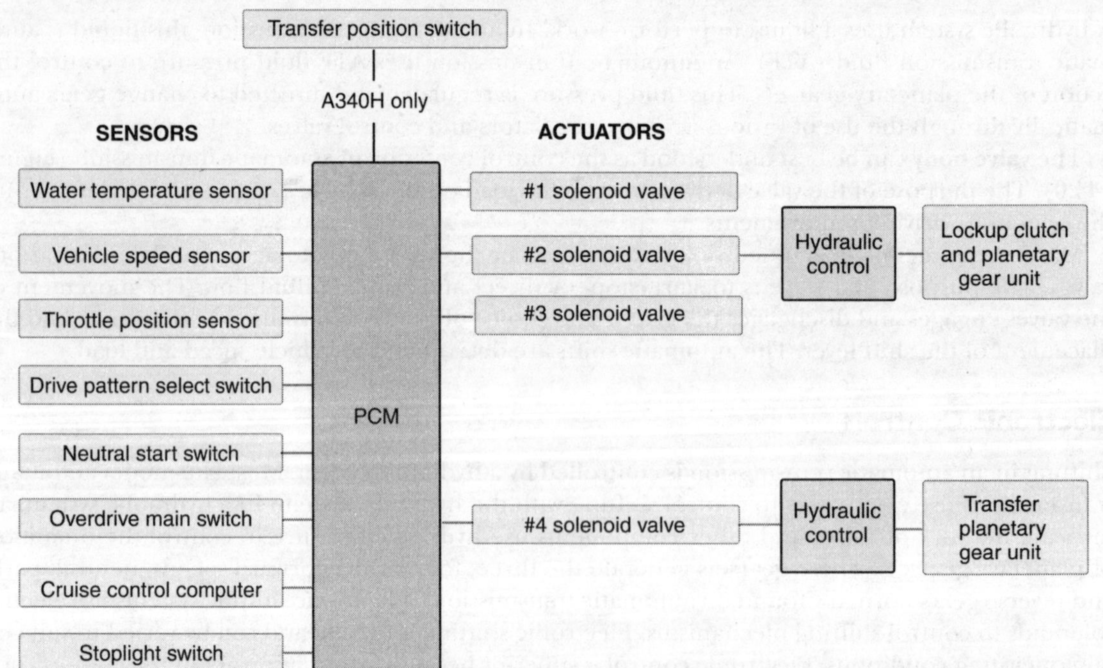

FIGURE 14-21 *Some of the sensors used by the PCM to determine optimum shift timing via shift solenoids.*

In order for the computer in an electronic control system to determine when to start a gear change, it must be able to refer to **shift schedules** that it has stored in its memory. A shift schedule contains the actual shift points to be used by the computer according to the input data it receives from the sensors. Shift schedule logic chooses the proper shift schedule for the current conditions of the transmission. It uses the shift schedule to select the appropriate gear, then determines the correct shift schedule or pattern that should be followed.

The first input a computer looks at to determine the correct shift logic is the position of the gear shift lever. All shift schedules are based on the gear selected by the driver. The choices of shift schedules are limited by the type and size of engine that is coupled to the automatic transmission. Each engine/transmission combination has a different set of shift schedules. These schedules are coded by selector lever position and current gear range and use throttle angle and vehicle speed as primary determining factors. The computer also looks at different temperature, load, and engine operation inputs for more information.

The shift schedules set the conditions that need to be met for a change in gears. Since the computer frequently reviews the input information, it can make quick adjustments to the schedule if needed and as needed. The result of the computer's processing of this information and commanding outcomes according to a logical program is optimum shifting of the automatic transmission. This results in improved fuel economy and overall performance.

The electronic control systems used by the manufacturers differ with the various transmission models and the engines they are attached to. The components in each system and the overall operation of the system also varies with the different transmissions; however, all operate in a similar fashion and use basically the same parts.

Electronic Transmission Controls, Inputs, and Outputs

Transmissions can be controlled by a separate computer called a **transmission control module**, or **TCM**, or the transmission control can be part of the function of the PCM. In either case, the transmission and engine share both information and sensors with other components to make shifting and driveability as smooth and efficient as possible. Additionally, the technician must be aware that a problem with an engine sensor may carry over into transmission operation. Electronic engine sensors and computers have taken the place of their vacuum and mechanical counterparts such as mechanical breaker points, vacuum advance, distributor flyweights, and thermostatic vacuum control valves. Transmissions have also benefited from advances in technology since electronic controls have replaced several traditional components. Three of the most basic mechanical controls that were in use have all been replaced by electronics (Figure 14-22).

In addition to updating the transmissions controls, some inputs and outputs were added that are basically for the transmission control system. Refer to Figure 14-23 for typical locations of these components.

The **transmission fluid pressure (TFP) switch** is used to determine the exact position of the manual valve. The manual valve is responsible for directing fluid pressure according to the gear selected. The PCM needs to know the position of the manual valve in order to follow the proper shift program. For example, in manual second position, many transmissions start out and stay in second gear. Some transmissions use a pressure switch assembly to confirm that a commanded shift has actually taken place by measuring apply pressure for a gear in a selected passage.

The **shift solenoid valves** are responsible for the control of transmission shifts. The solenoid valves are commanded on and off in specific combinations to produce shifting. Figure 14-24 shows a typical application chart for a Ford AX4N transmission. Shift solenoids made shift timing much easier to accomplish than the previous hydraulically controlled shift valves. Shift timing not only involves shifting the transmission at the proper time according to torque, but also the turning off and on

Component	Function	Replaced by
Vacuum modulator	**Engine load** Transmission shifting was altered according to manifold vacuum level.	**MAP, MAF, TPS** PCM can alter shifting via shift solenoids according to the load it sees.
Governor	**Vehicle speed** The governor used weights that moved an internal valve that changed hydraulic pressure into a speed signal used to time shifts according to vehicle speed.	**Vehicle speed sensor** The PCM knows the precise vehicle speed and can alter shifting based accordingly.
Shift (TV) cable	**Throttle position (load)** A cable was used to change position of a valve that altered hydraulic pressure to form a load (throttle position) signal.	**Throttle position sensor** The cable has been replaced by the TPS signal to the PCM.

FIGURE 14-22 *Older hydraulic controls and their electronic replacements.*

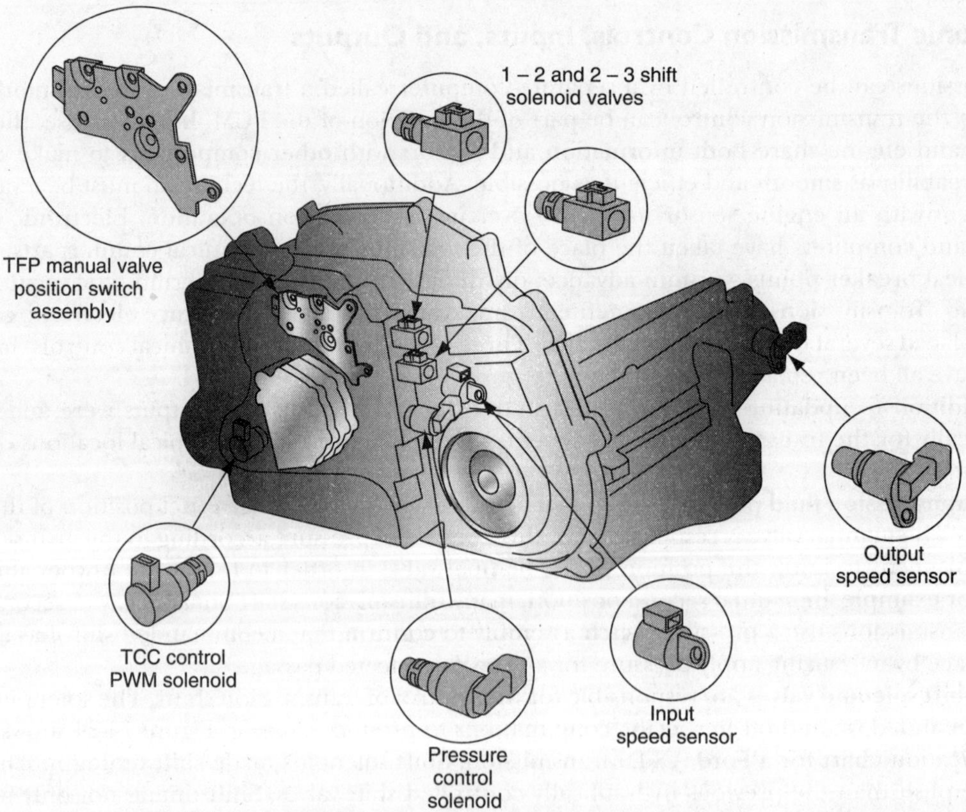

FIGURE 14-23 *Electrical components on a 4T40-E transaxle.*

SHIFT SOLENOID OPERATION CHART					
Transaxle range selector lever position	Powertrain Control Module Gear commanded	Eng braking	AX4N solenoids		
			SS 1	SS 2	SS 3
P/N[a]	P / N	NO	OFF[b]	ON[b]	OFF
R (Reverse)	R	YES	OFF	ON	OFF
Overdrive	1	NO	OFF	ON	OFF
	2	NO	OFF	OFF	OFF
	3	NO	ON	OFF	ON
	4	YES	ON	ON	ON
D (Drive)	1	NO	OFF	ON	OFF
	2	NO	OFF	OFF	OFF
	3	YES	ON	OFF	OFF
Manual 1	2[c]	YES	OFF	ON	OFF
	3[c]	YES	OFF	OFF	OFF
		YES	ON	OFF	OFF

a When transmission fluid temperature is below 50°, then SS1=OFF, SS2=ON, SS3=ON to prevent cold creep.

b Not contributing to powerflow

c When a manual pull-in occurs above calibrated speed, the transaxle will downshift from the higher gear until the vehicle speed drops below this calibrated speed.

FIGURE 14-24 *Shift solenoid reference chart for Ford's AX4N transmission.*

of components at the precise moment needed. Two gears cannot be applied at the same time. The timing of components is much like runners in a relay race, one member hands off to the next. This timing is easier to accomplish electronically than hydraulically. The electronically shifted transmission has on average one-half the number of valves that its totally hydraulic counterpart used. Also, should a common concern with transmission shifting occur, many times a software correction made by reprogramming the PCM with a manufacturer's update can relieve the problem.

The **pressure control solenoid** inside the transmission controls the line pressure of the transmission according to commands from the PCM. The control of transmission pressure allows the PCM to better adapt itself to driver habits and wear. It is also called **shift adapt**. If the PCM senses a shift that is occurring too slowly, it can increase transmission pressure for that particular shift and then return to normal for the next shift. The PCM can also alter ignition timing and transmission line pressure to make a shift occur smoothly if, for instance, a band applies too aggressively.

The **TCC control PWM solenoid** is used to control apply of the **torque converter clutch**. Many older torque converter clutches (TCC) applied noticeably especially during driving from 40 to 50 mph. Instead of applying the clutch either on or off all at once, the TCC control PWM solenoid feeds the apply solenoid with pulse width modulated fluid pressure. This is done to cushion apply of the torque converter clutch by gradually increasing the duty cycle of the PWM solenoid until the TCC is fully applied. The TCC can also be turned off in the same manner.

The **input speed sensor** is used to monitor the speed of the transmission's input shaft. This measurement is used along with the **output speed sensor** to calculate the gear range of the transmission. The PCM takes the two measurements and confirms that the gear commanded has actually applied and is not slipping. This information can also be used to measure how long it takes to complete a particular shift and use the information to help adapt shift pressure to conditions in the transmission or driver habits. If the gear range calculated is incorrect, the PCM can set an invalid gear ratio code. The vehicle speed sensor can also be used as the output shaft speed sensor in some applications.

DRIVELINE

Drivelines are used on rear-wheel drive vehicles and four-wheel drive vehicles. They connect the output shaft of the transmission with the gearing in the rear axle housing (Figure 14-25) on rear-wheel drive vehicles. They are also used to connect the output shaft to the front and rear drive axles on a four-wheel drive vehicle.

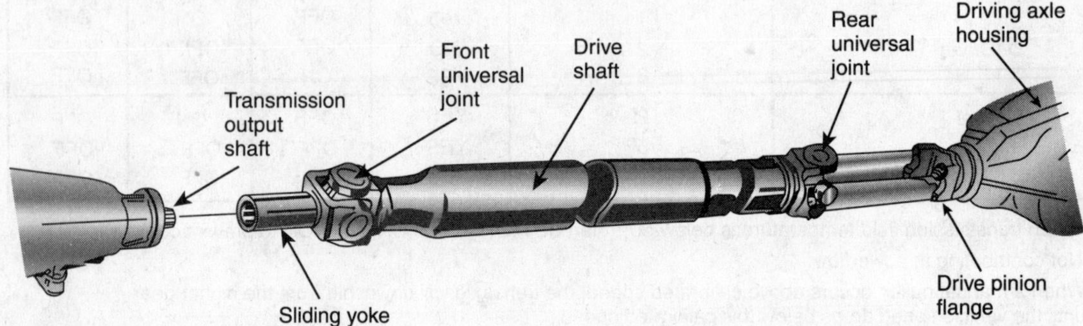

FIGURE 14-25 *Output power from the transmission is connected to the differential in the drive axle housing by a drive shaft.*

A driveline consists of a hollow drive or propeller shaft that is connected to the transmission and drive axle differential by universal joints. The drive shaft is nothing more than an extension of the transmission output shaft. The drive shaft transfers engine torque from the transmission to the rear driving axle.

The universal (or U-joint) allows two rotating shafts to operate at a slight angle to each other. Although simple in appearance (Figure 14-26), the universal joint is more intricate than it seems. This is because its natural action is to speed up and slow down twice in each revolution when operating at an angle. The rate of speed varies depending upon the steepness of the U-joint angle.

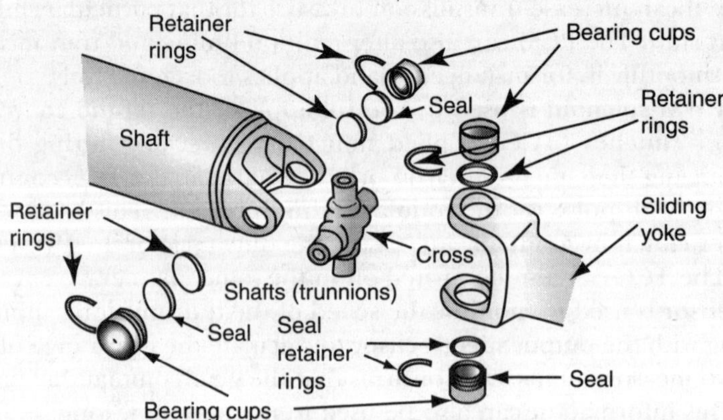

FIGURE 14-26 *Exploded view of Cardan universal joint.*

The universal joint operating angle is derived by taking the difference between the transmission installation angle and the drive shaft installation angle. For instance, in Figure 14-27, a true horizontal centerline is drawn through the transmission. In order to align better with the rear axle, the transmission is installed at an angle 5 degrees off the true horizontal line. The drive shaft installation angle is 8 degrees off the true horizontal. The difference between the transmission installation angle and the drive shaft installation angle is 3 degrees. Therefore, the universal joint operating angle is 3 degrees. When the universal joint is operating at an angle, the driven yoke speeds up and slows down twice during each drive shaft revolution. This acceleration and deceleration of the universal joint is known as speed variation or fluctuation.

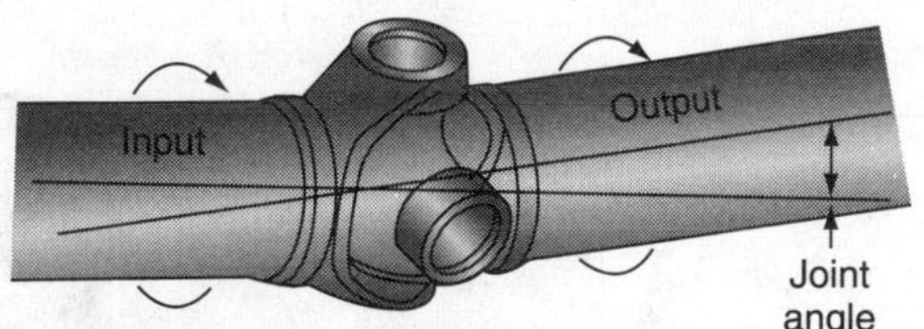

FIGURE 14-27 *U-joint action.*

The speed changes are not normally visible during rotation. They might be felt as torsional vibrations due to improper installation, steep or unequal operating angles, or high speeds.

Speed variations must be canceled at exactly the same point in drive shaft rotation. The two driving yokes at opposite ends of the drive shaft must be at the same point of rotation.

Vibrations can be reduced by using canceling angles (Figure 14-28). Carefully examine the illustration and note that the operating angle at the front of the drive shaft is offset by the one at the rear of the drive shaft. When the front universal joint accelerates causing a vibration, the rear universal joint decelerates causing a vibration. The vibrations created by the two joints oppose and dampen the vibrations from one to the other. The use of canceling angles provides a smoother drive shaft operation.

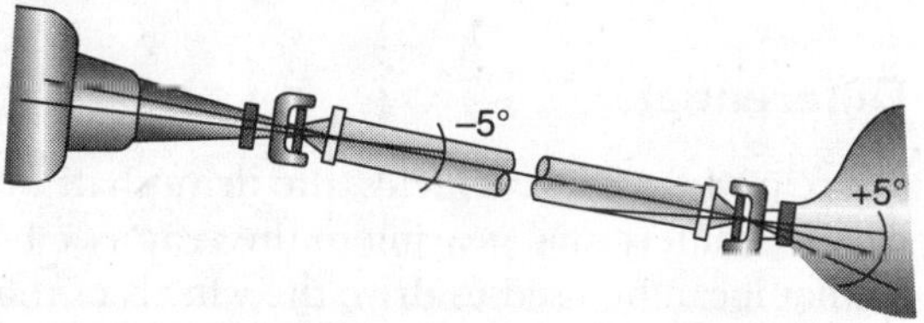

FIGURE 14-28 *Canceling angles reduce vibrations.*

Front-Wheel Drive Constant Velocity (CV) Joints

The driving axles of a front-wheel drive vehicle operate at higher angles than a rear-wheel drive driveshaft and have to be able to move with the suspension (Figure 14-29). A universal joint actually speeds up and slows down while turning. This speeding up and slowing down is more dramatic as the angle increases. A constant velocity joint such as found in a front-wheel drive vehicle (Figure 14-30) allows a constant speed during rotation.

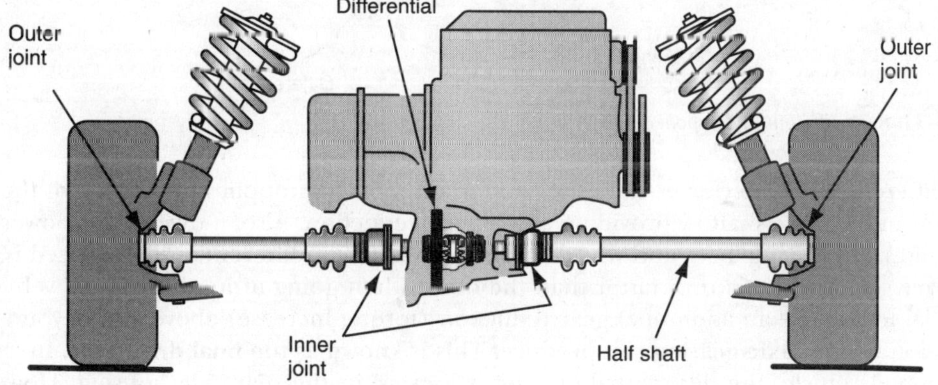

FIGURE 14-29 *A front drive axle with half shafts and CV joints.*

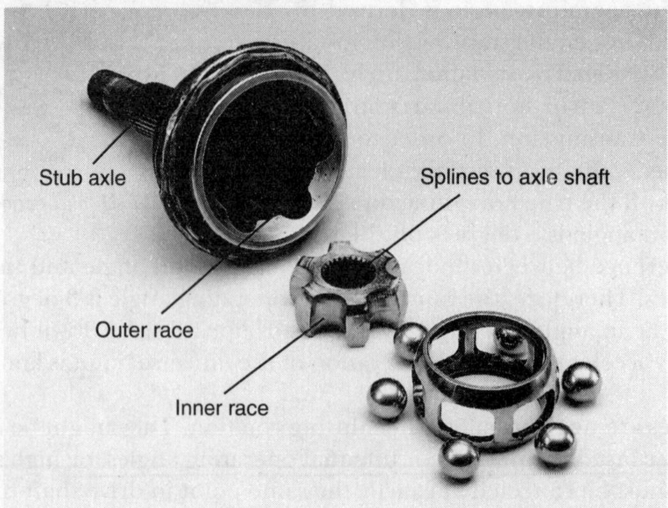

FIGURE 14-30 *A typical front-wheel drive CV joint. (Courtesy of Moog Automotive, Incorporated)*

Differential

On rear-wheel drive vehicles, the drive shaft turns perpendicular to the forward motion of the vehicle. The differential gearing in the rear axle housing is designed to turn the direction of the power so that it can be used to drive the wheels of the vehicle. The power flows into the differential where it changes direction, then to the rear axles and wheels (Figure 14-31).

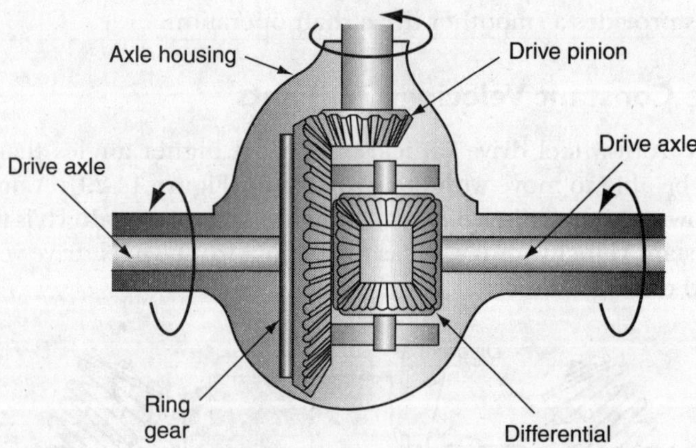

FIGURE 14-31 *Rear differential components.*

The differential also performs two other important jobs. It multiplies the torque of the power it receives from the drive shaft by providing a final gear reduction. Also, it divides this power between the left and right driving axles and wheels in such a way that a differential wheel speed is possible. This means one wheel can turn faster than the other when going around turns. All vehicles use a differential to provide an additional gear reduction (torque increase) above and beyond what the transmission or transaxle gearing can produce. This is known as the **final drive gear**. In a transmission-equipped vehicle, the differential gearing is located in the rear axle housing. However, in a transaxle, the final reduction is produced by the final drive gears housed in the transaxle case.

Driving Axles

Driving axles are solid steel shafts that transfer differential torque to the driving wheels. A separate axle shaft is used for each driving wheel. The driving axles and part of the differential are enclosed in an axle housing that protects and supports these parts.

Each driving axle is connected to the side gears in the differential. The inner or differential ends of the axles are splined to fit into the side gears. As the side gears are turned, the axles to which they are splined turn at the same speed.

At their outer or wheel ends, the axles are attached to the driving wheels. For attachment to a wheel, the outer end of each axle has a flange mounted to it. A flange is a rim for attaching one part to another part. Studs are attached to hold the wheel in place against the flange. Studs are threaded shafts resembling bolts without heads. One end of the stud is screwed or pressed into the flange. The wheel fits over the studs and a nut, called the lug nut, is tightened over the open end of the stud. This holds the wheel in place.

The inner end of each axle is supported by the differential carrier. The outer end of the axle shaft is supported by a bearing inside the axle housing. A bearing supports and holds a rotating part in place. This bearing, called the axle bearing, allows the axle to rotate smoothly inside the axle housing.

HEATING AND AIR CONDITIONING

An automotive air-conditioning (A/C) system is a closed pressurized system. It consists of a compressor, condenser, receiver/dryer or accumulator, expansion valve or orifice tube, and an evaporator (Figure 14-32).

In a basic air-conditioning system, the heat is absorbed and transferred in the following steps (Figure 14-33):

1. Refrigerant leaves the compressor as a high-pressure, high-temperature vapor.
2. By removing heat via the condenser, the vapor becomes a high-pressure, high temperature liquid.
3. Moisture and contaminants are removed by the receiver/dryer where the cleaned refrigerant is stored until it is needed.
4. The expansion valve converts the high-pressure liquid into a low-pressure liquid by controlling its flow into the evaporator.
5. Heat is absorbed from the air inside the passenger compartment by the low-pressure, low-temperature refrigerant, causing the liquid to vaporize.
6. The refrigerant returns to the compressor as a low-pressure, higher temperature vapor.

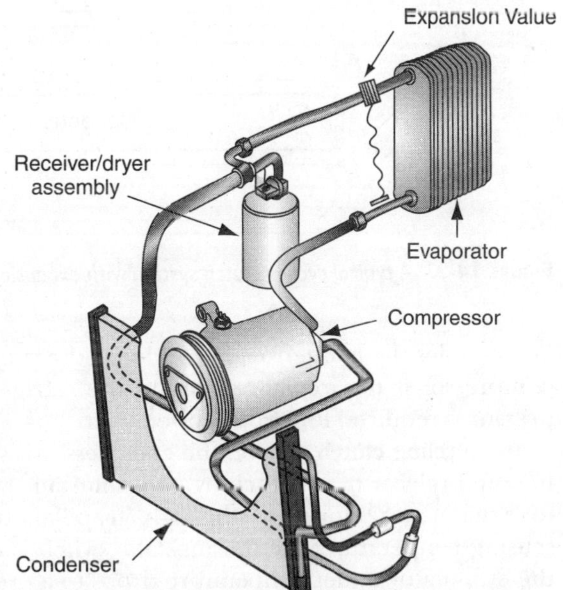

FIGURE 14-32 *An air-conditioning system using an expansion valve.*

The compressor is the heart of the automotive air-conditioning system. It separates the high-pressure and low-pressure sides of the system. The primary purpose of the unit is to draw the low-pressure vapor from the evaporator and compress this vapor into high-temperature, high-pressure vapor. This action results in the refrigerant having a higher temperature than surrounding air

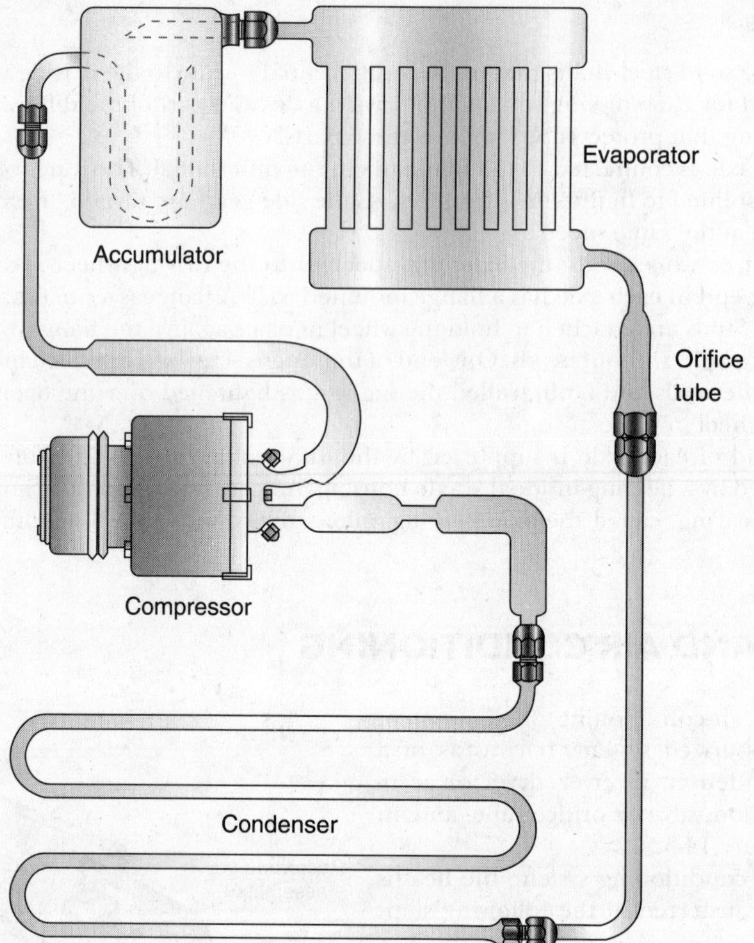

FIGURE 14-33 *A typical cycling clutch system with expansion (orifice) tube.*

and enables the condenser to condense the vapor back to a liquid. The secondary purpose of the compressor is to circulate or pump the refrigerant through the condenser under the different pressures required for proper operation.

In a **cycling clutch system**, the compressor is run intermittently through controlling the application and release of its clutch by a thermostatic switch. The thermostatic switch senses the evaporator's outlet air temperature through a capillary tube that is part of the switch assembly. With a high sensing temperature, the thermostatic switch is closed and the compressor clutch is energized. As the evaporator outlet temperature drops to a preset level, the thermostatic switch opens the circuit to the compressor clutch. The compressor then ceases to operate until such time as the evaporator temperature rises above the switch setting. The term "cycling clutch" is derived from this on and off operation.

When the temperature of the evaporator approaches the freezing point (or the low setting of the switch), the thermostatic switch opens the circuit and disengages the compressor clutch. The compressor remains inoperative until the evaporator temperature rises to the preset temperature, at which time the switch closes and compressor operation resumes.

Automatic Air Conditioning

Automatic air conditioning is in wide use today, and these systems have also felt the effect of technology. The A/C system has many of its own inputs and outputs, along with sharing some of the familiar inputs of the engine control system (Figure 14-34 and Figure 14-35).

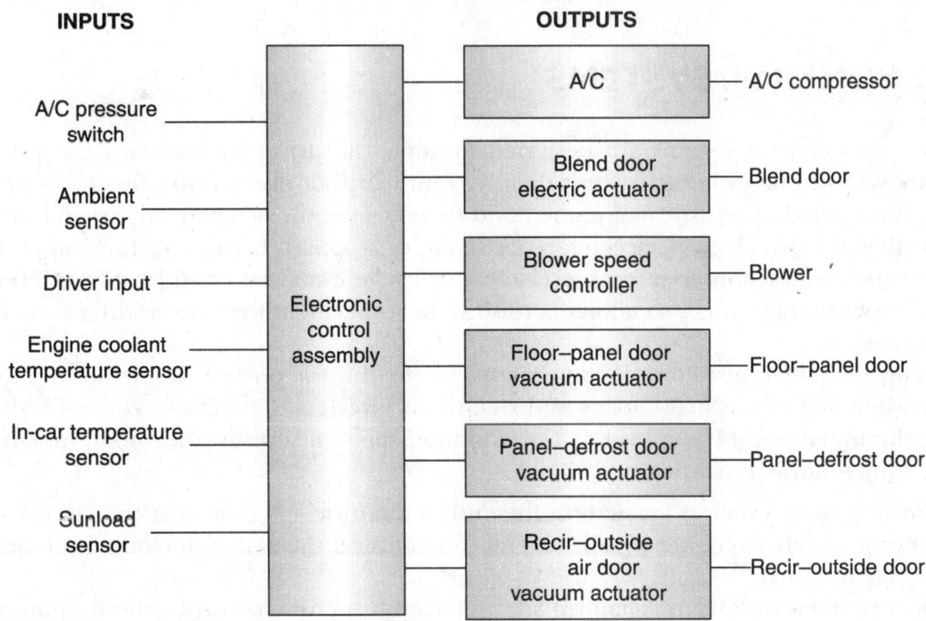

FIGURE 14-34 *Many vehicles use computers to monitor the operation of the air conditioning system, and some inputs are shared with the PCM.*

The **A/C pressure switch(s)** monitors the pressure of refrigerant in the A/C system. There are usually two on each vehicle, a high-pressure switch and a low-pressure switch. These switches can tell the PCM when the refrigerant pressure is too low to allow operation of the A/C or that the pressure is too high and the A/C system must be shut down to prevent damage.

The ambient temperature sensor is used to inform the A/C system controller of the outside air temperature. The ambient temperature sensor, combined with the in-car temperature sensor, allow the computer to calculate the load required. The A/C system then knows what position it will have to place the mode door's blower motor speed and determine whether cooling or heat is required to achieve the desired temperature in the shortest possible time. The sun load sensor allows the A/C controller to compensate for the effects of the sun on heating in the winter and cooling in the summer.

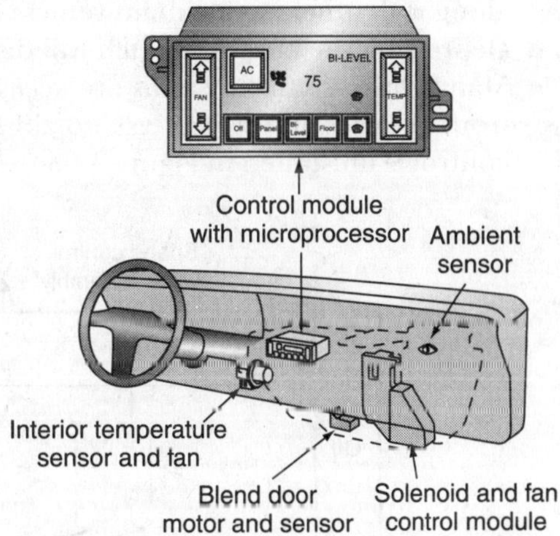

FIGURE 14-35 *A/C control module works to maintain a comfortable interior automatically with the help of several inputs.*

The engine coolant temperature sensor is used by the PCM and the A/C controller. Some systems do not start the heater blower motor until there is heat available. Also, if the engine temperature is too high, the PCM will not allow the A/C to come on because it would make the condition worse. Further, the PCM will usually shut the A/C down under wide-open throttle or high power steering loads. The cooling fan is also PCM controlled and generally runs on low speed when the A/C system pressures are moderate and high speed if the high-side pressure begins to climb. Most cooling fans are shut down over 35 mph because there is more air movement at that speed than the fan can deliver. To help monitor their operation, most automatic A/C systems can be accessed with a scan tool and have trouble codes to aid in diagnosis.

SPEED CONTROL SYSTEMS

Cruise or speed control systems are designed to allow the driver to maintain a constant speed (usually above 30 mph) without having to apply continual foot pressure on the accelerator pedal. Selected cruise speeds are easily maintained and speed can easily be changed. Several override systems also allow the vehicle to be accelerated, slowed, or stopped. Because of the constant changes and improvements in technology, each cruise control system may be considerably different. There are several types that are used, so always consult vehicle-specific information when servicing cruise control systems.

When engaged, the cruise control components set the throttle position to the desired speed. The speed is maintained unless heavy loads and steep hills interfere. The cruise control is disengaged whenever the brake pedal is depressed. The common speed or cruise control system components function in the following manner:

- The cruise control switch is located on the end of the turn signal or near the center or sides of the steering wheel. There are usually several functions on the switch, including off–on, resume, and engage buttons.
- A stepper motor and cable mechanism are used for most cruise control systems unless they have electronic throttle control (throttle-by-wire). The electronic throttle control vehicles do not require a stepper motor since there is already one in use for the throttle control. In either case, the cruise control module is usually built into the PCM and uses the vehicle speed sensor signal along with others to maintain vehicle speed.
- Depressing the brake or clutch will disengage the system.
- Many cruise control systems are accessible through the vehicle's PCM and may have diagnostic trouble codes and switch tests to aid in diagnosis. A typical block diagram for a modern cruise control is illustrated in Figure 14-36.

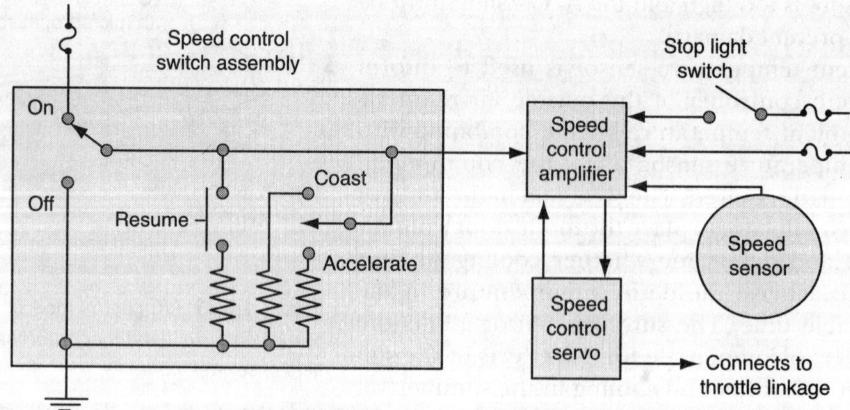

FIGURE 14-36 *Electronic cruise control uses an electronic control module (controller) to operate a servo that controls the position of the throttle.*

BRAKE SYSTEMS

Automobiles are stopped by activating the brake system (Figure 14-37). Brakes, which are located at each wheel, utilize friction to slow and stop the automobile.

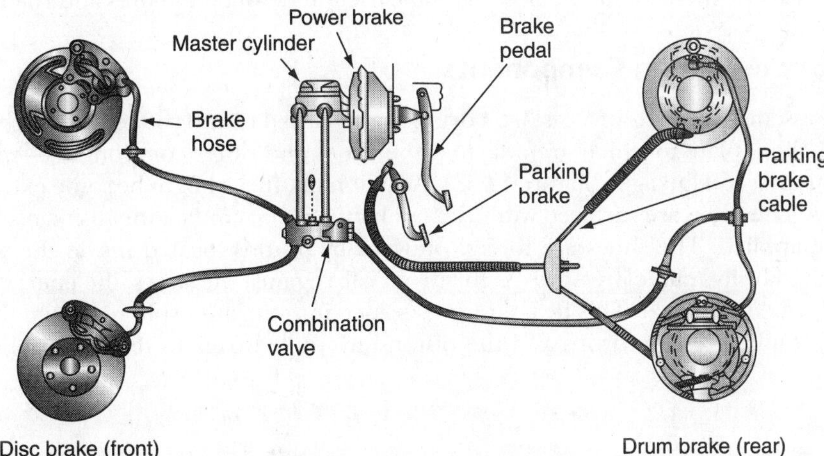

FIGURE 14-37 *Many automobiles feature a combination of drum and disc brakes.*

The brakes are activated when the vehicle operator depresses a brake pedal. The brake pedal is connected to a plunger in a *master cylinder*, which is filled with hydraulic fluid. When the brake pedal is depressed, a force is put onto the hydraulic fluid in the master cylinder. The force is increased by the master cylinder and transferred through brake hoses and lines to the four brake assemblies.

Two types of brakes are used on automobiles: disc brakes and drum brakes. Many automobiles use a combination of the two types; disc brakes at the front wheels and drum brakes at the rear wheels.

Most vehicles have power-assisted brakes. A brake booster typically uses manifold vacuum to increase the pressure applied to the plunger in the master cylinder. This lessens the amount of pressure that must be applied to the brake pedal by the operator and increases the responsiveness of the brake system.

The brake system is designed to slow and halt the motion of a vehicle. To do that, various components within a hydraulic brake system must convert the momentum of the vehicle into heat. They do so by using friction.

As the brakes on a moving automobile are actuated, rough-textured pads or shoes are pressed against rotating parts of the vehicle—either rotors or drums. The kinetic energy, or momentum, of the vehicle is then converted into heat energy by the kinetic friction of rubbing surfaces and the car or truck slows down.

When the vehicle comes to a stop, it is held in place by static friction. The friction between the surfaces of the brakes as well as the friction between the tires and the road resist any movement. To overcome the static friction that holds the car motionless, the brakes are released. The heat energy of combustion in the engine crankcase is converted into kinetic energy by the transmission and drivetrain and the vehicle moves.

Static friction also plays an important part in controlling a moving vehicle. The rotating tires grip the road, and the static friction between these two surfaces enables the driver to control the speed and direction of the car. When the brakes are applied, the kinetic friction of the rubbing brake components slows the rotation of the tires. This increases the static friction between the tires and the road, decreasing the motion of the car. If the kinetic or sliding friction of the brake components overcomes the static friction between the tires and road, the wheels lock up and the car begins to skid. Static friction then exists between the components in the brakes and kinetic friction between the skidding tires and the road—the car is out of control. Obviously, the most effective braking effort is achieved just below the brake component kinetic friction levels that result in wheel lockup. This is the role antilock braking systems play in modern vehicles. By electronically pumping the brakes on and off many times each second, antilock systems keep kinetic friction below the static friction between the tires and road.

Hydraulic Brake System Components

A drum brake assembly consists of a cast-iron drum that is bolted to and rotates with the vehicle's wheel and a fixed backing plate to which are attached the shoes and other components—wheel cylinders, automatic adjusters, and linkages (Figure 14-38). Additionally, there might be some extra hardware for parking brakes. The shoes are surfaced with frictional linings that contact the inside of the drum when the brakes are applied. The shoes are forced outward by pistons located inside the wheel cylinder. They are actuated by hydraulic pressure. As the drum rubs against the shoes, the energy of the moving drum is transformed into heat. This heat energy is passed into the atmosphere. When the brake pedal is released, hydraulic pressure drops and the pistons are pulled back to their unapplied position by return springs.

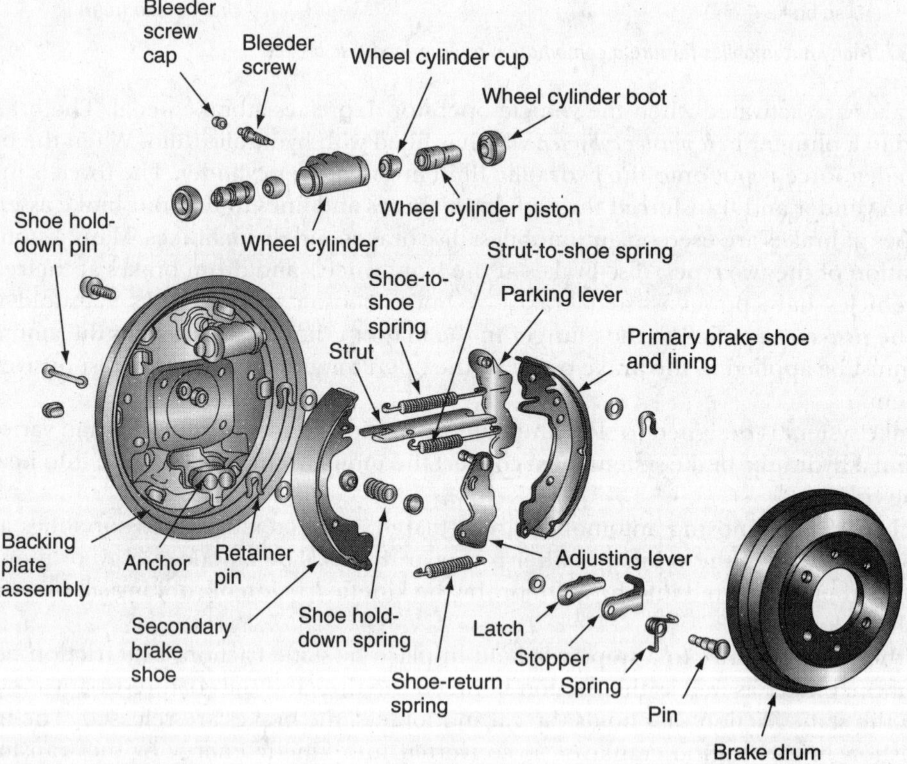

FIGURE 14-38 *Typical drum brake.*

Disc brakes resemble the brakes on a bicycle: the friction elements are in the form of pads, which are squeezed or clamped about the edge of a rotating wheel. With automotive disc brakes, this wheel is a *rotor* inboard of the vehicle wheel (Figure 14-39). The rotor is made of cast iron. Since the pads clamp against both sides of it, both sides are machined smooth. The pads are attached to metal

FIGURE 14-39 *A disc brake assembly.*

shoes, which are actuated by pistons, the same as with drum brakes. The pistons are contained within a caliper assembly, a housing that wraps around the edge of the rotor. The caliper is kept from rotating by way of bolts holding it to the car's suspension framework.

The caliper is a housing containing the pistons and related seals, springs, and boots as well as the cylinders and fluid passages necessary to force the friction linings or pads against the rotor. The caliper resembles a hand in the way it wraps around the edge of the rotor. It is attached to the steering knuckle.

Unlike shoes in a drum brake, the pads act perpendicular to the rotation of the disc when the brakes are applied. This effect is different from that produced in a brake drum, where frictional drag actually pulls the shoe into the drum. Disc brakes are said to be non-energized and so require more force to achieve the same braking effort. For this reason, they are ordinarily used in conjunction with a power brake unit.

SUSPENSION AND STEERING SYSTEMS

The suspension system on the automobile includes such components as the springs, shock absorbers, MacPherson struts, torsion bars, axles, and connecting linkages. These components are designed to support the body and frame, the engine, and the drivelines. Without these systems, the comfort and ease of driving the vehicle would be reduced. Figure 14-40 illustrates some of the components that are used in a suspension system.

Springs and torsion bars are used to support the axles of the vehicle. The two types of springs commonly used are the coil spring and the leaf spring. Torsion bars are made of long spring steel rods. One end of the rod is connected to the frame, while the other end is connected to the moveable parts of the axles. As the axles move up and down, the rod twists and acts as a spring.

Shock absorbers slow down the upward and downward movement of the springs. This is necessary to limit the car's reaction to a bump in the road.

The steering system allows the driver to control the direction of the vehicle. A steering system includes the steering wheel, **steering gear**, steering shaft, and **steering linkage**.

There are two basic types of steering systems used in today's vehicles: *rack-and-pinion* and *recirculating ball* systems (Figure 14-41). The rack-and-pinion system is commonly used in passenger cars. The recirculating ball system is normally used only on heavy vehicles such as large pickup trucks, station wagons, and full-size luxury cars.

Steering gears provide a gear reduction to make changing the direction of the wheels easier. On all but a few subcompact and compact car models, the steering gear is also power assisted to ease the effort of turning the wheels. In a power-assisted system, a pump provides hydraulic fluid under

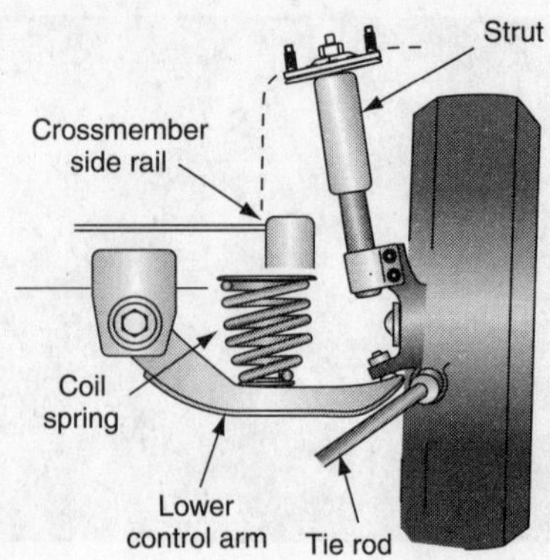

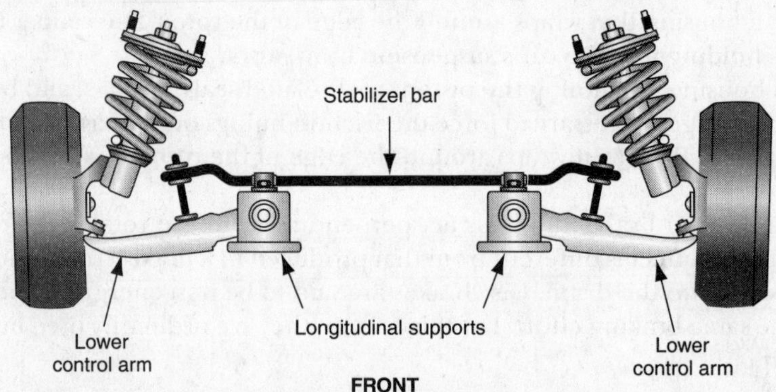

FIGURE 14-40 *Typical front and rear suspension systems.*

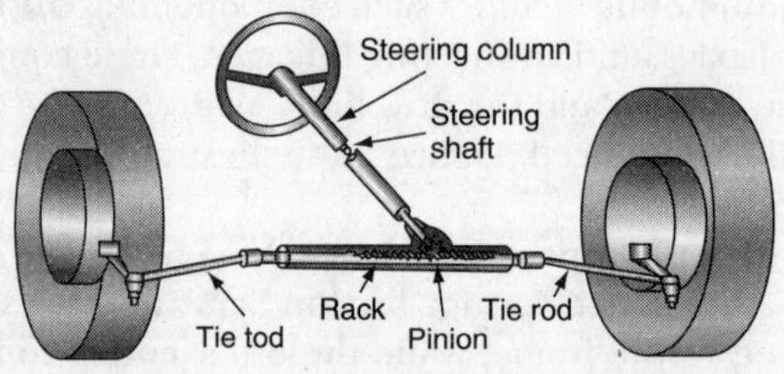

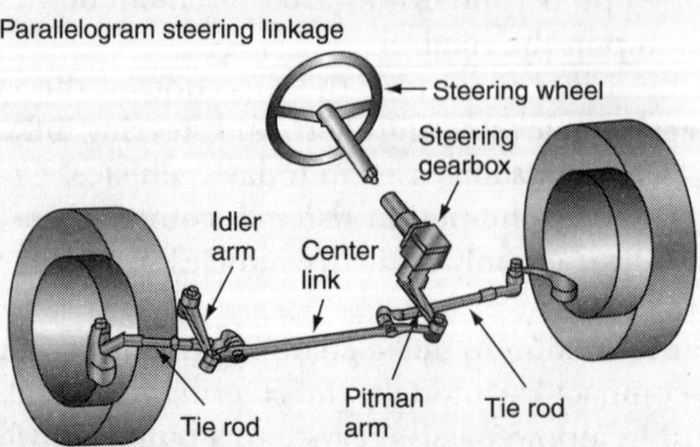

FIGURE 14-41 *Common steering systems.*

pressure to the steering gear. A spool valve directs fluid to one side or the other of the steering gear to assist the operator in turning the wheels.

Principles of Wheel Alignment

Wheel alignment allows the wheels to roll without scuffing, dragging, or slipping on different types of road conditions. This gives greater safety in driving, easier steering, longer tire life, reduction in fuel consumption, and less strain on the parts that make up the front end of the vehicle.

There is a multitude of angles and specifications that the automotive manufacturers must consider when designing a car. The multiple functions of the suspension system complicate things a great deal for design engineers. They must take into account more than basic geometry. Durability, maintenance, tire wear, available space, and production cost are all critical elements. Most elements contain a degree of compromise in order to satisfy the minimum requirements of each.

Most technicians do not need to be concerned with all of this. All they need to do is restore the vehicle to the condition the design engineer specified. However, to do this, the technician must be totally familiar with the purpose of basic alignment angles.

The alignment angles in the vehicle are designed to properly locate the vehicle's weight on moving parts and to facilitate steering. If these angles are incorrect, the vehicle is misaligned. The effects of misalignment are given in Figure 14-42. It is important to remember that alignment angles, when specified in the text, are those specific angles that should exist when the system is being measured

Problem	Effect
Incorrect camber setting	Tire wear Ball joint/wheel bearing wear Pull to side of most positive/least negative camber
Too much positive caster	Hard steering Excessive road shock Wheel shimmy
Too much negative caster	Wander Weave Instability at high speeds
Unequal caster	Pull to side most negative/least positive caster
Incorrect SAI	Instability Poor return Pull to side of lesser inclination Hard steering
Incorrect toe setting	Tire wear
Incorrect turning radius	Tire wear Squeal in turns

FIGURE 14-42 *Effects of incorrect alignment.*

under a given set of conditions. During regular performance, these angles change as the traveling surface and vehicle driving forces change.

Caster is the angle of the steering axis of a wheel from the vertical, as viewed from the side of the vehicle. The forward or rearward tilt from the vertical line (Figure 14-43) illustrates caster. Caster is the first angle adjusted during an alignment. Tilting the wheel forward is negative caster. Tilting backward is positive caster.

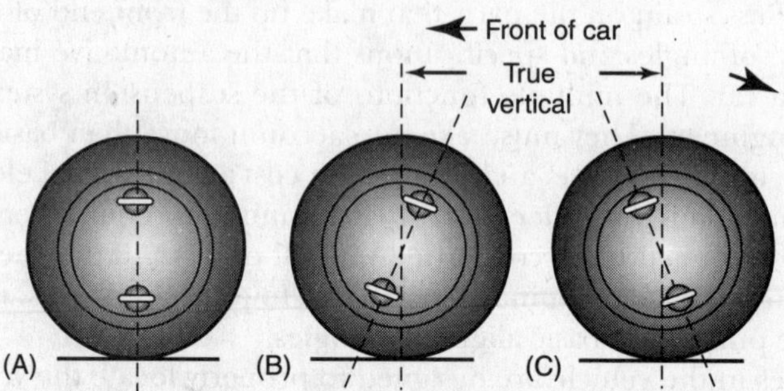

FIGURE 14-43 *Three types of caster: (A) zero, (B) positive, and (C) negative.*

Caster is designed to provide steering stability. The caster angle for each wheel on an axle should be equal. Unequal caster angles cause the vehicle to steer toward the side with less caster. Too much negative caster can cause the vehicle to have sensitive steering at high speeds. The vehicle might wander as a result of negative caster.

Camber is the angle represented by the tilt of either the front or rear wheels inward or outward from the vertical as viewed from the front of the car (Figure 14-44). Camber is designed into the vehicle to compensate for road crown, passenger weight, and vehicle weight. Camber is usually set equally for each wheel. Equal camber means each wheel is tilted outward or inward the same amount. Unequal camber causes tire wear and causes the vehicle to steer toward the side that is more positive.

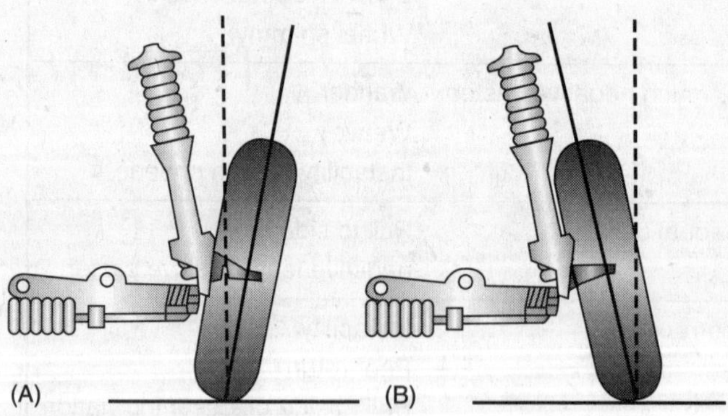

FIGURE 14-44 *(A) Positive and (B) negative camber.*

Toe is the distance comparison between the leading edge and trailing edge of the front tires. If the leading edge distance is less, then there is toe in. If it is greater, there is toe out (Figure 14-45). Toe is critical as a tire-wearing angle. Wheels that do not track straight ahead have to drag as they travel forward. Excessive toe measurements (in or out) cause a sawtooth edge on the tread surface from dragging the tire sideways.

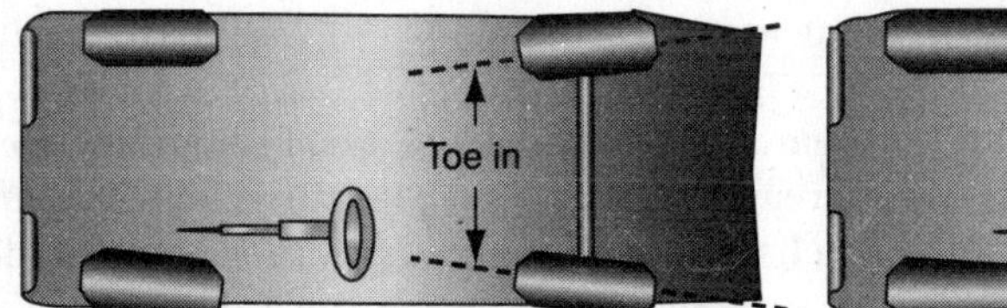

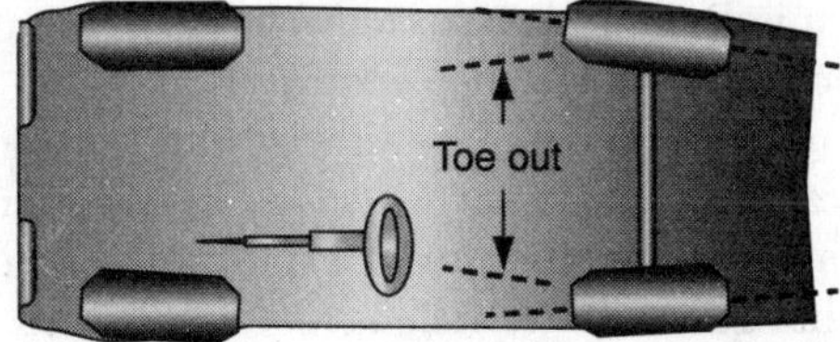

FIGURE 14-45 *Typical rear toe condition.*

A main consideration in any alignment is to make sure the vehicle runs straight down the road with the rear tires tracking directly behind the front tires when the steering wheel is in the straight-ahead position. The geometric centerline of the vehicle should parallel the road direction. This is the case when rear toe is parallel to the vehicle's geometric centerline in the straight-ahead position. If rear toe does not parallel the vehicle centerline, a thrust direction to the left or right is created (Figure 14-46). This difference of rear toe from the geometric center-line is called the **thrust angle**. The vehicle tends to travel in the direction of the thrust line rather than straight ahead.

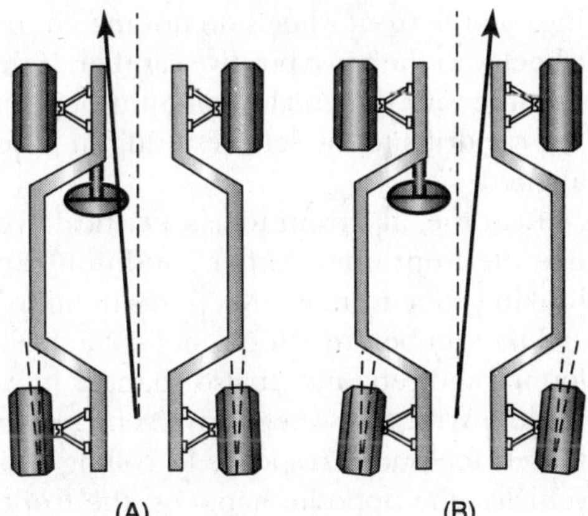

FIGURE 14-46 *(A) Left and (B) right thrust direction.*

Steering axle inclination (SAI) locates the vehicle weight to the inside or outside of the vertical centerline of the tire. The SAI is the angle between true vertical and a line drawn between the steering pivots as viewed from the front of the vehicle. It is an engineering angle designed to project the weight of the vehicle to the road surface for stability. The SAI helps the vehicle's steering system return to straight ahead after a turn.

Turning radius or cornering angle is the amount of toe out present in turns. As a car goes around a corner, the inside tire must travel in a smaller radius circle than the outside tire. This is accomplished by designing the steering geometry to turn the inside wheel sharper than the outside wheel. The result can be seen as toe out in turns. This eliminates tire scrubbing on the road surface by keeping the tires pointed in the direction they have to move.

All vehicles are built around a geometric centerline that runs through the center of the chassis from the back to the front. The thrust line is the direction the rear axle would travel if unaffected by the front wheels. This condition is also called tracking. An ideal alignment has all four wheels parallel with the centerline, making the thrust line parallel with the centerline. However, the rear-wheel thrust line of a vehicle might not always be parallel to the actual centerline of the vehicle, so the angle of the thrust line must be checked first.

Correct tracking refers to a situation with all suspension and wheels in their correct location and condition and aligned so that the rear wheels follow directly behind the front wheels while moving in a straight line. For this to occur, all wheels must be parallel with one another and axle and spindle lines must be at 90-degree angles to the vehicle centerline. Simply stated, all four wheels should form a perfect rectangle.

Rear Alignment

A car with a perfect front alignment can still experience poor handling and premature tire wear—particularly on front-wheel drive cars and cars with independent rear suspensions—if the rear suspension is misaligned. Approximately 80 percent of today's vehicles not only have front-end alignment specifications, but also require rear-wheel alignment.

Like front camber, rear camber affects both tire wear and handling. The ideal situation is to have zero running camber on all four wheels to keep the tread in full contact with the road for optimum traction and handling. Camber is not a static angle. It changes as the suspension moves up and down. Camber also changes as the vehicle is loaded and the suspension sags under the weight.

Besides wearing the tires unevenly across the tread, uneven side-to-side camber (as when one wheel leans in and the other does not) creates a steering pull just like it does when the camber readings on the front wheels do not match. It is like leaning on a bicycle. A vehicle always pulls toward a wheel with the most positive camber. If the mismatch is at the rear wheels, the rear axle pulls toward the side with the greatest amount of positive camber. If the rear axle pulls to the right, the front of the car drifts to the left, resulting in a steering pull even though the front wheels may be perfectly aligned.

Rear toe, like front toe, is a critical tire wear angle. If toed in or toed out, the rear tires scuff just like the front ones. Either condition can also contribute to steering instability as well as reduced braking effectiveness. (Keep this in mind with antilock brake systems.)

Like camber, rear toe is not a static alignment angle. It changes as the suspension goes through jounce and rebound. It also changes in response to rolling resistance and the application of engine torque. With four-wheel drive vehicles, the front wheels tend to toe in under power while the rear wheels toe out in response to rolling resistance and suspension compliance. With rear-wheel drive vehicles, the opposite happens: the front wheels toe out while the rear wheels on an independent suspension try to toe in as they push the vehicle ahead.

WHEELS AND TIRES

A vehicle's tires, wheels, and suspension and steering systems provide the contact between the driver and the road. They allow the driver to safely maneuver the vehicle in all types of conditions as well as ride in comfort and security. Tire design has improved dramatically during the past few years. Modern tires require increased attention to achieve their full potential of extended service and correct ride control. Tire wear that is uneven or premature is usually a good indicator of problems in the steering and suspension system. Tires become not only a good diagnostic aid to a technician, but they can also be clear evidence to the customer for the need to service the front end.

The primary purpose of tires is to provide traction. Tires also help the suspension absorb road shocks, but this is a side benefit. They must perform under a variety of conditions. The road might be wet or dry; paved with asphalt, concrete, or gravel; or there might not be a road at all. The car might be traveling slowly on a straight road, or moving quickly through curves or over hills. All of these conditions call for special requirements that must be present, at least to some degree, in all tires.

In addition to providing good traction, tires are also designed to carry the weight of the vehicle, to withstand side thrust over varying speeds and conditions, and to transfer braking and driving torque to the road.

There are many different designs of tires available today (Figure 14-47), the most common of which is the **radial ply**. Radial ply tires have body cords that extend from bead to bead at an angle of about 90 degrees "radial" to the tire circumferential centerline, plus two or more layers of relatively inflexible belts under the tread. This construction of various combinations of rayon, nylon, fiberglass, and steel gives greater strength to the tread area and flexibility to the sidewall (Figure 14-48). The belts restrict tread motion during contact with the road, thus improving tread life and traction. Radial ply tires also offer greater fuel economy, increased skid resistance, and more positive braking.

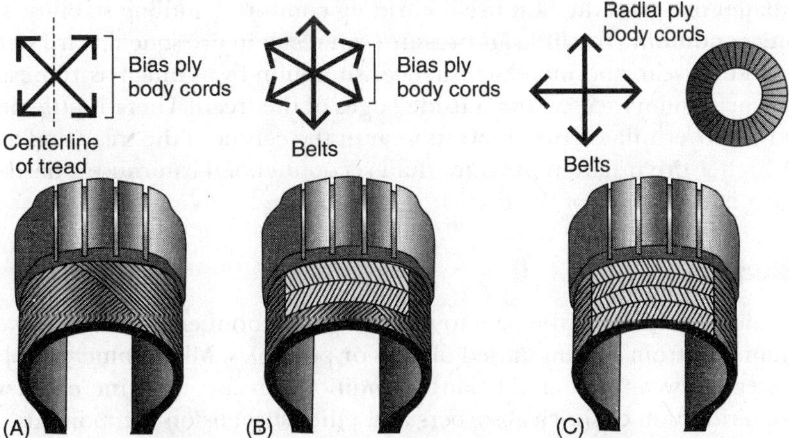

FIGURE 14-47 *Three types of tire construction: (A) bias ply; (B) bias belted; and (C) radial ply.*

Although the newer synthetics are being used more frequently in radial tires, steel is still the most popular belt material. Bias-ply and belted bias are available in all cord materials mentioned earlier, except amarid and kevlar. Non-radial belts are usually of the same material as the sidewalls.

Radial Bias-ply

FIGURE 14-48 *A radial tire's highly flexible sidewalls give maximum tread contact area during fast, hard turning.*

Combining Tire Types

As a general rule, tires should be replaced with the same size designation or an approved optional size as recommended by the auto or tire manufacturer. In addition to following the vehicle manufacturer's recommendations for tire size, type, inflation pressures, and rotation patterns, the following points should be observed:

1. Never mix size or construction types on the same axle.
2. Tires on the same axle should be of approximately equal tread depth.
3. All tires on station wagons and all other vehicles used for trailer towing should be of the same size, type, and load rating.
4. On some vehicles, the use of radial tires might hinder ride quality and control due to the design of the suspension system.
5. New tires should be installed in pairs on the same axle. When replacing only one tire, it should be paired with the tire having the most tread to equalize braking traction.
6. If radial tires are used on the car, combine them with radial snow tires on the driving wheels.
7. Snow tires should be of a size and type equivalent to the other tires on the vehicle. Otherwise, the safety and handling of the vehicle might be adversely affected.

Tire Care

To maximize tire performance, inspect for signs of improper inflation and uneven wear, which can indicate a need for balancing, rotation, or front suspension alignment. Tires should also be checked frequently for cuts, stone bruises, abrasions, blisters, and for objects that might have become imbedded in the tread. More frequent inspections are recommended when rapid or extreme temperature changes occur or where road surfaces are rough or occasionally littered with debris.

A properly inflated tire gives the best tire life, riding comfort, handling stability, and gas mileage for normal driving conditions. Too little air pressure can result in tire squeal, hard steering, excessive tire heat, abnormal tire wear, and increased fuel consumption by as much as 10 percent. An underinflated tire shows maximum wear on the outside edges of the tread. There is little or no wear in the center. Conversely, an overinflated tire shows its wear in the center of the tread and little wear on the outside edges. A higher tire inflation pressure than recommended can cause a hard ride, tire bruising, and rapid wear at the center of the tire.

Tire/Wheel Balance

Proper front-end alignment allows the tires to roll straight without excessive tread wear. The wheels can go out of alignment from striking raised objects or pot holes. Misalignment subjects the tires to uneven and/or irregular wear. An out-of-balance condition can also cause increased wear on the ball joints as well as deterioration of shock absorbers and other suspension components.

Should an inspection show uneven or irregular tire wear, wheel alignment and balance service is a must. Wheel balancing distributes weights along the wheel rim which counteract heavy spots in the wheels and tires and allow them to roll smoothly without vibration. There are two types of wheel imbalance: static and dynamic.

Static balance is the equal distribution of weight around the wheel. Wheels that are statically unbalanced cause a bouncing action called **wheel tramp** (Figure 14-49). This condition eventually causes uneven tire wear. As the name implies, static balance is balancing a wheel at rest. This is done by adding a compensating weight. Static balance is achieved when the wheel does not rotate by itself regardless of the position in which it is placed on its axis. A statically unbalanced wheel tends to rotate by itself until the heavy portion is down.

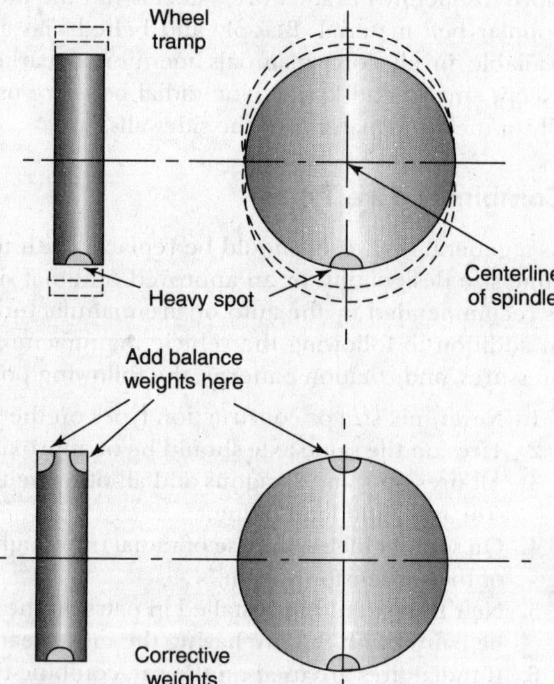

FIGURE 14-49 *Static unbalance causes wheel tramp.*

Dynamic balance is the equal distribution of weight on each side of the centerline. When the tire spins, there is no tendency for the assembly to move from side to side. Wheels that are dynamically unbalanced can cause **wheel shimmy** and a wear pattern (Figure 14-50). Simply stated, dynamic balance is balancing a wheel in motion. Once a wheel starts to rotate and is in motion, the static weights try to reach the true plane of rotation of the wheel because of the action of centrifugal force. In an attempt to reach the true plane of rotation when there is an imbalance, the static weights force the spindle to one side.

At 180 degrees of wheel rotation, static weights kick the spindle in the opposite direction. The resultant side thrusts cause the wheel assembly to wobble or wiggle. When severe enough, as already mentioned, it causes vibration and front-wheel shimmy.

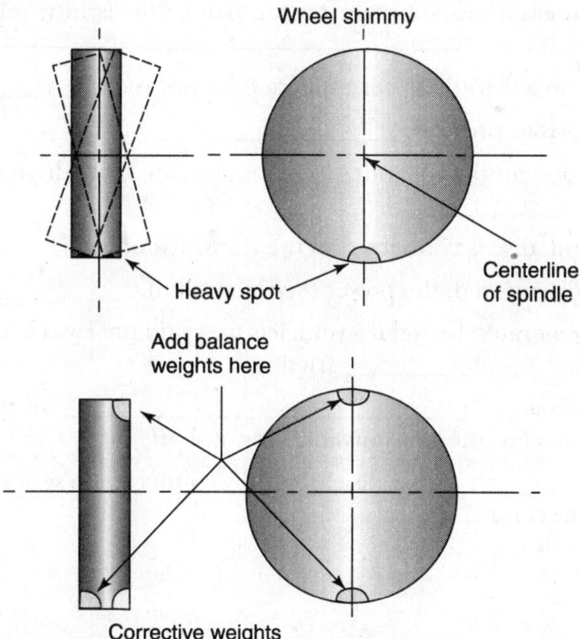

Figure 14-50 *Dynamic unbalance causes wheel shimmy.*

Review Questions

Short Answer Essays

1. Explain the operation of the manual transmission clutch?
2. Explain the terms constant mesh and fully synchronized.
3. Define final drive gear.
4. What component in an electronic cruise control system is used to monitor or sense vehicle speed?
5. Define dynamic and static wheel balance.
6. Briefly describe how an automatic transmission knows when to shift gears.
7. Explain the primary purpose of the torsional coil springs in the transmission's clutch disc.
8. Describe the purpose of a brake wheel cylinder.
9. Explain what happens during the coupling stage of conventional torque converter operation.
10. Explain what is necessary for torque converter clutch lockup engagement to take place.

Fill-in-the-Blanks

1. The ______________ converts the force on the brake pedal to hydraulic pressure that is sent to the individual wheel brake units.

2. The most commonly used brake system on the front wheels of a vehicle is _______________ brakes.
3. The cruiser control on a throttle-by-wire system does not require a _______________.
4. The main job of tires is to provide _______________.
5. The drive shaft component that provides a means of connecting driveline components together at an angle is the _______________.
6. The clutch, or friction, disc is connected to the transmission's _______________.
7. When the clutch is disengaged, the power flow stops at the _______________.
8. The friction that is generated between a vehicle's tires and the road when the vehicle is in a non-skidding state is called _______________ friction.
9. Automatic transmissions use a _______________ _______________ instead of a clutch to transfer power from the flywheel to the transmission's input shaft.
10. A _______________ _______________ is electrically connected in series with the compressor electromagnetic clutch to control it.

Multiple Choice

1. *Technician A* says that the clutch disc is also called the friction disc.

   Technician B says the clutch disc is splined to the transmission input shaft.

   Who is correct?

   A. Technician A   C. Both technicians

   B. Technician B   D. Neither technician

2. *Technician A* says an automatic transmission uses a torque converter instead of a clutch to transfer power from the engine to the transmission.

   Technician B says the torque converter allows the vehicle to stop and idle without releasing a clutch.

   Who is correct?

   A. Technician A   C. Both technicians

   B. Technician B   D. Neither technician

3. All of the following are parts of the torque converter ***except***:

   A. Impeller   C. Turbine

   B. Roller gear   D. Stator

4. *Technician A* says most automatic transmissions rely on planetary gears to transfer and multiply engine torque.

   Technician B says the planetary gear-set consists of four parts.

   Who is correct?

   A. Technician A   C. Both technicians

   B. Technician B   D. Neither technician

5. *Technician A* says a transmission *band* is hydraulically applied by a multiple disc clutch.

   Technician B says the purpose of a drum is to hold a drum and the connecting planetary gear member stationary.

Who is correct?

A. Technician A C. Both technicians
B. Technician B D. Neither technician

6. *Technician A* says the driveline connects the transmission output shaft to the gearing in the rear axle housing.
   Technician B says a driveline consists of a solid drive or propeller shaft connected to the transmission and differential by U-joints.
   Who is correct?
   A. Technician A C. Both technicians
   B. Technician B D. Neither technician
7. *Technician A* says that U-joints speed up and slow down as they rotate.
   Technician B says CV joints run at a constant rate of speed.
   Who is correct?
   A. Technician A C. Both technicians
   B. Technician B D. Neither technician
8. *Technician A* says the differential divides the power between the left and right axles.
   Technician B says the differential allows the rear wheels to turn at different speeds when going around corners.
   Who is correct?
   A. Technician A C. Both technicians
   B. Technician B D. Neither technician
9. While discussing the air-conditioning system;
   Technician A says the expansion valve converts high-pressure liquid into a low-pressure liquid.
   Technician B says the refrigerant enters the compressor as a low-pressure liquid from the evaporator.
   Who is correct?
   A. Technician A C. Both technicians
   B. Technician B D. Neither technician
10. *Technician A* says a common steering system is the rack and pinion.
    Technician B says another common system is the recirculating ball type.
    Who is correct?
    A. Technician A C. Both technicians
    B. Technician B D. Neither technician

INDEX